SOVIET GEOGRAPHY
ACCOMPLISHMENTS AND TASKS

AMERICAN GEOGRAPHICAL SOCIETY
OCCASIONAL PUBLICATION NO. 1

SOVIET GEOGRAPHY

ACCOMPLISHMENTS AND TASKS

A symposium of 50 chapters, contributed by 56 leading Soviet
geographers and edited by a committee of the Geographic
Society of the USSR, Academy of Sciences of the USSR.

I. P. GERASIMOV, *Chairman*   O. A. KONSTANTINOV

G. M. IGNAT'YEV, *Secretary*   E. M. MURZAYEV

S. V. KALESNIK   K. A. SALISHCHEV

Translated from the Russian by
LAWRENCE ECKER

English edition edited by
CHAUNCY D. HARRIS

AMERICAN GEOGRAPHICAL SOCIETY

Broadway at 156th Street, New York 32, New York

1962

SOVIET GEOGRAPHY
ACCOMPLISHMENTS AND TASKS

AMERICAN GEOGRAPHICAL SOCIETY
OCCASIONAL PUBLICATION NO. 1

Publication of this book has been made
possible by NSF Grant G20349 from
the National Science Foundation to
the American Geographical Society.

Library of Congress Catalog Card Number: 62-13659

INTRODUCTION
TO THE
ENGLISH-LANGUAGE EDITION

Soviet Geography: Accomplishments and Tasks (Sovetskaya Geografiya: Itogi i Zadachi) is a collective work by 56 leading Soviet geographers sponsored by the Geographic Society of the USSR under the Academy of Sciences of the USSR and edited by a committee of six. It briefly traces the rise and development of Russian geography and then examines in considerable detail each of the major fields of Soviet geography, some of the principal problems on which geographers work, the methods of geographic research, and the teaching and dissemination of knowledge about geography. The volume is devoted not to geography in general but to geography as developed in the Soviet Union. References to antecedents or parallel developments in other countries are rare. Nevertheless, as the most comprehensive review of Soviet geography ever issued, it deserves wide distribution and study. To that end, this book in its entirety is here made available in English translation.

The general contents and organization of the volume are explained in the Foreword by the Editorial Committee of the Russian edition. It may be useful, however, to summarize very broadly five of the major characteristics of Soviet geography as revealed in the pages of this volume.

Soviet geography has a very broad range. In the Soviet Union it is customary to speak of the geographical sciences as a whole family of closely related and interrelated fields ranging from climatology, glaciology, perma-frost study, hydrology, geomorphology, soil geography, plant geography, zoogeography, and general physical geography on one side to geography of population, settlements, industry, agriculture, and general economic geography on another side, or to regional geography (both economic and physical), or historical geography, or cartography, on yet other sides. The field of geography, or the fields of geography, include scientists both with broad interests, such as general physical geography on one hand, and with highly specialized research programs in narrow but important topics within the fields of glaciology or hydrology on the other hand. As a discipline or group of disciplines, geography in the Soviet Union has a somewhat broader range than in the United States. It also is characterized by a somewhat heavier emphasis on the various aspects of physical geography.

Soviet geography has a practical orientation. Although excellent research in some purely theoretical scientific questions has been carried on in the Soviet Union, geography as a whole is characterized by a concern for practical applications of its studies or for work on applied problems. Geographers are engaged in work on the "transformation of nature," a process which man has been carrying on, for good and ill, since he first became Man with bow, plow, axe, crops, fire, and domesticated animals. The utilization, preservation, and improvement of natural resources receive great attention in the Soviet Union. Geographers are engaged in practical work on hydroelectric and irrigation projects, settlement of new lands, control of soil erosion, agricultural land management, programs to reduce the load on the transportation system, exploration and development of Arctic areas, appraisal of vegetation, soil, and land resources, and mapping. But, just as in other countries, failures of communication sometimes develop between the geographer and the technical specialist, between the broad view of a problem as a whole within its areal setting and the more specialized view of a single aspect.

Research in geography tends to cluster around great problems. Research in the Soviet Union is somewhat less individualistic than in some other countries. Plans for research on broad major problems—scientific or practical—are characteristic of geographic establishments, whether in academies of sciences, government bureaus, or universities. Some of the major problems on which geographers are now working, in association with scientists from related fields, are the heat and water regime of the earth's surface, snow cover, establishment and characterization of natural regions, and economic regionalization of the Soviet Union. Great efforts are being expended in the development of such fields as paleogeography, medical geography, and the theory of zonality on land and sea.

THE SCALE OF GEOGRAPHIC WORK IN THE SOVIET UNION IS VERY LARGE. The Geographic Society of the USSR has about ten thousand members, said to be mostly geographers. Perhaps a more discriminating figure is given in Chapter 46 by Dean A. M. Ryabchikov of the Geography Faculty of Moscow State University: in the Soviet Union in 1958 some 1,440 geographers had completed a three-year postgraduate course and received the degree (rank) of candidate of geographical sciences. Only in the United States and in Germany are there comparable numbers of geographers with similar research degrees in geography. In terms of concentration of geographers in a geographic research establishment, the Institute of Geography of the Academy of Sciences of the USSR with its several hundred full-time research scientists stands unmatched in the world. The Geography Faculty of Moscow State University also appears to occupy first place among the universities of all countries in its numbers of teaching and research staff and students specializing in geography.

GEOGRAPHY AS A MAJOR RESEARCH, UNIVERSITY, AND SCHOOL SUBJECT IS RELATIVELY RECENT IN THE SOVIET UNION. Although antecedents of Soviet geography extend back several centuries to great explorers and universal scientists, although the Russian Geographical Society was founded in St. Petersburg in 1845, and although from 1884 D. N. Anuchin in the chair of geography at the University of Moscow trained many great geographers, the main expansion of Soviet geography dates only from the 1930's. The Institute of Geography of the Academy of Sciences of the USSR was established in 1931 (but with the name Geomorphological Institute from 1931 to 1934 and the name Institute of Physical Geography from 1935 to 1937).

Perhaps the key point in the development of geography in the educational system was the decree of May 16, 1934, which set up a substantial program in geography in the elementary and secondary schools of the Soviet Union. The need for teachers of geography provided the stimulus that led to the establishment of departments of geography in many pedagogical institutes and universities. The Geography Faculty of Moscow State University became a separate faculty in 1938 with responsibilities for teaching, for the training of teachers for secondary schools and institutions of higher learning, and for research. In 1953 it moved to its new quarters in the central skyscraper of the university campus on Lenin Hills.

Editing of *Soviet Geography: Accomplishments and Tasks* has had the aim of following as closely as possible the meaning of the original Russian text. The only changes have been (1) the numbering of the chapters and of the figures, (2) the addition of a list of the figures, (3) the addition of a list of authors and co-authors with some identifying notes on each, (4) the slight modification of the Foreword and Chapter 1 on the basis of additional later materials supplied directly in English by Academician I. P. Gerasimov, the chairman of the editorial committee for the Russian edition, and (5) the addition of an Appendix on "Soviet Serials Cited in this Book." The bibliographies which conclude most of the chapters follow the original text in alphabetization, according to the Russian order: *a, b, v, g, d,* etc.

Thanks are due to Lawrence Ecker for the excellent translation, and to G. M. Ignat'yev for supplying reproductions of the maps, charts, and portraits, and for his biographical notes on the authors. Publication of *Soviet Geography* has been made possible by a grant from the National Science Foundation to the American Geographical Society. Special thanks are owed to Wilfrid Webster of the Society's staff, who voluntarily assumed responsibility for final editing and seeing the volume through the press. The book has benefited greatly from his wide editorial and publication experience. Francis Barkóczy, of the cartographic staff of the Society, has been responsible for placing English place-name equivalents on most of the maps and on the diagrams. To keep the price of the book low and thus broaden its potential distribution, use has been made of offset reproduction and of other manufacturing economies. The basic surveys in this volume can be supplemented by following the current articles appearing in *Soviet Geography: Review and Translation,* published ten times a year by the American Geographical Society and edited and translated by Theodore Shabad.

CHAUNCY D. HARRIS
University of Chicago

FOREWORD

This collection represents a scientific work in the nature of a reference book. Its purpose is to give a comprehensive characterization of the present state of Soviet geography, its chief theoretical achievements, and its problems. The compilation from time to time of such fundamental reviews is in the interest of the development of science itself; it affords an opportunity to make a critical evaluation of the work done during the preceding period, and soundly to map out its further prospects. At present, such a review is especially necessary for Soviet geography, above all in connection with the imposing tasks of the current and prospective plans for the development of the national economy of our country, which provide for the thorough development of the productive forces of all its geographic regions and for the broad practical utilization of modern scientific achievements. Furthermore, it is important in view of the profound transformation of the classic methods of the geographic sciences, which are assimilating recent progress in geophysics and geochemistry, as well as in view of the growth of foreign scientific relations, the active participation of Soviet geographers in the work of international scientific congresses, and the further strengthening of the world prestige of Soviet science.

These main tasks have determined the program of the present symposium. Its contents are divided into the following main parts:

1. REVIEW OF THE HISTORY AND PRESENT STATE OF SOVIET GEOGRAPHY, presented separately for the general (synthetic) branches (physical geography of lands, physical geography of seas and oceans, economic geography, regional geography, cartography) and the specialized branches of geographic disciplines (climatology, glaciology, permafrost science, hydrology of the land, geomorphology, soil geography, plant geography, zoogeography, geography of population and settlements, and geography of industry, agriculture, and transportation).

2. A CHARACTERIZATION OF THE MAIN INTEGRATED (COMPLEX) SCIENTIFIC PROBLEMS AND TRENDS being worked out by Soviet geography: the paleogeography of the glacial period on the territory of the USSR; the paleogeography of the postglacial period; the heat and water balance of the earth's surface; the present state of the theory of geographic zonality on the land and in the World Ocean; snow cover; landscape science; physical geographic regionalization; integrated mapping; economic regionalization; economic-geographic study of the complex development of productive forces in the separate economic regions; problems of industrial, agricultural and transportation geography; medical geography; and toponymy; and an analysis of the role of geographers in the transformation of nature on the territory of the USSR (study of natural resources; exploration and development of polar regions; geographical study and transformation of the area of coniferous forests; transformation of the steppes and deserts; and geographical research on the improvement of agricultural land use).

3. A PRESENTATION OF ANALYTICAL AND EXPERIMENTAL METHODS OF GEOGRAPHIC RESEARCH in field and office (expeditions; air photography and photogrammetry; office physical geographic research; laboratory analysis and experiment; nature reserves and national parks of the USSR; and methods of economic-geographic research).

4. GENERAL INFORMATION ON THE SYSTEM OF GEOGRAPHIC EDUCATION AND THE PRINCIPAL MEANS OF POPULARIZING GEOGRAPHIC SCIENTIFIC KNOWLEDGE IN THE USSR (secondary and higher geographical education; amateur local studies of the separate districts [*krayevedeniye*] and their importance for Soviet geography; tourism and mountaineering; publishing of geographic literature; and a brief review of the history and activity of the Geographic Society of the USSR).

Only a group of authoritative scholars could insure a highly competent presentation of these diverse questions. In the production of the present work, about 50 authors took part—Soviet geographers working in diverse fields of the geographic sciences. The coordination of the activities of such an extensive group of authors and the harmonization of the results of their work presented a very difficult task. As may be seen from the following chapters, this task has not been fully achieved. The present collection contains certain contradictory elements, in part retained deliberately in the interest of the preservation of the authors' independence. The Editorial Committee of this volume has made great efforts to confine such conflicts to those based on a divergence of scientific views. The debatability of a number of theoretical questions in geography is quite natural; we regard the clash of conflicting views about them as one of the important stimuli for the further active development of the science.

The book is designed for various kinds of readers. In addition to professional geographers in the broad sense, i.e., scientific workers in the field of the geographic, geologic, economic, and biological sciences, as well as teachers in the corresponding departments of institutions of higher learning, it should interest many workers in the planning organs and designing institutions, economists working in industry, agriculture, or transportation, and other specialists concerned with the study of natural conditions, the utilization and preservation of natural resources, and the development of the productive forces of the various regions of our country.

THE EDITORIAL COMMITTEE

ABOUT THE AUTHORS

Order of information: FAMILY NAME, given name, patronymic; year of birth; academic degrees; position or place of work; fields of specialization. *E* indicates that the individual was a member of the Editorial Committee. Numbers indicate the chapters of which the named individual is the author (or co-author if followed by an *x*).

ALAMPIYEV, Petr Martynovich. 1900. Doctor of economic sciences. Scientific-research Institute of Economics of Gosplan. Economic geography of the USSR, theory of economic regionalization. *(28)*

ALISOV, Boris Pavlovich. 1891. Doctor of geographical sciences. Professor, Geography Faculty of the Lomonosov Moscow State University. Regional climatology. *(9x)*

ARMAND, David L'vovich. 1905. Doctor of geographical sciences. Institute of Geography of the Academy of Sciences of the USSR. General questions of physical geography. *(38, 41x)*

AVGEVICH, Vitol'd Ivanovich. 1906. Doctor of geographical sciences. Institute of Geography of the Academy of Sciences of the USSR. Cartography and photogrammetry. *(40)*

AVSYUK, Grigoriy Aleksandrovich. 1906. Corresponding member of the Academy of Sciences of the USSR. Professor, Institute of Geography of the Academy of Sciences of the USSR. Glaciology. *(10)*

BASS, Sergey Varfolomeyevich. 1921. Institute of Geography of the Academy of Sciences of the USSR. Hydrology. *(41x)*

BELOUSOV, Ivan Ivanovich. Doctor of geographical sciences. Institute of Complex Transportation Problems, Gosekonomsovet. Geography of transportation. *(31)*

BOGOROV, Veniamin Grigor'yevich. 1904. Corresponding member of the Academy of Sciences of the USSR. Institute of Oceanology of the Academy of Sciences of the USSR. Oceanology, biogeography of the ocean. *(23)*

BYAKOV, V. P. *(32x)*

BUDYKO, Mikhail Ivanovich. 1920. Doctor of physical-mathematical sciences. Professor, Voyeykov Main Geophysical Observatory, Leningrad. Climatology, hydrology, general questions of physical geography. *(21)*

CHOCHIA, N. S. *(41x)*

DAVITAYA, Feofan Farneyevich. 1911. Academician, Academy of Sciences of the Georgian SSR, Doctor of agricultural sciences. Main Administration of the Hydrometeorological Service. Director, Vakhushti Institute of Geography, Academy of Sciences of the Georgian SSR, Tbilisi. Agroclimatology, geography of agriculture. *(37)*

DOBROVOL'SKIY, Aleksey Dmitriyevich. Professor, doctor, chair of oceanology, Moscow State University. Oceanology. *(4)*

FORMOZOV, Aleksandr Nikolayevich. 1899. Doctor of biological sciences. Professor, Institute of Geography, Academy of Sciences of the USSR. Biogeography, zoology, ecology. *(16x, 41x)*

GAKKEL', Yakov Yakovlevich. 1901. Doctor of geographical sciences. Professor, Arctic Institute. Physical geography of the Arctic. *(35)*

GELLER, Samuil Yul'yevich. 1906. Doctor of geographical sciences. Institute of Geography of the Academy of Sciences of the USSR. Physical geography, geomorphology, geography of arid lands. *(13)*

GERASIMOV, Innokentiy Petrovich. 1905. Academician, Academy of Sciences of the USSR. Director, Institute of Geography, Academy of Sciences of the USSR. Physical geography, geography of soils, geomorphology, paleogeography. *(E, 1, 14, 19, 34, 42x)*

GLAZOVSKAYA, Mariya Al'fredovna. 1912. Doctor of geographical sciences. Professor, Moscow State University. Geography of soils, geochemistry, landscape. *(41x)*

GOKHMAN, Veniamin Maksovich. 1918. Candidate of geographical sciences. Institute of Geography of the Academy of Sciences of the USSR. Economic geography of the United States, geography of population and manufacturing, general questions of economic geography, geography of cities. *(6x)*

GRIGOR'YEV, Andrey Aleksandrovich. 1883. Academician, Academy of Sciences of the USSR. Institute of Geography of the Academy of Sciences of the USSR. Theoretical questions of physical geography, study of landscapes. *(2, 22)*

IGNAT'YEV, Grigoriy Mikhaylovich. 1925. Candidate of geographical sciences. Geography Faculty, Lomonosov Moscow State University. Physical geography, qualitative appraisal of land. *(E, 6x)*

IGNAT'YEV, Yevgeniy Ivanovich. Candidate of medical sciences. Institute of Geography of Siberia and the Far East, Siberian section of the Academy of Sciences of the USSR, Irkutsk. Medical geography. *(32x)*

ISAKOV, Yuriy Andreyevich. 1912. Candidate of biological sciences. Institute of Geography of the Academy of Sciences of the USSR. Terrestrial zoogeography. *(16x)*

IVERONOVA, Margarita Ivanovna. 1906. Candidate of geographical sciences. Institute of Geography of the Academy of Sciences of the USSR. Geomorphology. *(41x)*

KACHURIN, S. P. *(11)*

KALESNIK, Stanislav Vikent'yevich. 1901. Corresponding member, Academy of Sciences of the USSR. Professor, Geography Faculty, Leningrad University named for A. A. Zhdanov. Glaciology, general geography, study of landscapes. *(E, 3, 25, 50)*

KHMELEVA, Natal'ya Vladimirovna. 1922. Candidate of geographical sciences. Geography Faculty, Moscow State University. Geomorphology. *(42x)*

KHROMOV, Sergey Petrovich. 1904. Professor, Geography Faculty, Lomonosov Moscow State University. Climatology. *(9x)*

KIRIKOV, Sergey Vasil'yevich. 1899. Doctor of biological sciences. Institute of Geography of the Academy of Sciences of the USSR. Zoogeography. *(43)*

KLUPT, Veniamin Solomonovich. Professor, Leningrad Engineering - Economics Institute. Economic geography. *(18)*

KONSTANTINOV, Oleg Arkad'yevich. 1903. Doctor of geographical sciences. Herzen Leningrad Pedagogical Institute. Economic geography of the USSR, geography of cities. *(E, 5, 46x)*

KOTEL'NIKOV, Vasiliy Leont'yevich. Candidate of geographical sciences. Lenin Moscow State Pedagogical Institute. Physical geography. *(46x)*

LAVRENKO, Yevgeniy Mikhailovich. 1900. Corresponding member of the Academy of Sciences of the USSR. Botanical Institute of the Academy of Sciences of the USSR. Botanical geography. *(15)*

LEBEDEV, Dmitriy Mikhaylovich. 1891. Doctor of geographical sciences. Institute of Geography of the Academy of Sciences of the USSR. History of geographical sciences. *(8)*

L'VOVICH, Mark Isaakovich. 1906. Doctor of geographical sciences. Professor, Institute of Geography of the Academy of Sciences of the USSR. Hydrology. *(12)*

MAKKAVEYEV, Nikolay Ivanovich. 1908. Doctor of geographical sciences. Professor, Geography Faculty, Moscow State University. Geomorphology. *(42x)*

MARKOVIN, A. P. *(32x)*

MURZAYEV, Eduard Makarovich. 1908. Doctor of geographical sciences. Professor, Institute of Geography of the Academy of Sciences of the USSR. Physical geography of Asia, toponymics. *(E, 33)*

NEYSHTADT, Mark Il'ich. 1903. Doctor of geographical sciences. Professor, Institute of Geography of the Academy of Sciences of the USSR. Geobotany, bog studies, paleogeography. *(20, 42x)*

PEREL'MAN, Aleksandr Il'ich. Doctor of geological and mineralogical sciences. IGEM Academy of Sciences of the USSR. Geochemistry of the landscape. *(42x)*

POKSHISHEVSKIY, Vadim Vyacheslavovich. 1905. Doctor of geographical sciences. Professor, Institute of Geography of the Academy of Sciences of the USSR. Economic geography, geography of population. *(17, 44, 49)*

PREOBRAZHENSKIY, Vladimir Sergeyevich. 1918. Candidate of geographical sciences. Institute of Geography of the Academy of Sciences of the USSR. Physical geography of the USSR. *(39)*

RAKITNIKOV, Andrey Nikolayevich. 1903. Docent, Geography Faculty, Lomonosov Moscow State University. Geography of agriculture, economic geography. *(30)*

RAUNER, Yuriy L'vovich. 1930. Candidate of geographical sciences. Institute of Geography of the Academy of Sciences of the USSR. Climatology, general questions of physical geography. *(41x)*

RIKHTER, Gavriil Dmitriyevich. 1899. Doctor of geographical sciences. Professor, Institute of Geography of the Academy of Sciences of the USSR. Physical geography of the USSR and general questions of physical geography. *(24, 26)*

RYABCHIKOV, Aleksandr Maksimovich. 1918. Candidate geographical sciences. Docent, Dean, Geography Faculty, Lomonosov Moscow State University. Physical geography of foreign countries. *(46x)*

SALISHCHEV, Konstantin Alekseyevich. 1905. Doctor of technical sciences. Professor, Geography Faculty, Lomonosov Moscow State University. Cartography. *(E, 7, 27)*

SAUSHKIN, Yulian Glebovich. 1911. Doctor of geographical sciences. Professor, Geography Faculty, Lomonosov Moscow State University. Economic geography of the USSR, general questions of economic geography. *(29)*

SETUNSKAYA, Lyudmila Yevgen'yevna. 1924. Candidate of geographical sciences. Institute of Geography of the Academy of Sciences of the USSR. Physical geography. *(41x)*

SHOSHIN, Aleksey Alekseyevich. Candidate of medical sciences. Chairman of the Section on Medical Geography, Geographical Society of the USSR. Medical geography. *(32x)*

SOBOLEV, Leonid Nikolayevich. 1902. Candidate of biological sciences. Institute of Geography of the Academy of Sciences of the USSR. Botanical geography. *(41x)*

SOCHAVA, Viktor Borisovich. 1905. Corresponding member of the Academy of Sciences of the USSR. Institute of Geography of Siberia and the Far East of the Academy of Sciences of the USSR, Irkutsk. Physical geography, botanical geography. *(36)*

SOLOV'YEV, Aleksandr Ivanovich. 1907. Candidate of geographical sciences. Docent, Geography Faculty, Lomonosov Moscow State University. History of geography, physical geography. *(45)*

TUMANOVA, D. F. *(41x)*

VELICHKO, Andrey Alekseyevich. 1931. Candidate of geographical sciences. Institute of Geography of the Academy of Sciences of the USSR. Geomorphology, paleogeography. *(42x)*

YEFREMOV, Yuriy Konstantinovich. 1913. Museum of Geography, Lomonosov Moscow State University. Local studies. *(47, 48)*

CONTENTS

PART III

INTEGRATED SCIENTIFIC PROBLEMS AND TRENDS

PART IV

THE ROLE OF GEOGRAPHERS IN THE
TRANSFORMATION OF NATURE

PART V

METHODS OF GEOGRAPHIC RESEARCH

PART VI

GEOGRAPHIC EDUCATION AND POPULARIZATION OF SCIENTIFIC GEOGRAPHIC KNOWLEDGE

PART VII

THE GEOGRAPHIC SOCIETY OF THE USSR

MAPS AND DIAGRAMS

CHAPTER 1

GEOGRAPHY IN THE SOVIET UNION

AN INTRODUCTION

I. P. Gerasimov

Geographic science in the Soviet Union has traveled a prolonged and many-sided path of development. Arising after the Great October Socialist Revolution, Soviet geography received as a great and valuable heritage from pre-revolutionary Russian geography not only an immense store of geographic facts, but also a whole system of fruitful progressive scientific traditions, schools, and concepts, many of which have become classic. During its existence, Soviet geography has repeatedly enlarged its scientific heritage. It has gathered new factual materials, continued and enriched the progressive classic scientific trends, and created new theoretical concepts which have developed on the basis of scientific Marxism-Leninism and in close connection with the practice of socialist construction.

In present-day Soviet geography, the most important features of the world-wide evolution of science complexly intertwine and interact with the peculiarities in the development of Soviet socialist science. Somewhat schematizing this complex problem, one may characterize the world-wide tendencies in the development of Soviet geography in the following manner:

1. The immemorial general task of geography — one of the oldest sciences in the world — has always been and continues to be *the study of nature, population, and economy* on the territory of a given country, its various parts, other countries, and the earth as a whole. Such a study has as its object both an all-around characterization (description) and an explanation of the various features of similarity and difference in the natural conditions and local characteristics of the economy and population. The scientific results of geographic investigations have always been widely used for practical purposes, in revealing natural resources, the development of land for agriculture, in making a rational distribution of industrial enterprises, settlements, and communications, and for the purpose of developing the productive forces of various regions and countries.

2. One must categorically repudiate the view that geography has now in the main fulfilled its cognitive-descriptive functions and that the whole earth — or in any case the main inhabited part of it — has already been sufficiently studied geographically and therefore geography must now be regarded solely as a school discipline for general education, needed not so much for scientific and practical as for purely cultural purposes. Such a view of modern geography is profoundly erroneous and archaic.

Modern geography is a science of the present 20th century; it is no longer the former, principally descriptive-cognitive science which had as its main subject the hitherto unknown lands and countries. *This science is experimental and active (transformative) in character;* its basic objects are lands and countries long since discovered and now tamed by man, with nature thoroughly altered by man, dense population, and a complexly developed economy. The main task of modern geography throughout the world is not to lend aid in the pioneering of new lands and natural wealth, but to render many kinds of scientific service in mankind's great work of making varied and ever more intensive use of the natural resources already discovered, and of transforming nature and the economy of already developed regions and countries.

With the development of the powerful means of modern technology, these new tasks of geographic research are not simplified, but are becoming more and more complicated, since the efficient application of new technology demands an especially profound and differentiated knowledge of all the characteristics of the territory to be exploited or the properties of the natural phenomenon to be modified.

3. In order to insure a sufficiently precise and diversified geographic study of a territory and its typical phenomena, satisfying the demands of modern practice, and in order to give to geographic phenomena a full-valued scientific explanation, based on modern scientific concepts, it is necessary to have a much more profound and diversified scientific knowledge than formerly and to utilize many recent special methods of field and office investigation. All this taken as a whole cannot be accomplished, as a rule, at present within the framework of one science and by the efforts of one specialist alone. In the present stage of the development of geography, the former single science is being replaced by a system of sciences, and the single universal encyclopedist-scholar by the collective labors of many specialized geographers organized according to a unified plan.

Hence, *the foundation of modern geography in the USSR, as in other countries, is the complicated process of forming and developing a whole system of scientific disciplines,* arising in place of the former geographic science.

In the USSR, the main configuration of the modern system of geographic sciences, as well as the principles of their division and mutual relationship, have already become sufficiently clear.

From the viewpoint of Soviet geographers, it may be regarded as generally recognized that the subject of the study of the whole system of geographic sciences is the natural environment, i.e., the totality of the interrelated natural phenomena surrounding us on the earth's surface, the population, and production, as well as the relation of the natural environment to production and human life.

At present, the system of geographic sciences is divided first of all into two major divisions: *physical geography and economic geography,* including *population geography.* This division derives from the very nature of the objects studied by geography — the natural phenomena, on the one hand, and the social phenomena (population and production), on the other. It is based on methodological principles and on the relations of the corresponding geographic disciplines (from the series of physical or economic geography) to the natural or social sciences. Physical geography, taken as a whole, studies the geographic aspect of the phenomena of nature and thereby proceeds from the laws of the development of nature established by the natural sciences. Economic geography studies social phenomena (the characteristics and distribution of the economy and population) and so proceeds from the regularities characteristic of the structure and development of society and studied by the socio-economic or social sciences.

The further subdivision of physical and economic geography is based on the following principles.

The fundamental theoretical tasks of physical geography are the study of the mutually conditioned complex of natural phenomena constituting the natural geographic environment (sphere or envelope) as a whole, and also in its separate components and regions. The first of these tasks forms the *subject of the general division of physical geography,* or *knowledge of the earth* [*zemlevedeniye* = German *Erdkunde*], which investigates the natural geographic environment as a whole and on the scale of the entire terrestrial globe. The description and explanation of the causes of the similarity or difference of the geographic environment within the individual portions of the earth's surface (i.e., the study of the natural geographic regions or landscapes) form the subjects of the *regional division of physical geography,* or *landscape science* [*landshaftovedeniye* = German *Landschaftskunde*].

The direct objects of study of both the general and the regional divisions of physical geography [i.e., *zemlevedeniye* and *landshaftovedeniye*] are the intricate *combinations* or *complexes* of natural phenomena. That is why these geographical sciences are of a synthetic character summarizing and combining data of many other geographic sciences.

The study of the separate *components* of the natural geographic environment is the subject of a whole series of *particular, specialized, systematic, analytical* physical geographic scientific disciplines (for example, climatology, hydrology, geomorphology, soil science, plant geography, zoogeography, etc.), constituting altogether the third *special systematic, analytical division of physical geography.*

The geographic sciences forming this division are very closely interconnected with the sciences of the other two divisions. These latter, in their synthesis of scientific materials, are nourished by the special disciplines which in turn repose entirely upon the general and regional geographic regularities.

The main theoretical task of economic geography is the establishment of the regularities in the geographic distribution of population and production. For this reason, alongside the *general* and *regional divisions of economic geography,* investigating the distribution and composition of population throughout the world and the distribution of production as a whole or within individual countries or regions, separate subdivisions of the *special* or *branch divisions of economic geography,* such as, for example, population geography, and the geography of industry, agriculture, transportation, etc., are developing in the USSR and are being more or less distinguished from one another as independent scientific disciplines.

A somewhat special place in the system of geographic sciences in the USSR and in the whole world is occupied by two old divisions of geography, namely *regional geography* [*stranovedeniye* = German *Länderkunde*] and *cartography.* Having as their task the combining of scientific data on physical and economic geography for this or that territory by means of the literary or the cartographic method of presentation, these two independent geographic disciplines have always played an important role in the theoretical generalization, practical utilization, and popularization of scientific knowledge. In Soviet geography, both regional geography and especially cartography have developed very successfully.

The process of the formation and separation of the various divisions and disciplines in the present system of geographic sciences in the USSR, reflecting the general nature of the progress of science, is uneven and conflicting. The different degree of development and consolidation of this or that scientific geographic discipline and the unequal level of theoretical and practical achievements produce on the whole a rather complicated picture, in which many phenomena appear only temporary and fortuitous. The continual progressive development of everything new in the field of the geographic sciences is crowding the old, long-established concepts and positions. The latter, however, do not yield without a struggle, the temporary and particular result of which may be variable. All this is thoroughly reflected in the modern Soviet scientific geographic literature, the study of which in sequence yields rich material for clarifying the process of the rapid development of the whole system of geographic sciences under the conditions of a socialist social structure.

The general present state of Soviet geography and the level of theoretical and practical development attained by it is very clearly characterized by the most important tasks of scientific geographic work in the USSR and of the organization of that work. These tasks may be briefly formulated as follows:

1. Further expansion of integrated geographic expeditionary research and cartographic work, directed toward discovering new natural resources and developing the productive forces in all the regions of the Soviet Union, in conjunction with their economic exploitation and new major construction projects. Especially important now, in this respect, is the geographic work in the eastern regions of the Soviet Union—in Siberia and the Far East.

2. A scientific stock-taking, economic appraisal, and elaboration of rational methods of utilizing the diverse natural resources, with simultaneous protection of them from exhaustion and fundamental destruction. A systematic inventory of the natural resources (for example, the climatic, water, land, plant, and animal resources) discovered in the course of scientific research and scientific-production work, built on strictly scientific foundations and including an economic characterization of the resources, becomes, under conditions in the USSR, an indispensable element of national-economic planning. Such a stock-taking should include, first, a general survey of the available information on the natural wealth of the country and its separate regions and, second, a characterization of the present degree of utilization of that wealth. This information is equally indispensable for working out rational plans toward further research and practical activities having to do with the further study and exploitation of the natural resources of the whole country and its regions, as well as for establishing rational methods of protecting them from exhaustion and fundamental destruction.

3. The thorough development of scientific research connected with the purposeful transformation of natural conditions and the all-around utilization of the elemental forces of nature in the interest of further raising the productivity of the socialist national economy. Of especial importance in this area now is the work connected with the transformation of the natural water and heat regime of the developed territories, insuring the further raising of their productivity and the mitigation and liquidation of the harmful consequences of various unfavorable natural processes (for example, erosion, droughts, floods, etc.).

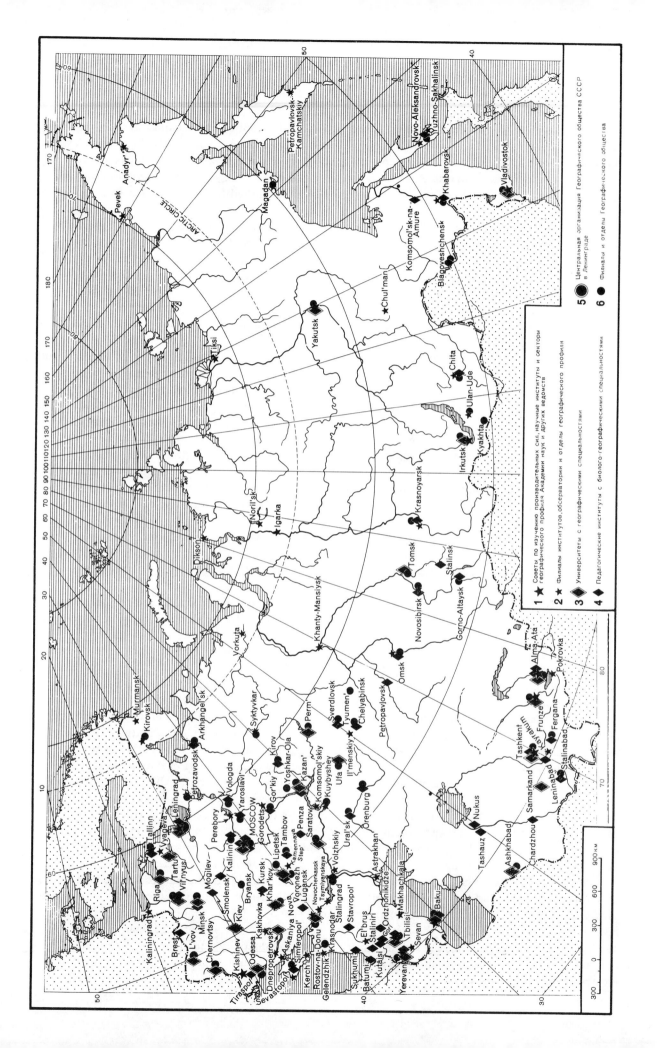

It is well known that for many centuries the various branches of the economy in Russia, especially agriculture, animal husbandry, and transportation, suffered from the periodic manifestation of the elemental forces of nature. Under the conditions of a socialist economy, their action has now been greatly moderated. However, the level of development of modern technology makes it possible, in a socialist state, to go considerably farther in this direction and not only to protect the socialist economy fully from the destructive effect of such elemental natural processes, but also, by overcoming their unfavorable effect, to place their forces in the service of mankind and turn their enormous power to the benefit of the economy. The chief role in the solution of this problem must belong to modern geography, especially to those scientific divisions of physical geography which are in closest contact with the fields of the physical sciences.

4. The study of the regularities in the geographic distribution of production, the territorial (geographic) division of labor, and the formation of economic regions; the study of population geography and related questions.

The further elaboration of all these important theoretical and practical questions of economic geography relates it most closely with the requirements of the national economy. Under the conditions of a socialist planned economy, the thorough scientific treatment of questions of natural and economic regionalization of the whole country or of its individual parts, of the rational distribution of enterprises and the various branches of production, and of the integrated economic development of the individual regions and the proper regulation of their economic ties, has immense practical significance and represents one of the most important tasks of scientific research work. Soviet geographers have long conducted such work both in the scientific and in the planning organs of the Soviet state; but owing to the continuous growth of the national economy this work needs further development and expansion.

5. The all-around scientific analysis of all the geographic characteristics of the country and of the changes produced on its territory by socialist construction, and the geographic study of other countries and the compilation on this basis of scientific surveys, summary maps, atlases, and monographs.

The results of the multiform scientific work on the study of the nature, economy, and population of the various continents, countries, provinces, and smaller territories have long been set forth in the form of geographic descriptions and series of maps. Hence, one of the most important and widespread forms of scientific production in the field of geography, thoroughly reflecting the manifold theoretical and practical achievements of the various geographic sciences, has always been and continues to be the scientific works of an integrated regional, physical-geographic and economic-geographic character, as well as various geographic maps and atlases. As knowledge broadens and scientific theory is developed, the contents of such works as well as the methods of compiling them have been continually perfected.

The present need for scientific geographic works of this type in the USSR is constantly increasing. Their theoretical content must fully reflect the radical changes in the content of modern geography mentioned earlier, and the methods of compilation — both literary and technical — need further perfecting.

There arises the question: In what concrete form and by what methods does Soviet geography solve at present or is it striving to solve in the near future all the complex and responsible tasks enumerated above?

Fig. 1. SCHEMATIC MAP OF THE DISTRIBUTION OF THE
GEOGRAPHIC INSTITUTIONS OF THE USSR
[numbers have been added to the original map]

[1] Councils for the Study of the Productive Forces. Scientific institutes and sectors having geographic interests, belonging to the Academy of Sciences and other official agencies.

[2] Branches of institutes, observatories, and sections having geographic interests.

[3] Universities with geographic specialties.

[4] Pedagogic institutes with biologic-geographic specialties.

[5] Central organizations of the Geographic Society of the USSR in Leningrad.

[6] Branches [filialy] and sections (otdely) of the Geographic Society.

The chief role in the development of the geographic sciences in the USSR and the main responsibility for the performance of the tasks put before them belong to the central scientific-research institutes of a geographic character (Fig. 1). Among them let us name the central Institute of Geography of the Academy of Sciences of the USSR and the newly created Institute of Geography of Siberia and the Far East; the geographic scientific institutions (institutes and sections) in the academies of sciences of the Union republics (Ukrainian, Georgian, Azerbaydzhan, Latvian, Lithuanian, Kazakh, etc.) and in the branches of the Academy of Sciences of the USSR (Komi and Urals branches; Eastern Siberian and Far Eastern branches of the Siberian section of the Academy of Sciences of the USSR, and others); the scientific institutes of the Main Administration of the Hydrometeorologic Service (Main Geophysical Observatory, State Hydrologic Institute, and others); the Central Scientific-Research Institute of Cartography, Aerial Photogrammetry, and Geodesy; the Arctic and Antarctic Institute of the Main Administration of the Northern Sea Route; the numerous geographic chairs and faculties of many universities (above all, Moscow, Leningrad, and Kiyev) and pedagogic institutes.

To these strictly geographic scientific institutions in the USSR are joined a broad system of geological, geophysical, biological, and economic scientific institutions (for example, the corresponding institutes in the academies of sciences), in which investigations of a geographic character are conducted (climatological, hydrological, geomorphological, soil-geographic, geobotanical and zoogeographic, economic-geographic, etc.). Finally, the widely ramified network of geographic research institutes of our country in its work leans upon a still broader network of practical scientific institutions — the planning organs of Unionwide, republic, oblast, or rayon significance and the system of hydrometeorologic and other geographic observation stations, and various project and prospecting enterprises (geologic engineering, hydrotechnical, reclamational, and others).

The total number of scientific workers and specialists active in the field of the geographic sciences in the USSR is rather large. Exact determination of it is rendered difficult by a certain indefiniteness in the criteria for delimiting the scientific specialty, research or practical scientific activity, as well as by the demarcation of researchers from teachers. However, it is significant that the number of active members of the Geographic Society of the USSR, uniting basically the geographers engaged in scientific work, reaches 10,000.

Owing to the great number of scientific and practical scientific institutions conducting work of a geographic character, a correct and reasonably organized co-ordination of scientific research is of especially great significance. The chief responsibility for the co-ordination of scientific work in our country rests upon the Academy of Sciences of the USSR; in the field of geographic research it is performed primarily by the Institute of Geography of the Academy of Sciences of the USSR, by the Council for the Study of Productive Forces under the Presidium of the Academy of Sciences of the USSR, and by other main scientific geographic institutions.

The Council for the Study of Productive Forces organizes and co-ordinates the work of the largest integrated expeditions of a geographic character. Soviet geography has a great deal of experience in conducting such expeditions. They were carried out formerly and are still now organized for the comprehensive geographic study of this or that part of the country and for the elaboration of scientific plans for the integrated utilization of their natural resources and the development of the productive forces. A mere enumeration of the titles of the series of integrated expeditions organized and carried out by the Council for the Study of Productive Forces of the Academy of Sciences of the USSR (SOPS) in Soviet times (Kola, Middle Asia, Caucasus, Urals, Pamir, Kazakhstan, Turkistan, Kulunda, Barabinsk, Yakut, Krasnoyarsk, Buryat-Mongolia, Amur, Tuva, Chita, Far East, Kamchatka, and many others) gives an idea of the territories of the Soviet Union that have been covered or are being covered by explorations of this type.

As is well known, major integrated scientific expeditions of a geographic character organized in the USSR in the most recent years have begun to go beyond the confines of the country. Thus, for example, Soviet geographers, in performing work for the establishment of the Northern Sea Route and the program of the International Geophysical Year, have conducted and are conducting extensive scientific work in the Arctic and Antarctic and adjacent seas.

The scientific institutes of the Main Administration of the Hydrometeorologic Service organize, conduct, and co-ordinate, together with the Institute of Geography of the Academy of Sciences of the USSR and other institutions, scientific-research work on the study of the hydroclimatic conditions of the country and investigation of the natural elemental phenomena. Among work of this sort in the plan of the Academy of Sciences of the USSR, special significance is attached to the study of the water and heat regime of the earth's surface, its role in the dynamics of natural processes, geographic differences, and methods of transformation of nature for practical purposes.

Such work is based on the idea that the water and heat regime, i.e., the heat and moisture circulation in the natural geographic environment, is the chief mechanism controlling the intensity and character of the dynamic changes in all the other forms of exchange of energy and matter between the components of the geographic environment. Hence, by keeping under scientific observation precisely this mechanism and purposefully acting upon it by means of various natural or artificial measures, significant desired changes can most easily be achieved in many important natural processes on the earth's surface.

This scientific trend is very important both for the development of the contemporary theory of physical geography and for the exploitation of its attainments in practice. From the viewpoint of many Soviet geographers, this trend builds a direct bridge between classic physical geography and modern geophysics, promoting the introduction of the achievements and methods of the so-called exact sciences into the field of the geographic sciences. On the other hand it is clear that the treatment of the problem of the water and heat regime of the earth's surface and the methods for its purposeful transformation is aimed directly at the creation of a deepened scientific foundation for various kinds of measures for the improvement of natural heat and water conditions (irrigation, drainage, etc.), the larger part of which, as is known, has been based up to the present time mainly on empirical estimates.

The scientific institutions of the Academy of Sciences of the USSR (including the Council for the Study of Productive Forces, the Institute of Geography and others), jointly with the geographic chairs and faculties of the universities and in close contact with the planning institutions, are organizing and carrying out extensive work in the natural and economic regionalization of the whole territory of the USSR and its separate parts. This work furnishes a very important scientific foundation for a comprehensive inventory of the natural conditions and resources of our country's vast territory and for the elaboration of plans for the rational geographic distribution of the national economy and the integrated development of the productive forces of the various regions.

In the process of performing this work, wide and creative discussions are being carried on regarding questions of the methodology of natural and economic regionalization. In the course of these discussions clashes arise between the various scientific approaches to this or that problem of regionalization which is being worked out by various Soviet geographers and their institutions; the scientific controversies and disagreements arising therefrom eventually make possible the finding of new interpretations and procedures based on a general scientific understanding of the object of geographic science and developing and supplementing earlier concepts. It is very important to emphasize that the general practical orientation of the scientific work on geographic regionalization makes it possible, in many theoretical discussions and disagreements, to rely on the control of scientific propositions by means of practical criteria.

The Institute of Geography of the Academy of Sciences of the USSR, jointly with the specially created State Publishing House for Geographic Literature and various scientific institutions, organizes and conducts in the USSR extensive work on the compilation and publication of regional physical geographic and economic geographic monographs. These books are devoted to the integrated geographic characterization of the major natural or economic regions of the USSR or of foreign countries and are based mostly on a scientific analysis of previously collected geographic materials.

Similar work on the compilation and editing of new general maps and atlases is being carried out by the institutes of the Academy of Sciences of the USSR and the institutions of the Main Administration of Geodesy and Cartography. As has already been noted, the demand for such geographic works in the USSR is very great. It is to be explained not only by the ever-growing cultural interests of the Soviet people and the rapid growth of international cultural relations, but, of course, most of all by the great practical significance of such work for the purposes of country-wide technical, managerial, and economic planning.

In recent years, Soviet geographers have been laboring more and more frequently in collaboration with geographers of the countries of the people's democracies in studying the territory of those countries. For example, major scientific monographs are being thus created on the physical and economic geography of Rumania and Bulgaria. This international scientific collaboration by geographers makes it possible to achieve a high theoretical level in the corresponding geographic monographs constructed on an especially broad and reliable factual basis. Still, such a form of scientific co-operation among the geographers of socialist countries as that found in recent years cannot, of course, by any means be regarded as sufficiently perfected and comprehensive. On the contrary, the generally successful experience in such joint scientific work points to the great and very fruitful opportunities for the further development both of this and of all other forms of scientific collaboration.

Of late, the international scientific ties of Soviet geography have developed very much. These ties have old historical roots. Of the nineteen international geographical congresses, Russian (Soviet) geographers have taken an active part in sixteen; thus, only the three congresses immediately prior to the last two were missed (in Washington, Lisbon, and Amsterdam). At the next-to-last, 18th International Geographical Congress in 1956 in Brazil (Rio de Janeiro), the Academy of Sciences of the USSR became a member of the International Geographical Union, and a number of Soviet geographers entered into the structure of leadership of various continuing commissions, dealing with the most important scientific problems of modern geography on the basis of international collaboration.

Such, in brief, are the basic methodological principles and the chief theoretical and practical tasks now confronting Soviet geography, and also the most important methods and main organizational forms whereby Soviet geographers are solving them.

In the present collection of articles, compiled by a large group of specialized geographers, all the questions touched on above will receive detailed and systematic elucidation. In particular, those present-day debatable theoretical and methodological questions which are exciting the Soviet geographic community and on which there is at times room for considerable differences of scientific views are set forth more concretely. These various scientific disputes and different conceptions among Soviet geographers in the main play an important positive role in the development of science. In the end they will make it possible to find one or another new theoretical interpretation or method, based on a harmonious understanding of the object of the geographic sciences and on the creative application to it of the scientific principles of advanced Marxist methodology.

Soviet geographers, like all Soviet people, take pride in the fact that they live and work in the great socialist country, which is confidently building communism, and this notable social conscience strongly unites, rallies, and inspires them with firm confidence in their own strength.

CHAPTER 2

RUSSIAN GEOGRAPHY*

A. A. Grigor'yev

Russians have long displayed great interest in traveling, to learn about the territories inhabited by them as well as neighboring countries. Thus, it is known that the Slavs of Kiyevan Rus (formed in the 9th-11th centuries) already had lively commercial and cultural relations with Byzantium and with the countries of the Orient and Western Europe. They were familiar with extensive territories of Eastern Europe and its most important rivers and had a good knowledge of the Black Sea region and the coasts of the Caspian Sea. Russian chronicles of the 12th century communicate very valuable information for that time about the nature and the population in Eastern Europe, and some information about the countries of Western Europe, about the sea routes from the Varangian Sea [Baltic Sea] to Rome, about Northern Africa, Asia Minor, Arabia, Persia, and India. Descriptions have also been preserved of travels by Russians to Oriental countries: the most important of these is the "Account" of Daniel, Father Superior of the Russian Land, to Palestine in 1106-1107. In the 12th-13th centuries Novgorod bodyguards crossed the Ural Ridge with fur trading as the objective. In the 13th century, Russians made voyages to Grumant (Spitsbergen). In the 13th-14th centuries, Muscovites and Novgorodians made a number of voyages on the White and Barents seas, penetrating far to the north. By the end of the 14th century, a broad belt of lands adjoining the shores of the Arctic Ocean, at least as far as the Ob', was well known to the Russians. In the 15th century, Novaya Zemlya was visited by them. In the middle of the 15th century, regular intercourse with Middle Asia** began to be established. In the second half of the same century, the Tver' merchant Afanasiy Nikitin was one of the first Europeans to make a journey through India. He spent three years there (1469-1472) and gave a noteworthy description of that country. At the end of the 15th century, Russians mastered the sea route from the White Sea to Western Europe. By this route the Russian ambassador Grigoriy Istomin traveled to Denmark in 1496. Acquaintance with navigation conditions in the Arctic Ocean gave Russians grounds for expressing, at the beginning of the 16th century, the thought that it was possible to travel to China and India by the northeastern sea passage, which produced a sensation in Western Europe and led to a persistent search for this route.

In the 16th century there began to be compiled cadasters and surveys as well as sketches (maps without degree grids) containing detailed geographic information about the territory of Rus, necessary for the government of the state. In the middle of this century the gathering of such information was organized throughout the country. At the end of the 16th century the "Great Drawing" [Bol'shoy Chertëzh] of all Rus was compiled, being accompanied by the "Book to the Great Drawing" [Kniga Bol'shomu Chertëzhu] with a description of the rivers, braided channels, lakes, wells, the adjacent towns and tracts, and the distances between them.

At the end of the 16th and in the 17th century Russian explorers discovered and investigated the immense territory of northern and eastern Asia in their search for new little empires

---

*Translator's note: In current Soviet usage, "Russian" always means exclusively "Pre-Soviet," i.e., "before the 1917 Revolution," save, of course, when applied to the language, to the Russian ethnic majority of the USSR, and to the Russian Socialist Federative Soviet Republic (RSFSR). In all other contexts, "Soviet" has systematically supplanted "Russian." Similarly, "Russia" always means "Pre-Soviet Russia." "Rus" is an early name for Russia or for its political or cultural predecessors.

**Translator's remark: "Middle Asia" ("Srednyaya Aziya") commonly and traditionally designates only that part of Central Asia (Tsentral'naya Aziya) which was annexed to the Russian Empire in the latter half of the 19th century and still forms a part of the Soviet Union.

rich in furs, walrus tusks, and minerals. Russian overland and maritime travelers covered the whole vast route from the Yenisey to the Pacific Ocean in only 30 years. In 1639, I. Yu. Moskvitin was the first European to reach the northwestern shores of the Pacific Ocean in the region of the Sea of Okhotsk. V. O. Poyarkov (1643-1646) and Ye. P. Khabarov (1647-1651) accomplished trips on the Amur. In 1648 S. I. Dezhnëv and Fedot A. Alekseyev-Popov were the first to pass through Bering Strait. To judge from the latest archeological data, one of the vessels of the Russian maritime travelers was in these years carried to the shores of North America, where apparently the first Russian settlement was founded. After Luka Morozko had penetrated to Kamchatka in 1696, V. V. Atlasov made the first exploration and description of it (1697-1698). In 1667 P. I. Godunov began the compilation of the first over-all sketch of Siberia, on which work continued until 1698. In 1701, S. V. Remezov completed the compilation of the first Russian "Atlas of Siberia" [*Chertezhnaya Kniga Sibiri*], a geographic atlas of world significance.*

The 17th century was also signalized by outstanding discoveries by Russian explorers in Middle and Central Asia and in the Far East, connected with the development of commercial relations between the Russian state and the Orient. The Russian embassies of Ivan Petlin in 1618-1619, of F. I. Baykov in 1654-1658 and of N. G. Spafariy in 1675-1678 discovered and described in detail the land routes to Mongolia and China.

Among the geographic explorations of the first half of the 18th century, especially outstanding results were yielded by those of D. Ya. Antsiferov and I. P. Kozyrevskiy, who discovered the chain of Kuril Islands in 1711-1713; the Caspian expedition of 1715-1720 by F. I. Soymonov and others, who compiled the first reliable map of the Caspian Sea; and the Kamchatkan expeditions of V. I. Bering and A. I. Chirikov, in 1725-1730 and 1733-1743, which discovered Alaska, a part of the northwestern coast of North America, and the Aleutian Islands, explored vast territories of Siberia, and surveyed for mapping the whole Arctic Sea coast from the Kara Sea to the mouth of the Kolyma River.

About 1746, A. I. Chirikov compiled a general map summarizing the results of the Russian geographic discoveries in the Pacific Ocean. The discovery of the northwest of North America, made by Russians, laid the ground for the Russian explorations of this part of the New World which were carried out in the 18th and first half of the 19th centuries and were accompanied by a series of important geographic discoveries.

The development of geography in Russia in the first half and the middle of the 18th century, along with the above-mentioned major geographic discoveries, was also marked by the creation of outstanding generalizing geographic works. The epoch of the collection of factual geographic material was gradually succeeded by the epoch in which the accumulation of further empirical material came to be combined with the development of scientific thinking about geographic theory.

The ground for this transition was laid by I. K. Kirilov in creating the regional geography of Russia under the title "The Flourishing State of the All-Russian Empire" and by the geographic works of V. N. Tatishchev, who was the first to examine from a theoretical standpoint the question of the subject and tasks of geography, as well as by the publication of the first atlases of the Russian Empire (I. K. Kirilov in 1734 and the Academy of Sciences in 1745) and particularly by the works of M. V. Lomonosov. As is known, this great Russian scholar, in all his investigations, including the physical geographic ones, proceeded from a recognition of the existence of the material world, the universality of the processes of development, and the causal relations of natural phenomena; he made wide use of the progressive comparative scientific method. "It must be firmly remembered," wrote Lomonosov, "that the visible physical objects on the earth and the whole world have not been, from the beginning of creation, in that state in which we now find them, but that great changes have occurred in them." Touching in his works upon various divisions of general physical geography, Lomonosov expressed entirely new ideas, deriving from the above-mentioned materialistic views. Thus, for example, he wrote about the formation and

---

*This has been republished recently as "The Atlas of Siberia by Semyon U. Remezov," facsimile edition with an introduction by Leo Bagrow. "Imago Mundi, A Review of Early Cartography, Supplement 1," ('s Gravenhage, Netherlands: Mouton & Co., 1958) — Ed.

long development of the major relief forms under the influence of processes arising from inside the earth, about the presence of powerful vertical movements in the atmosphere, about the moderating effect of the sea on the climate, about the necessity of creating a weather service, etc. In his work "Thoughts on the Origin of the Ice Mountains in the Northern Seas," Lomonosov was the first to prove the land origin of icebergs, and was the first to institute the idea of the Northern Sea Route. Directing the Geographic Department of the Academy of Sciences from 1757 to 1765, Lomonosov did much to create highly qualified geodetic specialists, laid the foundation for economic cartography, introduced this term, as well as the term "economic geography," into world usage, and was the initiator of the extensive economic geographic study of Russia.

Among the great Russian generalizing geographic works of the middle of the 18th century we note the "Description of the Land of Kamchatka" by Lomonosov's pupil, S. P. Krasheninnikov, compiled by him on the basis of many years of personal field observations. This is an outstanding work, in which special attention is paid to the integrated characterization of the productive forces of the region described. This monograph was followed by P. I. Rychkov's noteworthy work, "Topography of Orenburg," published in 1762. The works by Krasheninnikov and Rychkov were the first regional monographs which examined the interrelations and interactions of natural phenomena.

The greatest geographic scientific enterprise of the second half of the 18th century was the integrated "academic expeditions" (1768-1774), which together with subsequent explorations embraced the larger part of European Russia and a considerable part of the Urals and Siberia. Their program covered the study of nature, population, economy, and way of life. They were conducted under the guidance or with the participation of the greatest scholars of that epoch: I. I. Lepekhin, N. Ya. Ozeretskovskiy, V. F. Zuyev, P. S. Pallas, and S. G. Gmelin, who developed, in the published works of these expeditions, the advanced materialistic views held by Lomonosov.

Fundamental economic geographic works were also written in the 18th century: the many-volumed "Historical Description of Russian Commerce at all the Ports and Borders," by M. D. Chulkov, the works of A. N. Radishchev (in which the necessity of studying the country by regions, i.e., the necessity of regionalization, was emphasized), S. I. Pleshcheyev, M. M. Shcherbatov, and others.

Materialistic traditions in the field of the understanding of natural phenomena were also characteristic of the majority of the Russian geographic investigations of the 19th and beginning of the 20th century. In the first half of the 19th century, about forty Russian voyages around the world were made; this was a great development. Through these voyages, communication was maintained between European Russia and the Russian possessions in northeast Asia and northwestern North America. Many of these voyages also had exploratory purposes. During the voyages of I. F. Kruzenshtern and Yu. F. Lisyanskiy (1803-1806), V. M. Golovnin (1807-1809), M. P. Lazarev (1813-1816; 1822-1825), O. Ye. Kotsebu (1815-1818; 1823-1826) and F. P. Litke (1826-1829), numerous islands were discovered, observations of currents were made, depths were measured, and so forth. During the Antarctic voyage around the world by F. F. Bellingshausen and M. P. Lazarev (1819-1821) in January, 1820, the sloops "Mirnyy" and "Vostok" got all the way to the ice barrier of the continent of Antarctica. All these scientific oceanographic observations were based on the nascent world oceanography.

The celebrated expedition of A. F. Middendorf (1842-1845) to the least-studied regions of Siberia and the foundation in 1845 of the Russian Geographic Society were followed by great exploring expeditions. The northern regions of Russia were studied.

G. I. Nevel'skoy's expedition to the Amur and Ussuri explored a vast territory of the Russian Far East and discovered the Tatar Strait [*Tatarskiy Proliv*]. The renowned Russian travelers P. P. Semenov-Tyan-Shanskiy, N. M. Przheval'skiy, I. V. Mushketov, M. V. Pevtsov, V. I. Roborovskiy, V. A. Obruchev, G. N. Potanin, P. K. Kozlov, and many others opened up for science enormous territories of Middle and Central Asia. Great investigations in the geography of soils, geobotany, and other natural sciences were made in the same years by the so-called *zemstva* [district councils] and in the pre-revolution years of the 20th century by the expeditions of the Resettlement Administration.

The immense progress in the geographic study of the globe in the 19th and the beginning of the 20th century, in which Russian explorers held a conspicuous place, brought about further progress in our country in the working out of the theoretical problems of geography and the formation of the individual geographic sciences. Russian scholars took the most active part in the development of general and regional physical geography, geomorphology, hydrology of the land, oceanography, limnology, glaciology, and geobotany. Especially great has been the role of Russian scholars in the development of physical geography and geographic soil science, thanks to the innovational ideas of Vasiliy Vasil'yevich Dokuchayev, in climatology thanks to Aleksandr Ivanovich Voyeykov, and in zoogeography thanks to the works of Karl Frantsevich Rul'ye and Nikolay Alekseyevich Severtsov.

Materialistic views predominated in the theoretical works of Russian geographers of various specialties in the period described. Voyeykov examined climate in relation to all the other components of the natural environment. V. V. Dokuchayev created the study of natural zones and of integrated natural complexes in which all the component parts are in continuous interaction, changing and developing both in space and in time. Climatic zonality was known even in ancient times. The zonal distribution of vegetation was established by Alexander von Humboldt, but the discovery of the law of geographic zonality, i.e., the law of the zonal distribution of integrated natural complexes, represents the great scientific contribution of Dokuchayev. The Dokuchayev study of soils and of the zones of nature, supplemented and perfected by his numerous successors (especially in Soviet times) has established the basis for a genuinely scientific physical geography.

A major role in the creation of geographic theory was played by Dmitriy Nikolayevich Anuchin, who in his works proceeded from the idea of the development of nature and natural interrelations. He regarded geography as a whole system of sciences, distinguishing in it two major divisions (1892): (1) general geography [zemlevedeniye], study of the whole earth's surface, and (2) particular geography, or regional geography [stranovedeniye], the tasks of which embrace the investigation of the individual parts and sections of this surface. Both divisions exist and are developing jointly.

The development of physical geography in Russia around the beginning of the 20th century was marked, along with the development of a materialistic understanding of nature, by the appearance of a one-sided "spatial" trend in geography, founded in our country by Ye. Chizhov in 1896 and worked out in detail by Alfred Hettner in Germany from 1905 on.

As is known, this trend restricted the tasks of geography to a mere study of the spatial relations among the phenomena of the earth's surface, rejecting the study of geographic phenomena in their development and essence. Yet, for a genuinely scientific study of phenomena it is necessary to investigate them in all these relationships. The erroneousness of this trend was revealed rather quickly, and its influence on the development of geographic thought in Russia and the USSR came gradually to be reduced to nil.

To characterize the development of Russian economic geography in the 19th and the beginning of the 20th century, let us name the following basic works: the first experiments in the economic regionalization of Russia (by Konstantin Ivanovich Arsen'yev, Pëtr Petrovich Semenov-Tyan-Shanskiy and others); Nikolay Platonovich Ogarëv's investigation of the methodology of economic regionalization; the "Geographic-Statistical Dictionary of the Russian Empire," compiled by Pëtr Petrovich Semenov-Tyan-Shanskiy in 1863-1886, as well as the many-volume edition of "Russia: Complete Geographic Description of Our Fatherland," which also came out under his editorship; the valuable works of the zemstvo statisticians; works by Dmitriy Ivanovich Mendeleyev and Aleksandr Ivanovich Voyeykov on various questions of the economic geography of Russia; and a number of atlases and maps on branches of the national economy of Russia. Of especially great significance for the development of the theory of economic geography were Vladimir Il'ich Lenin's works: "The Development of Capitalism in Russia" (1899), "New Data on the Laws of the Development of Capitalism in Agriculture" (1917), "Imperialism as a Higher Stage of Capitalism" (1917), and others.

As has been pointed out above, Soviet geography, born after the Great October Socialist Revolution, was the direct and immediate heir of the classic heritage of Russian geography. This heritage has been rapidly enriched and expanded in the process of the development of Soviet geography.

The development of geography in the USSR was governed by the immense evolution of physical geographic and economic geographic investigations of all the territories of the Union, called for by the requirements of planning for the growing socialist economy. The orientation of these investigations was coordinated in the closest possible manner with the increasingly complicated practical demands of the building of a communist society. In response to these tasks there was also an extensive organization in the USSR of higher geographic education in the universities and teachers' colleges.

The decisive influence on the development of Soviet geography has been exerted by the wide dissemination in the USSR of the principles of dialectical and historical materialism, particularly the doctrine that various laws underlie the development of human society and nature. This has made it possible to demonstrate scientifically the fact that physical geography belongs to natural science and that economic geography belongs to the social sciences, with the existence of a very close connection between these sciences. This way of posing the question has been of outstanding significance for the progress of both the physical geographic and the economic geographic sciences.

Part I

THE HISTORY AND PRESENT STATE OF SOVIET GEOGRAPHY

V. V. Dokuchayev (1846-1903)

A. I. Voyeykov (1842-1916)

P. P. Semenov-Tyan-Shanskiy (1827-1914)

D. N. Anuchin (1843-1923)

CHAPTER 3

PHYSICAL GEOGRAPHY OF THE LAND

S. V. Kalesnik

Physical geography in the proper sense of the word occupies a special place among the geographic sciences in view of the complexity of the object of its study. This object is the geographic, or landscape, envelope of the earth — the natural system associated with the surface of our planet and including the troposphere, the hydrosphere, the biosphere, and the stratosphere. The complexity of the composition and structure of the geographic envelope sharply distinguishes it from the other parts of the globe. This is due to the fact that the geographic envelope exists and develops under the action of cosmic influences and of the internal forces of the earth, i.e., it serves as the arena for the encounter of exogenic and endogenic processes.

Physical geography studies the geographic envelope as an integral formation which possesses regional differences. The most general characteristics of the composition, structure, and development of the geographic envelope are the object of the attention of general physical geography [*zemlevedeniye*]. The regional differences of the geographic envelope are the object of regional physical geography [*landshaftovedeniye*]. The history of the development of the geographic envelope and of the individual geographic landscapes or groupings of them belongs to the jurisdiction of general and regional paleogeography. These branches of physical geography — general physical geography, regional physical geography, and paleogeography — are three sides of one and the same science, intertwined and inconceivable without each other, since genuine knowledge of the geographic envelope is impossible without investigating its qualitative characteristics and their changes in space and time. In the present essay only a general survey of the state of physical geography in the USSR is given. More detailed information is contained in other sections of this book.

The progress of any geographic research is determined by the requirements of society, by the character of the social structure, by the availability of research personnel and scientific-research institutions, by the organization and methods of investigation, and by the progress of the disciplines related to geography.

The main task of the socialist social structure — the continual raising of the material welfare and the fullest satisfaction of the cultural demands of the whole people — requires a constant search for new natural resources, and the rational utilization of the geographic environment as a whole. Hence, the geographic investigation of the territory of the USSR has in Soviet times acquired an unparalleled scope, insured by the systematic training of geographer-researchers and by the creation of dozens of institutions possessing the necessary personnel and funds to carry on scientific research in the various fields of geography.

In Tsarist Russia, geography chairs existed in only six universities, and there was not a single specialized independent geographic institution of higher learning. Such establishments arose only under Soviet rule. The first was the Geographic Institute in Leningrad, founded in 1918 and subsequently transformed into the Geographic Faculty of Leningrad University. Now there are geographic faculties and geographic departments in 27 universities of the country. It is principally here that physical geographers are trained for scientific research work.

In the first decade of Soviet rule there also arose a number of geographic scientific-research institutions of broad scope. Among them we note the Geographic-economic Scientific-Research Institute of Leningrad University, the Institute of Geography of Moscow University, the Institute of Geography of the Academy of Sciences of the USSR, the Arctic Institute of the Main Administration of the Northern Sea Route (now the Arctic and Antarctic Scientific-Research Institute). The institutes of geography in the Georgian and Azerbaydzhan academies of science, the geography sector in the Academy of Sciences of Kazakhstan, the Institute of Geology and Geography in Lithuania, etc., were created later. Recently the organization of the Institute of Geography of Siberia and the Far East in Irkutsk was initiated and the question of the creation of the Institute of Geography in Kiyev was decided in the affirmative. The functions of geographic scientific-research institutions are performed by some branches and sections of the Geographic Society of the USSR, as well as by the Council for the Study of Productive Forces (SOPS) under the Presidium of the Academy of Sciences of the USSR — one of the major centers for the organization of geographic investigation of our country's territory.

Characteristic of geographic research in the Soviet years has been the extensive application of the integrated method, as expressed in the formation of large expeditions, each of which has been composed of many working groups headed by various specialists — geologists, geomorphologists, soil scientists, botanists, and so forth. This method has been used in studying Central Yakutiya, the Kola Peninsula, Kazakhstan, Kirgiziya, Tadzhikistan, the Pamir, Karakalpakiya, the Buryat ASSR, the Karelian Isthmus, the Lake Ladoga region, the Volga region, the Crimea, Vologda oblast, the Onega-Dvina watershed, and other regions. The integrated expeditions have usually worked for many years and investigated not only the natural characteristics and natural wealth of a given district, but also its economy and the culture of the population.

The progress of physical-geographic research is always promoted by the availability of good topographic and general geographic maps. At present, in addition to large-scale maps for individual regions, Soviet geographers have at their disposal maps for the whole territory of the country and to scales of 1:1,000,000 and 1:100,000. If the size of the USSR (22 million square kilometers) is taken into consideration, it is easy to understand the immense scientific and practical significance of the 1:100,000 map — the fruit of the intense labor of Soviet aerial-photo surveyors and cartographers. It is evident that the compilation of such a map of itself leads to new geographic discoveries. In particular, it was aerial photo survey that prompted the discovery of new regions of present-day glaciation in Siberia—in the Suntar-Khayata Range, in the Buordakh massif (central part of the Khrebet Cherskogo) and in the Koryakskiy Khrebet, i.e., at places where the existence of glaciers was imagined to be improbable because of the dryness of the climate.

As a result of physico-geographic explorations on the territory of the Soviet Union from 1917 to 1959, not only was an enormous amount of new factual material collected on regions formerly but little or only partially studied, but new geographic objects were also discovered.

Let us mention first of all the major discoveries in the Soviet sector of the Arctic. The contours of the shoreline of Severnaya Zemlya had already been marked by Russian hydrographers in 1913 over a small stretch; but this archipelago, with an area of 37,000 square kilometers, was genuinely explored and put on the map in 1930-1932 by N. N. Urvantsev and G. A. Ushakov. Besides Severnaya Zemlya, many small islands were discovered in the Arctic, among them the ostrava (islands) Arkticheskogo Instituta, "Izvestiya TsIK," Sergeya Kirova, Voronina, Vize, Ushakova, and others. A scientific event of very great importance was the discovery in 1948 by Soviet geographers Ya. Ya. Gakkel' and others of the submarine range Lomonosova.

The systematic exploration being carried out in the Arctic with the aid of icebreakers, hydrographic vessels, airplanes, and stations drifting on icefloes, named "Severnyy Polyus" (nine such stations have already been organized), are contributing to an ever more thorough knowledge of the polar landscapes and the working out of plans for their economic conquest. The rich experience in Arctic exploration proved very helpful to Soviet geographers when they were engaged in the study of the Antarctic in connection with the International Geophysical Year. The Integrated Antarctic Expedition of the Academy of Sciences of the USSR, which began its activity in 1956 with the building of the research observatory "Mirnyy" on the shore of the South-Polar continent, enriched science with a number of substantial geographic discoveries and is continuing to work with unfailing success.

In Soviet times, new geographic names have appeared on the map of Middle Asia as well. Thus, for example, the Kavak-Tau (range) and the Pik Pobedy, 7,439 meters high (1943), have been discovered in the Tyan'-Shan, and Khrebet Akademii Nauk (1927), with the highest peak in the Soviet Union (Pik Stalina, 7,495 meters, 1928) and the mighty system of the Fedchenko Glacier, in the Pamirs. A multitude of new glaciers have been recorded in Middle Asia: in 1955, the glaciated area here was estimated at 17,000 square kilometers, whereas in 1930 only 9,000 square kilometers of glaciers were known.

In Middle Asia, not only the mountain regions, but also the desert areas, particularly the Kyzylkum, the Karakumy, the Muyunkum, the Betpak-Dala, and others, have been subjected to careful study. The Karakumy Desert, a depression lying 92 meters below sea level, was discovered in 1935. Repeated explorations of the Karagiye depression on the Mangyshlak Peninsula have shown that this is the deepest depression in the USSR, with an absolute depression of 132 meters below sea level.

Explorations of Siberia and the Far East have led to unexpected and very great geographic discoveries. Beyond the Arctic Circle and to the east of the Yenisey were discovered the Putorana Mountains with the summit Kamen' (1,664 meters); along the right bank of the same river a study was made of the Yeniseyskiy Kryazh [Ridge], extending southward from the mouth of the Podkamennaya Tunguska. To the east of the Verkhoyanskiy Khrebet (range) S. V. Obruchev discovered in 1926 the Khrebet Cherskogo—a mountainland not inferior in area to the Caucasus. The length of the range is 1,000 kilometers, its width is 300 kilometers, and its highest point, Gora Pobeda, rises to 3,147 meters. Among the new geographic objects discovered in Soviet times are also the Momskiy Khrebet (to the north of the Khrebet Cherskogo), Nerskoye Ploskogor'ye (plateau), El'ginskoye Ploskogor'ye, Oymyakonskoye Ploskogor'ye, Suntar-Khayata-Khebet (to the south of the Khrebet Cherskogo), Alazeyskoye Ploskogor'ye (between the Indigirka and the Alazeya), Yukagirskoye Ploskogor'ye, Anadyrskoye Ploskogor'ye, Penzhinskiy Khrebet, and others. On Kamchatka in the region of Kronotskiy Zaliv [Gulf] were discovered in 1941 more than 20 active geysers, i.e., the fourth great geyser focus on the earth (the first three are: Iceland, New Zealand, and Yellowstone National Park in the U.S.A.). As already noted, a new center of present-day glaciation was discovered in the basin of the Indigirka, where the area occupied by ice amounts to 255 square kilometers.

Geographic discoveries were also made in the European part of the USSR. For example, the Vetrenyy Poyas Kryazh, extending 200 kilometers along the southern shore of the Onega Bay of the White Sea was discovered in 1937 by N. M. Karbasnikov, and the highest point of the Ural Range, Narodnaya Gora (1,894 meters); and in the Polar Urals a group of unusual small glaciers was found (only one of them has a length as much as 2.5 kilometers).

From the foregoing it may be seen that the development of physical geography in the USSR has proceeded primarily along the line of accumulating new factual material. But still another important circumstance must be emphasized: the development of physical geography in the USSR has been accompanied by a break with, and revision of, the basic methodologic concepts of this science, which before the Revolution had in part become cluttered with elements of Hettnerianism. This revision took place in an atmosphere of heated controversy, which assumed an especially sharp character in the 1930's and in 1950-1951. However, it ultimately resulted in outlining the general contours of the theory of physical geography which have proved very fruitful for its further advance.

Without touching upon the theoretical achievements of regional physical geography, dealt with in other articles, we shall dwell briefly on the state of general earth science. In the first years of Soviet rule the most monumental production in this branch of knowledge was the "General Physical Geography" [*Obshcheye zemlevedeniye*] of A. A. Kruber. However, the last editions of this work came out without the author's participation: prominent but narrow specialists were engaged to supplement and rework the various chapters and in the end the "General Physical Geography," conceived by Kruber as an internally integrated work, was converted, in the hands of editors and co-authors acting, be it said, with the best of intentions, into an agglomerate of poorly interrelated essays on various particular branches of geographic knowledge. The value of this agglomerate consisted solely in the abundance of reliable factual material.

A serious contribution to the general theory of physical geography and to the theory of general physical geography in particular was made by the numerous works of A. A. Grigor'yev, especially the "Experiment in an Analytic Characterization of the Composition and Structure of the Physical Geographic Envelope of the Globe" (1937), "Experiment in a Characterization of the Basic Types of the Physical Geographic Environment" (1938-1942), and "On some Basic Problems of Physical

Geography" (1957). Grigor'yev demonstrated the qualitative difference of the geographic envelope of the earth from other layers of the planet, pointed out the importance of investigating the character of the interaction between the objects and phenomena in the geographic envelope, proposed a system of taxonomic units in physical-geographic regionalization, and, jointly with M. I. Budyko, formulated the periodic law of geographic zonality. (Concerning this law, see the article "Present State of the Theory of Geographic Zonality," Chapter 22 in the present book.) The groups of zones forming the periodic system of geographic zonality are distinguished on the basis of consideration of three closely interrelated factors: the yearly magnitude of the radiation balance of the earth's surface (i.e., the difference between the heat absorbed and the heat released by this surface); the yearly amount of precipitation; the ratios between this balance and precipitation (called the radiation index of dryness $K = \frac{R}{Lr}$, where R is the annual radiation balance, L the latent heat of evaporation, r the sum of precipitation). The investigation showed that the same values of K recur periodically in all groups of geographic zones, beginning with the subarctic and middle latitudes and ending with the tropical. Every such value determines the type of landscape zone, while the concrete aspect and character of the zone depend upon the magnitude of R.

A great contribution to the theory of general physical geography has been made by the works of V. B. Sochava, K. K. Markov, I. P. Gerasimov, A. G. Isachenko, D. L. Armand, and other geographers.

In addition to the multitude of separate articles devoted to diverse questions of geographic theory, summaries have begun to appear in recent years. The authors of these summaries attempt to give a general survey of the state of all the theoretical problems in geography or to examine the most important of them in detail. These works discuss such topics as the object of physical geography, the geographic landscape and its basic laws, the principles and methods of physical geographic regionalization, the typology of landscapes, geographic zonality, cultural landscapes, the classification of the geographic sciences, the general laws of the geographic envelope of the earth, systematization of geographic units, quantitative characteristics in geography, and so forth. Among the theoretical summaries of a monographic character are "Basic Questions of Physical Geography" by A. G. Isachenko (1953), "Basic Problems of the Theory of Physical Geography" by I. M. Zabelin (1957), "Basic Problems of Physical Geography" by F. N. Mil'kov (1959), "Theory of Physical Geography" by I. M. Zabelin (1959), and some others. The viewpoints of the authors of these books do not coincide on a number of questions, but they are all united by a common materialistic concept of nature.

The most important theoretical concepts of Soviet physical geography may be formulated in the following manner: the system of sciences historically evolved through differentiation of the once single science of geography embraces both the natural branches of knowledge (physical geography, geomorphology, climatology, oceanography, land hydrology, soil science, biogeography, and so forth), as well as certain sciences of the social series (economic geography, history of geography, and toponymy). Each geographic science has its own object of investigation (the geographic envelope of the earth, relief, climate, ocean, soil, and so forth) and is entirely independent in this respect.

The object of physical geography is the geographic, or landscape, envelope of the earth. Some authors identify this envelope with the geographic, or natural, environment. Most geographers, however, are not inclined to confuse the concept of the object of physical geography (the geographic envelope) with the general philosophical concept of the geographic (natural) environment.

The major parts making up the geographic envelope (relief, air masses, various forms of water accumulations, soil cover, biocoenoses) are called its components. The character of the interaction and interrelationship between the separate components is customarily called the structure of the geographic envelope. The heterogeneity of the structure in the different parts of the geographic envelope causes it to be broken up into a multitude of geographic landscapes or districts, differing both in external appearance and in internal build and content.

There are two categories of landscape units: the regional and the typological. Each regional unit possesses a continuous (unbroken) area, a distinct individuality (consequently, unduplicability in space) and a relative genetic unity of the territory occupied by it. In contrast, the typological units do not possess a continuous area. They may exist in the form of separate strips or spots and their distribution does not conform to the boundaries of the regional units. Both categories exist parallel to one another and at the same time are interrelated.

The latest summaries on general earth science, the "Fundamentals of General Physical Geography" (1947, 1955) and the "Short Course in General Physical Geography" (1957) have been written by S. V. Kalesnik. In these books the author establishes general physical geography as the branch of physical geography concerned with the geographic (landscape) envelope of the earth as a whole and with the most general characteristics of its material composition, structure, and development; in other words, as the science of the most general geographic laws of the earth.

Among the most general geographic laws of the globe are:

1. THE INTEGRITY OF THE GEOGRAPHIC (LANDSCAPE) ENVELOPE. Each component of this envelope, possessing, as it does, its own particular quality and existing and developing according to its own laws, is at the same time most closely related to other components, so that a change in one component sooner or later entails an associated change in all the other components.

2. THE PRESENCE, IN THE GEOGRAPHIC ENVELOPE, OF CIRCULATIONS OF MATTER AND RELATED ENERGY (intratropic circulation of the atmosphere, circular movements of water in the system of ocean currents, circulation of water in nature, circulation of oxygen, exchange of matter, etc.).

3. THE PRESENCE, IN THE GEOGRAPHIC ENVELOPE, OF RHYTHMIC PHENOMENA — daily, seasonal, perennial, secular, etc.

4. THE CONTINUITY OF DEVELOPMENT. The main cause of the development of the entire geographic envelope as a whole is the conflict between the exogenic and the endogenic processes; in other words, the struggle between zonal and azonal phenomena. In the process of development, the geographic envelope undergoes irreversible changes, although in form they sometimes are cyclical in character (for example, the Caledonian, Hercynian, and Alpine rhythms).

5. THE ZONALITY OF THE STRUCTURE OF THE GEOGRAPHIC ENVELOPE, governed by the form of the earth and its position with relation to the sun. The zonal distribution of a number of components has resulted, by virtue of the integrity of the geographical envelope, in the formation of landscape zones. Zonality changes with the change in the character of the environment (thus, it is expressed differently in the surface of the ocean than on the land), as well as under the effect of the interference of azonal factors. The cause of azonal factors, as is known, lies in tectonic phenomena such as oscillatory movements of the earth's crust, earthquakes, volcanism, and so forth. Zonality is evened out in epochs of major marine transgressions and becomes acute in epochs of regression; in mountain lands, zonality is transformed into vertical zonation, and the range of the zones varies with the relief. The predominance of azonal or zonal features in this or that section of the geographic envelope at any given moment depends upon the stage of development of the given section. The formation of zonality is subject to the periodic law.

As a result of intensive geographic investigations on the territory of the USSR, a very rich literature has been created, covering regional physical geography. Integrated regional characterizations in the form of physical geographic monographs generalize the materials from the branch geographic investigations concerning a given territory, describing its landscapes and giving a scheme of its natural regionalization. In their structure, the monographs usually fall into four parts: (1) *introductory* (history of the investigations, geographic position, toponymy); (2) *general* (characterization of the nature by separate components — climate, relief, hydrographic network, etc.); (3) *regional* (description of the recognized units of physical geographic regionalization; (4) *informational* (bibliography, index, etc.). Of course, this plan is not maintained in all the geographic writings, but it may be regarded as typical. Thus far there are still very few geographic monographs based on materials from a field landscape survey (see Chapter 25, "Landscape Science," in this book). In compiling a regional characterization the physical geographer is obliged, as heretofore, to use and synthesize materials on the study of the separate components of the landscape.

The literature on physical geography created in the USSR during the last 40 years is so abundant that it is not possible to give here an adequate presentation of it. From among the largest and most original summaries, we shall name "Geography of Russia, the Ukraine, and the Territories Adjoining Them on the West" by G. I. Tanfil'yev, "Geographic (Landscape) Zones of the Soviet Union," and the "Nature in the USSR"* by L. S. Berg, "Subarctic" by A. A. Grigor'yev, "Physical Geography of the USSR" (European Part and the Caucasus) by B. F. Dobrynin, and the "Physical Geography of the USSR" (Asiatic Part) by S. P. Suslov.** The Institute of

Geography of the Academy of Sciences of the USSR has published the series "Nature in the USSR," containing valuable summaries of materials on a number of regions of the country. (For further details see Chapter 6, "Regional Geography [*Stranovedeniye*]" in the present book.)

The compilation of a new series of scientific physical geographic monographs—12 in number— is planned to embrace the entire territory of the USSR. Two volumes have already been completed: "Forest-steppe and Steppe of the European Part of the USSR" and "Middle Asia."

To the above brief list should be added hundreds of large and small physical geographic and regional geographic monographs on all the natural regions of the USSR and on foreign countries, published by the State Publishing House for Geographic Literature, the branches and sections of the Geographic Society of the USSR, the oblast printing houses, etc. A four-volume "Short Geographic Encyclopedia" is being prepared for publication, which will reflect all the principal theoretical and practical achievements of geographic science in general and of Soviet physical geography in particular.

———

*[Available in English as *Natural Regions of the USSR* by L. S. Berg. Translated by Olga Adler Titelbaum and edited by John A. Morrison and C. C. Nikofiroff (New York: Macmillan, 1950), 436 pp. — Ed.]

**[Available in English as *Physical Geography of Asiatic Russia* by S. P. Suslov. Translated by Noah D. Gershevsky, and edited by Joseph E. Williams (San Francisco: W. H. Freeman, 1961), 594 pp. — Ed.]

BASIC LITERATURE

Armand, D. L. "On Some Theoretical Propositions of Physical Geography," *Izv. AN SSSR, seriya geogr.*, 1951, no. 3.

Berg, L. S. Geographic (Landscape) Zones of the Soviet Union (*Geograficheskiye [Landshaftnyye] Zony Sovetskogo Soyuza*), vol. I, 1947; vol. II, 1952.

Gvozdetskiy, N. A. "Research and Discoveries of Soviet Geographers," *Priroda*, 1957, no. 10.

Grigor'yev, A. A. "An Experiment in the Characterization of the Basic Types of the Physical Geographic Environment," *Problemy fiz. geogr.*, 1938-1942, vols. 5, 6, 7 and 11.

Grigor'yev, A. A. "From the History of Soviet Geography," *Izv. AN SSSR, seriya geogr.*, 1957, no. 5.

Grigor'yev, A. A. "On Some Basic Problems of Physical Geography," *Izv. AN SSSR, seriya geogr.*, 1957, no. 6.

Grigor'yev, A. A., and Budyko, M. I. "On the Periodic Law of Geographic Zonality," *Doklady AN SSSR*, vol. 110, 1956, no. 1.

Zabelin, I. M. Theory of Physical Geography (*Teoriya Fizicheskoy Geografii*), Moscow, 1959.

Isachenko, A. G. Basic Questions of Physical Geography (*Osnovnyye Voprosy Fizicheskoy Geografii*), Leningrad, 1953.

Kalesnik, S. V. Fundamentals of General Physical Geography (*Osnovy Obshchego Zemlevedeniya*), 2nd ed., Moscow, 1955.

Kalesnik, S. V. Short Course in General Physical Geography (*Kratkiy Kurs Obshchego Zemlevedeniya*), Moscow, 1957.

Kalesnik, S. V. "A General View of the Development of some Branches of Geography in the USSR during the Years of Soviet Rule," *Izv. VGO*, 1957, no. 5.

Kruber, A. A. General Physical Geography (*Obshcheye zemlevedeniye*), 5th ed., Moscow, 1938.

Makeyev, P. S. Natural Zones and Landscapes (*Prirodnyye Zony i Landshafty*), Moscow, 1956.

Markov, K. K. Paleogeography (*Paleogeografiya*), Moscow, 1956 (2nd ed., rotoprint).

Mil'kov, F. N. Basic Problems of Physical Geography (*Osnovnyye Problemy Fizicheskoy Geografii*), Voronezh, 1959.

Murzayev, E. M. "Results and Tasks of Physical Geographic Regional Geography (*Stranovedeniya*) in the USSR," *Izv. AN SSSR, seriya geogr.*, 1957, no. 5.

Polovinkin, A. A. General Physical Geography (*Obshchaya Fizicheskaya Geografiya*), Moscow, 1948.

CHAPTER 4

PHYSICAL GEOGRAPHY OF THE SEAS AND OCEANS

A. D. Dobrovol'skiy

Exploration of the seas in our country has developed to a large extent from the necessity of satisfying practical demands, above all for sea transportation and the fishing industry. Beside this, much influence has been exercised by the interests of the weather service, particularly in the field of forecasting, especially long-range. However, it is not only these applied purposes that have stimulated the development of the study of the ocean. This was required by the development of geography as a science.

At first, the study of the seas and oceans was confined to a determination of the contours of the land, to refinement of geographic maps, and only incidentally were scattered investigations made into the individual characteristics of the seas and oceans proper — the relief of the floor, the currents, the temperatures, etc.

Occasional oceanologic observations were made on the first Russian voyages around the world, at the beginning of the 19th century. The first major oceanologic work in our country was the well-known one by S. O. Makarov, "The *Vityaz'* and the Pacific Ocean" (1894). At about this same time oceanographic expeditions began their work on our seas (on the Black Sea by Shpindler and Vrangel' in 1890-1891 and on the Barents Sea by Knipovich in 1898, etc.).

After the October Revolution, exploration of the seas assumed a wide scope. In 1921, a special decree by V. I. Lenin created the special Floating Marine Scientific Institute, which, having begun its work on the White and Barents seas, later extended its explorations to other northern seas. The creation of the Hydrologic Institute within the Marine Department, and of the Arctic Institute, both of which began the study of the seas, dates from the same time.

In the first stages of the development of Soviet oceanology, a large role was played by the great scholars who had been trained even before the Revolution: Yu. M. Shokal'skiy and N. M. Knipovich, A. D. Arkhangel'skiy and V. I. Vernadskiy, S. A. Zernov and K. M. Deryugin, and others.

In 1929, an independent Hydrometeorologic Service was organized in the Soviet Union, in the system of which hydrometeorologic institutes were created on all the seas. Somewhat earlier, scientific institutes had been organized in the system of the fishing industry. Sea exploration institutions — stations, laboratories, institutes — were also developed in the Academy of Sciences of the USSR. If we add to all these institutions the Hydrographic Service of the Navy, we shall have defined the general system and design of oceanographic research in the USSR as it was established at the very beginning of the existence of the Soviet State and as it exists now. Both earlier and at present, the main purpose of scientific knowledge of the seas and oceans is assistance in the solution of the practical tasks of the national economy and the working out of the major theoretical problems of science.

Without describing in detail the course of the development of Soviet oceanology, let us endeavor to show the most significant results achieved by it.

The most important achievement of Soviet oceanology is the high degree of coverage in the study of the seas washing the shores of the USSR, which provides for the main requirements of the national economy. Furthermore, this research has made it possible to work out many theoretical propositions in the science of the ocean. Work was carried on with especial energy in the 20's and 30's on the Barents Sea by the forces of the State Oceanographic Institute, the "old" GOIN [Gosudarstvennyy Okeanograficheskiy Institut], created on the basis of the Floating Marine Scientific Institute and the Murmansk Biologic Station. Numerous expeditions on the vessels "Persey" and "N. Knipovich" and others furnished extensive material for an integrated oceanologic characterization of the Barents, Kara, Norwegian, Greenland, and other seas. It was essentially on the basis of this work that the new Soviet science of the sea was formed. From the GOIN of that time issued the great Soviet oceanologists, who created their own independent scientific trends, united by the common principles of materialistic science. It suffices to mention the names of I. I. Mesyatsev, A. A. Shorygin; and the following, all of whom are still living: L. A. Zenkevich, N. N. Zubov, M. V. Klenova, V. V. Shuleykin, V. B. Shtokman, V. P. Zenkovich, S. V. Bruyevich, L. K. Blinov, B. A. Skopintsev, B. P. Manteyfel', T. S. Rass, V. S. Samoylenko, and many others who began their work at the GOIN and have now become leading scholars in the respective fields of oceanology (the author also began his activity in this institute). In addition to the GOIN, oceanology was developed in the other above-mentioned institutions, which furnished science such names as Ye. F. Gur'yanov, V. V. Timonov, P. V. Ushakov, the deceased V. Yu. Vize, the deceased G. Ye. Ratmanov, and others.

In the development of Soviet oceanology the following stages may be distinguished:

1. First steps in the establishment of Soviet oceanology (1921-1931).

2. Broad evolution of oceanographic expeditions in the seas washing the shores of the USSR (1932-1940).

3. Curtailment of expeditionary work and evolution of exploration having defense significance (1941-1944).

4. Restoration and new broad evolution of exploration on the seas (1945-1949).

5. Change to the new technology, considerable growth of the scientific-research fleet in the oceanographic institutions (since 1949).

6. Finally, in the last few years, especially in connection with the International Geophysical Year, Soviet exploring vessels have gone out into the oceans and have established contacts and interaction with foreign exploration. This sixth stage is still continuing.

In the first stage, the already mentioned work was performed in the northern seas. Furthermore, in 1921-1927, expeditions operated in the Black Sea and the Sea of Azov under the direction of Yu. M. Shokal'skiy on the ship "Pervoye Maya" (later renamed the "Gidrograf") and of N. M. Knipovich on the ships "Tri Svyatitelya" (renamed the "Besstrashnyy"), and "N. Danilevskiy," and others; in the Far East B. V. Davydov and L. A. Demin operated on the vessel "Krasnyy Vympel" and others. And so forth.

An outstanding role in the development of the work of the second stage was played by exploration in accordance with the program of the Second International Polar Year (2 IPY, 1932-1933). Oceanographic work was included in this program at the proposal of the Soviet Union, and it was our country that developed it most extensively. At this time an expedition was conducted in accordance with a concerted program simultaneously on all the seas bordering our country's shores. This work, which furnished much completely new oceanographic information, was not discontinued upon termination of the 2nd IPY, but underwent further development.

During the war, expeditionary work was naturally almost entirely discontinued, and the main attention of theoretical research was directed toward insuring the country's defense.

In the first years after the war there was a restoration of the material base for the organization of oceanologic work. Created were the State Oceanographic Institute of the Hydrometeorologic Service (the "new" GOIN), and later the Institute of Oceanology and the Marine Hydrophysical Institute of the Academy of Sciences of the USSR, and others. The sharp qualitative growth of oceanologic research was connected with the creation of a new type of expeditionary vessel. In 1949, the "Vityaz'," the expeditionary vessel of the Institute of Oceanology of the Academy of Sciences of the USSR, put to sea. This large ship (5,500 tons displacement), with 13 laboratories and 60 places for scientists, provided with the latest technologic equipment, is able to operate for two or three months without returning to port. The very first voyages of the "Vityaz'" yielded exceptionally rich results, and each of its trips became an event in oceanography. It is a true floating institute, a real incarnation of the idea laid down in Lenin's decree of 1921: on the "Vityaz'" they not only observe, but also work up the material obtained and generalize it on the trip. By the time of the return from each regular voyage on the "Vityaz'" the report on the work has been entirely completed, with the materials worked up and with scientific articles on individual questions. What is more, the possibility of working up the material on board enables them to perfect operationally the plan of the trip in keeping with the results obtained.

In 1957 there appeared still another vessel of the "Vityaz'" type: the ship of the Marine Hydrophysical Institute of the Academy of Sciences of the USSR, "Mikhail Lomonosov." A still larger vessel (12,500 tons displacement) had been re-equipped by 1955 especially for work in Antarctic waters. This was the "Ob'," a diesel-electric icebreaker belonging to the Ministry of the Navy. Many other smaller vessels have been put into commission. Thanks to this, the Soviet Union occupied one of the leading places in oceanologic exploration under the program of the International Geophysical Year.

Work of a quite exceptional scope was performed in the Arctic Ocean. Its success was due to the use of airplanes. As is known, Russians were the first to employ airplanes in the Arctic (Nagurskiy, 1912). The development of Soviet Polar aviation proceeded very rapidly, and in 1937 it became possible to organize the first drifting station "Severnyy Polyus" (SP-1) in the region of the Pole on ice floes of the Central Arctic Basin. This station yielded unusually interesting materials. Subsequently, drifting stations have been repeatedly organized, and since 1954 ever more and more new "SP's" have been operating continuously in the Arctic.

Besides these stations moving with the ice, a large number of so-called "jumping" stations have been established, when the scientists were landed on the ice by planes to make single observations. Thanks to this, they have succeeded in covering the Central Arctic Basin with a dense network of oceanologic stations and gathering very rich material. This method, proposed by N. N. Zubov, was first employed in 1941. (I. I. Cherevichnyy's expedition to the region of the "Pole of Inaccessibility".)

Closely connected with the development of expeditionary exploration is the perfection of observation techniques and instruments. In this respect, especially great progress has been made since the remarkable exploring vessel "Vityaz'" was put into commission. True, our techniques are not equally good in all respects, but in many departments they are better than the foreign ones. Thus, our instruments for taking sample bottom cores are indisputably the best in the world. Suffice it to say that back in 1951 a bottom core about 34 meters long was obtained with one of them. Also excellent are the instruments for collecting matter suspended in the water, the optical apparatuses, the instruments for determining the elements of the currents (the Alekseyev self-recorder, the electromagnetic current meter, etc.), automatic installations for measuring currents, the electric thermograph and thermosonde, and others.

Great too are the results of the work in Soviet oceanology, which is advantageously marked by integration. Soviet scholars regard the ocean as a single whole, in which physical, chemical, biologic, and geologic phenomena and processes develop simultaneously, with all of them taking place in close interrelation with one another and with the phenomena and processes in the atmosphere.

Another characteristic feature of our science is its endeavor to satisfy the needs of the national economy. Individual objects—seas and oceans—have also been thoroughly studied in the interests of various branches of the economy. In ascertaining the laws and processes (general and particular), special stress has been laid on those which are important for different aspects of economic activity.

The largest geographic digest of accumulated data is the Marine Atlas [Morskoy Atlas], created by a large group of Soviet scholars. The first volume (1950) is composed of physical geographic maps of the seas and oceans, and the second volume (1953) gives a broad oceanographic characterization of the separate oceans and of the World Ocean as a whole. The third volume, which came out in 1957, is devoted to military history. This fundamental production summarizes and generalizes the most important information about the World Ocean available at the beginning of the 1950's.

Among the regional explorations, the most considerable results have probably been obtained in the Arctic Ocean. Here they have succeeded in making the greatest geographic discoveries of the last few decades: a submarine ridge which has been given the name of Khrebet Lomonosova [Lomonosov Ridge], extending from the Novosibirskiye Ostrova [islands] to Ellesmere Land, and also the neighboring Khrebet Mendeleyeva. This discovery has entirely changed our conception of the relief of the floor of the Arctic Ocean, its geologic structure, and its geophysical and oceanologic characteristics. The ice of this ocean has been studied in very great detail, which has made it possible to place on a firm scientific foundation ice forecasting and current hydrometeorologic services to transportation operations.

Not a little has been done, too, in the Far Eastern seas, where the employment of new techniques by the "Vityaz'" has revealed much that is new, especially with respect to the relief of the floor and the bottom deposits. In particular, it has effected a great change in our conception of the character of the bed of the western part of the Bering Sea and the central part of the Sea of Okhotsk, as well as in the region of the Kuril chain (here a submarine ridge, the "Khrebet Vityazya," has been discovered, which is a continuation of the Little Kuril chain), and also in the northwestern part of the Pacific Ocean.

In general, as has already been said, each of the seas bordering the shores of our country has now been sufficiently well studied in a first approximation, though not equally well in all respects. The least well ascertained are the laws of the variability of the hydrologic characteristics in time.

During the last few years Soviet scholars have done a very great deal for the study of the Pacific and Atlantic oceans and the Antarctic waters. On the voyages of the "Vityaz'," "Mikhail Lomonosov," and "Ob'," as well as the "Sedov" and "Sevastopol'," much diversified material was collected and many important discoveries were made in various fields of oceanology: concerning the relief of the floor, the bottom deposits, the sea currents, the systematic composition, distribution, and migration of sea animals, etc. The materials gathered by the "Ob'" in the Antarctic are of great value, especially for the study of the circulation of the waters and the water exchange between the oceans (V. G. Kort and others). Furthermore, many interesting data were obtained on the dynamics of the waters in the area of the hydrologic front in the Norwegian and Greenland seas, in the region of activity of the Soviet fishing fleet.

In the field of theory, Soviet oceanology has made great strides in several directions. First of all, perhaps, should be mentioned the work on the study of ice. For our country, investigation of the ice of the Arctic seas is important for both practical and theoretical reasons. This problem has many aspects: geographic, physical, technical, etc. In 1944 appeared N. N. Zubov's monograph, "Ice of the Arctic" [L'dy Arktiki], in which were collected the latest data thoroughly elucidating this subject. The book examines the conditions of ice formation in the sea, its development and physical properties, its movement, decay and disappearance, the distribution of ice, the variability of ice conditions, etc. Especially detailed is Zubov's treatment of the questions of the calculation of the age of ice, its movement under the influence of wind (ice drift by isobars). If we add to this the numerous works on the prediction of ice conditions—the greatest of them stems from V. Yu. Vize— this will suffice to enable one to see the leading role of Soviet scholars in the study of Arctic ice. We must not fail to mention certain works on Antarctic ice (V. Kh. Buynitskiy, V. L. Lebedev, and others), as well as on the characterization of the physical properties of ice (B. P. Veynberg, V. I. Al'tberg, B. A. Savel'yev, I. S. Peschanskiy, and others).

Exceptional progress has been made in the expeditionary study of the ice of the Arctic. Here new and very bold methods of investigation have been applied: aerial reconnaissance, icebreaker and plane expeditions and, finally, drifting stations. Thanks to the intensive development of these explorations, success has been achieved in clearing up the picture of the geographic distribution of ice in the Arctic, the laws of its movement, the changes in ice conditions in the various regions of the Arctic Ocean in the course of time, and so forth (M. M. Somov, P. A. Gordiyenko, A. F. Laktionov, N. A. Volkov, A. G. Dralkin, A. F. Treshnikov, and others).

In another very important theoretical direction, connected with the study of sea currents, mention must be made first of all of the work of V. B. Shtokman (theory of complete currents, influence of the irregularity of the wind, etc.), P. S. Lineykin (general theory of currents), N. N. Zubov (density currents, currents and level, the dynamic method, etc.), and A. I. Fel'zenbaum (currents in small seas, etc.). The employment of new instruments and methods in the study of currents, worked out by Soviet scientists, has resulted in obtaining fresh material straight from nature (V. V. Kuznetsov, Yu. K. Alekseyev, N. N. Sysoyev, and others). They have unexpectedly succeeded in discovering great velocities (10-20 cm/sec) in currents at ocean depths of the order of 1,000-2,000 meters (A. D. Dobrovol'skiy, N. N. Sysoyev, and others). The use of autonomous buoy stations has proved especially productive, when long observations can be made at several horizons with the aid of self-recording instruments (N. N. Sysoyev).

The study of tidal phenomena has undergone great development in our country. The new techniques have permitted a good study of the tidal phenomena in individual regions (I. V. Maksimov, V. V. Timonov, I. M. Soskin, and others). An especially large role has been played by the work on the pre-computation of the tide level (A. I. Duvanin, K. D. Tiron, N. P. Vladimirskiy, Ye. S. Stakhevich, and others), based on the new methods of pre-computation by solar, not by lunar, time. It has been possible to compile permanent tables of tides (A. I. Duvanin).

Very interesting are the investigations in the field of sea waves. Here a very great role has been played by the experimental work in a special circular basin for the study of the energetics of the processes (V. V. Shuleykin), as well as empirical investigations through observations straight from nature (A. P. Braslavskiy, N. A. Labzovskiy, L. F. Titov, and others). Considerable progress has also been achieved in the field of the theory of wind-driven waves (I. S. Brovikov, Yu. M. Krylov, and others) and the theory of long waves (L. N. Sretenskiy). In particular, certain achievements are connected with the work of the special commission on tsunamis of the Committee on Seismology of the Academy of Sciences of the USSR. Thus, it has been possible to compile a regionalization map of the Far Eastern coast of the USSR by the degree of danger from tsunamis (Institutes of the Academy of Sciences of the USSR: for Oceanology, for Marine Hydrophysics, and for Physics of the Earth), affording very interesting and important theoretical foundations for calculating and predicting tsunamis (D. N. Sretenskiy and others).

Soviet scientists pay great attention to questions of the intermingling of waters in the sea. The basic laws of the process of the winter vertical circulation have been studied and methods of calculation have been worked out (N. N. Zubov). Progress has also been achieved in the solution of the problem of the formation of a homogeneous surface layer, proceeding from the standpoint of the thermodynamics of the turbulent process (P. S. Lineykin, V. A. Tsikunov, A. G. Kolesnikov and others). Closely related with the problem of intermingling is the problem of water masses, which has undergone broad development (N. N. Zubov, A. D. Dobrovol'skiy, V. T. Timofeyev, A. K. Leonov, and others).

In recent years physical oceanology investigations have also been developed on the acoustics and optics of the sea.

Important results have been obtained in the field of marine forecasting. Soviet scientists have succeeded in finding fairly reliable methods of predicting the various elements of the ice regime, the water temperature, the non-periodic fluctuations of the level, etc. (N. A. Belinskiy, K. I. Kudryavaya, P. A. Gordiyenko, N. A. Volkov, S. D. Lappo, D. A. Drogaytsev, and others).

The present essay is devoted mainly to questions of physical oceanology, but one cannot fail to mention, at least briefly, the achievements in certain other departments of oceanology.

First of all, thanks to the fullness of the integrated exploration carried out in our country, it has been possible to formulate the doctrine of the zonality of phenomena in the ocean (V. G. Bogorov).

Furthermore, great progress has been made in studying the geomorphology of the sea floor. The development of the methods of echo sounding has permitted the employment of geomorphologic methods for the analysis of the elements of the relief of the ocean floor in almost as much detail as on land (G. B. Udintsev and others).

Extraordinarily effective have been the investigations of the dynamics of the seashores (V. P. Zenkovich, O. K. Leont'yev, A. V. Zhivago, V. V. Longinov, R. Ya. Knaps, and others). These investigations are being developed on the basis of the study of the characteristics of the dynamics of the waters along the shores (deformation of the waves, wave impact, alongshore and discontinuous [razryvnyye] currents, etc.) and its effects on the deformation of the shore (flows of alluvium, shore erosion, building of accumulational formations, development of a transverse shore profile, etc.).

Much new material has been obtained in the study of floor sediments (M. V. Klenova, P. L. Bezrukov, A. P. Lisitsyn and others). The field of activity of marine geology has now been greatly broadened and includes not only mineralogic, granulometric and chemical research, but also foraminifera analysis (A. P. Zhuze), diatom analysis (Kh. M. Saidova), the study of suspended matter in sea water (A. P. Lisitsyn), etc.

In recent years a new branch of oceanology has been developed, studying the characteristics of the processes in the region of river mouths (I. V. Samoylov and others).

Great progress has been achieved in chemical oceanology with respect to the methods of determination (S. V. Bruyevich, L. K. Blinov, N. I. Chigirin, and others), the problem of the geochemistry of the elements in the sea (A. P. Vinogradov, S. V. Bruyevich, L. K. Blinov, and others), and the study of organic matter in the sea (B. A. Skopintsev and others). Lately, oceanologist-chemists have paid much attention to the problem of primary production (jointly with the planktonologists) and to the problem of the carbon dioxide equilibrium in the ocean-atmosphere system. In addition, the chemistry of the ground and ooze waters is being studied, particularly in the aspects of paleogeographic reconstructions and metamorphosis (S. V. Bruyevich and others).

Finally, immense progress has been made in the study of the biology of the sea. Here it is impossible to enumerate even cursorily all the directions of investigation. It can only be noted that the main characteristic of Soviet biology of the sea is the development of quantitative methods in the investigation of processes in the sea (L. A. Zenkevich, V. G. Bogorov, Z. A. Filatova, and many others).

In conclusion, let us point out the most important of the monographs that have appeared in the last 20 years in the various fields of oceanology.

BASIC LITERATURE

Belinskiy, N. A. Marine Hydrometeorologic Information and Forecasts (Morskiye Gidrometeorologicheskiye Informatsii i Prognozy), Leningrad, Gidrometeoizdat, 1956 (2nd ed.).

Vize, V. Yu. Fundamentals of Long-range Ice Forecasts for the Arctic Seas" (Osnovy Dolgosrochnykh Ledovykh Prognozov dlya Arkticheskikh Morey), Moscow, Glavsevmorput', 1944.

Zenkevich, L. A. The Fauna and Biologic Productivity of the Sea (Fauna i biologicheskaya produktivnost' morya), vol. I, "The World Ocean (Mirovoy Okean), Moscow, "Sovetskaya Nauka," 1951; vol. II, Seas of the USSR (Morya SSSR), Moscow, Sovetskaya Nauka," 1947.

Zenkevich, L. A. The Seas of the USSR, their Flora and Fauna (Morya SSSR, ikh Flora i Fauna), Moscow, Uchpedgiz, 1956 (2nd ed.).

Zenkovich, V. P. The Dynamics and Morphology of the Seashores (Dinamika i Morfologiya Morskikh Beregov), Moscow-Leningrad, "Morskoy transport", 1946.

Zubov, N. N. Sea Water and Ice (Morskiye Vody i L'dy), Moscow, Gidrometeoizdat, 1938.

Zubov, N. N. The Ice of the Arctic (L'dy Arktiki), Moscow, Glavsevmorput', 1945.

Zubov, N. N. Dynamic Oceanology (Dinamicheskaya Okeanologiya), Moscow-Leningrad, Gidrometeoizdat, 1947.

Zubov, N. N. Fundamentals of the Doctrine concerning the Straits of the World Ocean (Osnovy Ucheniya o Prolivakh Mirovogo Okeana), Moscow, Geografgiz, 1956.

Zubov, N. N. Oceanologic Tables (Okeanologicheskiye Tablitsy), Leningrad, Gidrometeoizdat, 1957 (3rd ed.).

Klenova, M. V. The Geology of the Sea (Geologiya Morya), Moscow, Uchpedgiz, 1948.

Kudryavaya, K. I. Marine Hydrologic Forecasts (Morskiye Gidrologicheskiye Prognozy), Leningrad, Gidrometeoizdat, 1951.

Leont'yev, O. K. Geomorphology of the Sea Shores and Bottom (Geomorfologiya Morskikh Beregov i Dna), Moscow, MGU (Moscow State University), 1955.

Lineykin, P. S. Basic Questions of the Dynamic Theory of the Barocline Layer of the Sea (Osnovnyye Voprosy Dinamicheskoy Teorii Baroklinnogo Sloya Morya), Leningrad, Gidrometeoizdat, 1957.

Morskoy Atlas (Marine Atlas), vol. I, 1950; vol. II. Physico-Geographic, 1953; vol. III, Military History, part. 1, 1958; Leningrad, Glav. shtab Voyenno-Morskogo flota.

Samoylov, I. V. River Mouths (Ust'ye Rek), Moscow, Geografgiz, 1952.

Snezhinskiy, V. A. Practical Oceanography (Prakticheskaya Okeanografiya) (Work in the open sea), Leningrad, Gidrometeoizdat, 1954 (2nd ed.).

Chaplygin, Ye. I. Guide to Observation of Currents at Polar Stations and Observatories (Rukovodstvo po Nablyudeniyam nad Techeniyami na Polyarnykh Stantsiyakh i Observatoriyakh), Leningrad, "Morskoy transport," 1957.

Shtokman, V. B. Equatorial Countercurrents in the Oceans. Fundamentals of the Theory (Ekvatorial'nyye Protivotecheniya v Okeanakh. Osnovy Teorii), Leningrad, Gidrometeoizdat, 1948.

Shuleykin, V. V. Physics of the Sea (Fizika Morya), 1953 (3rd ed.).

Shuleykin, V. V. "The Theory of Sea Waves," Tr. Morskogo gidrofiz. int-a AN SSSR, vol. 9, 1956.

L. S. Berg (1876-1950)

A. A. Grigor'yev (born 1883)

Yu. M. Shokal'skiy (1856-1940)

N. M. Knipovich (1862-1939)

N. N. ZUBOV (born 1885)

N. N. BARANSKIY (born 1881)

B. F. DOBRYNIN (1885-1951)

I. A. VITVER (born 1891)

CHAPTER 5

ECONOMIC GEOGRAPHY

O. A. Konstantinov

As already noted in the introduction to the present collection, the system of geographic sciences is divided into two major subsystems: physical geography and economic geography.

In many countries there exist, alongside economic geography, still other geographic disciplines studying the various aspects of the life of human society: political geography, urban geography, population geography, cultural geography, and so forth. In the Soviet Union all these questions are encompassed by economic geography. The political phenomena examined by political geography for the most part ultimately represent the product of definite economic conditions. At the same time, political conditions exercise immense influence upon economic life. Hence, questions of political geography are closely related to those of economic geography and consequently there are not sufficient grounds for separating political geography from economic geography. In teaching economic geography there sometimes arises the necessity of paying special attention to political questions, as, for example, is the case in the party schools. In such cases the subject is called "economic and political geography." From this it must not be concluded that we have in this country two different scientific disciplines united in one educational subject. Actually, economic geography includes all questions of political geography as well.

Population geography in the Soviet Union is also regarded as one of the divisions of economic geography. The distribution of the population, the character of that distribution, the types of populated points, etc., to a considerable extent depend directly or indirectly upon the productive activity of people. Hence, all (or nearly all) questions of population geography can be examined within the framework of economic geography. This applies still more to urban geography, inasmuch as towns and cities are focal points of economic life and play a very active role in the geographic division of labor. (The question of why population geography and urban geography form an inseparable part of economic geography is discussed in more detail in Chapter 17, "Geography of Population and Populated Points.") It must, moreover, be taken into consideration that the geography of population and populated points, like political geography, has not yet undergone such development in this country as to be separated from economic geography and to form an independent scientific discipline.

By the term "cultural geography" is usually meant everything relating to the geography of human society and the products of its material and spiritual culture (economic geography, political geography, population geography, etc.), i.e., everything that in the Soviet Union is commonly called economic geography.

Understanding economic geography in a considerably broader sense than is customary in many other countries, Soviet scholars have made more than one attempt to give a definition of economic geography. At the Second Congress of the Geographic Society of the USSR (February, 1955) economic geography was defined as a social economic science studying the geographic distribution of production (by the latter is understood the unity of productive forces and productive relationships) and the conditions and characteristics of its development in different countries and regions. The resolutions of the Congress read: "The Congress considers the main tasks of economic geographic research to be the study of the laws of the geographic distribution of production, the territorial (geographic) division of labor and the formation of economic regions, the economic evaluation of the natural laws and resources, the combined study of the geographic distribution of the branches of industry, agriculture, and transportation and of regions on the basis of an integrated study of both, and the study of the geography of population." (*Izv. VGO,* 1955, no. 2, p. 99.)

Soviet economic geographic science consists of two main parts: the economic geography of the socialist countries and the economic goegraphy of the capitalist countries. The radical difference between these two parts is based on the fact that the laws of the distribution of production in the countries of the socialist camp differ entirely from those operating in the capitalist world. In the practice of the middle and higher schools, it is generally customary, for convenience in teaching, to distinguish the economic geography of the USSR as a separate subject, and to unite all the other socialist countries and the countries of capitalism under another subject, the economic geography of foreign countries.

A distinctive characteristic of economic geography in the Soviet Union is its close ties with practical economic construction, with the planning of the economy's development. As is known, socialism prevails absolutely in the USSR. The socialization of the means and tools of production creates the conditions for the state planning of the national economy, and consequently for the planned distribution of the productive forces. In pre-Revolution Russia the distribution of the economy was irrational, sometimes monstrous; considerable natural resources were unknown or lay unused. This retarded the economic development of the country. The Soviet State exploits its opportunities for economic planning to create a more rational geography of the economy.

A correct territorial organization of the productive forces, built on a scientific foundation, is of immense significance for the most efficient expenditure of material and labor resources, for the acceleration of the rate of our economic development, for the uplift of the welfare of the Soviet people, and for the strengthening of the country's defense capabilities. Hence, great attention is paid in our country to the rational territorial organization of the productive forces. Questions of economic geography are dealt with in the scientific-research institutes and in the chairs of the higher educational institutions, and to a still greater extent in the various governmental, party, planning, administrative, and economic organs both in the center and in the provinces, in the designing organizations, and so forth. The results of this great amount of work accomplished by the numerous cadres of scientific and practical operators in the field of the economic geography of the USSR are generalized in the resolutions adopted by the higher governmental and party authorities, including the congresses of the Soviets and of the Communist Party. The propositions formulated in these resolutions concerning the distribution of the productive forces and the territorial organization of the national economy of the USSR contain important economic geographic ideas. These resolutions are of immense significance for practical work on the planning of the distribution of the separate branches of the economy and of the objects of new construction, and also serve as a point of departure for the further elaboration of the theoretical questions of economic geographic science. Of great scientific and practical significance for the socialist construction of the USSR is the elaboration of questions of economic regionalization, as well as the regional and interregional problems of the integrated development of the productive forces of the Soviet Union. Chapters 28 and 29 in the present collection are devoted to these two problems.

The economic geography of the USSR consists of two main divisions, general and regional. The general division includes the economic evaluation of the natural conditions and natural resources, the distribution of the productive forces as a whole throughout the country, the geography of population, and the geography of the individual branches of the national economy of the Soviet Union (industry, agriculture, and transportation). The regional division includes questions of economic regionalization and the study of the economic geography of the separate republics and economic regions of the USSR.

Soviet economic geographers consider that both divisions are of equal significance; one division cannot develop without the other. As will be shown farther on, this follows the methodological principles of our science. Actually, however, in this country chief attention is paid to the regional division. This is partially due to the fact that the scholars of the allied sciences concern themselves to a certain extent and not without success with the questions relating to the general division. Thus, an economic evaluation of the natural conditions is contained in certain physical geographic works. A number of problems of the distribution of the productive forces of the USSR are treated from the theoretical aspect to some degree in works on political economy as well, and demographers sometimes deal with the geography of population. Specialists in various branches of the economy also concern themselves with the distribution of certain branches, especially separate branches of industry. But no allied sciences can concern themselves with the regional division, which is the specific sphere of economic geographic research, and it is no accident that Soviet economic geographers devote their chief attention to it. While there is a great multitude of economic geographic works devoted to the republics, economic regions, oblasts, and cities, there are comparatively few works on questions relating to the general division of the economic geography of the USSR.

Here we come to the essential difference between the levels of development of physical geography and economic geography in the USSR. The particular or analytical scientific disciplines studying the separate components of the natural geographic environment (geomorphology, climatology, hydrology, botanical geography, and so forth) have long existed as independent sciences, have undergone considerable development in the USSR, and have great scientific achievements to their credit. The particular or analytical disciplines studying the distribution of the separate branches of the economy (the geography of industry, the geography of agriculture, the geography of transportation, and so forth), on the contrary, have still not taken full shape and exist within the framework of the general division of the economic geography of the USSR as separate parts of it, not in the form of independent economic geographic sciences.

The economic geography of foreign countries has great general educational and political-propaganda significance, and also serves practical requirements of no small importance. The Soviet Union is pursuing an active international policy. It has manifold political, commercial, financial, and cultural relations with many countries, and the circle of these countries is continually expanding, and the kinds of ties with the various states are increasing. Especially to be noted is the disinterested aid lent by the Soviet Union to poorly developed countries that have thrown off the yoke of colonialism and entered upon the path of independent development. Under these conditions, a knowledge of the individual countries and the treatment of questions of the economic geography of the foreign world acquire great practical significance.

Economic geography, like any other science in the USSR, is being developed in the general interest of the people. The creation of a new, more rational territorial organization of the productive forces speeds up the rate of economic development and contributes to our approach to communism. Hence, the policy of the Soviet Government and Communist Party in the field of the distribution of productive forces and the territorial organization of the national economy of the USSR is warmly supported by the Soviet people, who are taking an active part in the creation of the new geography of production. At the appeal of the Soviet Government and the Communist Party, hundreds of thousands of persons have voluntarily left their old homes and resettled in the eastern regions of the country to work on building projects and industrial enterprises, on the virgin and fallow lands, and so forth. During 1939-1959 the population of the regions of the Urals and farther eastward increased by 18 million, while the number of inhabitants of the regions to the west of the Urals remained unchanged. These facts reflect the new geography of population, this most important productive force, and the active role of Soviet people in the creation of the new geography of the national economy of the USSR.

Economic geography, like any other science in the USSR, is developing on the basis of the tenets of dialectical and historical materialism. Soviet economic geographers reject idealistic, voluntaristic views of any sort, and so-called "geographic materialism." Unacceptable for us are the conceptions of anthropogeography, environmentalism, or any other conception having the philosophy of geographic determinism as its primary source. Let us recall that the division of the whole system of geographic sciences into two major subsystems (physical geography and economic geography) is based on the fact that physical geography studies the laws of nature, while economic geography studies the laws of human society. The confusion of these laws and the transfer of the laws of nature to human society and vice versa is resolutely rejected in Soviet geography.

Unlike the physical geographic disciplines, economic geography is a social, economic science. It reposes on the laws of Marxist-Leninist economics and at many points touches and is intertwined with the various economic sciences (the history of the national economy, the branches of economics, economic statistics, world economy). Unacceptable to us are the various location theories of foreign authors who proceed from the tenets of popular bourgeois economics. It is known that these theories do not reveal the laws of the distribution of the economy under capitalism and actually are incapable of explaining the distribution of the separate branches or single enterprises. All the more, the location theories prove completely unsuited for the planned territorial organization of production in the USSR and the other socialist countries. However, certain methodological procedures employed by the authors of the location theories may be utilized in the technical economic calculations necessary for the choice of location of this or that enterprise.

The distribution of production is a very complex phenomenon, and takes shape under the influence of diverse conditions. Among them, the aggregate of natural conditions plays an enormous, but by no means a decisive, role. A correct consideration of them requires not only a good knowledge of physical geography on the part of economic geographers, but also close everyday contact between the representatives of these disciplines. This close contact and interaction insure the necessary synthesis of the data of physical and economic geography, which does not mean at all the blending of physical and economic geography into a single geography, in which, as the works of the adherents of a unified geography maintain, there is an inevitable merging of the laws of nature and society. The Marxist-Leninist philosophy teaches that each phenomenon must be viewed in all its connections and intermediates. The natural conditions affect, in many cases very strongly, the distribution of production, but subject to the state of the socio-economic conditions at a given place. A thorough examination of the relations between human society and nature and the reflection of these relations in the distribution of production is a field in which there are boundless opportunities for joint work by the representatives of economic and physical geography, and one in which the greatest scientific results can be attained by close contact between the representatives of all the disciplines making up the system of geographic sciences.

THE HISTORY OF THE ORIGIN AND FORMATION
OF ECONOMIC GEOGRAPHY IN THE USSR

Before the Great October Socialist Revolution economic geography had not yet had time to take shape as an independent science. However, economic geographic research was conducted on a very considerable scale. It suffices to state that since the first quarter of the 19th century dozens of works devoted to the economic regionalization of Russia had been published. In the treatment of this problem, Russian science played a foremost role. Some expeditionary work was economic geographic in character: for example, the expedition for the investigation of grain commerce and productivity, made jointly by two scientific societies, the Geographic Society and the Free Economic Society. Much economic geographic material was contained in many zemstvo publications, and also in the publications giving the results of economic research done in connection with railroad construction and the resettlement movement. There were considerable economic geographic elements in the ethnographic, statistical economic and general geographic works. Such major works as "The Commerce and Industry of European Russia by Regions" (with a map) were published.

Of outstanding significance for the further development of economic geographic science (especially in the Soviet years) was V. I. Lenin's treatment of a number of problems leading directly to the solution of important questions of economic geography, including economic regionalization. These problems were treated in Lenin's works on the agrarian question in Russia and on the national [-minority] question, as well as in such publications of his as "The Development of Capitalism in Russia" and "New Data on the Laws of the Development of Capitalism in Agriculture."

Along with the capitalist development of Russia there arose the need for specialists having economic training, and this resulted in the appearance of economic geography as an independent educational subject. However, in pre-Revolutionary Russia it was taught only in the commercial schools and in a very few centers of higher education in economics. Economic geography was treated principally in the style of the so-called branch-statistical manner, whose most prominent representative was V. E. Den, professor in the Department of Economics of the St. Petersburg Polytechnical Institute.

In the first years after the Great October Socialist Revolution there began the great enterprise of creating a more rational distribution of productive forces. This found its expression above all in the elaboration of questions of economic regionalization in the higher party and government organs. The GOELRO plan (1920-1921) and the Gosplan's [State Planning Commission's] project of economic regionalization (1921) were drawn up, the commission on regionalization under the chairmanship of M. I. Kalinin (1921-1922) operated, regionalization questions were specially discussed at the Seventh Party Congress (1923), an experimental regionalization was made of the Ukraine (1923-1925), of the Urals (1923-1924), of the North Caucasus (1923-1924), and so forth (See Chapter 28, "Economic Regionalization" in this collection). In the course of this work new principles of regionalization were formulated, which were tested and refined in practice.

As the planning principle in the direction of the country's national economy became stronger and the planning methods improved, it became more and more possible to plan the distribution of separate branches and of the entire national economy as a whole. After the discussion of the draft of the first five-year plan at the Fifteenth Party Congress (1927), all the five-year and other national-economic plans were drawn up not only in the branch, but also the regional cross-section. The questions of the correct distribution of production assumed immense economic and political significance. They became a matter of country-wide importance and therefore the object of the attention of the higher party and government authorities, and their solution became the concern of the whole Soviet people.

This whole immense practical activity was accompanied by the elaboration of many theoretical questions of economic geographic science. At the same time, there was a wide dissemination of economic geography as a subject for instruction. It was necessary to arm the Soviet people with knowledge for conscientious work in the field of the distribution of the production of the USSR. Economic geography acquired especially great significance in the Soviet party schools and communist universities, which trained the cadres of local party and soviet workers. In the curricula and programs of the middle schools the significance of economic geography was so great that it even crowded out physical geography, which, of course, was to the detriment of the general education of the pupils, and also to the study of economic geography itself. In 1921 V. I. Lenin signed a decree concerning the inclusion of economic geography in the obligatory scientific minimum of the higher educational institutions, which served as the foundation for the spread of the teaching of this discipline in the higher schools.

Down to the beginning of the 1930's, various views and conceptions accepted in bourgeois science had wide currency among the scientific workers and teachers of economic geography. They were subjected to fierce criticism, and an ideological struggle began for the remodeling of our science on the basis of Marxism-Leninism. The remodeling of the economic geography of the USSR was greatly promoted by the strengthening of the ties with practical socialist construction, especially with the work on the new regionalization of the country.

A valuable contribution to economic geographic science was made by certain resolutions of the Comintern congresses and the plenums of its Executive Committee, containing Marxist-Leninist party characterizations of the development of individual countries and the phenomena of world economy and world politics. These characterizations were used in working out scientific problems and in teaching the economic geography of foreign countries.

All this helped to convert economic geography into a Marxist-Leninist party science, and on this basis there was a consolidation of all the forces engaged in scientific and teaching work in the field of economic geography. Among the outstanding figures in Soviet economic geographic science must be numbered first of all N. N. Baranskiy and I. A. Vitver, who trained a large number of pupils and played a very great role in strengthening and spreading economic geography as a subject for instruction in the higher and middle schools. N. N. Kolosovskiy made an immense contribution to the elaboration of questions of economic regionalization.

The development of economic geography as a science and as a subject for instruction had much support from the Soviet Government and the Communist Party of the Soviet Union. Of especially great significance was the decree of the Party and Government dated 16 May, 1934 "Concerning the Teaching of Geography in the Primary and Middle Schools of the USSR." This decree not only regulated the teaching of physical and economic geography in the middle schools, but also served as an impetus for the development of economic geography in the higher schools and scientific institutions, and contributed to the considerable quantitative and qualitative growth of the personnel in economic geography. Geographic faculties were created in the universities and pedagogic institutes, and their number gradually reached many dozens. In 1934, the Department of Economic Geography was created in-the Geographical Society in Leningrad, and economic geography sections later appeared in the regional branches of the Geographic Society. In 1937, work was also carried on in economic geography in the Institute of Physical Geography of the Academy of Sciences of the USSR, and it was converted into the Institute of Geography. Later, the Institute of Geography of the Academy of Sciences of the USSR was transformed into a leading scientific institution, in which a large number of economic geographers are now working.

The struggle on the ideological front, which has become intensified in the postwar years, has also found its expression in economic geography. The clash of opinions also manifested itself in the discussion of the basic methodological problems of economic geography at the Second Congress of the Geographical Society of the USSR in Moscow (February, 1955).

During the last few years, a considerable enhancement of economic geography has been observed in our country. It is being taught in more than two hundred higher educational institutions; economic geographers are working in dozens of scientific-research institutions, are taking part in many integrated geographic expeditions and various kinds of scientific deliberations and conferences, and are publishing a large number of books and articles. The ties between Soviet and foreign economic geographers are being strengthened.

MAIN SCIENTIFIC TRENDS, RESEARCH METHODS AND A CHARACTERIZATION OF THE RESULTS

Discussions and clashes of opinion over theoretical questions of economic geography have repeatedly occurred among Soviet scholars, and these discussions have been widely reflected in the press. In the heat of debate, unnecessary extremes have sometimes been permitted. From all this, the inexperienced reader might draw the conclusion that Soviet economic geographers are separated by these conflicts into at least two camps.

Such a notion would be wrong. The economic geographers of the Soviet Union proceed in their work from the Marxist-Leninist philosophy, from the basic tenets of dialectical and historical materialism. They are all guided by the resolutions of the Soviet Government and the Communist Party of the Soviet Union on questions of the distribution of production. Under these conditions there is not and cannot be in Soviet economic geography any ground for the appearance of mutually hostile trends or fundamentally different schools. Disagreements are possible here only on individual concrete questions, which is quite normal for a developing science. Furthermore, there are differences in the predominant *direction of interests,* which are quite inevitable in a science with so many sides and so many facets to its content as economic geography. In this sense, it is possible to speak of the following two trends in Soviet Union economic geography.

The one trend devotes especially great attention to the economic basis of the distribution of production as a whole or of individual branches of production, extensively revealing the relations between economic geography and the other economic sciences.

The other trend concerns itself principally with regional investigations, i.e., it studies individual localities (economic regions, republics, oblasts) and towns and cities. This trend devotes much more attention than the former to questions of the interaction between production and the natural environment. Hence, the connection of economic geography with the various physical geographic sciences is manifested with especial clarity in regional investigations.

As may be seen, the two trends supplement one another, and neither of them could develop successfully without the other. From this viewpoint, the existence of two trends has a very fruitful effect on science as a whole. Inasmuch as both trends in their theoretical tenets proceed from the Marxist-Leninist philosophy, their unity on basic principles is assured, despite the polemics regarding particular questions. Thus, in the Soviet Union economic geography as a science is united in its basic philosophical tenets, in aims and tasks, in its ties with socialist construction and the practical needs of the Soviet state, and in its negative attitude toward various kinds of anti-scientific concepts widespread among the economic geographers of capitalist countries.

Regarding the working methods of Soviet economic geographers, the following two main characteristics should be noted. Firstly, economic geographers are widely engaged in the numerous integrated expeditions covering a considerable part of our country's territory. The integrated character of these expeditions, requiring the participation of representatives of the various analytical physical geographic sciences (geomorphologists, climatologists, hydrologists, and others) and other specialists (geologists, engineers, agronomists, etc.), makes the task of synthesis very complex. As representatives of one of the synthesizing sciences, economic geographers have played and now play an active role in co-ordinating the work of the individual specialists, in generalizing the materials collected, in their national-economic evaluation, and in the compilation of practical recommendations aimed at the integrated development of the economy of the regions investigated.

The above refers exclusively to the work on the economic geography of the USSR. Since the Second World War, Soviet economic geographers have had an opportunity to visit other countries. In certain cases Soviet economic geographers have participated jointly with the scholars of certain countries of the socialist camp in the study of these states. However, most of the economic geographic works devoted to the foreign world have been written exclusively from published sources. Soviet economic geographers are fully aware of all the drawbacks of working on the study of this or that country without personal acquaintance with it. This mode of working is gradually beginning to be outlived.

Secondly, special field investigations have been widely developed in Soviet economic geography. (For more details on this see Chapter 44, "Methods of Research in Economic Geography.") This means that, in addition to the data borrowed from other sciences, economic geographers use the various materials that they themselves gather, in accordance with their own program and in application to their own aims and tasks. It may be mentioned, incidentally, that students of the geographic faculties are widely engaged in such field investigations. Their participation in field work and in the further working up of the material obtained has become an important means of instructing and training new specialists.

The scientific and practical activity in the field of economic geography has contributed to immense shifts in the distribution of the productive forces of the USSR. There have been radical changes in the geography of population, industry, agriculture, and transportation. On the basis of the consistent realization of Lenin's national [-minority] policy, a sharp rise has been secured in the economy and culture of the national [-minority] regions. The backwardness of the outlying districts has been liquidated and the contrast between the industrial and agrarian regions of the country has been destroyed. The specific weight of the eastern regions in the USSR economy is being continually strengthened.

The scientific and practical work in the field of economic geography has made a considerable contribution to the creation of a new, more rational distribution of the productive forces and the territorial organization of the national economy, which is rightly regarded as among the greatest achievements of the Soviet Union.

TASKS

The further development of economic geography in the USSR is connected with the great tasks now confronting our country. The Soviet Union, as is known, has reached such a high level of development of its productive forces that we have begun a gradual transition to communism. "The main practical task for our country at this time is the creation of the material-technical base of a communist society, a new and powerful uplift of the socialist productive forces" (N. S. Khrushchëv. "On the Control Figures for the Development of the National Economy of the USSR in 1959-1965," Gospolitizdat, Moscow, 1959, page 110). This new and powerful uplift of the productive forces is inconceivable without further planned shifts in their distribution, without the formation of new industrial nodes and regional territorial productional complexes, and without a new economic regionalization of the USSR. In the very near future it will be necessary to work out schemes for the distribution of the productive forces and economic regionalization in connection with the drafting of the prospective plan for the development of the national economy of the USSR for the next 15-20 years. Thus, the practical tasks now confronting economic geography are still more imposing than in the first stages of the existence of the Country of the Soviets.

The success of the policy of peaceful coexistence and the growth of the international relations of the USSR require the further considerable development of the economic geography of foreign countries.

Serving the practical requirements of the Soviet state is impossible without a thorough elaboration of the main scientific problems of economic geography. This will require the continuation of theoretical discussions and a further clash of opinions. We are faced by the task of continuing to take an active part in integrated geographic expeditions, in the activities of the planning organs, the designing and other organizations in which practical scientific work is being done in the field of economic geography. The preparation of monographs on countries, regions, and cities must be intensified, the deficiencies in textbooks and teaching aids must be removed, and the level of teaching in the middle and higher schools must be raised. All these tasks can be fulfilled only if economic geography is developed on the basis of Marxism-Leninism.

BASIC LITERATURE

See also the literature for Chapters 17, "Geography of Population and Populated Points"; 28, "Economic Regionalization"; 29, "Investigations into the Integrated Development of the Productive Forces of the Economic Regions of the USSR"; 45, "Geographic Education in Secondary Schools"; 46, "Geographic Education in Institutions of Higher Learning"; 49, "Publication of Geographic Literature"; and 44, "Methods of Research in Economic Geography."

Lenin, V. I. "The Development of Capitalism in Russia" (Razvitiye Kapitalizma v Rossii), Sochineniya (Collected Works) 4th ed., vol. 3, pp. 1-535.

Lenin, V. I. "Critical Remarks on the National [minority] Question", Sochineniya, 4th ed., vol. 20, pp. 1-34.

Lenin, V. I. "On the Right of Nations to Self-determination", Sochineniya, 4th ed., vol. 20, pp. 365-424.

Lenin, V. I. "New Data on the Laws of the Development of Capitalism in Agriculture," Sochineniya, 4th ed., vol. 22, pp. 1-89.

Lenin, V. I. "The Socialist Revolution and the Right of Nations to Self-determination (Theses), Sochineniya, 4th ed., vol. 22, pp. 132-145.

Lenin, V. I. "Imperialism as a Higher Stage of Capitalism," Sochineniya, 4th ed., vol. 22, pp. 173-290.

Lenin, V. I. "Draft of a Plan of Scientific-technical Work", April, 1918, Sochineniya, 4th ed., vol. 27, pp. 288-289.

Lenin, V. I. "The Infantile Disease of 'Leftism' in Communism." Sochineniya, 4th ed., vol. 31, chapter X, pp. 70-84.

Plan elektrifikatsii RSFSR (Plan of electrification of the RSFSR), Doklad VIII s"yezdu Sovetov Gosudarstvennoy Komissii po Elektrifikatsii Rosii. 1920, 2nd ed., Gospolitizdat, Moscow, 1955, 659 pp.

Pyatiletniy Plan Narodnokhozyaystvennogo Stroitel'stva SSSR (Five-year plan for national-economic construction of the USSR), Moscow, 1929, vol. II, part 1, 491 pp.; vol. III, 606 pp.

Vtoroy Pyatiletniy Plan Razvitiya Narodnogo Khozyaystva SSSR (1933-1937 gg.) (Second five-year plan for the development of the national economy of the USSR (1933-1937), vol. I, Moscow, 1934, 739 pp.; vol. II, 579 pp.

Tretiy Pyatiletniy Plan Razvitiya Narodnogo Khozyaystva SSSR (1938-1942) (Third five-year plan for the development of the national economy of the USSR (1938-1942), 1939. As a separate brochure or "The CPSU in the Resolutions and Decisions of the Congresses, Conferences, and Plenums of the CC," 7th ed., part II, 1953, pp. 879-909.

Zakon o Pyatiletnem Plane Vosstanovleniya i Razvitiya Narodnogo Khozyaystva SSSR na 1946-1950 gg. (Law concerning the five-year plan for the restoration and development of the national economy of the USSR in 1946-1950.) Gospolitizdat, Moscow, 1946, 95 pp.

Direktivy XIX S"yezda Partii po Pyatomu Pyatiletnemu Planu Razvitiya SSSR na 1951-1955 gg. (Directives of the 19th Congress of the Party concerning the fifth five-year plan for the development of the USSR in 1951-1955.) Gospolitizdat, Moscow, 1952, 30 pp.

Direktivy XX S"yezda KPSS po Shestomu Pyatiletnemu Planu Razvitiya Narodnogo Khozyaystva SSSR na 1956-1960 gg. (Directives of the 20th Congress of the CPSU concerning the sixth five-year plan for the development of the national economy of the USSR in 1956-1960.) Gospolitizdat, Moscow, 1956, 79 pp.

Kontrol'nyye Tsifry Razvitiya Narodnogo Khozyaystva SSSR na 1959-1965 gg. (Control figures for the development of the national economy of the USSR in 1959-1965), Gospolitizdat, Moscow, 1959, 112 pp.

Otechestvennyye Ekonomiko-geografy XVIII-XX vv. (Native economic geographers of the 18th-20th centuries.) Under the editorship of N. N. Baranskiy, N. P. Nikitin, Yu. G. Saushkin; Uchpedgiz, Moscow, 1957, 328 pp.

Baranskiy, N. N. Economic Geography. Economic Cartography (Ekonomichskaya geografiya. Ekonomicheskaya kartografiya.) Geografgiz, Moscow, 1956, 272 pp.

Vasyutin, V. F. "Fundamentals of the Distribution of Socialist Production and the Tasks of Economic Geography," "Izvestiya AN SSSR, seriya geogr.," 1950, No. 3, pp. 25-33.

Vitver, I. A. "Economic Geography of Foreign Countries in Moscow University." In the collection, Geografiya v Moskovskom Universitete za 200 Let, MGU (Moscow State University), Moscow, 1955, pp. 141-149.

Konstantinov, O. A. "Concerning the History and Present State of Economic Geographic Science in the USSR," "Izvestiya VGO," 1955, issue 3, pp. 259-266.

Konstantinov, O. A. "Economic Geography in the Geographic Society during Forty Years of Soviet Rule," Geograficheskiy sbornik, XI, Izd-vo AN SSSR, Moscow-Leningrad, 1957, pp. 131-187.

Saushkin, Yu. G. "Economic Geography of the USSR in Moscow University." In the collection, Geografiya v Moskovskom Universitete za 200 Let," MGU, 1955, pp. 111-134.

Feygin, Ya. G. "Distribution of Production under Capitalism and Socialism" (Razmeshcheniye Proizvodstva pri Kapitalizme i Sotsializme.) Institut Ekonomiki AN SSSR, 2nd ed., Moscow, 1958, p. 676.

CHAPTER 6

REGIONAL GEOGRAPHY [*Stranovedeniye*]*

V. M. Gokhman and G. M. Ignat'yev

Down to the end of the 19th century, geographic works embracing all sides of nature and life of different countries and peoples occupied a very important place among the geographic compositions published in Russia, as well as in other countries. The authors of fundamental works of such a "regional-geographic" [*stranovedcheskogo*] character were, as a rule, travelers. In these descriptions everything that attracted their attention found a place, and the very order of description was determined by the itinerary. Thus, in most of these works there was no strict system of distinguishing major division—nature, population, economy. The most vivid descriptions, from the pen of such outstanding Russian explorers as N. M. Przheval'skiy, M. V. Pevtsov, P. P. Semenov-Tyan-Shanskiy and P. K. Kozlov, have become classic geographic works that still present great interest not only for specialized geographers but also for wide circles of readers. This is evidenced, in particular, by the re-publication of these works in large editions since 1945.

The striving to create many-sided, all-embracing descriptions was characteristic of the geographers of that period. This tendency found its most vivid expression in the well-known multi-volume encyclopedic publication, *Rossiya*, which came out during the years 1899-1913 under the editorship of V. P. Semenov-Tyan-Shanskiy.

As a result of the development of the specialized geographic disciplines, which was especially intensified at the beginning of the 20th century, the situation changed substantially. In the first place, physical and economic geography became sharply separated. The progress in the field of the natural sciences contributed to a rapid growth of such physical geographic disciplines as geomorphology, climatology, hydrology, soil geography, geobotany, zoogeography, and others. The differentiation also affected economic geography, within which the geography of agriculture, industry, transportation, etc., were more or less set apart.

This differentiation was entirely natural and progressive. It contributed to the establishment of particular laws in the individual fields of geography and to the utilization of their results for practical purposes, and thereby certainly led to the further progress of geography. But differentiation sooner or later requires synthesis, and, if the specialized disciplines are necessary, the generalizing disciplines are equally necessary. In penetrating deeply into this or that narrow branch of knowledge, one must not lose sight of its connections with the related disciplines. This truth, applicable to any science, acquires special meaning with respect to geography, which constantly has to do with intricate complexes of the most heterogeneous but closely related processes peculiar to the territories and phenomena studied.

Within the specialized ("branch") disciplines, the factual material is examined by generic categories (rivers with rivers, mountains with mountains, etc.). However, functional relations exist not only between the objects of one and the same category, but above all between objects of different categories in space. Let us say, "not between the Ohio and the Kama and not between the

---

Translator's remark: This Russian term is a loan translation of German *Länderkunde:* "knowledge of a particular land, country, or state." While it is commonly rendered by "regional geography," some Soviet geographers have indicated their disapproval of its equation by foreign geographers to *regional'naya geografiya*. Certainly, it conflicts logically with "regionalization" [*rayonirovaniye*], which involves the breaking down of a *strana* (land, country, or state) into "regions" [*rayony*], whereas the *strana (-Land)* is precisely the highest unit of regionalization in the generally accepted Soviet system. The situation is further complicated, especially for the translator, by the fact that Soviet geographers sometimes contrast *rayon* to *région* (as a Russian word), which they indeed seem to equate to *strana* as a regionalization term in the same sense as in *stranovedeniye*. "Regional geography" has nevertheless been retained in this translation because there seems to be no alternative that would not be too unfamiliar and circumlocutional. The reader may overcome this drawback by bearing in mind the definition of *stranovedeniye* given below.

Obviously, to cite but one example, when the author speaks of "the general and regional [*regional'naya*] parts" of a monograph on *stranovedeniye*, he does not consider *regional'nyy* as equivalent to *stranovedcheskiy*. To guard the reader against the resulting confusion, the Russian terms are placed in brackets at critical points.

Appalachians and the Urals, but rather between the Ohio and the Appalachians on the one hand and the Kama and the Urals on the other. A flood on the Mississippi does not affect the Amur or any other river, but the surroundings of the Mississippi itself, the life and economy of the population living along its shores." (N. N. Baranskiy, "Regional Geography [*Stranovedeniye*] and Physical and Economic Geography," *Izv. VGO*, 1946, No. 1-2, pp. 18-19.) In other words, the real geographic object is primarily the country, the region. Hence, alongside of specialization in the separate components of nature and the branches of the economy, specialization in territories is continuing to develop and regional [*regional'nyye*] generalizing works of an integrated regional-geographic character are being created. However, the sharp separation of the two main branches—physical and economic geography—within geography has had the result that two principal trends have clearly asserted themselves in Soviet regional-geography literature: physico-geographic and economico-geographic regional geography [*stranovedeniye*].

The main task of regional geography [*stranovedeniye*], both physical and economic, is the study of definite territories (continents, countries, and major regions [*rayony*]). The regional geographer [*Geograf-stranoved*] collects, analyzes, and generalizes the data relating to concrete territories and ascertains how the more general laws, not peculiar to the given territory alone and ascertainable by physical and economic geography, manifest themselves in those territories. The discovery of such laws is not one of the tasks of regional geography, but inasmuch as the regional geographer is usually at the same time also a physical geographer or economic geographer, problems of a more general character are incidentally examined in the course of regional-geographic work on the basis of the materials on the territory under study. Still, work in regional geography is more descriptive in character than research in systematic physical geography or economic geography, which analyze the general laws usually not connected with only one concrete territory.

The development of the specialized geographic disciplines has made it possible to raise work in regional geography to a new level. Above all, a solid foundation has been built for a stricter selection of the most essential facts from among the boundless multitude of them, for their evaluation, and for the establishment of the mutual relations among them, primarily the genetic relations. Naturally, this could not fail to be reflected in the content and structure of characterizations in regional geography. The disorderly arraying of facts set down according to the explorer's itinerary has been replaced by a systematic description of the country or region studied according to the basic categories of interrelated phenomena.

Having independent scientific significance, such descriptions at the same time also represent a definite value from the viewpoint of the branch disciplines, inasmuch as they contribute to the accumulation of factual material and to the clarification of the interrelations between the phenomena of the different categories interacting on a concrete territory.

Along with this, works in regional geography, if written in a popular style and accessible for wide circles of readers, have great cultural educational significance, inasmuch as they endeavor to disseminate broadly knowledge about nature, population, and the economy of one's own country and foreign states. They thereby contribute to the development of a feeling of love for the Fatherland and at the same time to a better mutual understanding between peoples, which is important for strengthening universal peace and friendly relations between the different countries. Regional geography is of great importance as one of the general educational disciplines in the middle and higher schools and as a special discipline in the geographic faculties of the universities and teachers colleges, in the foreign-language institutes, and also in the institutions which train specialists on foreign countries.

A great role in the development of Soviet regional geography was played by N. N. Baranskiy, who did a great deal to work out its methodologic principles, formulated the tasks, and trained more than one generation of regional geographers. In his programmatic articles he comes out against a narrowing of the framework of regional geography, considering that it should be unified and should include a wide range of questions concerning the nature, history, economy, culture, and politics of a country [*strana*].

In the programmatic article "Regional Geography and Physical and Economic Geography," N. N. Baranskiy points out that in writing works in regional geography two basic methodological problems arise: the choice of factual material and the job of tying it together. Here the principal task of regional geography consists in creating, not "mechanical mixtures" of various information about a country, but characterizations containing a logical combination of the most important distinguishing features of each country or region, and in tying them as closely together as possible. These features are selected from different fields and are bound together into a single integral image. "These features to be selected should satisfy three conditions:

(a) they should be *unique,* distinguishing a given country [*strana*] from other countries;

(b) they should be *essential,* especially important for the understanding of the country;

(c) they should be *capable of being tied together* (mutually explained) with other features." (*Ibidem,* p. 21.)

As in the past, serious works in regional geography result from the generalization of the results of personal research and published materials. The widest use is made of personal observations in describing the territory of the Soviet Union. Major works on the regional geography of foreign countries are based principally on primary statistical sources, original detailed descriptions, including reports on field work, and other literary materials. Here, the regional geographer specializing on foreign countries has to deal with research written up from other methodological and methodical standpoints. Hence, a "re-interpretation" of both the factual material and the conclusions and explanations occupies an important place in the creative work of the regional geographer.

In recent years, owing to the growth of communications and the expansion of the collaboration between peoples, opportunities have arisen more and more frequently for visits to foreign states and for joint investigations with geographers of other countries.

Works in regional geography, of course, differ substantially one from another in both content and form of presentation. However, in the overwhelming majority of cases the authors endeavor to adhere to a definite structure, constituted on the basis of the unity of methodology. The descriptions are made by generic categories (by the components of nature in the physical geographic essay, by branches of the economy in the economic geographic essay), a considerable space being taken up by a portrayal of the interrelations existing between them. Here, showing the interrelations between the generic categories is not, generally speaking, an end in itself, but it cannot be dispensed with in analyzing the cause-and-effect relationship of phenomena, because the cause of the peculiarity of one category (or even of the origin of the phenomenon itself) must often be sought in the characteristics of others. This essential feature of the modern monograph, in regional geography, which, as a rule, was lacking in the works composed in the past century, is, to a considerable extent due to the progress of the particular sciences, which reveal many characteristics of the generic categories.

In studying cause-and-effect relationships wide use is made of the historical method of analyzing phenomena, which, in particular, finds its reflection not only in the content, but also in the structure of the essays themselves. Thus, in monographs in physical geography, independent paleogeographic sections appear more and more often, and in monographs on economic geography there are usually sections on historical geography. "In many many cases," remarks N. N. Baranskiy, "the historical background in works in economic geography — especially in countries and regions that are already old — proves more important for the understanding of modern economic geography than the natural background." (*Ibidem,* p. 15.)

In analyzing cause-and-effect relationships geographers have occasion to encounter quite different laws governing the development of nature and society. This has obviously contributed to a departure from the once-existing general unified regional geography and to the formation of physical geographic and economic geographic orientations to some degree isolated from one another. Physical geographers concentrate their whole attention on nature and only now and then touch on those aspects of man's economic activity which lead to changes in it, such as the replacement of the natural vegetation by cultivated vegetation, the regulation of rivers, and so forth. Economic geographers, on the other hand, work mainly on the economy and population and usually do not endeavor to penetrate into the essence of the laws determining the uniqueness of the natural conditions. The latter are necessarily examined in such works, but usually only as a background against which economic activity takes place.

An important feature affecting the construction of an essay in regional geography is the necessity of ascertaining and portraying the general and local characteristics inherent in each natural or economic region. As a rule, this circumstance determines the proportion between the general and regional parts making up the main subdivisions of the essays. Characteristic of the present period is the change in the relationship in favor of the regional part, especially in physical geographic essays, where the latter often occupies not less than two-thirds of the volume.

Of great importance for regional geography is the scientific elaboration of regionalization problems. Even the meatiest monograph in regional geography will not prove to have full value if it does not repose on a scientifically grounded system of taxonomic units — regions [rayony] and subregions [podrayony] of different orders. The very breakdown of the territory under examination is found to be different in works in regional geography with a physical geographic, and those with an economic geographic orientation. Inasmuch as regionalization essentially determines the structure of the regional part of the work, the non-coincidence of the networks of natural and economic geographic regions of itself forces the author to give the regional geography work either a physical geographic or an economic geographic character.

A physical geographic regional monograph usually begins with a characterization of the geographic position, in which the location of the given region is fixed in the system of objects of the regional and zonal categories of the higher ranks (for major territories these are continents, belts, or geographic zones), which, on the basis of the general laws, permits one immediately to point out certain important characteristics of the territory. The general part, in which the main features of nature are examined successively by components in their historical development — geologic structure, relief, climate, inland waters, soils, vegetation and animal life —, is frequently of subordinate importance. Here are noted the general features of nature, inherent in the territory as a whole, and the internal differences which permit the differentiation of physical geographic regions are established. The latter become the object of examination in the following regional part of the monograph. There is no general order or established sequence of presentation in the characterization of regions. The structure of this part depends in each individual case upon the geographic characteristics of the regions and is subordinate to the necessity of showing the peculiarity of the territory most precisely and vividly.

In works in economic regional geography the characterization of the geographic position of the country or region is followed by a chapter on the physical geographic characteristics, in which main attention is paid to an economic evaluation of the natural conditions and resources. Then usually follows a sketch in historical geography, showing the formation of the territory of the country, its population, and present economy. If no special section is devoted to these questions, great attention is paid to them in one way or another in other chapters of the work. An important place is occupied by the chapter on population geography, containing information on its composition and dynamics, distribution, populated points and, in some works, on the customs, habits and culture of the population. Man, as the chief productive force, is rightly assigned much space in all the other chapters as well, including the regional section. The bulkiest part of the general survey in monographs is occupied by an essay on the geography of the economy, which includes a general characterization and a number of chapters devoted to the separate branches (agriculture, industry, transportation, etc.). The general survey is concluded with an examination of the external economic relations. The regional survey, occupying as much as one-half the volume, gives a characterization of the internal differences by economic regions and subregions, and a description of the major cities and typical populated points.

As already pointed out, regional geography [stranovedeniye] has a wide range of consumers with the most varied demands. For this reason, the literature in regional geography may be most varied in character, ranging from voluminous scientific monographs and teaching aids for institutions of higher learning down to popular books, brochures, and articles. Among these must also be classed, with some reservations, the articles in encyclopedic publications, particularly in the Great Soviet Encyclopedia and especially in the Short Geographic Encyclopedia [Kratkaya Geograficheskaya Entsiklopediya], 4 volumes. [Volumes I and II appeared in 1960-1961.—Ed.]

With respect to the topics, substantial differences are also observed between the works on the USSR and those on foreign countries. Naturally, the territory of the USSR is examined with a smaller degree of generalization in Soviet literature on regional geography, while in works on a foreign territory economic geographers usually have to deal with countries or even groups of countries, and physical geographers with continents or major parts of continents. In describing the

USSR the objects are most often Union republics, or economic regions and so-called physical geographic "lands" [*strany*] or "provinces" [*provintsii*] and oblasts.

Among the Soviet works in regional geography differing in character and subject, the most prominent place is occupied by economic geographic monographs on separate parts of the USSR. Since 1948 and especially in the period 1954-1958 more than 20 monographs devoted to separate republics and regions of the Soviet Union have been issued. The main work in this field is being carried out by the Institute of Geography of the Academy of Sciences of the USSR and the academies of the Union republics. The majority of the works are collective, and in a number of cases collaborators of various local institutions and of the Institute of Geography of the Academy of Sciences of the USSR have worked jointly. Such monographs have now been published on all the Union republics, while the RSFSR, owing to its great size and the complex diversity of its nature and economy, is described not only in a general monograph but also in a number of works devoted to individual major regions. During these years works devoted to the following areas have been published: the Volga region, Karelia, North Caucasus, Urals, Western Siberia, the Far East, and others. Works are being prepared on the Center and the Northwest of the European part of the USSR and Eastern Siberia. Thus, the publication of a series of monographs on all the regions and republics of the USSR will in a short time have been generally completed.

Within these works there is a considerable volume of detailed research. Especially outstanding in this respect are the "Kazakh SSR" by a group of authors headed by O. R. Nazarevskiy, which came out under the editorship of N. N. Baranskiy, and "Western Siberia" by M. I. Pomus. Alongside preparation of the works of this series, further work is being done on regions characterized earlier. Expanded and revised volumes on certain territories, for example, Turkmenia, are already published.

Similar work on foreign countries is being done chiefly at the Institute of Geography of the Academy of Sciences of the USSR and in the geographic faculty of Moscow State University.

In the development of the study of the economic geography of foreign countries, a prominent place belongs to I. A. Vitver and his numerous pupils. Vitver's monographs which appeared already in the early 30's on the countries of Latin America still remain models of work on major regions embracing several states. I. A. Vitver and A. Ye. Sluka's "France," published in 1958, is one of the best works in regional geography of recent years.

Since 1952, more than 20 monographs devoted to the countries of the people's democracy and to capitalist states have come out, including those on Czechoslovakia, Hungary, Bulgaria, Albania, Germany, France, Great Britain, the Irish Republic, Sweden, Spain, Korea, Egypt, the Sudan, Chile, and others. A series of works is also being created on the chief economic regions of the major foreign countries: China, the United States, and India. Already published are "Eastern China," "Northern India," "Western India," "Kashmir," "The South of the USA," "The North of the USA," and others.

Along with these are being published many popular books, chiefly of small size, designed for wide circles of readers. Among them should be noted the series "Of the world map" *(U karty mira),* in which 50 booklets have come out since 1950, each being typically devoted to a separate state. Thus, in this series basic information may be found on almost all countries.

Among the major works in physical regional geography must be classed a number of textbooks for students of the geographic faculties of the universities and pedagogic institutes. Such are, above all, "Middle Asia" by I. S. Shchukin; "Physical Geography of the USSR (Asiatic Part)" by S. P. Suslov; "Physical Geography of the USSR (European Part and Caucasus)" and "Europe Beyond our Borders" [*Zarubezhnaya Yevropa*] by B. F. Dobrynin; "Africa" by A. S. Barkov; a collective work by six authors under the editorship of B. F. Dobrynin and E. M. Murzayev on "Asia Beyond our Borders" [*Zarubezhnaya Asiya*]; "The Caucasus" by N. A. Gvozdetskiy; and "South America" by Ye. N. Lukasheva. The appearance of these works as instructional aids is no accident. It is due to the great importance of physical regional geography as an educational discipline. Moreover, all the above-mentioned books in their contents go far beyond the bounds of the ordinary educational literature and hold great interest not only for students, but also for a wide range of physical geographers with different interests and qualifications.

In addition to this, a number of monographic characterizations of the natural conditions of major regions of the USSR have been published, such as Siberia, the south of the Far East, and others. Systematic work on the creation of monographs on the physical regional geography of individual regions of the USSR is being accomplished in the Institute of Geography of the Academy of Sciences of the USSR, which has issued books devoted to the European North, the Soviet Arctic, the Lower Volga region, the Middle Volga region, the Lower Don and the North Caucasus, the Northwest of the RSFSR, the Central Chernozem oblasts, Western Siberia, Middle Asia, the Far East, the Kuril Islands, Kazakhstan, the Moscow region, and Kamchatka. In the Institute's new series it is proposed to give in 12 monographs a detailed survey of all the natural regions of the Soviet Union.

During the last 15-20 years there have also appeared a considerable number of books containing a characterization of the natural conditions of many foreign countries and regions, particularly, Rumania, Hungary, Norway, Yugoslavia, India, and on China (Tibet), Mongolia, Algeria, New Zealand, the non-Soviet North and others. Among the books enumerated, we should especially note the excellently written book by E. M. Murzayev on Mongolia, based to a considerable extent on materials from many years of investigation by the author.

Thus, it may be observed that a large number of works in regional geography have appeared in the last 15-20 years. The unity of the methodological viewpoints of the authors has contributed to the creation of definite types of monograph in regional geography in which a common structure and approach are combined with a consideration of the peculiarity of the territory, which determines the individual characteristics of the various works. At the same time, two trends stand out distinctly in Soviet literature in regional geography: the physical and the economic. The small number of works in which nature, the population, and the economy of the countries or regions are characterized essentially in equal detail do not constitute an exception, since they usually represent a mere combination of a physical geographic characterization (in the first part) with an economic geographic one (in the second part).

The existence of two different forms of synthesis of geographic material reflects the characteristics of a definite stage in the development of geographic science, characterized by the rapid development of the special disciplines. Along with this it may be supposed that the development of these trends is not to be in the direction of further isolation, but, on the contrary, toward their mutual rapprochement. These tendencies are manifesting themselves ever more insistently in the field of both economic and physical geography. The economic geographer, in going deeply into the study of the geographic characteristics of man's economic activity, is obliged to penetrate ever more deeply into the essence of the laws of physical geography, inasmuch as the natural objects are the most important ones with which human society has to deal in the process of production. This is especially evident in the economic geographic study of agriculture, in the process of which one more and more frequently encounters the necessity of analyzing the natural factors affecting crop yields and other characteristics of agricultural production. On the other hand, the deliberate alteration of nature by man, as well as the whole array of methods now being perfected for such transformations, urge the introduction of material-technical means of acting upon nature into the range of objects for physical geographers, and, along with these means, also the introduction of definite problems of an economic character. All this leads to an erasure of the boundaries between the spheres of physical and economic geography and thereby creates opportunities for the appearance of new and fuller organic forms of synthesis of geographic material.

BASIC LITERATURE

Anuchin, V. A. "Concerning the Theoretical Questions of Regional Geography *(Stranovedeniye),*" *Voprosy geografii,* No. 37, 1955.

Baranskiy, N. "Regional Geography and Physical and Economic Geography." *Izv. VGO,* 1946, No. 1.

Dmitriyevskiy, Yu. D. "The Study of Nature in Foreign Countries by Soviet Scholars (1917-1957)." *Izv. VGO,* vol. 91, 1959.

Dobrynin, B. F. "Methodological Principles of Modern Research in Physical Regional-Geography," *Voprosy geografii,* No. 40, 1957.

Murzayev, E. M. "Results and Tasks of Physical Regional Geography in the USSR," *Izv. AN SSSR, seriya geogr.,* 1957, No. 5.

Ryazantsev, S. N. "Results and Tasks of the Work on Economic Regional Geography Done by the Institute of Geography of the Academy of Sciences of the USSR," *Izv. AN SSSR, seriya geogr.,* 1957, No. 5.

CHAPTER 7

CARTOGRAPHY

K. A. Salishchev

The development of cartography in pre-revolutionary Russia was determined chiefly by the interests of the army. The topographic study of the country was done by the Military Topographic Service. Its century-long activity resulted in the appearance of topographic maps for an immense area of about ten million [square] kilometers.

Especially accurate and detailed were the 1:21,000 and 1:42,000 surveys of the western border area, with relief and contour lines. Considerable cartographic material for a knowledge of Russia and the contiguous countries was furnished by numerous expeditions of the Geographic Society, which studied Siberia, the Amur region, and Middle and Central Asia. This material had the value of pioneer reconnaissance exploration. However, at the time of the revolution the central part of the country, the Urals, and other economically important regions still had only completely obsolete topographic maps, or were entirely deprived of them.

The outstanding figures of Russian science, Academicians V. I. Vernadskiy (1863-1945) and D. N. Anuchin (1843-1923) came out not long before the revolution with an appeal for the planned investigation of the productive forces of Russia based on a systematic mapping of the country, but at that time these ideas could not be realized. Special-purpose surveys were made regularly for geologic purposes, but with only modest forces. The work in the other branches of special-purpose mapping, due primarily to the initiative and activity of individual scholars, was episodic in character. A brilliant example of this was the research done by V. V. Dokuchayev (1846-1903), who worked out the scientific principles of soil mapping. Among the solid achievements of pre-revolutionary cartography must be classed a number of economic-cartographic publications, from early ones dating back to the middle of the 19th century (the "Map of the Industry of European Russia," 1842, and the "Economic-Statistical Atlas of European Russia," 1851, and others) to, finally, the integrated "Atlas of Asiatic Russia," 1914. But these examples are isolated ones. Under the conditions of the planless, spontaneous development of a capitalist economy, work on special-purpose mapping was very small in volume and proceeded without general organized supervision, without a strict system or sequence.

In keeping with the general state of pre-revolutionary cartography, aimed principally at providing the army with topographic maps, theoretical research was concentrated on questions of geodesy, topographic surveying, and cartographic projections. It found its generalization in the "trilogy" of the well-known military geodesist Prof. V. V. Vitkovskiy (1856-1924): "Practical Geodesy," "Topography," and "Cartography." Map compilation proper was held to simple technical operations. (Similar views of cartography may be found abroad even in our days. Thus, in the book "American Geography: Inventory and Prospect," published in 1954 by the Association of American Geographers, it is stated that cartography "embraces geodesy, geodetic and topographic surveying (including photogrammetry), and all the *crafts* and *techniques* (the italics are mine — K. S.) connected with the compilation, drafting, and reproduction of printed maps" (page 529 in the Soviet edition of 1957 and page 555 in the original). Such a narrow approach to cartographic questions proper finds a certain explanation in the fact that, according to the testimony of this book, work for the army, for war, has been and remains the incomparably greatest stimulus for the development of cartography in the United States in the current century. (Pp. 531-532 in the Russian edition and pp. 555-556 in the original.)

★ ★ ★

The Great October Socialist Revolution, which opened up a new era in the history of mankind, offered boundless opportunities for the planned advancement of the productive forces. The investigation of the rich natural resources, their involvement in economic production, the scientifically based distribution of the productive forces—all this required a detailed study of the whole territory of the country and called for comprehensive maps of it. Cartography was confronted by new goals and new problems, whose solution was accompanied by the energetic development of cartographic production and science.

On 15 March, 1919, V. I. Lenin signed the decree concerning the organization of the State Cartographic-Geodetic Service (called at that time the Supreme Geodetic Administration), as is stated in the decree: "for the study of the territory of the RSFSR with respect to topography, for the purpose of advancing and developing the productive forces of the country." The new institution was entrusted with the unification of all geodetic activity, the making of systematic surveys over the whole expanse of the country, the compilation and publication of maps of country-wide significance necessary for the national economy, as well as the preparation of maps requested by the individual official agencies and scientific institutions.

In turning state cartography to the service of the national economy, the decree of 15 March, 1919 advanced a broad program of measures necessary for the unification, scientific organization, and development of all cartographic-geodetic work. This program comprised: the training of young scientific forces; the organization of scientific work in all fields of cartography and geodesy; the creation of technical instructions establishing unified methods and working procedures; and the gathering, systematizing, working up, and preserving of all the results obtained. The fundamental propositions of the decree of 15 March, 1919 defined the primary interests of Soviet geography in the period of its inception, and the scale of subsequent actions. These propositions have retained their significance down to our times.

Another decree of the Council of People's Commissars, signed by Lenin on 7 August, 1919, concerning the preparation of cartograms, diagrams, carto-diagrams, and other graphic representations for the purpose of disseminating among the worker and peasant population correct information about the activity of Soviet institutions and knowledge about the national economy, confronted cartography with tasks of cultural-educational significance.

These documents determined the goals and organizational principles of Soviet cartography. Its methodological foundations were laid in the letters written by Lenin in 1920-1921 regarding the preparation of the first Soviet geographic atlases ("Works" [*Sochineniya*], vol. 35, p. 427; "The Lenin Collection" [*Leninskiy Sbornik*], **XX**, Moscow, 1932, pp. 317-323). From these letters emanated principles important not only for atlases but also for geographic maps in general: fullness and wholeness of content; multilateral characterization of phenomena, with an indication of their connections, dependences, and contradictions; portrayal of phenomena in their dynamics (in their historical development); modernity of data (or association with definite characteristic dates); distinguishing of the principal and the dominant; and legibility and accessibility of the maps.

A characteristic feature of Soviet cartography is its constant, close, organic connection with geography—a fact that has contributed to their development and to their mutual enrichment and enhancement of their value for practical purposes. The foremost Russian geographers have had a good understanding of the nature of this connection. D. N. Anuchin repeatedly noted the importance of maps in geographic investigations and the ability of maps "to lead to further conclusions from them" and, on the other hand, emphasized the necessity of fundamental geographic knowledge for successful map making. However, in pre-revolutionary years geographers received in the universities a very scant fund of knowledge about cartography and did not take part in state mapping; the latter was viewed almost exclusively from the geometric viewpoint.

The solution of the tasks set by the decree of 15 March, 1919, required the preparation of new personnel, particularly specialists with higher qualifications. Great credit in this matter belongs to the Moscow Surveying Institute (transformed in 1930 into the Institute of Engineers for Geodesy, Aerial Photogrammetry, and Cartography), which developed in accordance with the ideas of the great Soviet geodesist, F. N. Krasovskiy (1878-1948). At his initiative the Scientific-Research Institute of Geodesy and Cartography was also created in 1928. It was F. N. Krasovskiy and especially A. A. Borzov who worked for the introduction of the geographic orientation in cartography. Under their influence, the geographic-cartographic specialty was founded in 1923 in the Surveying Institute [*Mezhevoy Institut*] — the first higher cartographic school not only in the USSR, but in the whole world. Its curriculum comprised the series of geographic disciplines: physical geography and topology, geomorphology of Russia, economic geography, methods of natural-history field exploration, and organization of cartographic-geographic investigations. Much was also done by A. A. Borzov to extend geographic influence directly to cartographic-geodetic production.

The inclusion of university geographers in cartographic work has been facilitated by the fact that in Soviet times courses in geodesy and cartography have become obligatory in the training of geographers of all specialities. Of great significance for the further development of the geographic orientation in cartography has been the organization of the cartographic specialty in the geographic faculties of a number of universities. The ground was laid by A. A. Borzov in 1929 at Moscow University. In this university alone, about 320 persons have received the geographer-cartographer diploma in the course of thirty years (1929-1959).

The mapping of the country and the training of personnel for it have been accompanied by the energetic development of scientific research on all questions of cartography. The content of cartography as a science has been defined. In pre-revolutionary years its interests were confined to cartographic projections, i.e., a purely mathematical task. In Soviet times, the issuance of a large number of diversified maps and atlases has required the study of the methods and processes of making them. In the 1930's, all scientific-technical processes of the compilation and reproduction of maps began to be assigned to cartography. The next step was connected with the inclusion, in map-making tasks, of a systematic study of the maps themselves, their nature, elements, types, and development, i.e., that department of cartography which has received the name of map science [*kartovedeniye*] and which has permitted the analysis, evaluation and, most important, the drawing of new maps to be placed on really scientific foundations.

The geographic map is not merely the product of production; it is valuable as a means of practical work and scientific research. It is important not only to make a good map, but also to be able to use it in the best manner. Naturally, cartography also had to address itself to the theoretical elaboration of the questions of map use. Ultimately, cartography included in the field of its scientific interests the thorough study of the nature of geographic maps and the working out of methods and processes for making and using them. It was subdivided into a number of divisions: map science, mathematical cartography, the compiling and editing of maps, and the final editing of maps. Cartography has come to embrace the publication of maps, as well as the organization and economics of cartographic production. Substantial progress has been made in the elaboration of each of these divisions, although the movement in different directions has, of course, not been equal.

The historical investigations of A. I. Andreyev, O. A. Yevteyev, S. E. Fel', F. A. Shibanov, and others, which have been reflected in numerous articles, have revealed and permitted us to re-evaluate the high achievements of our native cartography in the past stages of its development. The results obtained down to 1948 have been summarized by K. A. Salishchev, "Principles of Map Science" [*Osnovy Kartovedeniya*] (1948). A. I. Preobrazhenskiy (1953) has published a monographic investigation on the history of Russian economic cartography.

Much attention has been paid to the search for scientifically based principles of the *analysis and evaluation of maps* — this fundamental task of map science (Salishchev, 1944; Byushgens, 1957, and others). Works on the concrete description of maps and atlases have been published by N. V. Vinogradov (1946), Yu. V. Filippov, Yu. G. Kel'ner, and L. M. Byushgens (1958).

Solid progress has been achieved in the field of *mathematical cartography and cartometry*. On the analysis, investigation, and calculation of projections, over 150 studies have been published.

The groundwork for major generalizations was laid by V. V. Kavrayskiy (1934). Later, detailed courses in cartographic projections were compiled by A. V. Grauer (1938), M. D. Solov'yev (1937, 1946), N. A. Urmayev (1941) and A. P. Yushchenko (1941, 1953). The elaboration by N. A. Urmayev (1947, 1950) of a method of finding projections by the assigned distribution of distortions opened a new stage in the development of the theory of cartography projections, already a well-established division of cartography. G. A. Ginzburg, in a number of works (for example, 1952) showed the necessity of examining, in conjunction with cartographic projections, the questions of the composition of maps, the co-ordination of the allotment and scales of maps, the density of the graticule network, etc., and gave the basis for a proper broadening of the tasks and content of mathematical cartography. N. M. Volkov (1950) examined and generalized in a monographic investigation the principles and methods of cartometry and their application in the field of geography. For mathematical cartography, there is a detailed survey of its development and achievements in the USSR, a description of the mathematical foundation of Soviet maps, and a complete annotated index of the literature (Ginzburg and others, 1955).

Very diversified are the scientific works on the *compilation and editing of maps*. It is precisely in this department of cartography that theoretical research has especially been closely connected with practical requirements, has been stimulated by it, and has in turn aided the development of cartographic production. Here should be mentioned, in the first place, the elaboration of the principles and method of scientific generalization, aimed at bringing out both the expressive portrayal of typical features and the characteristic peculiarities of the phenomena to be mapped. The essence of generalization, its factors and methods, have been demonstrated by N. N. Baranskiy (1946), K. A. Salishchev (1947), A. M. Komkov (1951), and others. In its application to topographic maps, generalization has been worked out most systematically in the five-volume "Practical Handbook on the Compilation of Topographic Maps" (1943-1951). Works by Yu. V. Filippov (1946) and V. I. Sukhov (1947) have also been devoted to the representation and generalization of relief and populated points on topographic maps. With regard to general geographic maps on a small scale, a number of generalization questions have been examined in a collective work under the editorship of Yu. V. Filippov (1955). Ways of establishing standards of selection are being sought (Borodin, 1948; Sukhov, 1947; Bocharov and Nikolayev, 1957).

To improve the organization of cartographic production and raise the quality of the maps, it has proved especially valuable to introduce the *editing of maps* [*redaktirovaniye kart*], the establishment of its principles and content as a system of unified scientific-technical supervision, exercised at all stages of map making. The editing of maps, which constitutes a characteristic peculiarity of Soviet cartography, has been reflected above all in instructions and directions on the making of maps (the most important of which are indicated in the bibliography). These encompass both the practical experience and the achievements of science. Its utilization at the various stages of development has been implemented in the basic courses on the compiling and editing of maps (Salishchev and others, 1947; Komkov and others, 1958) and, in its application to topographic maps, has been discussed in a special work under the editorship of Komkov and Kudryavtsev (1952).

The considerable progress in the *technology of map compilation* is due to the rationalization and the introduction of new working methods, new apparatus and materials. Of the greatest significance has been the wide use of phototechnology and the mechanization of compilation processes. Many articles have been written on these questions. A theoretical basis for methods and techniques of transferring the image from the sources to the original of the maps being compiled has been propounded by N. A. Urmayev (1956).

The *final editing of maps* has been perfected principally as a result of experimental work, thanks in many respects to the experience and taste of those who produce the maps. In the last few years, however, investigations with a view to a theoretical interpretation on individual questions have begun to appear; for example, the basis of the size and drawing of the symbols (Vasmut, 1958; Kopylova, 1956).

Many scientific investigations on cartography are built on a solid geographic basis. It is recognized as necessary even in editing of maps, particularly for the logical classification of the symbols. But there are in cartography tasks that are geographic by nature, for example, the generalization of the relief in the contour lines, which has the purpose not only of showing the altitude relationships on the map, but also of portraying the morphology of the locality. It is precisely here, in the field of hypsometry, that Soviet cartography has achieved outstanding success, thanks in many respects to the works of Yu. M. Shokal'skiy, A. A. Borzov, T. N. Gunbina (1938), and I. P. Zarutskaya (1958).

The development of other branches of map making, connected with specialized geographic sciences, has led to the formation of a number of *special divisions of cartography*. In this connection, one must mention the works by A. I. Spiridonov (1952) on geomorphologic mapping, by I. P. Gerasimov (1949) and I. F. Sadovnikov (1952) on soil cartography, A. I. Preobrazhenskiy (1953) on economic cartography, and M. I. Nikishov (1957) on the cartography of agriculture, all of which have exerted a considerable influence on raising the scientific level of the respective maps. The works of M. A. Tsvetkov (1950), V. I. Sukhov and others (1937) have contributed to the systematization of the compilation of forest and agricultural maps. A book by K. A. Bogdanov (1954) is devoted to marine cartography.

The technical progress in *cartographic production*, the raising of the labor productivity, and the improvement of the quality of cartographic products have been promoted by scientific research and the generalization of practical experience in the field of map publication, the organizing and planning of production, but a review of them lies outside the tasks of the present collection. The bibliography gives only the works of a summary nature: V. V. Puskov (1954) and A. P. Safonov (1955) on the publication of maps; V. A. Merkulov (1954), I. N. Rusinov and A. V. Naumov (1954) on organization and planning.

The introduction of the results of scientific research into production is aided by the diversity of the *cartographic literature*. The main scientific-research institutions and educational establishments publish their own works. Monographic investigations are printed principally by specialized publishing houses (for geodetic literature and geographic literature). Articles on cartography are printed regularly in the monthly journal "Geodeziya i Kartografiya," the organ of the Main Administration of Geodesy and Cartography, and in the geographic journals.

The socialist system of economy has engendered a diversified need for geographic maps and has thereby predetermined the broad development of cartographic works. Placing them on a solid scientific foundation and training qualified personnel have insured the success of the enterprise and the high quality of the maps. The chief efforts have been directed toward the topographic study of the country "for the purpose of stimulating and developing the productive forces." The most important result has been the creation, by means of aerial photogrammetry, of the state topographic map to a scale of 1:100,000 for the whole territory of the USSR. The survey is being intensively expanded to scales of 1:25,000 and 1:10,000. For example, maps to a scale of 1:10,000 are already available for extensive areas in the European part of the USSR, Transcaucasia, Middle Asia, and Kazakhstan. The completion of large-scale mapping for all the most important regions of the country is a matter of the near future.

An obligatory precondition for topographic surveys is the creation of a geodetic support. Its fulfilment according to the scheme proposed by F. N. Krasovskiy has not only insured the unity of the coordinates, but has also made it possible to use geodetic data for scientific conclusions and generalizations. An example is the computation of the size of the terrestrial ellipsoid (the so-called Krasovskiy ellipsoid), which has now been adopted for geodetic and cartographic work in the USSR and the countries of the people's democracy.

The use of methods of photogrammetry and stereotopography has resulted in a speeding up and refining of the surveys (especially in regions difficult of access) and has furnished an efficient means of enriching the maps. The quality of the topographic maps has been improved, especially thanks to the introduction of geography into cartography, and to the geographic interpretation of survey work. In the course of time, the maps have not merely been filled up with new signs. Rather, their improvement has been directed toward the fullest possible and scientifically best characterization of the locality and its natural and economic conditions. This lengthy and continuing process has been promoted by the geographic training of topographers, based on A. A. Borzov's idea that "it is impossible to portray any locality realistically on a map unless the cartographer is capable of distinguishing and understanding the characteristic features of the area to be represented." Geographic editing has become an important link in the processes of making topographic maps (Gol'dman, 1954; Podobedov, 1950). It insures the identification of typical features and the characteristic peculiarities of a locality and the working out of methods for the geographically correct reproduction of them on maps.

The mapping of sparsely inhabited territories of the USSR has been accompanied by many geographic discoveries. Topographic maps have furnished an accurate representation of the country, comparable for all regions. In them, geographers have received not only a foundation for special-purpose investigations, surveys and maps, but also a noteworthy means of ascertaining the characteristics and laws of distribution, and the combinations and spatial relationships of many geographic phenomena, as shown, for example, by N. S. Podobedov (1957).

The 1:100,000 map serves as a source for the mutually related series of maps to scales of 1:200,000, 1:300,000, 1:500,000 and 1:1,000,000, destined to satisfy various practical demands and research work. Especially interesting is the 1:1,000,000 map, conforming to the principles of the international map to that scale, but richer in content.

Models among the general geographic maps to smaller scales are the maps of the major reference work "World Atlas" [*Atlas Mira*], 1954, rich in content (there are over 205,000 names in the index) and very complete in the hypsometric portrayal of the relief of the land and the floor of the World Ocean. This Atlas reflected (at the time of its preparation) the results of the topographic study of the USSR, generalized the data on the topographic coverage of the planet as a whole and showed the high grade of the Soviet hypsometric school. In the establishment of the latter a noteworthy role was played by the hypsometric maps of the European part of the USSR to a scale of 1:1,500,000 (1941) and of the USSR to a scale of 1:2,500,000 (1949). It was on these maps that methods were worked out for generalizing the isohypses, and constructing variable section scales on the basis of a preliminary regionalization of the relief and construction of typical profiles of the terrain. Their success in conveying, by means of horizontal contour lines, the morphologic characteristics of different landscapes and the distribution of the basic types of relief demonstrated with particular clarity the fruitfulness of a geographic foundation of cartographic work and at the same time the indispensability of a scientific cartographic approach to the making of special-purpose maps, particularly in working out generalization questions.

The state and progress of special-purpose map making have been shown in the chapters on the specialized geographic sciences, and integrated map making has been examined in a separate chapter. Hence, in conclusion, it suffices to dwell solely upon one of the cultural-educational tasks of Soviet cartography, namely providing schools with instruction maps. In this branch of cartography there is constant contact between the producing cartographers and the geographer-teachers (as well as the historian-teachers for historical maps). The significance of the map in the teaching process is underscored with great force in the decrees of the directive organs dated 25 August, 1932, and 16 May, 1934, concerning the teaching of geography in the middle school. In accordance with the decision of the Government, a series of 10 school wall maps, marked by internal unity and high quality, was published in 1938 with a total edition of about three million copies. The co-ordination and consistency between the maps intended for the various classes of the middle school have also been developed in subsequent editions. The maps were issued by series; for example, a series of nature maps, a series of economic school maps, etc. Altogether, more than 100 different geographic maps and about 70 historical wall maps for the middle school and 13 atlases — 6 geographic and 7 historical — have appeared. In addition, over a million and a half albums or sets of colored maps have been issued on the yearly average to each of the six school geography books and to each of the eight school history books. The improvement of the school maps and atlases has been promoted by special-purpose research; the questions of the compilation of school maps have been generalized initially by I. B. Sukhodrev (1939), and later by G. N. Bashlavina (1954), who included in her work a survey of the development of Soviet school maps.

An entirely new enterprise, for which there are no parallels abroad, was the making of geographic wall maps for the higher schools, undertaken in 1950 at the initiative and under the editorial direction of the geographic faculty of Moscow University. Altogether, about a hundred maps have appeared. They are maps forming a number of series and are uniform, within each series, in general contents, degree of generalization, and type of make-up. At the same time, each map of the series represents an independent teaching aid. Very interesting, among the available series, are the maps of nature in the USSR to a scale of 1:4,000,000 — hypsometric, geologic, tectonic, geomorphologic, soil, vegetation, and zoogeographic (Salishchev and Zarutskaya, 1953).

BASIC LITERATURE

Baranskiy, N. N., "Generalization in Cartography and in Geographic Text Description." *Uchenyye zapiski MGU*, no. 119, Moscow, 1946.

Bashlavina, G. N., Features of the Compilation of General Geographic School Wall Maps *(Osobennosti Sostavleniya Stennykh Obshchegeograficheskikh Shkol'nykh Kart)*, Moscow, 1954.

Bogdanov, K. A., Marine Cartography, part 1, Soviet Marine Navigation Charts, their History and Description *(Morskaya Kartografiya, ch. 1, Sovetskiye Morskiye Navigatsionnyye Karty, ikh Istoriya i Opisaniye)*, 1954.

Borodin, A. V., "Concerning the Question of the Choice of Populated Points on General Geographic Maps." *Sb. GUGK*, no 18, Moscow, 1948.

Bocharov, M. K., and Nikolayev, S. A., Mathematico-statistical Methods in Cartography *(Matematiko-statisticheskiye Metody v Kartografii)*. Moscow, 1957.

Byushgens, L. M., "Analysis and Evaluation of Foreign General Geographic Maps as Materials for Compilation." *Tr. TsNIIGAiK*, no. 116, 1957.

Vasmut, A. S., "Visual Perception of the Symbols on Geographic (topographic) Maps." *Voprosy geografii*, sb. 42, Moscow, 1958.

Vinogradov, N. V., "Maps of Foreign States and the International 1:1,000,000 Map of the World" *(Karty Inostrannykh Gosudarstv i Mezhdunarodnaya Millionnaya Karta Mira)*. Moscow, 1946.

Volkov, N. M., Principles and Methods of Cartometry *(Printsipy i Metody Kartometrii)*, Moscow-Leningrad, 1950.

Vitkovskiy, V. V., Practical Geodesy *(Prakticheskaya Geodeziya)*, St. Petersburg, 1898; 2nd ed., St. P., 1911.

Vitkovskiy, V. V., Topography *(Topografiya)*, St. Petersburg, 1904; 4th ed., Leningrad, 1940.

Vitkovskiy, V. V., Cartography *(Kartografiya)*, St. Petersburg, 1907.

Geodeziya i kartografiya, journal of the Main Administration of Geodesy and Cartography, since 1956; its predecessors were the journal *Geodezist* (1925-1940) and the collections *(sborniki)* of scientific-technical and productional articles of the Main Administration of Geodesy and Cartography, nos. 1-31, 1940-1955.

Gerasimov, I. P., "Draft Program of the State Soil Map of the USSR." *Pochvovedeniye*, 1949, No. 10.

Ginzburg, G. A., "Mathematical Basis of the Maps of Integrated World Geographic Atlases." *Tr. TsNIIGAiK*, No. 91, 1952.

Ginzburg, G. A., Karpov, N. S., and Salmanova, T. D., "Mathematical Cartography in the USSR; part 1, Historical Sketch and Reference Data," *Tr. TsNIIGAiK*, no. 99, 1955; "part 2, Annotated Index of Literature on Mathematical Cartography and Cartometry," *Tr. TsNIIGAiK*, no. 108, 1955.

Gol'dman, L. M., "The Editing of Topographic Maps to a Scale of 1:10,000." *Tr. TsNIIGAiK*, no. 101, 1954.

Graur, A. V., Mathematical Cartography *(Matematicheskaya Kartografiya)*. Leningrad, 1938; Geodezizdat, Leningrad, 1956.

Gunbina, T. N. and Spiridonov, A. I., Under the editorship of Borzov, A. A., "An Experiment in Working Out the Question of the Representation of Relief on School Physical Maps." *Tr. TsNIIGAiK*, no. 21, 1938.

Zarutskaya, I. P., Methods of Compiling Relief on Hypsometric Maps *(Metody Sostavleniya Rel'yefa na Gipsometricheskikh Kartakh)*. Moscow, 1958.

Instruktsiya po Sostavleniyu, Vycherchivaniyu i Izdaniyu Karty Masshtaba 1:200,000 (Instructions on compiling, drawing and publishing the 1:200,000-scale map). Moscow, 1942.

Instruktsiya po Sostavleniyu, Vycherchivaniyu i Izdaniyu Karty Masshtaba 1:500,000 (Instructions on compiling, drawing and publishing the 1:500,000-scale map). Moscow, 1945.

Kavrayskiy, V. V., Mathematical Cartography *(Matematicheskaya Kartografiya)*. Moscow-Leningrad, 1934.

Komkov, A. M., "Concerning the Question of the Nature and Methods of Generalization in Cartography." *Voprosy geografii*, sb. 27, 1951.

Komkov, A. M., and Kudryavtsev, M. K. (editors), Fundamentals of Editing Topographic Maps *(Osnovy Redaktirovaniya Topograficheskikh Kart)*. Moscow, 1952.

Komkov, A. M., Nikolayev, S. A., and Shilov, N. I., Under the editorship of M. K. Kudryavtsev. The Compilation and Editing of Maps *(Sostavleniye i Redaktirovaniye Kart)*, parts 1 and 2. Moscow, 1958.

Kopylova, A. D., "On the Scientific Foundations for Establishing the Sizes and Form of Cartographic Symbols." *Geodeziya i Kartografiya*, 1956, no. 10.

Merkulov, V. A., The Organization and Economics of Cartographic Production. *(Organizatsiya i Ekonomika Kartograficheskogo Proizvodstva)*. Moscow, 1954.

Nastavleniye po Sostavleniyu, Vycherchivaniyu i Podgotovke k Izdaniyu Karty Masshtaba 1:100,000 (Directions for compiling, drawing and preparing for publication the 1:100,000-scale map). Moscow, 1940.

Nastavleniye po Sostavleniyu i Podgotovke k Izdaniyu Gosudarstvennoy Karty SSSR v Masshtaba 1:1,000,000 (Directions for compiling and preparing for publication the State Map of the USSR to a scale of 1:1,000,000). Moscow, 1940.

Nastavleniye po Sostavleniyu i Podgotovke k Izdaniyu Karty Masshtaba 1:1,000,000 (Directions for compiling and preparing for publication the 1:1,000,000-scale map). Moscow, 1951.

Nikishov, M. I., Agricultural Maps and Atlases *(Sel'skokhozyaystvennyye Karty i Atlasy)*. Moscow, 1957.

Podobedov, N. S., "The Editing of the 1:100,000-scale Topographic Map in Mapping the Little Explored Regions of the USSR." *Tr. TsNIIGAiK*, no. 80, 1950.

Podobedov, N. S., "The 1:100,000-scale Topographic Map and its Significance for Physical Geography." *Geodeziya i kartografiya*, 1957, no. 8.

Prakticheskoye Posobiye po Sostavleniyu Topograficheskikh Kart (Practical aid in compiling topographic maps): issue 1, Komkov, A. M. and Kostrits, I. B., "Populated Points, their Choice, Generalization and Representation on Topographic Maps," Moscow, 1943; issue 2, Komkov, A. M. and Kostrits, I. B., "The Hydrographic Network and its Representation on Topographic Maps," Moscow, 1945; issue 3, Lyubvin, N. I. and Spiridonov, A. I., "Relief and its Representation on Topographic Maps," Moscow, 1951; issue 4, Nikolayev, S. A., "The Road Network and its Representation on Topographic Maps," Moscow, 1947; issue 5, Nikolayev, S. A., "The Soil and Plant Cover," Moscow, 1946.

Preobrazhenskiy, A. I., Russian Economic Maps and Atlases *(Russkiye Ekonomicheskiye Karty i Atlasy)*, Moscow, 1953.

Preobrazhenskiy, A. I., Economic Cartography *(Ekonomicheskaya Kartografiya)*. Moscow, 1953.

Pus'kov, V. V., The Technology of Publishing Maps *(Tekhnologiya Izdaniya Kart)*. Moscow, 1954.

Rusinov, I. N., Naumov, A. V. and Bendovskiy, M. K., The Organization and Planning of Cartographic Production. *(Organizatsiya i Planirovaniye Kartograficheskogo Proizvodstva)*. Moscow, 1954.

Sadovnikov, I. F., Soil Cartography *(Pochvennaya Kartografiya)*. Moscow, 1952.

Salishchev, K. A., Fundamentals of Map Science *(Osnovy Kartovedeniya)*. General part *(obshchaia chast')*, 2nd ed., Moscow, 1944; 3rd ed., Moscow, 1959.

Salishchev, K. A., (with the participation of V. I. Sukhov and Yu. V. Filippov). The Compiling and Editing of Maps *(Sostavleniye i redaktirovaniye Kart)*. Moscow, 1947.

Salishchev, K. A., "Cartography, its Object and Certain Problems." *Voprosy Geografii*, sb. 9, 1948, pp. 111-118.

Salishchev, K. A., Fundamentals of Map Science *(Osnovy Kartovedeniya)*. Historical part and cartographic materials. *(Chast' istoricheskaya i kartograficheskiye materialy)*. Moscow, 1948.

Salishchev, K. A., and Zarutskaya, I. P., "Geographic Maps for the Higher School." *Izv. AN SSSR, seriya geogr.*, 1953, No. 4.

Salishchev, K. A., "The Mapping of the USSR, its Results and Geographic Significance." *Izv. AN SSSR, seriya geogr.*, 1957, No. 5.

Safonov, A. P. and Abol'yan, A. M. (editors), Publication of Topographic Maps *(Izdaniye Topograficheskikh Kart)*. Moscow, 1955.

Solov'yev, M. D., Cartographic Projections *(Kartograficheskiye Proyektsii)*. Moscow-Leningrad, 1937; Moscow, 1946.

Spiridonov, A. I., Geomorphologic Map-making *(Geomorfologicheskoye Kartografirovaniye)*. Moscow, 1952.

Sukhov, V. I., "The Representation of Populated Points of the USSR on Topographic Maps." *Tr. TsNIIGAiK*, no. 48, 1947.

Sukhov, V. I., Yurovskiy, Ya. I., Liodt, G. N., and Nikishov, M. I., The Compilation of Agricultural Maps *(Sostavleniye Sel'skokhozyaystvennykh Kart)*. Moscow, 1957.

Sukhodrev, I. B., The Compilation, Editing, and Preparation for Publication of School Maps *(Sostavleniye, Oformleniye i Podgotovka k Izdaniyu Uchebnykh Kart)*. Moscow, 1939.

Urmayev, N. A., Mathematical Cartography *(Matematicheskaya Kartografiya)*. Moscow, 1941.

Urmayev, N. A., Methods of Finding New Cartographic Projections *(Metody Izyskaniya Novykh Kartograficheskikh Proyektsiy)*. Moscow, 1947.

Urmayev, N. A., "The Search for Some New Cylindrical, Azimuthal, and Pseudocylindrical Projections." *Sb. GUGK*, no. 29, 1950.

Urmayev, N. A., "The Theory of Homolographic Transformation and its Application to Mathematical Cartography and to the Compilation of Maps. *Tr. TsNIIGAiK*, no. 113, 1956.

Filippov, Yu. V., "The Fundamentals of the Generalization of Relief on Topographic Maps." *Tr. TsNIIGAiK*, no. 47, 1946.

Filippov, Yu. V., editor, "Fundamentals of Generalization on Small-scale General Geographic Maps." *Tr. TsNIIGAiK*, no. 104, Moscow, 1955.

Filippov. Yu. V., Kel'ner, Yu. G., and Byushgens, L. M., "Maps of Nature in Foreign General Reference Atlases (of states and regions)" *Tr. TsNIIGAiK*, no. 125, 1958.

Tsvetkov, M. A., Forest Maps and Methods of Compiling Them *(Lesnyye Karty i Metodika ikh Sostavleniya)*. Moscow-Leningrad, 1950.

Yushchenko, A. P., Cartography. The Theory of Cartographic Projections *(Kartografiya, Teoriya Kartograficheskikh Proyektsiy)*. Leningrad-Moscow, 1941; 2nd ed., Leningrad-Moscow, 1953.

CHAPTER 8

RESEARCH IN THE HISTORY OF GEOGRAPHIC KNOWLEDGE

D. M. Lebedev

The beginning of publication in the Russian press of investigations into the history of geographic knowledge dates back to the 1740's, when works on this subject by the St. Petersburg Academicians G. F. Miller and, somewhat later, S. P. Krasheninnikov appeared. M. V. Lomonosov devoted attention to these same problems; unfortunately, his works in this field were published considerably later. During the 19th and early 20th centuries, both the circle of Russian scholars working on the history of geography and the range of problems covered by them were greatly expanded. But these investigations have undergone their greatest development in Soviet times.

The object of the history of geography as a science is a very comprehensive one. It embraces not only the history of geographic discoveries and explorations of the land and the sea basins, but also the history of the development of theoretical geographic views, the development of the individual geographic sciences, and of all of physical and economic geography as a whole. Within its province are also the study of the activity of the individual institutions and organizations conducting research of a geographic character and thus contributing to the development of these sciences and, finally, the activity of individual persons whose lives and labors have made some contribution or other to the history of geography.

All the above-mentioned main questions are covered (to different degrees, of course, as we shall endeavor to show later) by Soviet scholars working in the field united by us under the broad term "history of geographic knowledge." In their research they strive to take into account the concrete historical circumstances as they have taken shape in this or that epoch. Such an approach to a characterization of the diverse sides of the history of geography in the works of Soviet scholars is generally recognized. (Hence, it is not noted in the separate parts of this essay). This makes it possible not only to take note of this or that characteristic in the development of geographic knowledge in definite historical periods, but also to explain the causes of these differences, produced by the profound action of the historical environment.

We shall endeavor to show only the principal problems that have attracted the attention of Soviet scholars, grouping all the works on the history of geography in several major divisions, more or less separated from one another in their topics.

A very large number of works are devoted to the history of geographic discoveries and the related history of geographic exploration of the land and the sea basins. In this extensive and complex division, it is necessary to distinguish several separate groups of problems, depending upon the territories (or sea basins) whose history of discovery and exploration has been studied by Soviet scholars. One of these groups, which long attracted special attention, includes the Eurasian sector of the Arctic Ocean with its European coastal regions, Siberia, the Far East, and the northern part of the Pacific Ocean with the adjacent territories of Northwestern America. The discovery and the exploration of these vast areas were closely connected with one another historically and were wholly or preponderantly the result of the activity of a multitude of native navigators, travelers, and scholars, which continued for centuries. In significance, they occupy one of the most important places in the history of world geographic discoveries.

The works of many Soviet scholars, taken altogether, examine a vast range of questions on the history of discovery and exploration in the above-mentioned territories during a period of six or seven hundred years, down to our times, inclusive. Among them one may (with, of course, a high degree of conventionality) distinguish works dealing principally with:

1. The history of the development of ideas about the existence of a strait separating the Northeast of Asia from the Northwest of America and the history of the discovery, exploration, and mapping of the sea route from Europe via the Arctic Ocean to the Pacific in the 15th-16th and especially in the 17th-18th centuries. In the course of these centuries all the separate parts of this route were discovered and the groundwork was laid for its exploration and conquest (L. S. Berg, M. S. Bodnarskiy, M. I. Belov, V. Yu. Vize, and many others).

2. The history of the successive study and conquest of the Northern Sea Route and of the Eurasian Arctic seas in general (the extensive work by V. Yu. Vize, embracing the period from ancient times to the 40's of the 20th century and containing information about foreign travelers as well).

3. The history of discoveries and explorations in Siberia and the Far East, principally in the 17th-18th centuries, and the development, in these same centuries, of cartographic representations of them, especially of the extreme Northeast and East (A. I. Andreyev, S. V. Bakhrushin, L. S. Berg, A. V. Yefimov, and others).

4. The history of the discovery and exploration, in the 18th and a part of the 19th century, of the Kurils (O. A. Yevteyev, I. I. Ogryzkov, and others), and of the Aleutian Islands and Alaska with the adjacent regions (A. I. Andreyev, L. S. Berg, R. V. Makarova, and others).

5. Works characterizing the significance of the First and Second Kamchatka Expeditions of 1725-1743, which constituted an epoch in the study of this immense area (L. S. Berg, G. V. Yanikov, and others).

To the same group of problems also belong numerous works specially devoted to individual native seafarers, travelers, and scholars who made a substantial contribution to the discovery and study of Siberia and the Far East, of the north of the Pacific Ocean, and of Northwestern America. Thus, for example: in the 17th-18th centuries S. I. Dezhnev, who actually discovered Bering Strait jointly with Fedot Alekseyev (Popov) in 1648; the leaders of the Kamchatka expeditions of 1725-1743, V. J. Bering and A. I. Chirikov and some outstanding participants in them; the explorers of Kamchatka, V. V. Atlasov, and S. P. Krasheninnikov; the outstanding Siberian geographer, hydrologist, and cartographer F. I. Soymonov; M. V. Lomonosov, as the author of the first scientific project of an expedition for the exploration of the Northern Sea Route and as a historian of geographic discoveries in Africa; and the industrialist and explorer of the Aleutian Islands, G. I. Shelikhov. To this galaxy belong, in the 19th-20th centuries: the explorer of Alaska, L. A. Zagoskin; the explorer of Sakhalin and the Amur region, G. I. Nevel'skoy; the explorers of Siberia and the Far East, P. A. Chikhachev, P. A. Kropotkin, I. D. Cherskiy, V. A. Obruchev, V. K. Arsen'yev; the explorers of the Arctic, F. P. Litke, F. P. Vrangel' [Wrangel], V. A. Rusanov, G. Ya. Sedov, and some others.

Altogether, the works of the numerous Soviet scholars mentioned above (and many others) have, above all, refined and considerably amplified the notions about the discoveries within the above-noted limits that were to be found in the pre-revolutionary Russian and foreign literature. Furthermore, many of their aspects were put in a new light on the basis of the extensive literature and documentary sources (both published and archival). For example, the mass character of the movement of Russian seafarers and travelers of the 16th-18th centuries eastward beyond the Urals, which led to the discovery of the Northern Sea Route and the above-mentioned areas, has been portrayed against a broad historical background. The significance of many unknown or insufficiently appreciated individual participants in these discoveries, as well as of certain scholars of the 18th and succeeding centuries, has been brought out.

These works have shown the development, considerable for those times, of Russian cartographic representations in the 18th century. These led, in particular, to a decisive refinement in the concepts about the configuration of the Northeast of the Asiatic continent and the opposite part of the Northwest of America, as well as the Kuril and Aleutian Islands. They have characterized the great influence exercised by these cartographic works on Western European cartography. They have illuminated the picture of the profound and thorough study and conquest of the Northern Sea Route and the Eurasian Arctic seas in Soviet times by native navigators, aviators, and scholars.

The second group of problems forming a part of the same division, which attracted the attention of Soviet scholars includes the Caspian and Aral seas and the territories now forming a part of the

Kazakh and Middle Asiatic Soviet Republics. Such are the works dealing with: (1) the history of the study of the Caspian and Aral seas, known already to ancient (especially Arab) scholars, but represented quite incorrectly in Western European cartography down to the Russian explorations of the 18th century, and (2) the so-called "Amu-Dar'ya problem," i.e., the history of the question of the reality of channels once uniting this river with the Caspian.

Soviet scholars made much more precise the main stages of the history of these closely interrelated Russian explorations, and the role of the chief participants in them: A. Bekovich-Cherkasskiy, A. I. Kozhin, F. I. Soymonov, K. Verden, A. I. Butakov, and certain others. In particular, they discovered the unknown first Russian maps of the Caspian and Aral seas and new data on the historically important expeditions of A. Bekovich-Cherkasskiy and A. I. Kozhin (works by L. S. Berg, Ye. A. Knyazhetskaya, K. I. Shafranovskiy, and others).

As for the territory of the Kazakh SSR and the Middle Asiatic Soviet Republics (Uzbek, Turkmen, Kirgiz, and Tadzhik), a number of works have been devoted to them: (1) surveys of the history of their exploration and mapping, by L. S. Berg, N. L. Korzhenevskiy, and others, (2) works characterizing the contributions of individual Russian travelers of the 17th-18th centuries to the geographic study of Middle Asia; for example, I. Unkovskiy, the compiler of the first map of the "*kontayshiny* possessions," and F. S. Yefremov, who for many years made "wanderings" through Middle Asia as well as through Iran and India and left valuable notes on them, (3) and works characterizing the significance of the native scholars of Middle Asia, Al-Biruni and Al-Khorezmi.

Special attention was paid to Russian scholar-explorers of the Middle Asiatic areas in the 19th century: P. P. Semenov-Tyan-Shanskiy, A. P. Fedchenko, G. N. Potanin, N. A. Severtsov, V. A. Obruchev, and I. V. Mushketov, who were the first to reveal to world science these vast areas about which—up to that time—there had been only very fragmentary and inaccurate information.

Such are the main groups of problems embracing (with certain exceptions) the history of the exploration of the territories now forming a part of the USSR.

A survey by N. A. Gvozdetskiy, devoted to the exploration of these territories by Soviet scholars in the 40 years since the October revolution, shows their extent and the resulting elimination of many "blank spots" that had existed theretofore.

To the third group of problems may be assigned the works on the history of the geographic exploration done by individual Russian travelers on territories now forming a part of the Chinese and Mongolian People's Republics, and also characterizing the significance of individual travels to certain other countries of the world. A brief summary characterization of the outstanding significance of our scholar-explorers of Central Asia [outside the Soviet Union] is given by V. A. Obruchev; a work by N. M. Shchukina is devoted to the creation of maps of Central Asia through the labors of Russian explorers of the 19th and early 20th centuries and to a characterization of them; a review of the explorations made on the territory of the Mongolian People's Republic from the most ancient times down to 1946 is given by E. M. Murzayev (also containing information about certain foreign travelers).

Much attention has also been paid to (1) the analysis of the main stages of the discovery in the 17th century of land routes from Russia via Siberia to Mongolia and China by the Russian ambassadors V. Tyumenets, Ivan Petlin, I. Baykov, N. G. Spafariy, and I. Ides, and the use made by Western European scholars of the itineraries and descriptions composed by them of the countries visited; and (2) a characterization of the activity of individual Russian scholar-travelers of the 19th and early 20th centuries through Central Asia. An analysis has been made of the great changes brought about in the concrete notions concerning its geography and in the cartographic representations of it that heretofore existed in Western European science, as well as in certain theoretical questions of physical geography elucidated by the materials from these travels. Such, for example, are the works about the life and activity of N. M. Przheval'skiy, G. N. Potanin, G. Ye. Grumm-Grzhimaylo, P. K. Kozlov, V. I. Roborovskiy, and M. V. Pevtsov.

Among the many individual travels to other countries, there has been detailed treatment of the travels [*Khozheniye*] to India in the 15th century by the Tver' merchant Afanasiy Nikitin. Soviet scholars have subjected to analysis the variants of the many texts of Nikitin's notes that have come down to us have ascertained his itineraries more precisely, and have shown their value for the study of the history and geography of the India of that time. In addition to the many works devoted to them, Nikitin's notes have been published by the Academy of Sciences and provided with voluminous articles and commentaries, characterizing their significance for science from various angles.

Finally, in 1960 the "Travels Across Three Seas" [*Khozhdeniye za Tri Morya*] was published by Geografgiz. This book contains the notes discovered in the chronicles of the Troitskiy Monastyr' (Trinity Monastery), and a translation of them into modern Russian, Hindi, and English. This unique publication was made by artists of Palekh, a village in Ivanovo oblast, famed for its art craftsmen.

The travels to Indo-China, the Malayan Archipelago, and New Guinea by N. N. Miklukho-Maklay have also been a subject for research by Soviet geographers. His works have been republished in full, some of them for the first time. The results of the travels to Africa by the 19th-century Russian scholars Ye. P. Kovalevskiy, V. V. Yunker, A. V. Yeliseyev, as well as of G. I. Langsdorf to Brazil have likewise been elucidated.

A special research division is formed by the extensive special literature devoted to the numerous long-distance voyages of our native sailors and scholars not only in the Arctic and the north of the Pacific Ocean, but also on many other seas and oceans. Special attention is paid therein to voyages around the world in the first half of the 19th century. Soviet scholars endeavor to refine the information about the itineraries and the circumstances of these voyages, about the discoveries and explorations made, and also to analyze the great contribution made by Russian voyages around the world to the special science of oceanology which is taking shape.

Such are: (1) generalizing surveys embracing considerable historical periods, exemplified by L. S. Berg's survey of Russian explorations in the Pacific Ocean in the 17th-19th centuries, and especially by N. N. Zubov's work, which for the first time systematically and comparatively fully characterizes our native voyages in the different seas and oceans from ancient times down to 1941; (2) works examining individual native expeditions, especially those around the world, for example: the voyages made under the leadership of I. F. Kruzenshtern and Yu. F. Lisyanskiy, V. M. Golovnin, S. O. Makarov, and others. Among them stand out numerous works elucidating the significance of the F. F. Bellingshausen-M. P. Lazarev expedition, which constituted an epoch in the history of discovery and exploration in the Antarctic Ocean and Antarctica (L. S. Berg, N. V. Vvedenskiy, S. G. Grigor'yev, Yu. M. Shokal'skiy, and many others.)

In concluding this division, let us note two surveys devoted principally to the history of our native geographic discoveries and explorations, by L. S. Berg from antiquity down to 1923, and by M. S. Bodnarskiy, down to the first half of the 19th century.

The history of the development of cartographic representations of the earth's surface and especially of the territory of Russia and the USSR is continuously connected with the history of geographic discoveries and explorations, as a result of which the respective maps were usually compiled or refined. Still, it is necessary to distinguish especially the problems dealing with certain questions, not sufficiently treated in the Russian pre-revolutionary literature, concerning the *history of the cartographic representations of territories and sea basins*. Among these, for example, principal attention has been given to:

1. The analysis of documents confirming the compilation of many Russian maps ("sketches") down to the 16th century, inclusively, and the demonstration of the wide use of these maps by Western European cartographers.

2. The history of the compilation and characteristics of the General Map of Russia from around the beginning of the 17th century, the so-called "Great Drawing" [*Bol'shoy Chertëzh*], according to the preserved "Rospis'" of it, i.e., the text characterization of its content. An analysis of the numerous variants of this "Rospis'" has led to the establishment of the fullest and most reliable text of it and has confirmed: (a) the coverage by the "Great Drawing" not only of the whole territory of the Russia of those times, but also of certain contiguous countries, (b) its great accuracy and detail, and (c) the recording on it of certain objects unknown to Western European cartographers; particularly the Aral Sea and the Syr-Dar'ya, which empties into it (works by F. A. Shibanov, I. I. Starostin, and many others). We note especially the investigations by K. N. Serbina, who also prepared the academic edition of the "Book to the Great Drawing" [*Kniga Bol'shomu Chertëzhu*], provided with a comprehensive historical analysis.

3. The detailed survey of the development of many-sided economic mapping (maps and atlases of the separate branches of the national economy, general economic and regional maps, etc.) in Russia and the USSR, from the 17th century down to our days (A. I. Preobrazhenskiy).

4. The history of the creation of certain Russian atlases: the general Russian atlases (including that of I. K. Kirilov and the Academic Atlas of 1745), world atlases, and specialized Russian atlases — statistical, industrial, forest, school and other atlases of this sort.

5. The tracing (or precise determination) of the itineraries of certain journeys and expeditions from the preserved data.

6. A number of works characterizing the outstanding significance, for the history of our native cartography, of certain of its figures; for example, I. K. Kirilov and Bagrationi Vakhushti.

7. Brief surveys of the history of pre-revolutionary Russian (for example, S. E. Fel') and Soviet (for example, K. A. Salishchev) cartography.

8. The generalizing characterization of the development of cartographic representations of the earth's surface from antiquity down to our days in many countries of the world, and especially in Russia and the USSR, given by K. A. Salishchev.

A large number of Soviet investigations are devoted to the significance of outstanding figures in the history of geography. In addition to their activity directly connected with travels, which naturally relates to the groups of problems examined above, a special division is formed by the extensive literature, which (1) elucidates from various angles the biographies of the individual scholars and the significance of their activity in the history of geographic knowledge, or (2) confines itself to an analysis of the contribution made by the scholar to this or that field of the theory of geography. The range of persons to whom such Soviet investigations have been devoted is also very broad. Let us name, by way of example, a few of them. For the 18th century, the economist and creator of the first All-Russian atlas, I. K. Kirilov; the first Russian theoretician in the field of geography, V. N. Tatishchev; M. V. Lomonosov as a geographer; the regional geographer, P. I. Rychkov; Academicians S. P. Krasheninnikov, I. I. Lepekhin, and V. F. Zuyev; for the 19th-20th centuries — N. A. Severtsov, G. I. Tanfil'yev, and A. A. Borzov. Some scholars (D. N. Anuchin, L. S. Berg, A. I. Voyeykov, V. V. Dokuchayev, V. L. Komarov, M. V. Lomonosov, V. A. Obruchev, and Yu. M. Shokal'skiy) have had devoted to them not only numerous separate works but also special collections of articles characterizing various aspects of their lives and activities, and likewise a part or all of their works have been re-published.

One of the most important and difficult divisions of the history of geography is devoted to the analysis of the development of the individual geographic sciences, the history of the development of the theoretical conceptions in the field of the physical geographic and economic geographic sciences in specific epochs. We still have no finished detailed (monographic) generalizations of this sort, but very many Soviet scholars are paying attention to this field, discussing in a number of articles (and in the historical sections of their own geographic works) the history of the development of our pre-revolutionary and Soviet geomorphology, hydrology, climatology, paleogeography, permafrost science, oceanology, limnology, and other separate physical geographic sciences.

Brief surveys of the development of physical geography, principally in the 19th-20th centuries in Russia and the USSR (for example, by L. S. Berg, A. A. Grigor'yev, and V. A. Obruchev) have also been published.

To a special group of problems may be assigned the investigations concerning the significance, in the history of geography, of our major institutions and organizations that have played, and are playing, an outstanding role in the development of geographic knowledge in Russia and the

USSR: the Academy of Sciences, the Geographical Society, and the universities. Such, for example, are the works written on the basis of archive data by V. F. Gnucheva concerning the role of the Academy of Sciences, which in the 18th-19th centuries organized a number of highly important expeditions headed by the well-known scholars P. S. Pallas, I. I. Lepekhin, I. A. Gil'denshtedt, V. F. Zuyev, K. M. Ber, A. F. Middendorf, and many others, and concerning the significance of its Geographic Department, which in the 18th century was the center of cartographic work in Russia; and the survey of the century-long activity of the Geographical Society, by L. S. Berg.

Less attention has been paid specifically to the history of our native economic geography. Certain features of its development, particularly the level of economic-geographic knowledge in this or that historical epoch, have been treated in works characterizing the significance, for science, of the numerous travels and expeditions which have studied not only nature, but also the population. Furthermore, the attention of Soviet geographers has been attracted to such problems as the history of the attempts at economic regionalization of Russia in the 18th-19th centuries (for example, B. A. Val'skaya), the initial periods of the inception of economic geography as a special science (for example, N. P. Nikitin), the significance of the activity of the Siberian vice-regencies and other particular problems.

A somewhat isolated trend in the field of the work on the history of geographic knowledge is represented by the research which, for the first time, sets as its task the integrated generalizing characterization of the development of geography in Russia in the separate major stages of its history. Embracing to one extent or another the basic divisions and groups of problems distinguished by us above, these works endeavor to characterize, within the framework of the periods discussed, the features peculiar to the development of geography in Russia in its diverse manifestations in the field of both physical and economic geography (works by D. M. Lebedev relating to the 15th-18th centuries).

★ ★ ★

In conclusion, let us dwell briefly upon one more aspect of Soviet works on the history of our native geography which contribute to a fuller and more accurate elucidation of certain important sides of it. We have in mind the publication of much archival material, usually accompanied by introductory articles and commentaries. Such, for example are (a) two collections of numerous documents on the activities of Russian travelers in Siberia and the Far East and of polar navigators of the 17th century, compiled by M. I. Belov and N. S. Orlova; (b) a collection of documents on the Second Kamchatka Expedition of 1733-1743, compiled by A. Pokrovskiy; (c) the manuscript of S. Vaksel', steersman of the vessel "Svyatoy Petr" (under the captainship of V. I. Bering) and the logbook of the vessel "Svyatoy Pavel," which sailed under Captain A. I. Chirikov to the coasts of Northwestern America; (d) a collection of documents concerning Russian discoveries in the Pacific Ocean in the 18th-19th centuries, compiled by A. I. Andreyev; (e) the diary notes of the scholar-explorer of the Aral Sea, A. I. Butakov; and (f) manuscript works on geography by M. V. Lomonosov, V. N. Tatishchev, and others. Photocopies of many manuscript maps of the 17th-18th centuries relating chiefly to Siberia, the Far East, and the north of the Pacific Ocean have also been published in the works of Soviet scholars.

Finally, it is necessary to point out also the re-publication (and, in part, new publication) of many works of outstanding native figures in the field of geography, usually accompanied by their biographies and extensive introductory articles written by Soviet scholars. Such, for example, are (1) the description, by G. A. Sarychev, an outstanding hydrologist, geographer, and cartographer of the 18th century, of his journey through the Far East and the north Pacific Ocean; descriptions of certain travels published by the Russian explorers of the Arctic, Siberia, the Far East, Middle and Central Asia, or by the round-the-world, Antarctic, and other navigators who have been mentioned in the respective divisions of the present chapter; (2) the re-publication of certain works by major scholars, for example those of S. P. Krasheninnikov, D. N. Anuchin, A. I. Voyeykov, and others.

Such is the very extensive range of problems investigated by Soviet scholars in the field of the history of our native geography. But the history of geographic knowledge in the countries beyond the borders of the USSR does not remain outside their field of vision. A literature is devoted to it which embraces all periods from antiquity down to the 20th century, inclusive. A chief place in this literature is held by numerous works characterizing the significance of individual major figures in the geographic and certain allied sciences. In this division one may note several thematic groups:

1. The classic writers of antiquity, for example Eratosthenes, Strabo, and Ptolomy; and then many scholars who have made an outstanding contribution to the theory of geography or to regional geography, principally in the 19th century: Alexander von Humboldt, Charles Darwin (as a traveler and geographer), William Morris Davis, Alfred Hettner, Eduard Suess, Albrecht Penck, Elisée Reclus, Paul Vidal de la Blache, Ferdinand von Richthofen, and others.

2. Great attention has been paid to the explorers of the Arctic and Antarctic. Such, for example, are: Willem Barents, Gerrit de Veer, James Cook, John Franklin, John Ross, A. W. Greely, K. J. V. Rasmussen, Fridtjof Nansen, Otto Sverdrup, Julius Payer, Roald Amundsen, Robert E. Peary, G. W. De Long, A. E. Nordenskjöld, C. E. Borchgrevink, Jean Baptiste Charcot, Robert F. Scott, Richard E. Byrd, Ernest H. Shackleton, and others.

3. Many works have been devoted to famous travelers of the Middle Ages, such as Marco Polo, Christopher Columbus, Ferdinand Magellan, and Antonio Pigafetta.

The works of most of the travelers named under points 2 and 3 have been published in Russian translations and are accompanied by biographic information, commentaries, and an evaluation of their significance. The travels of David and Charles Livingstone and Henry M. Stanley in Africa have also been published.

A number of works by Soviet scholars represent generalizing surveys of separate aspects of the history of geography in foreign countries. They may also be divided into several groups:

1. Investigations characterizing the works and accounts of many foreign travelers in Russia which have afforded a knowledge of its geography, principally before the 17th century. These investigations analyze the sources of such information and are accompanied by translations into Russian. Among them we note especially the works by Yu. V. Got'ye on English travelers in Russia in the 16th century, and by M. P. Alekseyev on information concerning Siberia gathered by foreigners from the 13th to the 17th century.

2. The extensive research by I. Yu. Krachkovskiy on Arabic geographic literature since ancient times.

3. Brief information about travelers in ancient China and geographic explorations in the Chinese People's Republic (V. T. Zaychikov).

4. A characterization of the main stages of the history of the discovery of the North Pole and of the exploration of the central Arctic areas by travelers and expeditions from many countries of the world, including Russian pre-revolutionary and Soviet ones (A. F. Laktionov).

5. Description of the main stages of the history of discoveries and explorations made in Antarctica and the Antarctic Ocean by travelers and scholars from many countries of the world (for example, A. Z. Aleyner and S. G. Grigor'yev), and of the development of cartographic representations of Antarctica and the Antarctic Ocean from the oldest times down to our days (A. Z. Aleyner).

6. A special place is held by I. P. Magidovich's comprehensive generalizing work, crammed with factual material and devoted to one of the major divisions of the history of geography — world geographic discoveries from antiquity to 1956.

★ ★ ★

Such are the main trends in the research being carried out in the USSR on the history of geography. Alongside the continuation of the work of penetrating in greater depth and detail into individual problems from among those outlined above, it is necessary to concentrate attention upon the history of the development of theoretical geographic knowledge during the 19th-20th centuries, as well as upon the history of geographic exploration of the territory of the USSR since the Great October Socialist Revolution.

BASIC LITERATURE

Alekseyev, M. P. Siberia in the Accounts of Western European Travelers and Writers *(Sibir' v Izvestiyakh Zapadnoyevropeyskikh Puteshestvennikov i Pisateley)*. 2nd ed., Irkutsk, 1941.

Andreyev, A. I. Essays on the Source Science of 17th-century Siberia *(Ocherki po Istochnikovedeniyu Sibiri XVII v.)*. Leningrad, 1940.

Bakhrushin, S. V. Essays on the History of the Colonization of Siberia in the 16th and 17th Centuries *(Ocherki po Istorii Kolonizatsii Sibiri v XVI i XVII vv.)*. Moscow, 1927.

Belov, M. I. Arctic Navigation from the oldest Times down to the Middle of the 19th Century *(Arkticheskoye Moreplavaniye s Drevneyshikh Vremen do Serediny XIX v.)*. Moscow, 1956.

Berg, L. S. The All-Union Geographic Society during one hundred years *(Vsesoyuznoye Geograficheskoye Obshchestvo za Sto Let)*. Moscow-Leningrad, 1946; Selected Works, vol. I, The History of Science *(Istoriya Nauki)*, Moscow, 1956; The Discovery of Kamchatka and Bering's Expeditions of 1725-1742 *(Otkrytiye Kamchatki i Ekspeditsii Beringa 1725-1742)*. Moscow-Leningrad, 1946; Sketch of the History of Russian Geographic Science (down to 1923) *(Ocherk Istorii Russkoy Geograficheskoy Nauki Vplot' do 1923 g.)*. Leningrad, 1929.

Vize, V. Yu. The Seas of the Soviet Arctic *(Morya Sovetsoy Arktiki)*. Moscow-Leningrad, 1948.

Gvozdetskiy, N. A. Forty Years of Exploration and Discovery *(Sorok Let Issledovaniy i Otkrytiy)*. Moscow, 1957.

Gnucheva, V. F. The Geographic Department of the Academy of Sciences in the 18th Century *(Geograficheskiy Departament Akademii Nauk XVIII v.)*. Moscow-Leningrad, 1946.

Grigor'yev, A. A. Progress in Soviet Physical Geography during Thirty Years *(Uspekhi Sovetskoy Fizicheskoy Geografii za Tridtsat' Let)*. In the book: *Obshcheye Sobraniye AN SSSR, Posvyashchennoye Tridtsatiletiyu Velikoy Oktyabr'skoy Sotsialisticheskoy Revolyutsii*, Moscow-Leningrad, 1948; "From the History of Soviet Geography," *Izvestiya AN SSSR, seriya geogr.*, 1957, No. 5.

Yefimov, A. V. From the History of the great Russian Geographic Discoveries in the Arctic and Pacific Oceans in the 17th and first half of the 18th Centuries *(Iz Istorii velikikh russkikh Geograficheskikh Otkrytiy v Severnom Ledovitom i Tikhom Okeanakh XVII—pervaya polovina XVIII v.)*, Moscow, 1950.

Zubov, N. N. Native Navigator-Explorers of the Seas and Oceans *(Otechestvennyye Moreplavateli-Issledovateli Morey i Okeanov)*, Moscow, 1954.

Krachkovskiy, I. Yu. Arab Geographic Literature *(Arabskaya Geograficheskaya Literatura)*. Izbrannye Sochineniya (Selected Works), vol. 4, Moscow-Leningrad, 1957.

Lebedev, D. M. Geography in Russia in the 17th Century (pre-Peter epoch) *(Geografiya v Rossii XVII v. [dopetrovskoy Epokhi])*, Moscow-Leningrad, 1949; Geography in the Russia of Peter the Great *(Geografiya v Rossii Petrovskogo Vremeni)*, Moscow-Leningrad, 1950; Essays on the History of Geography in the Russia of the 15th and 16th Centuries *(Ocherki po Istorii Geografii v Rossii XV i XVII vv.)*, Moscow, 1956. Essays on the History of Geography in the Russia of the 18th Century (1725-1800) *(Ocherki po Istorii Geografii v Rossii XVIII v. [1725-1800])*, Moscow, 1957.

Magidovich, I. P. Essays on the History of Geographic Discoveries *(Ocherki po Istorii Geograficheskikh Otkrytiy)*. Moscow, 1957.

Murzayev, E. M. The Geographic Exploration of the Mongolian People's Republic *(Geograficheskoye Issledovaniye Mongol'skoy Narodnoy Respubliki)*. Moscow-Leningrad, 1948.

Salishchev, K. A. Fundamentals of Cartography *(Osnovy Kartovedeniya)*. Historical Part and Cartographic Materials. Moscow, 1948.

Part II

THE SPECIALIZED
GEOGRAPHIC SCIENCES

M. I. SUMGIN (1873-1942)

V. G. GLUSHKOV (1883-1939)

M. A. VELIKANOV (born 1879)

YA. S. EDEL'SHTEYN (1869-1952)

CHAPTER 9

CLIMATOLOGY

B. P. Alisov and S. P. Khromov

Russian climatology in the second half of the 19th and early 20th centuries was in the front line of world science. On the one hand, an exemplary system of climatologic study of the country had been created in the Russian Empire and by the end of the 19th century the climatic conditions in this vast country had received an adequate treatment on a macrogeographic scale through the efforts of Vil'd and his collaborators in the Chief Physical Observatory. On the other hand, the great A. I. Voyeykov had, by his own labors and influence, established such vital traditions of Russian climatology as its practical, national-economic orientation, the elaboration of problems of climatology in close connection with the whole geographic complex and — as inevitably follows therefrom — the devotion of special attention to the broad theoretical problems of the formation of climate.

Soviet climatology in the last four decades has organically continued and developed these traditions of the preceding epoch. But, of course, new factors have also entered, imparting to this development new quantitative scales and, to a definite degree, a new quality. To these factors belong (1) the extraordinarily enlarged volume of factual material from observations, including aerological and actinometric ones, which throws light on the country's territory, especially its eastern regions and the Arctic, (2) the creation of numerous regional centers for the climatological study of the country alongside of the Chief Geophysical Observatory, (3) new trends in the general development of the meteorological sciences in general and, above all, a system of frontological synoptics and an ever-increasing introduction of the methods of physico-mathematical analysis into meteorology.

The diversity and wide scope of climatological research in the USSR in our times can not, of course, be reflected adequately in a brief essay. Hence, we shall necessarily confine ourselves to a very short exposition of the state of only a few problems that are basic in our opinion. Numerous other investigations, relating especially to the climatology of the country, cannot even be mentioned. This does not mean that the authors of this article underestimate the immense contribution of many dozens and even hundreds of Soviet climatologists to the study of the climatic conditions of the Soviet Union. In the summary works given in the list of literature, the reader will find an extensive bibliography numbering in the hundreds of titles.

We confine ourselves to a survey of the questions of climatology proper. Meteorological problems, even those underlying climatology, could not be given consideration in this essay, nor shall we touch upon so-called applied climatology, with the exception of certain agroclimatic works possessing geographic significance. Still less shall we examine the numerous problems related to climate in the allied geographic disciplines, for example, botanical geography, soil geography, economic geography, and so forth.

CLIMATOLOGICAL WORKS

The main difficulties in the development of climatographic research are due, as is known, to the inadequate uniformity of observations, owing mainly to the variability of the meteorological regime in individual years. This renders difficult a comparison of the data for different periods of observation. The first works in which attempts were made to eliminate this lack of uniformity date back to the 70's of the past century (Vil'd). An orderly and scientifically based technique has now been created for the statistical handling of the meteorological elements, to the construction of which Soviet climatologists, especially the workers of the Chief Geophysical Observatory (A. A. Kaminskiy, Ye. S. Rubinshteyn, O. A. Drozdov, T. V. Pokrovskaya, S. A. Sapozhnikova, I. A. Gol'tsberg, and others) have made important contributions.

The technique of the climatological handling of the observations from the meteorological networks is designed above all to obtain many-year mean characterizations of the climate by separate elements, which are supplemented by the extreme values and probabilities (frequencies of recurrence) by definite gradations. In spite of a certain abstractness in the characterizations obtained, their scientific and practical value is very great, and the lightweight criticism of "classical climatology," which has sometimes been made, especially in the 30's, has in no way shaken this significance. The extraction of many-year averages is the only means of reducing to a system the voluminous and rather unhomogeneous observation material. The physical sense of average values consists, of course, not in their giving an idea of any "average condition," but in their characterizing the many-year sum of action of this or that element: insolation, temperatures, precipitation, etc. Average data by elements also represent a convenient form for mapping, which in turn serves as a basis for deducing very important climatological laws.

The determination of the probabilities of meteorological phenomena is related to an understanding of climate as the many-year regime of the weather. Only in connection with weather and with consideration of the influence of local factors do climatological deductions about the daily course and periodic changes of the elements, their extreme values and inter-year variability acquire the necessary concreteness and practical significance. Ye. Ye. Fedorov laid the groundwork for the special technique of studying climate as a many-year weather regime (1925). This technique of so-called integrated climatology was perfected by him in the course of a number of years (Chubukov, 1949). On its basis a number of studies have been made in the Institute of Geography of the Academy of Sciences of the USSR and in the academies of sciences of the Union Republics, including the work by Ye. Ye. Fedorov and A. I. Baranov on the climate of the Russian Plain (1949). Fedorov's technique has been repeatedly expounded in the press, and we shall not here speak about it in detail.

Coming now to the concrete works on the climatology of the USSR and the globe which have been completed in the Soviet period, we shall confine ourselves to mentioning those which we regard as most important with respect to science and production. Above all, these are works relating to the whole territory of the country or to its largest subdivisions. Generalizing works in this direction dating back to the early period of Russian climatology are the "Climate of Russia" by K. P. Veselovskiy (1857) and "Climates of the Globe, particularly of Russia" by A. I. Voyeykov (1884).

In the last decades of the 19th century and in the first 15 years of the 20th, there appeared an extensive series of monographs on the distribution of the various elements of climate over the territory of the country, which were compiled by Vil'd and his collaborators. These investigations were summarized in the "Climatic Atlas of The Russian Empire" under the editorship of M. A. Rykachev (1900). Not long before the Revolution there appeared the important Atlas supplement, "Monthly and Yearly Precipitation Sums for European Russia" by S. I. Nebol'sin (1916). In 1926, the Chief Geophysical Observatory began publication of a new series of monographs, "The Climate of the USSR," for which a number of authors, especially A. A. Kaminskiy, Ye. S. Rubinshteyn, O. A. Drozdov, and T. V. Pokrovskaya reworked and carefully mapped the augmented observation material on air temperature, pressure and wind, precipitation, etc. In 1931-1932, the important digest of statistical data, "Climatological Handbook of the USSR" [*Klimatologicheskiy Spravochnik SSSR*], was published; later, the voluminous climatic material contained in the "Water Cadaster of the USSR" [*Vodnyy Kadastr SSSR*] was revised and published. In the postwar period, a series of handbooks on the oblasts of the USSR has been issued. Several large series of climatic maps of the country and of the whole globe have also been published in various atlases of a general character, including the Great Soviet Atlas of the World [*Bol'shoy Sovetskiy Atlas Mira*] (1937) and in the second volume of the Marine Atlas [*Morskoy Atlas*] (1952).

Even during the Great Patriotic War the task was set of creating a new, comprehensive climatological atlas of the USSR; the fulfillment of this task at the Chief Geophysical Observatory occupied a number of years, and only now is the atlas (in two volumes) ready for printing.

In the last few years a start has been made with the publication of a series of climatic descriptions by regions of the country under the title "The Climate of the USSR" in accordance with the general program. By 1959, the first issues of this series had come out, being devoted to the European part of the USSR and the Far East (1958).

The Institute of Aeroclimatology has also done a great deal of work in the processing of aerological material on the climatological level, and has issued corresponding reference handbooks and series of maps both for the territory of the USSR and for the whole globe. There has been a separate processing of the climatological observations made by the Arctic network of stations at the Arctic and Antarctic institutes of the Main Administration of the Northern Sea Route, and a number of reference publications have been issued, which have thereupon served as a basis for much research work.

In addition to these major works, which have had a view to the systematization and generalization of material on the climatic conditions of the country, and sometimes also of the whole globe, works have appeared on the climatic conditions of individual regions of the country, by various researchers in the Hydrometeorological Service, the Main Administration of the Northern Sea Route, the universities, the academies of sciences, and other institutions. Many climatic descriptions and reference handbooks have also been issued on individual cities of the country. Some of these regional works — descriptions, atlases, handbooks, and monographs — have been executed from the agroclimatic angle. One cannot fail to note the great amount of work by G. T. Selyaninov, F. F. Davitaya, P. A. Koloskov, I. A. Gol'tsberg, and S. A. Sapozhnikova on the agroclimatic study of the country, particularly its subtropical and arid regions.

HEAT BALANCE

We come now to the most important scientific problems of a theoretical order. Among the most important tasks of modern climatology are (1) the study of the condition of climate formation, i.e., the laws of the radiation regime and circulation of the atmosphere, which determine the heat and moisture exchange on the earth's surface and in the atmosphere, in conjunction with the geographic location and local physical geographic characteristics, (2) climatic regionalization, and (3) investigation of the secular changes in the climate and the connection between climate and solar activity.

The climatological and microclimatological study of the heat balance of the active surface has assumed the widest scope in the USSR, especially in the last ten years. A detailed bibliography of the many works on the determination of the components of the radiation balance in the various oblasts and points of the USSR and on the seas, which appeared in the 30's and 40's, may be found in the monograph by M. I. Budyko (1955).

Since 1948, the study of the heat balance in the USSR has been conducted principally at the Chief Geophysical Observatory under the direction of M. I. Budyko and with the active participation of T. G. Berlyand, already on a macro-scale. The goal has been set of ascertaining the broad geographic laws governing the distribution of the components of the heat balance. The technique worked out at the Chief Geophysical Observatory for calculating the radiation and heat balance from direct and indirect data, while still needing substantial improvement, has already made it possible to compile maps of the geographic distribution of all the components of the heat balance for the surface of the USSR, as well as for almost the entire globe, with the exception of the high latitudes. The components of the heat balance have thereby been brought into the circle of climatological elements.

From an analysis of the maps compiled, the following most interesting conclusions have been drawn:

1. The radiation balance as deduced for the year is positive throughout the globe, with the exception of the regions with a permanent snow cover (central Greenland, the Antarctic and others).

2. The radiation balance on the land depends not only on the geographic latitude but also on

the humidity (or dryness) of the climate. In deserts it is much less than in the humid regions, owing to the great reflecting power of the deserts and the heightened effective radiation because of the dryness of the atmosphere.

3. Under conditions of a sufficiently humid or excessively humid climate the radiation balance of the active surface represents a factor determining the magnitude of the evaporation.

4. Over the preponderant part of the globe (with the exception of the circumpolar regions) the flow of heat in the process of turbulent exchange is, on the yearly average, directed from the earth's surface into the atmosphere.

5. As deduced for the year, the greatest quantity of heat in evident form enters the atmosphere from the surface of the tropical deserts, since the loss of heat in evaporation is small there, while the insolation is abundant. The chief source of moisture in the air and of heat in latent form is the oceans in the trade-wind zones of the Northern and Southern hemispheres.

These calculations and the maps constructed on them need, of course, to be refined and further enriched with new materials.

The investigation of the heat balance of the various regions of the globe has built a firm bridge between geophysics and geography, and this fact must be regarded as a great scientific event.

ATMOSPHERIC CIRCULATION

The geographic distribution of heat and moisture depends on the radiation regime and on the circulation of the atmosphere. The question of the relation of the geographic types of climate with the peculiarities of the circulation of the atmosphere occupies one of the first places in climatology. In the past century the study of atmospheric circulation as a climate factor was confined to the establishment of the many-year mean distribution of pressure and wind. In our times maps of long-run mean pressures have also been used to ascertain the mean positions of the tropospheric fronts. Such maps of climatological fronts have been constructed for the globe by S. P. Khromov (1940, 1950). The expansion of the radar network has enabled Kh. P. Pogosyan to be one of the first (1947) to construct climatological maps of barometric topography for the Northern Hemisphere and, on the basis of an analysis of them, to draw conclusions about the seasonal fluctuations of the atmospheric circulation. More recently, he has also worked on the question of the geographic distribution of jet streams.

Especially inadequate and sometimes downright false notions have survived down to our times regarding atmospheric circulation in the polar regions. For the Arctic, these notions have been modernized, particularly by B. L. Dzerdzeyevskiy, who has not only constructed new maps of the mean distribution of pressure in the Arctic basin (1945), but has also come to important conclusions on the basis of synoptic materials. Finally, an end has been put to the myth about a stationary and permanent polar anticyclone as the basis of Arctic circulation: it has been pointed out that the Polar basin represents an area of lively cyclonic activity, closely connected with processes in the lower latitudes. More recently, no small amount of research has been done at the Arctic Institute on the synoptics, aerology and climatology of the Arctic.

In the last few years the augmented observation material in the Antarctic has also permitted the first steps to be taken in the direction of revising the earlier, almost entirely hypothetical notions, about the Antarctic circulation of the atmosphere. Soviet researchers have quickly joined this trend, and serious investigations have already been published, notably by G. M. Tauber (1956) and S. S. Gaygerov (1958). Well-founded doubts have been expressed about the stability of the Antarctic anticyclone; it has been pointed out that central cyclones arise in certain seas of the Antarctic and that the meridional type of processes plays a considerable role in the winter season. Cyclonic activity in the Antarctic seas has been studied in fairly close detail, as have also the peculiarities of the weather regime connected with Antarctic cyclones. Much attention has also been attracted by the glacier (runoff) winds on the periphery of the Antarctic continent. Of course, with the appearance of a number of stations in the heart of the continent, each year will bring important new data on the characteristics of the Antarctic circulation of the atmosphere and will bring us closer to the construction of a satisfactory picture of the climatic conditions over the continent of the Antarctica.

The employment of synoptic material in the study of the processes of the general circulation has made it possible to set the task of ascertaining the types of circulation and their time sequence. Not infrequently, the work in this direction is inspired by the requirements of long-range forecasting, but its climatological significance is obvious. It includes, for example, the treatments by B. P. Mul'tanovskiy by types of synoptic processes, continued by his numerous successors. Since the War, G. Ya. Vangengeym, following E. S. Lir and F. Baur, has established three basic types of circulation in the temperate latitudes and has introduced the principle of characterizing the circulation regime of long intervals of time by the predominance of this or that type of circulation. The laws governing the appearance and succession of circulation types, derived from data extending over many years, also belong to the factors of the climatic regime and its short-period fluctuations. B. L. Dzerdzeyevskiy (1945), on the basis of many-year synoptic material on the Northern hemisphere, has distinguished 13 types of so-called elementary circulation mechanisms over the hemisphere, basing them on the types of circulation relationship between the high and low latitudes, i.e., the geographic characteristics of Arctic irruptions. The general atmospheric circulation of the season and of the year is composed of such elementary circulation mechanisms, succeeding one another in one sequence or another. The statistical laws governing the recurrence and succession of the types of circulation mechanisms have been determined. Catalogs of the processes, constructed by Dzerdzeyevskiy, Vangengeym, and their collaborators, are already being used for numerous climatological comparisons and conclusions. Other researchers are working in related directions, particularly L. A. Vitel's, who has ascertained the types of "baric-circulation regime" over the more restricted territory of Europe (1949).

Particular investigations into the conditions of the atmospheric circulation in individual areas of the world, in addition to those already mentioned on the Arctic and Antarctic, have been made for a number of regions. In particular, the study of the atmospheric circulation in Middle Asia has occupied V. A. Dzhordzhio, V. A. Bugayev, and their collaborators. A number of their works have been summarized in the collection "Synoptic Processes of Middle Asia" [*Sinopticheskiye Protsessy Sredney Azii*] (1947). A number of investigations have been devoted to the Far East (N. V. Stremousov, A. I. Shtabova, and others).

A very important factor in the heat and moisture exchange between the latitudes and between the continents and oceans is the monsoon activity, represented by one of the forms of general atmospheric circulation. In hydrodynamic models of the monsoon circulation, "monsoon" has usually meant the system of components in the general transfer of air due to the thermal contrasts between land and sea. S. P. Khromov (1950, 1956) had proposed that the term "monsoon" be given back its concrete geographic content as the real transfer of air in specific regions of the earth, which is stable during the season and sharply changes its direction from the one half of the year to the other. A map of the geographic distribution of monsoons has been constructed as a result of the analysis of the seasonal change in the predominant direction of the wind over the globe. It has been stressed that the monsoon circulation both in the tropics and in the extratropical latitudes does not oppose cyclonic activity, but is effected through cyclonic activity, being a special form of it which is connected with the relative seasonal stability of the baric regime in specific regions of the earth. A definite zonality has been discovered in the distribution of monsoons, and from the statistical aspect they are represented by the result of the seasonal displacement of the planetary zones of pressure and wind.

MOISTURE CIRCULATION

The question of the moisture circulation is also related to the progress of our knowledge about the synoptic and climatological aspect of the general circulation of the atmosphere. Since the War, the so-called internal moisture circulation, i.e., the role of evaporation from the land surface in precipitation on the same territory or on adjacent territory, has attracted special attention. At the beginning of the 20th century, this problem was being given solutions involving fundamental errors (Yu. Brikner, I. I. Kasatkin, and G. N. Vysotskiy), and after the War it became the object of fantastic fabrications by certain non-specialists, who "proved," for example, that the planting of forest belts in the south of the European part of the country was capable of increasing the amount of precipitation by 150 per cent with all the ensuing consequences for crop yield.

However, a synoptic-aerological calculation of the transfer of moisture by air currents has shown the very modest role of the internal moisture circulation in the precipitation regime on the land. According to estimates by O. A. Drozdov and M. I. Budyko (1950-1952 and following years), on the yearly average only about 15 per cent of the precipitation over the land is from moisture evaporated from its surface. To be sure, a certain amount of additional precipitation results from the fact that the local evaporation, by raising the humidity of the atmosphere, serves as a catalyst to precipitate additional moisture. Inasmuch as the role of the internal moisture circulation in the total precipitation is so insignificant, forests do not furnish any substantial increment of precipitation on a given territory or adjacent ones. The additional evaporation from the forest vegetation is so small that it can raise the small internal moisture circulation to only an insignificant degree. Moreover, certain investigations show that a small increment of precipitation in a forest region may result from ascending air movements on the forest margins. But it is impossible to bring about a substantial increment of precipitation through a certain increase in the evaporation as a result of afforesting a locality, and still less by planting forest belts.

It is easy to estimate that the effect on the amount of precipitation from bringing water to steppe and desert regions can be only very insignificant. Thus, a correct conception has been created of the climatic effect of forest-reclamation and irrigation measures. Despite their considerable microclimatic role, they cannot exert any substantial influence upon the macroclimate.

Another important climatological question connected with moisture circulation is humidity. Soviet, as well as foreign, investigators have done a great deal of work on methods for best expressing humidity conditions. Most popular is the empirical hydrothermal coefficient proposed by G. T. Selyaninov, which represents the ratio of the sum of active temperatures (above 10°) to the annual precipitation.

N. N. Ivanov has proposed that the ratio of the total precipitation to the evaporability, computed from the air temperature by an empirical formula, be used as the humidity coefficient. The possibility of using the coefficient thus obtained for purposes of climatic regionalization has been illustrated by him with the example of the regionalization of Eurasia and tropical countries (1956).

A new approach has been made to the question by M. I. Budyko, who has related the water balance to the heat balance and proposed the ratio of the radiation balance to the sum of heat necessary for evaporation of the precipitation for the characterization of humidity on plains territory. Budyko (1948) has proposed a scheme showing the concordance of the magnitude of the radiation balance, which determines the heat regime, and of the magnitude of the humidity index with the character of the various physico-geographic zones. (For more details see Chapter 3, "Physical Geography of the Land" and Chapter 21, "The Heat and Water Regime of the Earth's Surface.")

CLASSIFICATION OF CLIMATES AND CLIMATIC REGIONALIZATION

These tasks are closely interrelated, but the purposes and means of their solution are different. Classification has the object of singling out from among the great diversity of climatic conditions on the earth's surface those which are most typical, depending on geographic latitude, position in the system of atmospheric circulation, and the character of the underlying surface. Naturally, a more objective classification of climate should be based on a study of the genesis of its regional characteristics. Climatic regionalization concerns itself with the determination of the boundaries along which step-wise qualitative changes in the climate take place, with the term "quality of the climate" meaning the character of its influence upon the other elements of the natural environment. It is obvious that, to find such climatic boundaries, the cause-and-effect relationships must be established between the climate and the other most important elements of the geographic environment, especially the soil and plant cover. Here, of course, climate must not in any way be deprived of its meteorological concreteness.

As early as 1920, L. S. Berg proposed a climatic regionalization of the land of the globe which essentially coincided with its division into geographic zones in the aggregate of geographic conditions, above all in vegetation conditions. The boundaries of Berg's climatic zones coincide closely with the boundaries of the major subdivisions on Köppen's widely known map of climates. Later, in his remarkable monographs, "Fundamentals of Climatology" [*Osnovy klimatologii*] and "The Geographic Zones of the USSR" [*Geograficheskiye zony SSSR*], Berg gave excellent characterizations of these zones, especially on the territory of the USSR.

Subsequently, B. P. Alisov has worked on the construction of a genetic *classification of types of climate* for the whole surface of the earth (1936-1950). This classification is based on a scheme of the dependence of the regime of the air temperature, humidity, and precipitation upon the geographic types of air masses predominating during the year or by seasons and upon the characteristics of their circulation. The types of air masses are here regarded as complex indices of the radiation regime, the circulation conditions, and the effect of the underlying surface, thus reflecting the whole aggregate of climate-forming factors. The climatic types distinguished are characterized by the magnitude and annual course of the temperature and humidity, as well as by the seasonal characteristics of the weather. The climatic regionalization of the continents and oceans of the globe, as well as of the Soviet Union, was carried out according to this scheme. The boundaries of the distribution of the main types of air masses in winter and summer were established mainly from maps of climatological fronts. Each climatic belt so distinguished is broken down into climatic areas [*oblasti*] depending upon the peculiarities of the atmospheric circulation and the character of the earth's surface, with consideration for the type of soil and plant cover.

N. N. Ivanov (1956) proposed a climatic regionalization of Eurasia, basing it on Alisov's scheme of circulation zones, the degree of continentality of the climate according to his own criterion (see below), the degree of atmospheric humidity of the locality (ratio of precipitation to evaporability), as well as the orographic limits and the character of the underlying surface. He distinguished 60 climatic areas for Eurasia, some of which are further broken down into subareas [*podoblasti*].

G. T. Selyaninov (1956) worked out his scheme of climatic regionalization of the USSR from the agroclimatic angle. He takes the sums of the temperatures of the growing period as the main criterion of subdivision into climatic zones; the further subdivision into areas [*oblasti*] is made by types of humidity and annual course of precipitation, and the areas are divided into provinces [*provintsii*] according to various features, particularly the degree of continentality of the climate, which the author judges from the severity of the winter. Let us mention further A. I. Kaygorodov's classification and regionalization of the climates of the globe (1955), based on the regime of air temperature and precipitation.

Related to the questions of climatic regionalization are the world maps of temperature iso-anomalies newly constructed by Ye. S. Rubinshteyn (1953), which have made it possible to re-compute the characteristics of the planetary distribution of temperature refined by comparison with Meinardus's results; A. I. Kaygorodov's map of precipitation iso-anomalies, apparently the first experiment of this sort; and N. N. Ivanov's evaporation map (world and USSR). It is not necessary here to mention the works on the characterization of the continentality of climate. The proposals by N. N. Ivanov and S. P. Khromov (1953, 1956) have developed further the idea of the annual range of temperature as the most rational indicator of continentality. Ivanov believes that continentality of climate is characterized by the difference between the annual temperature range, averaged for the circle of latitude, and the annual temperature range at a given point $A \phi - A$, which leads, among other things, to the concept of negative continentality. An influence of the latitude upon the annual range is not, however, ruled out, and the data on the Northern and Southern hemispheres are found to be especially non-comparable. Hence, Khromov has proposed that continentality be characterized by the expression

$$K = \frac{A - Am \sin \phi}{A},$$

where $Am \sin \phi$ is the so-called purely oceanic temperature for a given latitude, and the numerical value of Am is determined by the range for the region of the Southern Pacific Ocean most remote from the continents. Thus, the ratio shows what proportion of the annual temperature range at a given place is determined by the influence of the land. This proportion is found to be very considerable even in the most sharply pronounced marine climates on a continent. Both authors have proposed corresponding maps of the distribution of continentality. (N. N. Ivanov's posthumous work, in which the new continentality index is proposed, was published at the end of 1959.)

L. G. Polozova (1954) has introduced the substantially new principle of expressing continentality separately for winter and summer by comparing the temperature anomalies with the extreme anomalies for a whole circle of latitude (as determined from Rubinshteyn's maps). The continentality for January is charcterized by the ratio (in percentages):

$$K_1 = \frac{\overset{+}{amx} - a}{\overset{+}{amx} - \overset{-}{amx}} \cdot 100,$$

where the numerator contains the difference between the maximum positive anomaly and the anomaly at a given point, and the denominator the difference between the maximum positive anomaly and the maximum negative anomaly on the same circle of latitude; a similar formula is given for July. Thus, the degree of continentality is determined from its ratio to the maximum continentality on a given latitude.

LOCAL FEATURES OF CLIMATE. MICROCLIMATE.

Substantial attention has been paid by Soviet climatologists to the study of local circulations and local manifestations of the general atmospheric circulation connected with local climatic features. Numerous authors have studied the phenomena of the foehn and the bora, mountain-and-valley and land-and-sea breezes in a number of regions, and glacier winds under mountain range conditions in the USSR and in the Antarctic. Also the object of attention have been various local winds such as the *afganets,** the *ursat'yevskiy veter*** and so forth. Many works have been devoted to the dry winds [*sukhovei*] of the southeast of the European part of the USSR in connection with their effect on agriculture.

These concrete investigations have led to a revision and more precise definition of many fundamentally important questions. Thus, the Caspian Lowland has been distinguished on the maps of Ye. Ye. Fedorov and A. I. Baranov as the main focal point of dry winds. The notion of the Middle Asiatic origin of the dry winds, so popular until quite recently, has been resolutely disproved by the works of P. K. Yevseyev (1949) and others. It is not the advection of air masses from the deserts, but the summer transformation of the air over the southeast of the European part of the Union that is the decisive factor in the rise of dry winds. I. V. But has definitively shown (1939) that the Novorossiysk bora is not the effect of the radiational chilling of the air in the North Caucasus, as was once supposed, but is formed as a result of the advection of cold air masses behind a cold front crossing the range without any preliminary accumulation, etc.

Many phenomena in the thermal regime and moisture circulation have also been studied on the regional level. It is impossible to indicate here all the numerous works on the climatic aspect of frosts, droughts, fogs, thunderstorms, gales, and hailstorms, produced principally by climatologists on the separate oblasts and national republics.

The study of microclimate, i.e., the influence exerted on climate by local physical geographic factors — exposure and forms of relief, vegetation, bodies of water, etc. — is growing into a major problem of national-economic significance. A special impetus to the development of field investigations in this direction has been furnished by the planting of forest belts in the steppe and forest-steppe zones, by irrigation and the provision of water in steppe and desert regions, by the creation of new reservoirs, etc. It was essential to study the climatic effect of the measures already carried out in order to make recommendations for the rationalization of further work. In particular, a study was made of the influence of irrigation on the climate of farm fields, especially in Middle Asia, and very many researchers have worked to ascertain the climatic effect of forest belts. The leading link in the first case is the change in the radiation-heat balance of the underlying surface under the influence of the change in the albedo and additional evaporation, and in the second case is the weakening of the wind, entailing changes in the evaporation conditions. The extent and spatial distribution of the changes, depending upon the scale of the measures, have been ascertained. In the

---

*A local wind of the upper reaches of the Amu-Dar'ya. It blows from the southwest (from Afghanistan, hence the name) and is very dusty. At Termez it occurs on 40 to 70 days a year. Tied to the incursion of cold air masses into the Turanian lowland, it is observed in advance of fronts and ends after their passage.—Ed.

**A strong wind observed near the entrance to the Fergana Valley at Ursat'yevsk, hence the name, occurring as a result of the effect of the pass through the mountains on the general circulation of the air.—Ed.

Caucasus, the Pamir, and the Urals microclimatic investigations (chiefly into the heat balance) have also been instituted on the glaciers in accordance with the program of the International Geophysical Year.

Microclimatic investigations have brought forth the task of working out a technique for constructing large-scale climatic maps. The mapping of mean long-run values of the air temperature and precipitation under low relief conditions can now be done to a scale of 1:1,000,000, in view of the sufficiently dense network of meteorological stations. For the whole European part of the USSR, the Chief Geophysical Observatory has compiled temperature and precipitation maps to a scale of 1:2,500,000 which makes it possible to trace fairly well the influence of the valley-and-gulch relief upon the mean and especially the minimum values of the air temperature.

The microclimatic field investigations which are now being expanded over the territories of the European and Asiatic parts of the USSR give a still more detailed idea of the influence of the local conditions upon individual phenomena that are especially important from the practical viewpoint. Thus, for example, according to I. A. Gol'tsberg (1958), the comparative frost danger to individual sections of agricultural lands can, after microclimatic investigation, be represented with a precision corresponding to mapping on a scale of 1:500,000.

The study of the climatic rôle of local factors should now be instituted on an especially broad basis in connection with the fulfillment of two major tasks: the physical geographic regionalization of the USSR for agricultural purposes and the compilation of comprehensive oblast geographic atlases.

FLUCTUATIONS OF CLIMATE

The problem of changes in climate in the geologic past relates to historical geology rather than to climatology, and remains outside the bounds of this essay. The attention of Soviet climatologists has been directed to a greater extent toward the fluctuations of climate in the postglacial and especially the historical epoch. Some important guiding ideas in this respect have been based on the works of L. S. Berg in the pre-Revolution and Soviet periods. He came to the conclusion that the climate of historic times, at least in Europe and Middle Asia, has been cooler and more humid than that of the preceding epoch; that there have been no progressive changes in the climate in the historic epoch; and that it has only been subject to fluctuations of the order of tens of years. Later, A. V. Shnitnikov (1956), on the basis of an analysis of the fluctuations of the levels of lakes and the regimes of glaciers, as well as archeologic and historical sources, showed that in climatic changes periods of the order of 40 years and 1,850 years are experienced. Besides A. V. Shnitnikov, P. P. Predtechenskiy (1948) has confirmed the existence of cycles close to 2,000 years, and evidence in favor of this is also to be found in the publications of other authors.

Short-period changes in temperature in Europe during the 19th century have been investigated in special detail by Ye. S. Rubinshteyn (1946). I. I. Buchinskiy (1957), on the basis of an analysis of the results of instrumental observations, has established four warmer periods in 140 years in the Ukraine, which is very close to the celebrated Brückner cycle.

The present warming-up period, which began in the second half of the last century or in the beginning of our century and has embraced chiefly the Arctic, but also the temperate latitudes, has been studied by V. Yu. Vize, L. S. Berg, Ye. S. Rubinshteyn, L. A. Vitel'son, and others. There is no divergence of opinion as to the fact that this is a temporary fluctuation of the climate and that its immediate cause, as well as the cause of short-period fluctuations of climate in general, is the fluctuations in the character of the general circulation of the atmosphere, the more remote cause being the fluctuations of solar activity. I. V. Maksimov explains the intensity of the present heating-up process by the superimposition of the phases of two fluctuations causing climatic changes: the 80-90-year cycle of solar activity and the 250-year periodic change in the velocity of motion of the earth.

M. S. Eygenson has developed the thought (close to the views independently expressed by Villette), that the climatic changes in geologic epochs have also been due to changes in the general circulation caused by hypothetical supra-secular fluctuations of solar activity.

The idea of the influence of solar activity upon the fluctuation of climate, which not long ago was still treated with mistrust, is now receiving ever wider recognition in Soviet climatology, though there has been no special progress in the question of the intermediate mechanism of the relation between the processes on the sun and climate.

THE NEXT TASKS OF CLIMATOLOGY

The rapidly growing circle of questions of national economy and the logic of the development of climatology itself confront it with a number of tasks in the near future. Perhaps the most essential are those relating to humidity. Among them, the calculation of evaporation is especially complicated. There now exist several methods of calculating evaporation, which do not always yield concordant results, and it is urgently necessary to work out a uniform method. The results of direct measurements of the amount of precipitation, even from a fairly dense network, cannot produce a homogeneous field and require spatial generalization. There is thus far no uniform technique for such generalizations. Finally, it must be taken into consideration that precipitation and evaporation are bound together by a physical geographic factor, the runoff, in the equation of the water balance, which must be made a means of verifying the correctness of the values entering into it.

As has been pointed out, an exceptionally important role in climatic phenomena, belongs to the radiation and heat balance of the active surface. But the balance is thus far calculated for the horizontal surface. The next stage is to work out a technique for calculating the balance under the conditions of dissected relief.

It is obviously necessary to develop further the synoptic (dynamic) method in climatology, i.e., the study of the regional characteristics of the atmospheric circulation and their relation to the climatic conditions on the earth's surface. Related to this problem is the very important methodical task of working out a technique for investigating the long-run weather regime as one of the most important components of climate. The great variability of the weather does not permit one in a given case to resort to the usual procedures of climatology — deducing the mean values and estimating the number of days with this or that state of the weather. It is necessary to make an estimate and construct characteristic curves, including a synoptic one, not of the individual interconnected days, but of weather periods of different types. Work in this direction is being carried on particularly by the chair of climatology of the geographic faculty of Moscow State University.

The practical application of climatological data, especially in agriculture, is made difficult by the lack of techniques for large-scale climatic mapping. It is necessary to concentrate our efforts upon working out such techniques.

The tasks of so-called applied climatology consist in establishing the characteristics of climate in application to questions of the various branches of the national economy. Such specialized characterizations of climate can be worked out only with the cooperation of specialists in the respective branches of the economy.

Thus far one of the aspects of climate most important for biology, including agriculture, has not yet been characterized, namely, the exposure to direct and diffuse solar radiation. It is necessary to organize instrumental network observations of this exposure.

BASIC LITERATURE

Alisov, B. P. The Climatic Areas of Foreign Countries (Klimaticheskiye Oblasti Zarubezhnykh Stran). Moscow, 1950.

Alisov, B. P. The Climate of the USSR (Klimat SSSR). Moscow, 1956.

Berg, L. S. Fundamentals of Climatology (Osnovy Klimatologii), 2nd ed., 1938. Extensive bibliography in the text.

Berg, L. S. Climate and Life (Klimat i Zhizn'), 2nd ed., 1947. Extensive bibliography in the text.

Budyko, M. I. (editor). Atlas of the Heat Balance (Atlas Teplovogo Balansa). Leningrad, 1955.

Budyko, M. I. The Heat Balance of the Earth's Surface (Teplovoy Balans Zemnoy Poverkhnosti). Leningrad, 1956. Bibliography of 259 titles.

Davitaya, F. F. (editor). The Agroclimatic and Water Resources of the Regions of Reclamation of Virgin and Idle Lands (Agroklimaticheskiye i Vodnyye Resursy Rayonov Osvoyeniya Tselinnykh i Zalezhnykh Zemel'). Leningrad, 1955.

Dzerdzeyevskiy, B. L., Kurganskaya, V. M., and Vitvitskaya, Z. M. Typing of Circulation Mechanisms in the Northern Hemisphere and Characterization of the Synoptic Seasons (Tipizatsiya Tsirkulyatsionnykh Mekhanizmov v

Severnom Polusharii i KHarakteristika Sinopticheskikh Sezonov). Moscow, 1946.

Drozdov, O. A. (editor). Methods of Climatological Processing of Meteorological Observations *(Metody Klimatologicheskoy Obrabotki Meteorologicheskikh Nablyudeniy).* Leningrad, 1957. Bibliography of 85 titles.

Ivanov, N. N. The Landscape-climatic Zones of the Globe *(Landshaftno-klimaticheskiye Zony Zemnogo Shara).* Leningrad, 1948. Extensive bibliography.

Ivanov, N. N. Atmospheric Humidity of the Tropical and Adjacent Countries of the Globe *(Atmosfernoye Uvlazhneniye Tropicheskikh i Sopredel'nykh Stran Zemnogo Shara).* Moscow-Leningrad, 1958. Bibliography of 208 titles.

Kaminskiy, A. A. Air Pressure and Wind in the USSR (Davleniye Vozdukha i Veter v SSSR). *Klimat SSSR,* part 2, Leningrad, 1932.

Klimat SSSR (The Climate of the USSR), no. 1. European part of the USSR (A. N. Lebedev); no. 6, the Far East (A. A. Zanina), Leningrad, 1958.

Meteorologiya i Gidrologiya v Uzbekistane (Meteorology and Hydrology in Uzbekistan). Collection of articles *(Sbornik),* Tashkent, 1955. Extensive bibliography.

Pogosyan, Kh. P. (editor). "Changing the Climate in Connection with the Plan of Transforming the Nature of the Arid Regions of the USSR" *(Izmeneniye Klimata v Svyazi s Planom Preobrazovaniya Prirody Zasushlivykh Rayonov SSSR),* Leningrad, 1952. Bibliography of 141 titles.

Rubinshteyn, Ye. S. Air Temperature in the USSR; the Climate of the USSR *(Temperatura Vozdukha v SSSR, Klimat SSSR),* part I, Leningrad, 1927.

Rubinshteyn, Ye. S. Concerning the Problem of Changes in Climate *(K Probleme Izmeneniy Klimata),* Moscow, 1946.

Rubinshteyn, Ye. S. (editor). Course in Climatology *(Kurs Klimatologii),* parts 1 and 2, 1952; part 3, 1954. Bibliography of over 200 titles.

Sapozhnikova, S. A. Microclimate and Local Climate *(Mikroklimat i Mestnyy Klimat),* Leningrad, 1950.

Sovremennyye Problemy Klimatologii i A. I. Voyeykov (Present-day Problems of Climatology and A. I. Voyeykov). Collection of articles *(Sbornik),* Leningrad, 1957.

Shnitnikov, A. V. "Variability of the General Humidity of the Continents of the Northern Hemisphere," Moscow-Leningrad, Izd-vo AN SSSR, *Zapiski VGO,* vol. 16, 1957.

CHAPTER· 10

GLACIOLOGY

G. A. Avsyuk

Of late, the proposal is being advanced that glaciology should be understood to mean the science of all the forms of natural ice on the earth: not only glaciers, but also the motionless ice on the earth's surface, the underground, sea, and river ice, the snow cover, the ice in the atmosphere, and the frozen rocks. Such a broad treatment of the subject of glaciology is, of course, possible. However, it does not rule out — on the contrary, it necessitates — an independent investigation of the individual kinds of natural ice within the framework of the separate scientific disciplines. This is required because the different forms of natural ice, in addition to the properties common to them, differ in the particulars of their appearance and genesis and in a large number of specific laws. Hence it appears to us that the designation "glaciology" should be reserved for the science studying the present-day glaciers of the land, in keeping with established terminology and scientific tradition. For the science uniting the study of all kinds of natural ice, it is necessary to choose another, new designation. It is from the standpoint of this narrower interpretation of glaciology that the following discussion is conducted.

Glaciology is a relatively young science, for less than two centuries have elapsed since the first scientific glaciological observations were made on Alpine glaciers. In Russia, observations of glaciers began much later — not until the 60's of the last century. Thus, glaciological research in our country does not yet count a full hundred years.

The development of our native glaciological research may conventionally be subdivided into four main periods. The first of these embraces the time from the 1860's to the beginning of the Second International Polar Year.

The second period relates to the Second International Polar Year, i.e., it embraces the period 1932-1933. The third period started after the Second IPY and continued to the beginning of the Second Geophysical Year. Finally, the fourth period embraces the International Geophysical Year (1957-1959). We are now entering the second phase of the fourth period, when field observations have been completed and all efforts are concentrated on the processing and topical assimilation of the data accumulated under the IGY program.

In the first period descriptive glaciological work was done, on the basis of which it was possible to constitute the first conception of present-day glaciation on our country's territory. Glacier tongues were almost exclusively the objects of study; the upper areas of glaciers, as a rule, were not visited and were described crudely. Because almost no precise surveys of glaciers were made, the sizes and areas of glaciers were estimated only roughly; nor were there systematic observations made of glacier processes. Relatively little attention was paid to characterizations of the types of glaciers and to the processes taking place on them: they were judged chiefly on the basis of speculative conclusions, not infrequently based on concepts mechanically borrowed from Swiss Alpine glaciology. Investigation of glaciers in this period was largely casual in character. Glaciological observations were usually incidental to geological explorations, sometimes to botanical or zoogeographic ones, and played a secondary role. Observations were executed mostly by non-specialists in glaciology and by persons having other specialties. The investigations were made principally with a geologic-geomorphologic bent and were mainly confined to the study of the accumulative and erosional activity of both modern and ancient glaciations. It must be stated that even Alpine glaciology in this period also developed chiefly in the geologic-geomorphologic direction.

Despite the unfavorable conditions for the development of Russian glaciology in the first period, the accumulation of information about the glaciers of our country proceeded rather swiftly. The great Russian scholars of those times such as, for example, A. I. Voyeykov, P. A. Kropotkin, I. V. Mushketov, and B. A. Fedchenko, were aware of the imperfection of the glaciological work being done and in their works repeatedly pointed out the necessity of a broader and more thorough approach to the study of glaciers, the inadmissibility of a mechanical transfer of the laws observed on the Alpine glaciers to the glaciers of any other regions, especially continental ones. These scholars, in spite of the imperfection and relatively small amount of observational material at their disposal, created great classical scientific works which have exerted enormous influence upon the further development of our native glaciology and have not lost their significance even in our times. It suffices, for example, to point out the widely known work by P. A. Kropotkin, "Investigations into the Ice Age" [*Issledovaniya o Lednikovom Periode*] or the work by A. I. Voyeykov, "The Climatic Conditions of Glacial Phenomena, Present and Past" [*Klimatologicheskiye Usloviya Lednikovykh Yavleniy, Nastoyashchikh i Proshedshikh*].

Since the Great October Socialist Revolution the rate of glaciological research in the Soviet Union has grown rapidly, and has undergone special development in the mountain regions of Middle Asia. It has begun to assume independent significance and to embrace a considerably wider range of scientific theoretical questions, while still retaining a strong geologic-geomorphologic trend.

By the 1930's, glaciological research in the USSR had become especially intensified and, alongside the former geologic-geomorphological orientation, a new approach to the study of glaciers was developed which may be called the hydrometeorological approach. In contrast to the canons of "Alpine glaciology," new tendencies took shape which consisted primarily in giving proper consideration, in the study of glacial phenomena, to the characteristics of the physical-geographic conditions in the different glacier areas.

The end of the 1920's was marked by the discovery in the USSR of a large number of new glaciers in the Altay, the Tyan'-Shan' and the Pamir, and of a new glacier region in the Sub-Polar Urals. In the Pamir, the Fedchenko Glacier, the largest mountain glacier in the world, was first fully examined in this period.

The Second International Polar Year (1932-1933) occupies a special place in the development of Soviet glaciology. Let us recall that the proposal to expand the glaciological-exploration program of the Second International Polar Year — namely, the inclusion in it not only of the glaciers of polar countries but also of the areas of present-day mountain glaciation in the temperate latitudes — was made by the Soviet committee for the execution of this international scientific enterprise. The proposed program was subsequently put into effect solely in the Soviet Union.

By the beginning of the work on the Second International Polar Year the view had become confirmed among most Soviet glaciologists that an integrated geographic approach to the study of glaciers was necessary. Especially great attention was devoted to glaciers as hydrometeorological objects, which manifested the practical trend in glaciological investigation.

In this period, the special "Glacier Expeditions of the 2nd IPY" were created. The work of these expeditions embraced simultaneously almost all the then-known regions of glaciation on the territory of the USSR: the Caucasus, the Altay, the Pamir, the Tyan'-Shan', the Sub-Polar Urals, and the Arctic islands.

Temporary meteorological stations were organized on the glaciers, and numerous measurements of ablations and rates of ice movement were made for the first time. Much attention was paid to the study of the morphology of glaciers, to the description of the structure of the ice, of the different glacial formations on the surface of glaciers, etc. Hydrometric work was done on the streams flowing out from glaciers. Many glaciers, especially their terminal parts, were covered with instrumental surveys. The volume of material gathered proved to be truly enormous and sufficiently varied. To be sure, in the glaciological work of the 2nd IPY success was not attained in the proper uniformity in observation techniques, and the procedures themselves were not noted for their great perfection, so the data obtained differed both in quality and in amount of detail.

The results of the glaciological investigations of the 2nd IPY were recorded in the six volumes of the "Work of the Glacier Expeditions of the 2nd IPY" [*Trudy Lednikovykh Ekspeditsiy 2 MPG*], which appeared in the years 1935-1936. This contains a wealth of factual material and theoretical conclusions, in most cases original in character. It reflects the new general direction of glaciological work — the integrated geographic approach to the study of glacial phenomena so characteristic of the Soviet glaciology of that period. From the present-day viewpoint, a basic shortcoming of the 1932-1933 work was the still-inadequate attention paid to the study of the quantitative side of the various glacial processes, the slight employment of geophysical methods of observation and the inadequate attention to investigation of the physics of the processes.

All the investigations under the 2nd IPY have been summarized in the work by S. V. Kalesnik, "The Mountain Glacier Regions of the USSR" [Gornyye Lednikovyye Rayony SSSR], published in 1937. This book generalizes all the information on USSR glaciers, furnishes a picture of our present knowledge of the glacier areas of our country, and sets in high relief the progress in the development of Soviet glaciology due to the work of the 2nd IPY. In conclusion, it formulates the tasks for further glaciological exploration.

In this period, the majority of Soviet glaciologists became confirmed in the belief that a glacier represents a unique physical geographic object, a fruitful scientific study of which can only be made on the basis of an integrated geographic approach, with the required employment of precise and systematic methods of observation.

During the third period of development of Soviet glaciology, from the 2nd IPY to the beginning of the International Geophysical Year, i.e., from 1933 to 1957, there was further deepening and widening of glaciological exploration in all the glacier regions of our country. Systematic working methods and precise quantitative observation procedures are more and more being introduced. Glacial research, as a rule, is conducted with the employment of photogrammetric methods of measurement and various geophysical observation techniques, and is based on the data from crystallographic analyses, etc. The balance method of studying the matter and energy of glaciers is gaining ever-greater recognition and is being introduced into practical glaciological work. During the investigation of glaciers, precise surveys are made of them, and the distribution of temperatures throughout the ice. The processes of ice formation, feeding, thawing, and runoff are studied, and much attention is paid to the study of the structure of the ice, firn, and snow, the movement of ice in glaciers, and the climatic and radiation conditions. In a word, the whole complex of natural processes peculiar to glaciers lies within the sphere of interest of Soviet glaciologists. Major researches of the stationary type on Arctic glaciers are being conducted on Franz Josef Land. Since 1947, uninterrupted stationary glaciological observations have been organized in the Tyan'-Shan'.

At the same time, the areas of glaciation and the number of glaciers in different parts of the country are being determined considerably more precisely, the differences in the types of glaciers are being established, and catalogs of glaciers are being compiled for a number of regions. In this same period new, formerly unknown, regions of present-day glaciation have been discovered in the northeast of the country (on the upper course of the Indigirka), and in the Polar Urals.

A special study is being made of the various factors of glaciation, and its connection with the orographic and climatic conditions. The problems of the evolution of glaciation are continuing to be worked out. Great attention is being directed toward the zonal characteristics of the development of glaciation and glacial processes. Finally, a laboratory study is being made of the properties of ice, and experimental work is being conducted under natural conditions on the glaciers themselves with respect to the artificial intensification of their thawing.

On the basis of numerous new factual data, a number of original works are being created on the most varied questions of glaciology. Alongside of explorations of a regional character to throw light on the laws of glacial phenomena peculiar to specific glaciers and glacier regions, works having a comparative purpose are also being created to elucidate the character and state of glaciers of various regions. Among this rather numerous group one may mention, for example, M. V. Tronov, "The Glaciation of the Altay" (1949); N. N. Pal'gov, "Present-day Glaciation in the Trans-Ili Alatau" (1958), R. D. Zabirov, "The Glaciation of the Pamir" (1955); P. A. Shumskiy, "The Present-day Glaciation of the Arctic" (1947); G. A. Avsyuk, "Glaciers of Flat Summits" (1950), "The Glaciers of the Mountain Node of the Khan-Tengri" (1950), and "Some Data on the Glaciation and Orography of the Ak-Shiyryak Massif" (1952). Works of a general theoretical character are also being published. To this second group belong, first of all, the works by S. V. Kalesnik, "General Glaciology" (1939), M. V. Tronov, "Questions of Mountain Glaciology" (1954) and "Questions of the Connection between Climate and Glaciation" (1956); G. A. Avsyuk, "The Temperature of the Ice in Glaciers" (1956); P. M. Shumskiy, "The Energy of Glaciation and the Life of Glaciers" (1947) and "Fundamentals of Structural Ice Science" (1955). [For the Russian titles see the "Basic Literature" at the end of this chapter.]

During the period under discussion Soviet glaciology has been enriched by a large amount of new and more perfect material from actual observations. The series of original works, both regional and general theoretical, produced chiefly on this new basis, have made it possible to record a considerable advance in this branch of knowledge. As an example, let us name at least the very successful treatment of such a progressive trend in glaciology as is structural ice science [ledovedeniye]; great progress in this direction is due to the works by P. A. Shumskiy. A certain indication of the general recognition of the achievements of Soviet glaciology in this field is the translation of the book by P. A. Shumskiy, "Fundamentals of Structural Ice Science" [Osnovy Strukturnogo Ledovedeniya] (1955), into French and English and its publication in a number of countries.

Also of great significance have been the results of the investigations of the temperature regime of the ice of glaciers and its zonal distribution, and the proposed classification of glaciers by this feature. The study of the interdependence between climate and glaciation (both present and ancient) has undergone substantial development and has had considerable success. Here attention has chiefly been paid to those features of the development of glaciers which depend indirectly upon changes in the climatic conditions. This field of glaciology has even received the special, separate designation of "glacioclimatology" from certain Soviet glaciologists. No less progress has been made in the study of glaciers as hydrogeologic objects, especially in the establishment of the empirical dependences between thaw and runoff of thaw waters and the discharge of water in glacier-fed rivers.

The general consequence of the theoretical development of Soviet glaciology has been a more profound and broader understanding of its problems. At present, the majority of Soviet glaciologists understand the main general task of modern glaciology to be to study the processes of accumulation, transformation, consumption, and movement of ice in land glaciers depending upon the water and heat regime (including balance in this term) of the earth's surface. In this connection, it has been found necessary to make a scientific investigation both of the general laws of development and dynamics inherent in all land glaciers and of the zonal and regional characteristics of the manifestation of these laws. An especially large amount of attention should be paid to the study of the matter-and-energy balance of glaciers.

The further successful development of Soviet glaciology depends primarily upon how widely the new modern methods of observation and measurement can be introduced into the practice of glaciological explorations. These methods, along with a quantitative characterization, would permit the determination of the physical laws and causal functional relations in the development of glacier processes in their diverse forms and combinations. A knowledge of this sort of dependences would permit the creation of a glaciological theory close to the universal one, in which the time and space characteristics of the appearance and development of glaciation would find a sufficiently full and trustworthy explanation, and to calculate forecasts of glacier phenomena it would only be necessary to make a well-grounded choice of the respective parameters and dependences reflecting the general functional relations. This path of further development for glaciology will also create all the necessary preconditions for a wide and efficient use of its achievements for the needs of modern practice. Thus, the further development of glaciological work presents itself chiefly as the development of stationary investigations with employment of the latest techniques, embracing long intervals of time, at least annual cycles, and located in regions of present-day glaciation differing in natural conditions.

The development of the general theory of Soviet glaciology has brought forth a large number of new major problems. Among the most important we shall mention, for example, the interaction between glaciation and climate, the role of glaciers in the circulation of water on our planet, the zonal and regional characteristics of the formation and development of glaciation (including the characteristics of the natural processes peculiar to the glaciers of different areas), the laws of the spatial distribution and capacity of glaciation, the general direction of its evolution, and other problems. In order to work out these questions, it is necessary not only to refine and fill out our information about the spatial condition and distribution of glaciers, their size, the features of the tendency of their development, etc., but also to make investigations of the main glacier processes, since a considerable part of them are still far from having been sufficiently studied. With the exception of a small number of precise data, our present knowledge of glacier processes is confined, as a rule, mostly to general qualitative information — this applies above all to the zonal and regional characteristics of the manifestations of glacier processes. The main attention should be paid to a study of such processes as the matter and energy balance of glaciers, the supply and consumption of matter in glaciers, the transformation of accumulated precipitation into firn and ice, the further metamorphoses of glacier ice, the processes and conditions of phase conversions of water in glaciers, its migrations in the layers of firn and ice (in the liquid, solid, and gaseous states), the movement of ice in glaciers, the temperature regime and the heat balance of glaciers, the heat exchange between glacier surfaces and the atmosphere, the physical-mechanical properties of glacier ice and firn layers, the general structure of glaciers and glacier ice, the runoff of thaw waters, the formation of glacial deposits and the erosional work of the ice, the snow-nival processes in the glacier zones, and so forth.

Soviet glaciology has since 1957 proceeded on a broad front to work out the scientific questions which had been singled out by the end of the third period, i.e., since the beginning of the work under the program of the International Geophysical Year.

Glaciological explorations under the IGY program were organized in accordance with the tasks and requirements set forth above. These aims were general ones for the glaciological explorations of all countries doing work under the IGY program and were adopted as the obligatory direction of explorations at the Third Assembly of the Special IGY Committee in 1955 at Brussels. Thus, the IGY investigations were, for Soviet glaciology, a direct continuation of the previous work.

Before the beginning of the IGY, preparatory work was done to unify the programs and research methods as much as possible both between the individual countries and within them. The Soviet IGY Committee's working group on glaciology, which united the glaciologists of our country, prepared and published sixteen issues of basic methodological instructions on all the main kinds of glaciological investigations. Provisions were made to carry out the work by the most modern methods. Let us note that in the IGY period such modern measuring methods were employed as the electrometric (especially for measuring temperatures throughout the ice), the crystallo-optic, the photogrammetric and, finally, the seismic method, which had earlier been employed only on a limited scale in glaciological investigations.

The IGY program of glaciological work embraced a very wide range of glacial phenomena and was done by modern methods. Observations under this program were carried out by 26 countries in a large number of diverse regions of present-day glaciation, situated throughout the whole expanse of our planet—from both poles to the equator. Glaciological exploration was especially extensive in Antarctica and, we assume, will yield original and important results for the further development of glaciology. Glaciological observations were made uninterruptedly throughout the whole period of the International Geophysical Year and embraced considerable sections of time, in any case not less than one full annual cycle, and at most points of observation more than two annual cycles. It is important that these observations were made synchronously.

From 1957 to the end of 1959, the glaciologists of our country conducted continuous systematic observations in ten regions of present-day glaciation on the territory of the Soviet Union. Work was done on Franz Josef Land (on Hooker Island, or Ostrov Gukera), on Novaya Zemlya (in the region of Russkaya Gavan'), in the Tyan'-Shan' (in the Trans-Ili Alatau and Terskey-Alatau Ranges), in the Pamir (on the Fedchenko Glacier), in the Altay and in Eastern Yakutia (in the Suntar-Khayata Range). Besides this, experimental comparative glaciological observations were instituted at Zagorsk. A number of seasonal inspections were also made of the glaciers (under the IGY program) in the Tyan'-Shan', the Pamir, the Caucasus, the Altay, in the Kodar Range, in the Polar [i.e., within the Arctic Circle] and Sub-Polar Urals, in the Franz Josef Land Archipelago and in other regions. Finally, a very considerable volume of very complex glaciological work, well equipped with modern technology, was accomplished by the Soviet explorers in Antarctica. From 1956 to 1959, systematic stationary observations were made in the region of the stations Mirnyy, Pionerskaya, Oazis, Komsomol'skaya, Vostok, Lazareva, Ostrov Drigal'skogo, Mount Gauss, and so forth. In addition, during thousand-kilometer sled-and-tractor treks into the heart of the continent, they made many glaciological observations, accompanied by measurements of the thickness of the ice cover, the temperatures in it, studies of its structure, and that of the surface, and so forth. Soviet glaciologists have made a great contribution to the study of the glaciation of the Antarctic continent; in its total volume, the work they performed here can be compared only with the work done by the scientists of the United States of America.

The field observations under the IGY program have now been completed, and we have entered the second phase of the fourth period of development of Soviet glaciology, the chief task of which consists in the topical assimilation of the IGY data. On the basis of these materials, one should confidently expect the appearance of new and original works on the basic glaciological problems and the vigorous general progress of this science. Since even the primary processing of the observational materials accumulated during the IGY period had not been completely finished during the composition of the present chapter and the data have not yet been received from other countries, it is still impossible fully to evaluate and characterize the achievements in the field of glaciology due to the IGY work. However, it is already clear that an immense amount of new and unique factual material has been obtained, equipped with precise quantitative data and embracing a wide range of glacial phenomena. It characterizes the zonal and regional features of manifestation and combination for practically all the areas of present-day glaciation of our planet, including Antarctica — an area completely unknown heretofore. There has never before been such a precedent in the history of glaciology.

It may be assumed, therefore, that the IGY materials will make it possible to penetrate deeply into the physical nature of glacial phenomena and to establish with sufficient reliability the causal relations between them and other natural processes. Thus, even now there are grounds for stating that on the basis of the IGY materials both the general glaciological laws and their zonal and regional features will be ascertained and that it will be possible to relate them chiefly to the water-and-heat regime of the earth's surface. It is in this direction that we envisage the immediate prospects for the development of glaciology. That the assimilation of the IGY materials will create a new period in the development of glaciology is confirmed at least by the fact that, on the basis of only a small part of the materials collected on the Antarctic, a number of essential and complex questions have already been worked out, relating to the movement of ice (the type of flow, the mechanism of the metamorphosis of the ice in the process of movement) and theoretical explanations of the form and thickness of the ice sheets depending upon the conditions of movement, feeding and ablation, the temperature and physical mechanical properties of the ice, and so forth. Some of the respective works (by P. A. Shumskiy, V. N. Bogoslovskiy, S. S. Vyalov, and L. D. Dolgushin) were reported on by Soviet glaciologists in September, 1958, at the symposium in Chamonix (France) on the physics of the movement of ice, held by the Snow and Ice Commission of the International Geodetic and Geophysical Union.

Contemporaneous glaciation on the territory of the Soviet Union is developed in 17 regions with different physical geographic conditions — from the extreme Arctic to sultry Middle Asia. Of these seventeen areas of glaciation, four are on islands of the Soviet Arctic and thirteen are on the continental part of the territory of the USSR. In the Arctic, glaciation is developed on the Franz Josef Land Archipelago (including Victoria Island), on Novaya Zemlya, on Severnaya Zemlya (including Shmidt and Ushakov islands) and on the De Long Islands. On the continent, there are glaciers in the Polar and Sub-Polar Urals, on the Taymyr Peninsula, in the Khariulakh Range (northern spur of the Verkhoyansk Range), on the headwaters of the Indigirka, in the Koryak Range (Chukotka Peninsula), on Kamchatka, in the Caucasus, in the Altay, in the Saur Range, in the Sayans, in the Kodor Range, in the Tyan'-Shan' (including the Dzhungarskiy Alatau) and in the Pamir. The total area of contemporaneous glaciation on the territory of the USSR is estimated at about 77,500 sq. km., 55,000 of which are located on the islands of the Arctic and 22,500 in the mountain regions of the continental part of the territory of the USSR. In the latter more than 6,500 separate glaciers are counted.

Such a varied geographic location of the regions of present-day glaciation creates an extraordinary diversity of combinations and manifestations of glacier processes on the territory of our Fatherland, which, on the one hand, renders the tasks of Soviet glaciologists difficult. On the other, the diversity is favorable to the fullest study of glacier phenomena both as a whole and in their zonal and regional features. In view of the great diversity in the occurrence of glacial processes, it is quite impossible to use any universal empirical interdependences for the practical economic exploitation of the glacier regions and for forecasting glacial phenomena. Here there is need for rather precisely established general physical laws and a knowledge of the causal, functional interrelationships between the numerous glacial phenomena. Only on this scientific foundation is it possible to work out rationally the questions of the utilization of glaciers in the modern practice of civilian, industrial, and transport construction and the operation of public works in high-mountain and polar areas, and, in the regions of glacier-fed rivers, also for the needs of irrigation and hydro-power. Only on this foundation, too, can methods of forecasting glacial phenomena be worked out. Our country's glaciologists are confronted by the task of perfecting by every possible means the theory of Soviet glaciology and are paying special attention to the practical application of their achievements.

BASIC LITERATURE

Avsyuk, G. A. "Artificial Intensification of the Thawing of the Ice and Snow of Mountain Glaciers."
    Tr. In-ta Geogr. AN SSSR, vol. 56, 1953.
Avsyuk, G. A. "The Temperature Condition of Glaciers," *"Izv. AN SSSR, Seriya geogr.,"* 1955, No. 3.
Avsyuk, G. A. "The International Geophysical Year and the Glaciological Investigations of the USSR in this Period,"
    "Izv. AN SSSR, Seriya geogr.," 1955, No. 6.
Avsyuk, G. A. "Certains Renseignements sur le Mouvement de la Glace dans les Glaciers du Tian-chan,"
    Symposium de Chamonix, Publ. No. 47, de L'Association Supernationale d'Hydrologie Scientifique, 1958,
    Gentbrugge, Belgique.
Avsyuk, G. A., Markov, K. K., Shumskiy, P. A. "The Cold Desert in the Antarctic." *Izv. AN SSSR, Seriya geogr.,*
    1956, No. 4.
Bogoslovskiy, V. N. "Application des Méthodes Géophysiques aux Investigations du Glacier et de Moraine Touyuksou."
    Symposum de Chamonix, Publ. No. 47, de L'Association Supernationale d'Hydrologie Scientifique, 1958.
    Gentbrugge, Belgique.
Berman, L. L. "Present-day Glaciation of the Upper Course of the Indigirka River," *Voprosy Geografii*, sb. 4, 1947.
Vyalov, S. S. Regularities of Glacial Shields Movement and the Theory of Plastic Viscous Flow [in English].
    Symposium de Chamonix, Publ. No. 47, de l'Assoc. Sup. d'Hydr. Scient., 1958, Gentbrugge, Belgique.
Vyalov, S. S. Regularities of Ice Deformation [in English]. *Symposium de Chamonix*, Publ. No. 47, de l'Assoc. Sup.
    d'Hydr. Scient., 1958, Gentbrugge, Belgique.
Dolgushin, L. D. "Glaciological Observations in Antarctica." *"Izv. AN SSSR, Seriya geogr.,"* 1958, No. 6.
Dolgushin, L. D. Les Particularités Morphologiques Essentielles et les Régularités des Mouvements des Glaciers de la
    Marge de l'Antarctide Orientale, *Symp. de Chamonix*, Publ. No. 47, de l'Assoc. Sup. d'Hydr. Scient., 1958.
    Gentbrugge, Belgique.
Dolgushin, L. D., and Kemmerikh, A. A. "New Glaciers in the Urals." *"Izv. AN SSSR, Seriya geogr.,"* 1957, No. 6.
Zabirov, R. D. The Glaciation of the Pamir *(Oledeneniye Pamira)*. Geografgiz, 1955.
Kalesnik, S. V. Mountain Glacier Regions of the USSR *(Gornyye Lednikovyye Rayony SSSR)*, 1937.
Kalesnik, S. V. General Glaciology *(Obshchaya Glyatsiologiya)*, Uchpedgiz, 1939.
Makarevich, K. G., and Zenkova, V. A. "Some new Data on the Dynamics of the Glaciers of the Dzhungarskkiy
    Alatau." *Vestn. AN Kaz. SSSR*, No. 7, 1956.
Pal'gov, N. N. "Investigations of the Glaciers of Kazakhstan from 1936 to 1946." *Vestn. AN Kaz. SSR*, No. 7, 1947.
Pal'gov, N. N. "Some Results of the Latest Investigations of the Glaciers of Kazakhstan." *Izv. AN SSSR, Seriya geogr.,*
    1954, No. 4.
Pal'gov, N. N. "Determination of the Thickness of Mountain Glaciers by the Method of Balances." *Vestn. AN Kaz.
    SSSR*, No. 4, 1956.
Popov, V. I. "The Second International Polar Year and the observations of glaciers." *Izv. GGI*, No. 46, 1932.
*Programma i Obshchiye Ukazaniya po Provedeniyu Glyatsiologicheskikh Issledovaniy Mezhdunarodnogo Geofizicheskogo
    Goda* (Program and General Instructions for Conducting Glaciological Investigations for the International
    Geophysical Year). Pub. by the IGY Committee, Moscow, 1957.
Tronov, M. V. Essays on the Glaciation of the Altay *(Ocherki Oledeneniya Altay)*, 1949.
Tronov, M. V. Questions of Mountain Glaciology *(Voprosy Gornoy Glyatsiologii)*, 1954.
Trudy Lednikovykh Ekspeditsiy Komiteta SSSR po Provedeniyu 2-go Mezhdunarodnogo Polyarnogo Goda (Works of
    the Glacier Expeditions of the USSR Committee on the Conduct of the 2nd International Polar Year),
    under the editorship of S. V. Kalesnik, issues I, II, III, IV, V and VI, 1935-1936.
Shumskiy, P. A. "Present-day Glaciation in the Soviet Arctic," *Voprosy Geografii*, sb. 4, 1947.
Shumskiy, P. A. The Energy of Glaciation and the Life of Glaciers *(Energiya Oledeneniya i Zhizn' Lednikov)*. 1947.
Shumskiy, P. A. Fundamentals of Structural Ice Science *(Osnovy Strukturnogo Ledovedeniya)*. 1955.
Shumskiy, P. A. "The Mechanism of Ice Straining and its Recrystallization" [in English]. *Symp. de Chamonix*,
    Publ. No. 47, ASHS, 1958, Gentbrugge, Belgique.

CHAPTER -11

PERMAFROST SCIENCE (GEOCRYOLOGY)

S. P. Kachurin

Permafrost science [*Merzlotovedeniye*] is one of the young geographic disciplines. It has taken shape in the Soviet period under the influence of urgent practical demands in conjunction with the winning of vast territories in the northern and eastern parts of the Soviet Union, over which perennially frozen (or perpetually frozen) rocks are widely distributed.

In the process of the economic and industrial conquest of the northern and eastern territories it has become obvious that the experience in managing the economy, construction, and operation of the various routes and great public works (railroad depots, electric power stations, etc.), which has been acquired outside the areas of distribution of perennially frozen rocks, is entirely inadequate for the same kind of work on dispersed frozen rocks. Here other approaches and methods are needed in economic activity and construction, without which it is impossible to conduct a rational economy and firm, stable construction.

Inadequate consideration of local geologic-geographic characteristics in the development and structure of the upper layers of the perennially frozen rocks very often results in considerable loss to the economy. As a result of serious deformations, roads, many expensive buildings, and other engineering works are rapidly destroyed, and this has necessitated considerable annual repairs and rebuilding, which have made operation complicated and costly. From the literature it is known (Sumgin, 1927) that in pre-Soviet times the repairing of track damage from various frost processes cost the state the huge sum of some fifty million gold rubles a year on the Trans-Baykal railroad alone, to say nothing of the material losses from breakdowns and interruptions of operation.

The isolated investigations and incidental observations made formerly during investigations for other purposes, although helping to clarify certain causes of this or that frost phenomenon, did not furnish all the materials required for working out the theory and adequate foundations for a purposeful management and reliable construction under the conditions outlined.

Not until Soviet times did the possibility present itself of commencing planned and systematic investigations of frozen rocks, the phenomena and processes taking place in them, and of working out the proper practical measures for overcoming their unfavorable characteristics. The efforts of specialists during the comparatively short period of 20 to 25 years have resulted in obtaining such a large amount of new factual data on frozen rocks, their properties and the related phenomena and laws governing them, as had not been gained during the period of more than two centuries extending from the initial observations of frozen rocks down to the time when the science of frozen subsoils and rocks was created.

Of importance in the shaping of *merzlotovedeniye* as a science was the monographic work by M. I. Sumgin, "Perpetual Frozenness of the Soil Within the Boundaries of the USSR" [*Vechnaya merzlota pochvy v predelakh SSSR*]. In this work the author, who personally engaged for many years in field investigations in Siberia and the Far East of the USSR, summarized everything that was known about frozen rocks, critically examined the theories of the origin of frozen rocks, gave an explanation of the facts personally studied by him, pointed out the principal directions and paths for further investigation of permafrost and proposed a large number of practical measures to combat the harmful effect of this phenomenon on construction and agriculture.

The appearance of M. I. Sumgin's book served as an impetus to the organization of a special institution, the Commission for the Study of Permafrost, created in 1930 as a part of the Academy of Sciences of the USSR at the initiative of Academician V. I. Vernadskiy. The Commission's tasks embraced the systematic study of frozen rocks and the processes and phenomena accompanying them, as well as the co-ordination of the problems and the immediate research work on the study of frozen rocks with all the other institutions and the organizations of the USSR interested therein.

In the very first year of its operation, the Commission, directed by V. A. Obruchev and M. I. Sumgin, organized a large and active group of young researchers and has displayed very energetic activity. Field investigations of frozen rocks have been evolved—both in special expeditions and at stations—and a theoretical analysis has been made of the collected literature and manuscript materials to explain the principal laws in the development and appearance of perennially frozen rocks. Owing to a considerable expansion of its functions, the Commission was soon reorganized into a Committee and later into the V. A. Obruchev Institute of Permafrost Science of the Academy of Sciences of the USSR. At the same time, scientific-research permafrost stations were organized in a number of the northern regions of the country. Thus, a solid scientific basis was established for the further development of the new science.

Before the organization of the Institute of Permafrost Science, Soviet permafrost researchers had studied almost exclusively perennially frozen rocks (permafrost), distributed principally in the east and north of our country, but the work program of the new institute, in addition to the chief object of investigation, perennially frozen rocks, embraced the study of seasonally frozen soils and rocks ("seasonal frost"), encountered throughout almost the whole remainder of the vast territory of the Soviet Union. In the course of time the range of questions studied by permafrost scientists has expanded more and more (Fig. 2).

Permafrost science in our country, like other branches of geographic knowledge, is developing both theoretically and practically. If one compares the range of questions being dealt with by this science 20 to 25 years ago with what makes up its content at present, the progress will become especially clear. In the initial period of its existence (Obruchev, 1947), investigations were conducted principally in two main directions: on the one hand, into questions of general permafrost science — the study of the general physical and geologic-geographic laws — and, on the other hand, into questions of engineering permafrost science relating to different kinds of construction on frozen rocks and to a lesser extent in the field of agriculture. These directions were united on the basis of general laboratory and experimental research.

Later, especially since the Great Patriotic War, new trends, each of which has in turn been differentiated, have emerged in Soviet permafrost science and have begun to be elaborated with success. Subjects with a geographic content have constituted a considerable proportion of the questions of theoretical and applied significance, as heretofore. At the same time, the list of topics having geophysical, construction-engineering, and other orientations has been enlarged.

The Academy of Sciences and certain other scientific institutions of the Union have engaged in both the geographic and the applied study of frozen rocks in about equal degrees, but a large number of government agencies — the Ministries of Means of Communication, Road Construction, Hydro-energy and others — have conducted and are conducting investigations of frozen rocks chiefly in the interest of the construction done in realizing the plans for the development of the national economy in the east and north of our country.

The geographic topics in permafrost science are distributed among five main fields of research. The first field, one of the most complex and diversified with respect to its topics, embraces questions of the regional geologic-geographic laws of the development of the rock strata, and the processes and phenomena occurring in perennially frozen and seasonally frozen rocks. The most important question among those making up this field is the ascertainment of the laws of development and geographic distribution of the various types of frozen rocks in the different landscape zones, the study of the structure, composition, and properties of frozen rocks, their dependence upon the natural geographic factors of the immense territory of the country and other factors.

A very important section of this field is the surveying and mapping of various types of frozen rocks and the accompanying phenomena: bulging, *naled'* formation [secondary formation of a sheet of ice from water forced out from a frozen stream or other source], thermo-karst, solifluction, and many others, as well as regionalization of the area of distribution of frozen rocks and distinction of comparable territories by a complex of geographic features.

In the last few years a larger-scale (1:10,000,000) and more detailed permafrost (geocryological) map of the USSR (Baranov, 1958) has been created than the well-known schematic maps of M. I.

Sumgin and V. F. Tumel'. Based on extensive factual material, the new map for the first time unites data both for the area of distribution of perennially frozen, and for seasonally frozen, soils and rocks. This map has attracted much attention from workers in the various scientific and producing institutions. Work on maps to other scales is continuing.

The second field is connected with the study of the physical geographic, principally thermo-physical, conditions of the development of the strata of perennially frozen rocks. Here the main task is to investigate the heat exchange in the materials in the atmosphere — soil — lithosphere system at a negative temperature level in the upper layers of the earth's crust. Work is continuing along this line on such scientific questions as the study of the thermics [*termiki*] of the strata of perennially frozen rocks, the theory of the development of perennially frozen rocks, the questions of the dynamics of the temperature regime of the strata of perennially frozen rocks and the dynamics of the southern boundary of the area of distribution of perennially frozen rocks in time and space, the migration of moisture and humid masses under the influence of external actions (changes in the temperature gradients, humidity in the rock strata, and so forth), the heat balance in the rock strata with consideration of the phase conversions of water, and many others.

The physical processes had in some part also been the objects of study in the preceding period of investigation into perennially frozen soils and rocks, but the physical-chemical and chemical processes did not begin to be studied until very recently. The results obtained therefrom testify to the importance of the change in the chemistry of the soils and rocks both for the development of the frozen strata (cryogenesis) and for the accompanying phenomena (Tyutyunov, 1951).

The third field relates to the genesis of subterranean ice and its interrelation with above-ground processes and ice. In the light of the latest data, this problem becomes one of the cardinal ones in studying a large number of other problems of geography and of Quaternary geology. Thanks to the laws established, it is possible to judge not only the course of development of subterranean ice in the Quaternary period, but also the strata of the frozen rocks containing it. The structure of ice, its textural properties, and the distribution of ice in the rocks in combination with the litho-morpho-logical conditions serve as the principal indicators of the genesis of rock strata. On the basis of these features it is easy to establish the type of process by which the stratum was formed: syngenetic, epigenetic, or polygenetic (Popov, 1957; Baranov, 1958; and others). The organic remains in ice and the mineral masses, as well as the geomorphologic data, contribute to the ascertainment of the relative age of a dispersed mass of frozen rocks.

Under subarctic conditions, subterranean ice, which often interacts with surface (glacier) ice, becomes simultaneously an object of both permafrost-science and geologic investigation. Only through such an integrated study of it can more reliable information be obtained in many cases about the modes, conditions, and time of its formation. The ice in a stratum of frozen rocks is one of the most important components upon which depend many properties of the rocks containing it. The investigation of this natural formation has only just begun—a great deal of work is still to be done.

The fourth field in the geographic study of frozen rocks concerns one of the vitally important problems of permafrost science, namely the laws governing the interaction between the perennially frozen rocks and the underground waters. The formation of ground-water horizons in perennially frozen rocks proceeds differently than it does outside the frozen strata. The distribution of the liquid phase of the water among the strata of frozen rocks is subject to special laws, in which the heat factor plays a leading role on the same footing as the geologic structure of the containing strata. The immense practical significance of ground waters and their appearance on the surface of the earth is related to the task of supplying water to populated points over vast expanses with frozen rocks of considerable thickness, but without surface sources of water (for example in Central Yakutia), as well as to the questions of water-and-heat reclamation in the regions of distribution of perennially frozen rocks. A vivid illustration of the latter under natural conditions is the development of thermo-karst under the most severe conditions of the Far North, with the absence there of degradation of frozen rocks but with an abundance of surface water in small bodies.

The fifth field of present-day permafrost science is the study of the history of the development and paleogeography of perennially frozen strata in the Quaternary period, in combination with the development of ancient glaciations and the accompanying processes over the vast territory of the country, with consideration of all the other components of the geographic environment. The beginning

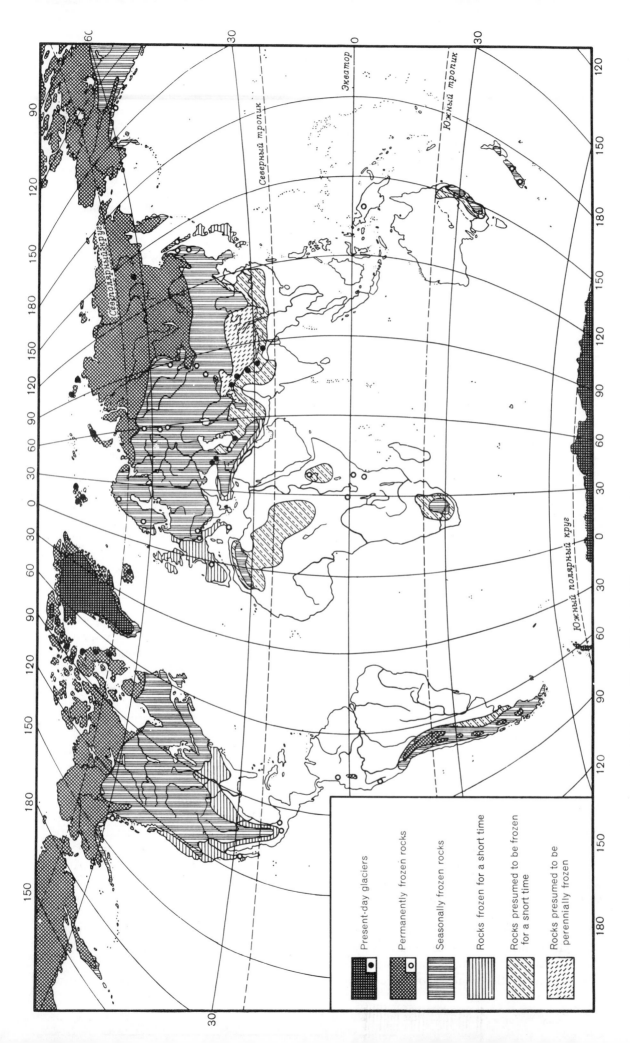

Fig. 2. RANGE OF DISTRIBUTION OF THE VARIOUS TYPES OF FROZEN ROCKS ON THE GLOBE

Present-day glaciers

Permanently frozen rocks

Seasonally frozen rocks

Rocks frozen for a short time

Rocks presumed to be frozen for a short time

Rocks presumed to be perennially frozen

Северный тропик

Экватор

Южный тропик

Южный полярный круг

Северный полярный круг

of the Quaternary period, or Anthropogene as it has now begun to be called, coincided with the beginning of a chilling of the climate, considerably intensified in the Pleistocene, which to an equal extent was a precondition for the development of widely distributed and enormous-surface glaciers and of great thicknesses of perennially frozen rocks, in which subterranean ice played and still plays a leading role. The study of the history of the development of ancient glaciation in Eurasia and the north of America, as well as the history of the development of strata of perennially frozen rocks aids mutually in many ways in the study of the traces of both phenomena in the so-called periglacial zone. This topic has in recent years attracted the attention of a wide circle of investigators: permafrost scientists, geographers, geologists, etc.

Among the permafrost questions important from a national-economic viewpoint are investigations of biological objects in the field of the distribution of perennially frozen rocks, although this problem relates only partially to permafrost science, primarily with respect to taking into account the laws governing the humidity (multiphase) regime of soils in regions with a negative mean annual soil temperature. These questions have been investigated periodically by permafrost agrobiologists (botanists) under the conditions of the Soviet Arctic, so that some new interrelationships have been ascertained between the underground parts of plants and cold soils (Dadykin, 1952), but on the whole this area of research awaits further thorough field, experimental, and production treatment.

To a still lesser degree, work is being done on the questions of the life and preservation of animals and micro-organisms (anabiosis) under the conditions of perennially frozen soils and rocks, although they are important from both practical and scientific (paleoclimatic) standpoints (Shmidt, 1948).

Of course, the above-enumerated directions of geographic research in permafrost do not exhaust all the questions that make up its list of topics in one way or another (Shvetsov, 1958).

As has been noted, a considerable part of the content of permafrost science is formed by questions of applied (engineering) significance which may be united into a special field, namely, investigation of the basic physical geographic and geologic laws and processes governing the freezing and frozen rocks for the purposes of forecasting the development of various phenomena—heaving during freezing, sagging upon the thawing of rocks, and other phenomena—, as well as the working out of rational methods of construction and special measures to prevent the harmful effect of these phenomena on various structures. For each zone and for each type of frozen rocks, proper measures are being elaborated, which are being continually improved and typed. This field reposes to a considerable degree upon the achievements of the physical, physical geographic, construction-engineering, and other sciences.

In the light of the main tasks which permafrost science solves, it belongs, on the one hand, to the series of sciences termed natural history, primarily geography, physics, and geology, and to a large extent uses the research methods worked out by them, interpreting the methods for the purposes of studying frozen rocks, ice, and the inclusions in them. On the other hand, permafrost science belongs to the series of engineering and other applied sciences and uses their achievements and methods with respect to the interaction of frozen, freezing, and thawing rocks and various man-made structures (Tsytovich, 1945; Krylov, 1952; Yanovskiy, 1936). Lying on the boundary line between a large number of sciences and utilizing their research methods, permafrost science, which has its own specific object of study, has also worked out special research methods that are not generally applicable to any other science.

The wide range of questions, the diversity of the regional geographic and geologic conditions (from the Arctic, Antarctic, and Subarctic to the subtropics), and hence the abundance of problems of geographic significance in which thermal (cryogenic) factors play a leading role in their complex interaction with the surrounding environment necessitate the conduct of integrated investigations with simultaneous consideration of many factors. This greatly complicates the tasks confronting permafrost scientists. For some tasks only approximate solutions have thus far been found (for example, the determination of the quantity of non-freezing water in the rock); for other tasks, only an empirical approach has been worked out (for example, in the determination of the depths of freezing and thawing of rocks, etc.). In this connection, even with the many achievements already attained by Soviet permafrost scientists in a large number of directions and problems, they are still faced by many ever more complex tasks. The solution of them has aided and will aid the development of the country's national economy and the improvement of living conditions in the field of the distribution of frozen rocks and their seasonal freezing to great depths.

BASIC LITERATURE

Baranov, I. Ya. "Some Laws Governing the Development of Strata of Perennially Frozen Rocks and the Seasonal Freezing of the Soil." *Izv. AN SSSR, Seriya geogr.*, 1958, No. 2.

Vernadskiy, V. I. "On the Areas of Chilling in the Earth's Crust." *Zapiski Gos. gidrol. in-ta,* vol. 10, Leningrad, 1933.

Dadykin, V. P. Peculiarities of the Behavior of Plants on Cold Soils. *(Osobennosti Povedeniya Rasteniy na KHolodnykh Pochvakh).* Izd-vo AN SSSR, 1952.

Krylov, M. M. "The Transformation of Nature through Hydrothermal Reclamation." *Voprosy geografii,* sb. 28, 1952.

Kudryavtsev, V. A. "The Dynamics of the Southern Boundary of Distribution of Perpetual Frost." *Tr. In-ta merzlotovedeniya im. V. A. Obrucheva,* vol. 12, Izd-vo AN SSSR, 1953.

Obruchev, V. A. The Progress of Permafrost Science in the USSR. *(Uspekhi merzlotovedeniya v SSSR).* Jubilee collection of articles dedicated to the 30th Anniversary of the Great October Socialist Revolution, Izd-vo AN SSSR, 1947.

Popov, A. I. "The History of Perpetual Frost in the USSR in the Quaternary Period." *Vestn. MGU, Seriya biol., pochvoved., geologii i geografii,* No. 3, 1957.

Saks, V. N. "An Experiment in the Reconstruction of the History of the Development of Siberia in the Quaternary Period." *Materialy po Chertvertichnomu Periodu SSSR,* issue 3. Komissiya po izucheniyu chetv. perioda, AN SSSR, 1952.

Sumgin, M. I. Perpetual Frozenness of the Soil in the USSR *(Vechnaya Merzlota Pochvy v Predelakh SSSR),* first ed., Vladivostok, 1927; 2nd ed., AN SSSR, Moscow, 1937.

Sumgin, M. I. "On the Degradation of Permafrost in a Certain Part of the Territory Occupied by it in the USSR." *Tr. Komissii po izucheniyu vechnoy merzloty AN SSSR,* vol. I, Leningrad, 1932.

Sumgin, M. I., Kachurin, S. P., Tolstikhin, N. I., and Tumel', V. F. General Permafrost Science *(Obshcheye Merzlotovedeniye).* Izd-vo AN SSSR, 1940.

Tumel', V. F. Permafrost Science and the Work of the Academy of Science on Perpetual Frost *(Merzlotovedeniye i Raboty Akademii Nauk po Vechnoy Merzlote).* Ocherki po istorii Akademii nauk. Geol.-geogr. nauki, 1945.

Tyutyunov, I. A. The Migration of Water in Peat-and-gley Soil in the Periods of Freezing and its Frozen State under Conditions of Shallow-seated Perpetual Frost *(Migratsiya Vody v Torfyano-gleyevoy Pochve v Periody Zamerzaniya i Zamerzshego yeye Sostayaniya v Usloviyakh Neglubokogo Zaleganiya Vechnoy Merzloty).* Izd-vo AN SSSR, Moscow, 1951.

Fedosov, A. Ye. "The Mechanical Processes in the Subsoil when the Liquid Phase Freezes in Them." *Tr. In-ta geol. nauk AN SSR,* issue 35, *seriya inzhen. geol.,* No. 4, Moscow, 1940.

Tsytovich, N. A. "Concerning the Theory of the State of Equilibrium of Water in Frozen Subsoils." *Izv. AN SSSR, seriya geogr. i geofiz.,* vol. IX, Nos. 5-6, 1945.

Tsytovich, N. A., and Sumgin, M. I. Fundamentals of the Mechanics of Frozen Subsoils *(Osnovaniya Mekhaniki Merzlykh Gruntov).* Izd-vo AN SSSR, 1937.

Shvetsov, P. F. "The Content and Tasks of Soviet Geocryology." *Sovetskaya geologiya,* no. 12, 1958.

Shmidt, P. Yu. *Anabioz* (Anabiosis). Izd-vo AN SSSR, 1948.

Shumskiy, P. A. Fundamentals of Structural Ice Science *(Osnovy Strukturnogo Ledovedeniya).* Izd-vo AN SSSR, 1955.

Shumskiy, P. A. "Investigation of the Glacier Cover of the Antarctica." *Priroda,* no. 7, 1957.

Yanovskiy, V. K. "On the Question of the Methods of Investigating Perpetual Frost for Purposes of Planning Engineering Works." *Tr. I geol.-razv. Konferentsii Glavsevmorputi,* 1936.

CHAPTER 12

HYDROLOGY OF THE LAND

M. I. L'vovich

Hydrology, which belongs to the young geographic sciences, has developed in Soviet times in two main directions: the theoretical and the engineering. Investigation on the theoretical side has been mainly connected with geography, hydrophysics, and hydrodynamics. It has laid the groundwork for the shaping of hydrology as the science of the water envelope — the hydrosphere — of the earth, which studies the circulation of water in the atmosphere, on the surface of the earth, and in its depths, in its three aggregate states — vapor, liquid, and solid — and in its interaction with other elements of nature.

The engineering side of hydrology has developed in connection with practical demands. However, the practical requirements of the rapidly developing national economy have outstripped the growth of theoretical research. Hence, purely empirical treatments, which insure the safety of hydrotechnical structures but do not always solve the task efficiently enough from the economic viewpoint, have largely predominated for some time in applied hydrological work, especially on stream runoff. Moreover, the division of hydrological research into theoretical and engineering is in part merely schematic. Theoretical investigations have made no small contribution to national-economic construction and the engineering side has, in turn, enriched certain aspects of theoretical research.

The role of theoretical research in Soviet hydrology is greater than it is in many other countries. This applies especially to the methods of hydrological generalizations, which make possible the solution of complex problems of science and practice with a relatively small volume of initial hydrometric data. Under conditions where the methods of generalization and the theoretical side in general are not properly developed, the solution of scientific and practical problems is completely dependent upon the volume of available initial hydrometric data. With such an approach, hydrometric work is the principal object of development. When one considers the manifold water-economy problems in the different parts of a country, the demands on the network of hydrometric posts and stations are essentially unlimited. In the USSR a relatively small volume of hydrometric data is supplemented by scientific research. Here, the methods of theoretical analysis and generalization permit a sufficiently well-grounded solution for the complex problems of hydrology in conformity with the demands of the national economy. This applies both to the characterization of the various elements of the hydrological regime and to the elucidation of the hydrology of any point of the country.

Soviet science must now insure the most productive utilization of the country's water resources, with a maximum efficiency of water-economy measures. Realization of this requires the thorough development of theoretical hydrological research and the utilization of its results in the practice of socialist construction.

Hydrological work and investigations in pre-revolution Russia had undergone a rather substantial development. In the general level of the development of hydrology, Russia was not behind other foremost countries, and in some questions it occupied a foremost position. This, however, does not mean that the volume of hydrological research corresponded to practical demands. On the contrary, there was a considerable lag, which became especially perceptible after the Great October Socialist Revolution, when the tempestuous development of the whole national economy of the country had its inception.

In the very first years of Soviet rule, hydrological research assumed a wide scope, and hydrological science began to develop at a rapid rate. In the Academy of Sciences of the USSR, the Hydrological Commission was created, on the basis of which the Hydrological Institute — the first integrated scientific-research institution in this field — was organized in 1919 on the initiative of V. G. Glushkov. The Institute evolved methodical work on hydrological forecasting, investigation of the ice regime, the dynamics of ground water, and a number of other questions.

In the first years after the October Revolution, leading hydrologists (V. G. Glushkov, Ye. V. Bliznyak, and others) took part in working out the hydro-energy part of the GOELRO plan. Hydrology expanded greatly as a result of the experience with great national-economic construction projects such as the Volkhovstroy, the Dneprostroy, and the Svir' hydroelectric stations, the Caucasian and Middle Asiatic hydroelectric stations and irrigation systems, the White Sea and Moscow canals, and many others. Hydrologists solved the problems of water supply to Magnitogorsk, the Kuzbass, and Karaganda, and to the Turksib Railroad. In the first five-year plans, the practical demands were so great that hydrological research was hardly able to keep up with them and, hence, they developed principally in an empirical direction. Great use was made of statistical procedures of investigation. It was often necessary to solve practical problems with insufficient initial data and on an insufficiently developed theoretical basis. Among the investigations that played a great role in the solution of practical problems and at the same time contributed to theory should be noted the works of the well-known hydrologist D. I. Kocherin, as well as B. V. Polyakov, B. D. Zaykov, D. L. Sokolovskiy, S. N. Kritskiy and M. F. Menkel', A. V. Ogiyevskiy, M. F. Sribnyy, and others.

The basis for the solution of the practical problems of hydrology was the "Water Cadaster of the USSR," compiled by the Hydrometeorological Service of the USSR. This grand publication, comprising over 7,000 printed sheets [of 16 pages each], contains all the basic information about the hydrology of water objects in the USSR down to 1935, inclusive. In continuation of the "Water Cadaster," hydrological yearbooks have been published by the Hydrometeorological Service.

In connection with the demands of a planned economy, much attention has been paid to hydrological forecasting, which was at first connected with such major water-economy measures as irrigation in Middle Asia (L. K. Davydov), the building of the Volkhov and Dnepr hydroelectric stations (V. N. Lebedev, F. I. Bydin, and A. V. Ogiyevskiy). Later, the Hydrological Institute, the Central Forecasting Institute, and all the territorial administrations of the Hydrometeorological Service began to issue forecasts. The forecasting methods worked out in the USSR concern all the main elements of the hydrological regime in all water objects. Short-range forecasting techniques, which have been developed since the end of the last century, have in the last few decades received a new scientific basis, especially for the forecasting of rain floods (Ye. V. Berg, G. P. Kalinin, M. I. L'vovich, and others). Much attention has also been paid to the long-range forecasting of spring high waters (V. D. Komarov, V. A. Nazarov, Ye. G. Popov, and others), the mean low runoff and volume of mountain rivers (Z. V. Dzhordzhio, and others), the break-up of ice and the freezing of streams (G. R. Bregman, L. G. Shulyakovskiy, and others) and other elements of the hydrological regime. A considerable role in raising the quality of forecasting has been played by the technique of evaluating the reliability of the forecasting methods and the justification of operating forecasts, which was worked out by the Hydrological Institute in 1939.

Alongside the investigations directed toward satisfying the demands of the national economy, the theoretical foundations of Soviet hydrology have also been successfully worked out. Thus, hydrology in the USSR has been developed as an integrated science and has been grounded on A. A. Grigor'yev's doctrine of the interrelationship between the components of the water and heat balance of the earth's surface and the whole complex of natural elements.

Great progress has been achieved in studying floods (M. A. Velikanov, V. G. Glushkov, G. A. Alekseyev, G. P. Kalinin, and others), erosion processes and the dynamics of stream channels (M. A. Velikanov, V. G. Glushkov, V. M. Makkaveyev, K. I. Rossinskiy, and N. I. Makkaveyev), as well as in the hydrophysical investigation of evaporation (L. K. Davydov, B. D. Zaykov,

Z. A. Vikulina and A. P. Braslavskiy, M. I. Budyko, A. I. Budagovskiy, and others), the ice regime (Ye. V. Bliznyak, B. P. Veynberg, V. I. Bydin, B. V. Proskuryakov, and others) and the regime of snow cover and snow thaw (G. D. Rikhter, N. P. Kuz'min, and others).

A considerable role in the recognition of the geographic laws governing the hydrological regime has been played by summary works on the stream runoff in the USSR (B. D. Zaykov, K. P. Voskresenskiy, B. V. Polyakov, P. I. Kuzin, V. A. Troitskiy, G. I. Shvets, and others), on the typology of the regimes of rivers of the USSR and the globe (M. I. L'vovich), the investigation of evaporation from the land (M. I. Budyko), on solid runoff (G. V. Lopatin and G. I. Shamov), on the hydrochemistry of stream waters (V. I. Vernatskiy, O. A. Alekin, and others), on the mouths of the rivers of the globe (I. V. Samoylov), on the hydrology of the forest (A. D. Dubakh, A. A. Molchanov and V. I. Rutkovskiy) and a number of other investigations. Along with this, integrated hydrographic investigations have been conducted on the USSR as a whole (L. K. Davydov, Ye. V. Bliznyak, A. A. Sokolov, L. L. Rossolimo), on separate parts of the country or on individual rivers (V. L. Shul'ts, S. G. Rustamov, D. O. Abramovich, B. D. Zaykov, and others), as well as separately on large lakes: Baykal (G. Yu. Vereshchagin), Balkhash and Issyk-Kul' (L. S. Berg), Onega (I. V. Molchanov, V. K. Davydov), Teletskoye (A. A. Alekin), Sevan (V. K. Davydov, B. D. Zaykov), the Caspian (B. D. Zaykov, B. A. Apollov) and others. The small lakes of Western Siberia and Northern Kazakhstan have been studied by A. V. Shnitnikov. The techniques of limnological investigation have been worked out by G. Yu. Vereshchagin, L. L. Rossolimo, and others. The groundwork for an integrated hydrological study of swamps has been laid by A. D. Dubakh and is being successfully developed by N. Ye. Ivanov.

The initial data for all hydrological research is furnished by a network of hydrological stations, of which there are about 5,000 on the territory of the USSR. The work of the hydrological stations embraces a wide range of questions and is complex in character. The stations keep a record of the liquid and solid runoff, make observations of the ice regime of rivers and lakes, and study the chemical composition of the surface waters. Considering the immense size of the country and the diversity of the hydrological conditions on its territory, the number of points of hydrological observation cannot be recognized as great. Nevertheless, this network permits the solution of the main practical and scientific problems of hydrology: the numerical insufficiency of the network of hydrological stations, as has been stated, has been compensated for by the high level of the theoretical treatment and the interpolation of data. This has obviated the necessity of an excessively dense network of hydrological stations. The increased demands of the national economy, particularly the winning of new regions in the North, East, etc., will require additional development of this network in Siberia and in certain other less well studied territories. There is also the task of the further technical equipment of the hydrological stations, the introduction of automatic procedures for making observations and transmitting their results over long distances.

Forming a part of the hydrological network are the specialized hydrological observatories and stations at the big reservoirs, as well as swamp and runoff observation stations. The latter study the runoff in the initial stage of its development — in the small drainage areas and on the slopes. The idea of organizing these stations was first advanced by M. A. Velikanov more than thirty years ago. Subsequently, similar stations have also begun to appear in other countries. The main purpose of these stations is to study the runoff factors. In our country there exist about a score of runoff stations. Among them, the Valday Hydrological Laboratory occupies a leading position with respect to the breadth of its investigations and technical equipment (V. A. Uryvayev, 1953).

Hydrological investigations in the USSR are made by the scientific-research institutes of the Hydrometeorological Service, the Academy of Sciences of the USSR and the academies of the union republics, as well as by the official institutions of the Ministry of Agriculture, the Ministry of Electric Power Stations, the Ministry of the River Fleet and, finally, by the educational institutions— the geographic faculties of a number of universities and the hydrometeorological institutes.

In the above survey, we have tried to characterize the principal trends and the content of certain concrete hydrological investigations as a historical background for an understanding of the problems and tasks of hydrological science.

MAIN PRACTICAL TASKS OF HYDROLOGY

The thorough development of the productive forces and the construction of the material and technical base of communism which has been evolved in our country confront hydrology with a number of responsible tasks, among which the following are the most important:

Firstly, the rational distribution of the productive forces imposes the task of the economic utilization of the enormous raw-material and energy resources of the eastern regions of the country. The correct resolution of the questions of the water economy plays an enormous role in this matter. In certain regions the development of industry and agriculture is limited by the water resources. Among these regions is, for example, Northern Kazakhstan, where the development of metallurgy and agriculture requires the building of a large water-supply canal from the Irtysh River to Karaganda. Unique in character are the questions of insuring a water supply to the industrial and power enterprises in Eastern Siberia and the Far East, especially in the regions of distribution of permafrost. The industrial conquest of certain desert regions and the development of animal husbandry have required searches for new sources of water supply under the difficult conditions of an arid climate. The results from the investigations made in the last few years successfully solve this problem through the lenses of ground water discovered or created artificially (V. N. Kunin). Further searches and development of water-balance investigations in the deserts are required. The correct solution of these questions of water economy is possible only with an integrated approach and joint work by hydrologists and hydrogeologists with hydrotechnicians and economists.

Secondly, in order to raise farm productivity it is necessary to bring about a regulation of the water balance of the territory for the purpose of creating favorable conditions for raising the yield of agricultural crops.

The third practical task is connected with the development of the forest economy. The great growth of capital construction requires the expansion of logging and its transfer to regions difficult of access, and much labor and money will be spent on hauling wood out of them. On the other hand, the forests, as is known, are regulators of the water balance; hence, their destruction has a negative effect upon the water regime of rivers. It is found that the system of water-conserving forests created almost 25 years ago with the setting aside along rivers of broad (up to 20 kilometers) forest belts forbidden to industrial logging and based on the allegedly existing conflict between the water-conserving action of forests and the industrial cutting of timber, is not accomplishing its object. Theoretical research and practical experience show that with the right kind of logging the water-regulating properties of the forest are not only not reduced, but in certain cases are even enhanced, a fact which must be taken into consideration in planning water-conserving forests. The solution of this important problem requires additional investigation, in which hydrologists, climatologists, and specialists in forest exploitation must participate.

The fourth major practical problem of modern hydrology is connected with hydrotechnical construction. The practice of hydrological estimates has developed principally in an empirical direction and rests largely on probability statistics, based on the law of large numbers and allowance for accident in the formation of hydrological phenomena. Hydrological calculation based on this principle represents essentially a projection into the future, i.e., the period of operation of public works, of the hydrological observation data obtained for the longest possible number of preceding years. As shown by experience, estimated hydrological values obtained by such techniques often prove completely unrealistic and contain an unjustified margin unnecessarily adding to the cost of hydrological works. In the past, these estimating techniques have been justified to some extent, but at the present level of development of science estimated hydrological characteristics can be evaluated on the basis of an analysis of the physical possibility of their formation. In this respect, a wealth of experience has been obtained in practical hydrological forecasting, the techniques of which differ little in principle from the possible procedures used in hydrological estimates. The change in the hydrological estimating procedures will help to cheapen hydrotechnical works and make their operation more efficient and economical.

The fifth practical problem of hydrology relates to the big reservoirs created in recent years. In the conditions of their exploitation, these reservoirs differ substantially from lakes and navigation conditions on them are also peculiar. Being new bodies of water, the reservoirs are in the stage of an unestablished regime; this applies especially to the shaping of the shores and to silting in the zone where the pressure tapers off. Some experience has now been gained in planning and operating the new artificial bodies of water and the groundwork has been laid for the hydrology of reservoirs as a special department of the hydrology of the land (S. L. Vendrov and others). These investigations require further development and should be integrated in character. Intensified attention should be given to the economic questions related to the creation and operation of reservoirs. This problem is closely allied to questions relating to the further development of the construction of small reservoirs and the exploitation of lakes.

The sixth problem concerns questions of channel erosion. Although many navigable rivers have been regulated by reservoirs, navigation on the larger part of our waterways is done under the conditions of free river beds. Hundreds of millions of rubles are spent yearly on the maintenance of navigable depths over rapids. For this reason, the already comparatively old question of the regulation of rapids still remains one of the important tasks of modern hydrology. Closely allied with this problem is the question of solid stream runoff.

The seventh problem is devoted to the pollution of streams, lakes, and reservoirs by industrial and urban sewage. With the development of industry and the growth of cities, the pollution of the surface waters has been growing, so that the tasks of water supply and the fishing industry require intensified attention to this problem and appropriate investigations. A substantial change in the sanitation of stream and lake waters should be brought about by the measures for the use of sewage for agricultural irrigation.

There should be an intensified systematic control of the chemical and biological composition of of stream waters, and investigations should also be continued into the water, chemical, and biological balances of the fields irrigated with waste waters. Closely allied to this problem are investigations of the chemical, gaseous, and biological composition of natural waters as sources of water supply and as a habitat for fish. The study of rare chemical elements occurring in stream and ground waters, for the purpose of searching for minerals, is acquiring great significance.

The eighth important task consists in raising the quality and increasing the range of hydrological forecasts, as well as in intensifying forecasting work for the water objects in the newly won regions of Siberia. The solution of this task requires the development of hydrological theory. It cannot be said that the possibilities of empirical research in this direction have been fully exhausted, but further improvement of the accuracy of forecasts, with an increase in their range, necessitates an intensification of the search for new methods.

The main problems enumerated above do not exhaust all the practical tasks facing the hydrology of the land in connection with the realization of the grand plan for the development of the national economy. In the process of developed large-scale construction, new problems may, of course, arise, for the solution of which hydrological science must be prepared. With a purely utilitarian development, if it solves only those questions with which production is today confronting science, hydrology will not be able to insure the solution of this task. Hydrologists must look far ahead and possess a "reserve fund," the liquidation of which may be required at any time by practical demands.

SOME SCIENTIFIC PROBLEMS OF HYDROLOGY AND THE MAIN METHODS OF STUDYING THEM

The satisfaction of practical demands requires the development of hydrological scientific research, the content and framework of which must be fixed by proceeding from historical premises and the present state of science. It is very important to choose the methods of investigation correctly. In this connection it is appropriate to recall A. I. Herzen's thought that method in science is the embryology of truth. Indeed, the results of scientific research, the completeness of our knowledge of natural laws, and, consequently, the correctness of the measures for utilizing the country's waters, largely depend upon applied method.

In investigations of the water balance, stream runoff, and hydrological regime it is extremely important to make a correct analysis of the factors in their formation and their interrelationship with other elements of nature. Of course, results are derived from a climatological analysis of the hydrological phenomena, and in this substantial progress has been made. But in recent years the climatological explanation of the origin of the water balance and runoff has proved insufficient. A more thorough analysis of the origin of hydrological phenomena has necessitated the involvement of other factors, primarily those characterizing the environment in which they develop, i.e., the soil-and-plant and the geologic-morphologic conditions. Hydrology has thereby begun to switch over to the integrated course of investigation for which V. V. Dokuchayev and A. I. Voyeykov laid the groundwork.

The problem of an integrated hydrology, especially its soil-and-botanical component, is assuming ever greater significance, since it permits us to deepen our concepts of the origin of hydrological phenomena and processes and thereby substantially increase the accuracy of their analysis, and consequently the accuracy of the solution of practical tasks.

Closely related to the integrated trend in hydrology, especially to the study of soil hydrological factors, are the questions of the changes in water balance, runoff, and regime under the influence of man's activity, mainly under farming and forestry. In the perennial dynamics of the hydrological regime, particularly runoff, two causes must be distinguished. The first, natural-historical in character, is related chiefly to the cyclic fluctuation of the climate; the second is of anthropogenic origin. The study of fluctuations and changes in the hydrological regime requires not only a joint consideration of these causes, but also a different approach to them.

Closely akin to the problem of the development of an integrated hydrology are the questions of generalization, particularly the mapping of the characteristics of the elements of the hydrological regime and the application of the method of analogues. Until recently, hydrology had at its disposal hydrometric observation data principally on the large and medium-sized streams. The mapping of the hydrological characteristics of these streams reflects fairly well the general zonal laws. But when it is a matter of intra-zonal features, mass hydrometric data are too general and inadequate. The sharp variability of the soil cover and vegetation, and sometimes also of the geologic structure, from one area to another causes the characteristics of the hydrological regime to vary substantially and sharply even within the confines of small stream drainage areas, sometimes unevenly. Ascertainment of these peculiarities requires an integrated analysis of the factors of the hydrological regime. Hence, the task of developing geographic hydrological research based on experimental investigations of the water balance and runoff consists in comparing the character of the formation of the hydrological regime under elemental conditions. Here, all the hydrological factors in the objects studied should be equal or as nearly alike as possible, except the one factor whose role is ascertained in the course of a given investigation.

It appears to us that the development of theoretical and experimental research in the genetic direction in hydrology opens up prospects for generalization, particularly the mapping of the elements of the hydrological regime on a new methodological basis. These investigations will undoubtedly show that mapping the elements of the regime of land waters, which in nature are discrete in character, cannot be based on simple causal dependences. A hydrological map must reflect the principal factors of the complex of physical geographic conditions and the features of the environment in which the hydrological regime is formed.

A start toward mapping, based on such a principle, has already been made—proposals of corrections in the general runoff maps for adjustment to concrete conditions are appearing more and more frequently in the literature. Active research work, however, is needed to give this technique proper development in accordance with ever-growing practical demands.

It appears to us that in hydrology it is now time to take up the question of deepening the analysis of the water balance, which may be based on the following general expression of the water balance for perennial characterizations:

$$R = S + U; \quad P = S + U + E; \quad W = P - S = E + U,$$

where R is the total stream runoff, S, the surface (flood) runoff, U, the underground (basic) runoff, E, the evaporation, P, the precipitation, and W, the total soil moisture.

This expression differs from the well-known Penck-Oppokov equation of the water balance in that the stream runoff in it is differentiated into two main components. Such an apparently small supplementation of the water-balance equation opens considerable prospects for a further deepening of the analysis of this process.

The main factors in the foregoing have been reflected in the program of the great integrated problem concerning the study of the water and heat balance of a territory, which is being worked out by the institutes of the Academy of Sciences of the USSR jointly with other scientific institutions.

The improvement of hydrological estimates for the purpose of developing methods of planning water resources, lowering the construction costs of hydrotechnical works, and rationalizing the exploitation of water-economy measures, as has been noted above, is impossible if based on the statistical methods widely employed in practical work. In order to overcome this limitation, the following would appear to us to be required as first steps:

1. Intensify research on the long-range fluctuations of stream runoff and, on this basis work out techniques for objectively evaluating the runoff norms without resorting to long series of observations, which cannot be dispensed with if one follows the main premise of variation statistics—the law of large numbers. Long-range series of observations suffer from the drawback that they relate to different economic conditions and in some cases are not comparable with each other for different periods.

The results of the investigation of long-range fluctuations made by A. V. Shnitnikov and A. V. Agupov represent a considerable contribution to the solution of this question.

2. In those regions where economic conditions change substantially during the period of observation (because of the development of farming and forestry), it is necessary to ascertain these changes and introduce corrections in the values of the runoff of different periods. Investigations in this direction have been developing more and more with each succeeding year both in the USSR and in a number of foreign countries, especially in China (S. L. Vendrov, I. A. Kuznik, M. I. L'vovich, and others).

3. The results of the statistical estimates of extreme hydrological values, used in planning hydrotechnical works, for example those of maximum runoff, must be evaluated from the viewpoint of the physical possibilities of the formation of these phenomena under actual physical geographic conditions. The physically possible maximum or minimum is the sole reliable criterion for any practical conclusions. Experience shows that such an approach increases the efficiency of hydrotechnical works. In recent years hydrotechnicians have begun to make more efficient estimates of this sort, which has already been reflected in the dimensions of certain hydrotechnical nodes, making it possible to lower their cost. An important task of science is the theoretical and empirical basis for these hydrological estimates.

Of substantial significance for the development of hydrological research in the geographic direction are geophysical and hydrodynamic methods of investigation. This concerns primarily the study of the elemental hydrological processes — ice formation, snow melt, evaporation and transpiration, infiltration, movement of water in the soil, and so forth. Hydrodynamic investigations are necessary for the study of the processes of erosion, movement of sediments, formation of stream channels, and duration of slope and channel runoff. All these investigations afford a physical foundation for geographic hydrological research. For this reason, the ever increasing penetration of geophysical and hydrodynamic methods into hydrology must be recognized as entirely legitimate.

Special mention must be made of the problem of studying floods, which are the most striking hydrological phenomenon. The theory of floods, mainly created by Soviet hydrology, as was also the solution of the practical problems of forecasting and estimating the basic elements of floods, has undergone considerable development. In this question, too, further steps must be made in the direction of working out and subsequently perfecting methods of the consistent precomputation of all the elements, for both snow and rain floods. In doing so, it is necessary to strive toward a closer unification of the theoretical and the empirical precomputation procedures.

To the important questions of the flood problem belongs the investigation of infiltration and the duration of the flood runoff. Of great significance also is the study of the soil runoff as a component of the flood runoff. The few facts thus far available show that this kind of runoff under certain conditions plays an essential role in the formation of floods. The main paths of this research are clear and they now need to be developed.

The growth of industry, power, and agriculture in the East of the country requires greater attention to the study of the water resources of those regions. No "blank spots" have remained in the USSR with respect to the geographical, particularly the hydrological, study of the country. However, the coverage of certain water features in Siberia does not fully meet the rapidly growing demands of the national economy. In this connection it is necessary to conduct integrated hydrological investigations of certain streams and lakes and extend to them the network of hydrological stations. The results of these investigations might well be published in the form of special monographs similar to those issued by the Hydrological Institute in the form of handbooks on the water resources of the USSR, or as separate regional monographs for the southern half of the European part of the USSR (K. P. Voskresenskiy), on Western Siberia (P. I. Kuzin) or on the areas of reclamation of virgin and idle lands ("Water Resources of Akmolinsk Oblast," published by GGI, 1958). The study of large lakes must, of course, be individual in character. But the small lakes must be investigated on the basis of typological principles and by type lake regions. The outcome of these investigations should be a monograph on the small lakes of the USSR.

In connection with the task of raising the accuracy of hydrological forecasting and lengthening its range, it appears essential to us to develop the above-mentioned investigations of the factors and processes of the formation of the hydrological regime. However, in addition to this, great significance attaches to the organization of information work—its expansion with respect to snow cover, principally in mountain regions and on the plains, calculation of the characteristics of the intra-zonal distribution of thundershowers, and, in regions where forecasts of rain floods have great significance, humidity and state of the soil, and the like. It appears to us that, in addition to expanding these observations, the time is now ripe technically to examine the question of their extensive automation by means of radioactive isotopes and the autonomous automatic transmission of these data over long distances. This technique has become rather widespread in scientific research work, but it is important to introduce it widely into operative forecasting practice. It should be stressed that automation represents not only a means of raising the operating capacity, but also opens possibilities of expanding observations in regions difficult of access; for example, in mountain areas, where the organization of high-mountain stations and the maintenance of a special staff under difficult conditions would otherwise be required.

This brief survey of the tasks and content of research in the hydrology of the land lays no claim to completeness. With the general geographic orientation of these investigations, as has been stated above, the application of geophysical hydrodynamic methods of investigation is required. The history of science and the accumulated experience show that investigations, including hydrological ones, conducted on the border line between two or more disciplines yield the most fruitful results. Hence, one must strive toward their possible expansion.

BASIC LITERATURE

Alekin, O. A. General Hydrochemistry (Obshchaya Gidrokhimiya). Gidrometeoizdat, 1948.

Alekseyev, G. A. Estimates of the Flood Runoff of the Streams of the USSR (Raschety Pavodochnogo Stoka Rek SSSR), Leningrad, 1955.

Appolov, B. A. Studies of Rivers (Ucheniye o Rekakh). Izd. MGU, 1951.

Bliznyak, Ye. V. Water Investigations (Vodnyye Issledovaniya). Moscow, 1952.

Bregman, G. R. Atlantic Influences Upon the Processes of Freezing and Opening of Streams (Atlanticheskiye Vliyaniya na Protsessy Zamerzaniya i Vskrytiya Rek). Tr. GGI, no. 10. Voprosy Gidrolog. prognozov, Leningrad-Moscow, 1946.

Budagovskiy, A. I. The Absorption of Water by the Soil (Vpityvaniye Vody v Pochvu). Moscow, Izd-vo AN SSSR, 1955.

Budyko, M. I. The Heat Balance of the Earth's Surface (Teplovoy Balans Zemnoy Poverkhnosti). Gidrometeoizdat, Leningrad, 1956.

Velikanov, M. A. The Channel Process (Fundamentals of the Theory) (Ruslovoy Protsess [Osnovy Teorii]), Moscow,

Velikanov, M. A. The Hydrology of the Land (Gidrologiya Sushi), Leningrad, 1948.
    Fizmatgiz, 1958.

Vendrov, S. L. Change in the Maximum Runoff of Plains Streams due to the Transformation of Nature (Izmeneniye Maksimal'nogo Stoka Ravninnykh Rek v Svyazi s Preobrazovaniyem Prirody), Moscow, 1953.

Vernadskiy, V. I. The History of the Minerals of the Earth's Crust. vol. II, The History of Natural Waters (Istoriya Mineralov Zemnoy Kory. t. II, Istoriya Prirodnykh Vod), part. I, issue I, 1933.

Voyeykov, A. I. Man's Action upon Nature (Vozdeystviye Cheloveka na Prirodu). Geografgiz, Moscow, 1949.

Glushkov, V. G. "On Hydrology." Gidrol. vestn., 1915, No. 1.

Grigor'yev, A. A. "On some Geographic Laws of Heat Exchange and Water Exchange on the Surface of the Land and Paths of Further Study of the Exchange of Matter and Energy in the Geographic Environment." Izv. AN SSSR, seriya geogr., 1958, no. 3.

Davydov, L. K. The Volume of the Rivers of the USSR, its Fluctuation and the Influence of Physico-geographic Factors upon it. (Vodonosnost' Rek SSSR, yeye Kolebaniye i Vliyaniye na neye Fiziko-geograficheskikh Faktorov). Gidrometeoizdat, Leningrad, 1947.

Davydov, L. K. The Hydrography of the Rivers of the USSR (Gidrografiya Rek SSSR), parts I and II, publ. by Leningrad State Univ., 1953-1955.

Dubakh, A. D. The Forest as a Hydrological Factor (Les kak Gidrologicheskiy Faktor). Moscow, 1951.

Zaykov, B. "Mean Runoff and its Distribution in the Year over the Territory of the USSR." Tr. NIU GUGMS SSSR, seriya IV, no. 40, GGI, Leningrad, 1946.

Zaykov, B. D. Essays on Limnology (Ocherki po Ozerovedeniyu), Leningrad, 1955.

Ivanov, K. Ye. The Hydrology of Swamps (Gidrologiya Bolot). Leningrad, Gidrometeoizdat, 1953.

Kalinin, G. P. "The Fundamentals of the Technique of Short-range Forecasting of the Water Regime." *"Tr. TsIP,"* no. 28 (55).

Komarov, V. D. The Hydrological Analysis and Forecasting of Spring Floods in Plains Rivers *(Gidrologicheskiy Analiz i Prognoz Vesennego Polovod'ya Ravninnykh Rek)*. Leningrad, Gidrometeoizdat, 1955.

Lopatin, G. V. The Alluvial Deposits of the Rivers of the USSR *(Nanosy Rek SSSR)*. Moscow, Geografgiz, 1952.

L'vovich, M. I. "Elements of the Water Regime of the Rivers of the Globe", *Tr. NIU GUGMS SSSR,* seriya IV, no. 18, GGI, Sverdlovsk, Moscow, 1945.

Makkaveyev, N. I. The Bed of a River and the Erosion in its Basin *(Ruslo Reki i Eroziya v yeye Basseyne)*. Moscow, Izd-vo AN SSSR, 1955.

Molchanov, A. A. The Hydrological Role of Pine Forests on Sandy Soils *(Gidrologicheskaya Rol' Sosnovykh Lesov na Peschanykh Pochvakh)*. Moscow, 1952.

Ogiyevskiy, A. V. Hydrology of the Land *(Gidrologiya Sushi)*. Sel'khozgiz, 1952.

Ol'dekop, E. M. On the Evaporation from the Surface of River Basins *(Ob Isparenii s Poverkhnosti Rechnykh Basseynov)*. Yur'yev, 1911.

Polyakov, B. V. Hydrological Analysis and Estimates *(Gidrologicheskiy Analiz i Raschety)*. Gidrometeoizdat, 1946.

Popov, Ye. G. Hydrological Forecasts *(Gidrologicheskiye Prognozy)*. Leningrad, Gidrometeoizdat, 1957.

Samoylov, I. V. The Mouths of Rivers *(Ust'ya Rek)*. Moscow, Geografgiz, 1952.

Sokolovskiy, D. L. Stream Runoff *(Rechnoy Stok)*. Gidrometeoizdat, 1952.

Sribnyy, M. F. Calculation of the Maximum Shower Runoff *(Raschet Maksimal'nogo Livnevogo Stoka)*. Sbornik (Collection of articles) *Maksimal'nyy Stok s Malykh Basseynov* (Maximum Runoff from Small Basins). Transzheldorizdat, 1940.

Troitskiy, V. A. Hydrological Regionalization of the USSR *(Gidrologicheskoye Rayonirovaniye SSSR)*. Moscow, 1948.

Trudy Gidrometricheskoy Chasti Turkestanskogo Kraya (Works of the Hydrometric Department of the Turkestan Kray), 1911-1914.

Uryvayev, V. A. Experimental Hydrological Investigations in the Valday Hills *(Eksperimental'nyye Gidrologicheskiye Issledovaniya na Valdaye)*. Gidrometeoizdat, 1953.

Shamov, G. I. River Alluvial Deposits *(Rechnyye Nanosy)*. Leningrad, Gidrometeoizdat, 1954.

Shvets, V. I. The Distribution of the Runoff of the Streams of the Ukrainian SSR by Seasons and Months *(Raspredeleniye Stoka Rek USSR po Sezonam i Mesyatsam)*. Izd-vo AN USSR, 1946 (in Ukrainian).

Shnitnikov, A. V. The Variability of the Total Moisture of the Continents of the Northern Hemisphere *(Izmenchivost' Obshchey Uvlazhnennosti Materikov Severnogo Polushariya)*. Moscow-Leningrad, Izd-vo AN SSSR, 1957.

Shul'ts, V. A. The Rivers of Middle Asia *(Reki Sredney Azii)*. Geografgiz, Moscow, 1949.

CHAPTER 13

GEOMORPHOLOGY

S. Yu. Geller

The broad scope assumed by geomorphologic research in the last few decades in a number of countries, including the Soviet Union, and the ever-growing role of this research in the solution of important practical questions have led to a substantial overestimation of the significance of certain theoretical concepts that have long had scientific currency. Some investigators are inclined to regard this as a sign of an open crisis in geomorphology, whereas the revision of a number of its most important theories, which is taking place in our days, reflects in the main the inevitable and entirely normal course of the progressive development of science.

A revision of the basic scientific theories in this or that field of knowledge is usually accompanied by increased attention to the history of its development. In the process of such a revision there is, as a rule, a second birth of certain theoretical tenets that have apparently become hopelessly obsolete and have long since been filed away in the archives of science.

Among geomorphologists one has lately observed a definite intensification of attention to questions concerning the history of the study of the earth's relief. In spite of the unquestionable progress in this field, however, thorough coverage and the requisite objectivity are still far from having been attained in the evaluation of the whole aggregate of geomorphological investigations that have been conducted in the course of many decades by the scholars of various countries. The solution of this task encounters ever-growing difficulties: throughout an already long period there has been a sharp increase each year in the number of publications on questions of geomorphology, which naturally affects the possible completeness of any survey of the achievements in the study of the relief forms of the earth's surface. This could not fail to result, also, in a certain incompleteness of coverage and a certain amount of subjectivity in the choice of the most important works in the present examination of the general features of the development of geomorphology in the Soviet Union.

As a preliminary, let us dwell at least briefly upon the geomorphological investigations conducted by Russian scholars before the October Revolution. This will permit the reader to conceive more clearly the development of geomorphology in the USSR, successor to the research done in pre-Revolutionary Russia.

The most important propositions of geomorphology were clearly formulated almost two hundred years ago by the great Lomonosov (1763). For the first time in the history of science, he advanced the idea that the forms of the earth's surface were produced in the process of the interaction between internal (endogenic) and external (exogenic) forces. Stressing the necessity for studying relief in its development, M. V. Lomonosov paid especially great attention to tectonic processes, regarding them as the leading relief-forming factor. In his opinion, vertical movements — fast or slow, including oscillatory ones — play a decisive role in the formation of the face of the earth.

The notion of the great relief-forming significance of vertical movements was reflected in a book by the Russian Academician P. S. Pallas, published in German in St. Petersburg in 1777, which became widely known abroad.

Later the complete domination of the contraction theory for a long time almost entirely excluded the notion of the immense role of vertical movements in the creation of the earth's face. This was exactly what happened in the countries of Western Europe. In Russia, the fate of the concepts introduced into science by Lomonosov proved to be a different one. In the years during which the contraction theory flourished, the great role of oscillatory movements in the formation of relief was clearly demonstrated by N. A. Golovkinskiy (1869), and somewhat later it received a thorough foundation in the outstanding works of A. P. Karpinskiy (1883, 1887, 1894), A. P. Pavlov (1887, 1896, 1901, 1902, 1909), and F. Yu. Levinson-Lessing (1893). The works by A. P. Karpinskiy and A. P. Pavlov laid down the basic principles of modern morphotectonic analysis.

Along with the ascertainment of the character of the endogenic factors in the formation of relief, Russian scholars made a great contribution to the development of correct notions about the role of exogenic processes. Their investigations concerned almost all the principal factors of denudation and accumulation.

As is known, the proposition of the genetic relation of streams and valleys, worked out around the beginning of the 19th century by James Hutton and John Playfair, was abandoned for a long time, and the dominance of various fantastic views became established in world science. Not until almost three quarters of a century later was there a return to the correct conceptions. Among the first who addressed themselves to these were I. F. Levakovskiy (1869), V. V. Dokuchayev (1872, 1878), P. A. Kropotkin (1873, 1875), and I. D. Cherskiy (1878, 1882). Especially great contributions to the solution of this problem are the work by V. V. Dokuchayev, "Modes of Formation of the Stream Valleys of European Russia" [*Sposoby Obrazovaniya Rechnykh Dolin Yevropeyskoy Rosii*], as well as the numerous publications by S. N. Nikitin, which followed soon after its appearance, beginning in 1884, and in which the close genetic connection between rivers and their valleys was patently established for vast expanses of plains.

V. V. Dokuchayev introduced into science the important concept of the absolute and relative age of relief. In his works, he used terms that somewhat later gained wide distribution in conjunction with W. M. Davis's works: "senility," "maturity," "youth," and "infancy" of relief. He also contributed in a substantial degree to the elaboration of the concept of the types of relief, was one of the first to apply the quantitative-cartometric method in the study of ravine-and-gulch relief and gave concrete descriptions of the various types of erosional relief of plains. The relief types of mountain lands and the stages of their denudational development (for example in Eastern Siberia) were examined in the works by P. A. Kropotkin and I. D. Cherskiy.

The questions of the formation of plains relief under the action of surface and ground waters was extensively treated in a number of works by A. P. Pavlov, especially in his famous monograph, published in 1898. Alongside the examination of the activity of linear erosion, Pavlov gave a profound analysis of the relief-forming significance of the processes of sheet erosion, the products of which are deluvial deposits [*delyuvial'nyye otlozheniya*] (Pavlov's term). Pavlov paid great attention also to the morphological role of suffosion [*suffoziya*] (Pavlov's term), by which were originally meant both the carrying out of soluble substances by ground waters and the washing out of dust particles. Subsequently, the name proposed by Pavlov was retained only for the process of mechanical outwash by ground waters. With suffosion he particularly connected the formation of the gently sloping local sags of the earth's surface. These interesting thoughts of Pavlov's did not, however, receive wide distribution in pre-Revolutionary times. Russian scholars turned their attention somewhat later to the study of the action of ground waters on relief, particularly to the study of karst processes, and the development of these investigations here at home lagged for a rather long time behind similar investigations abroad. Not until shortly before the Revolution, in 1915, was A. A. Kruber's monograph published, which was devoted to an analysis of the development of karst in the Crimea. At about the same time (1916) was published the interesting work by A. D. Natskiy, examining the conditions of the occurrence of karst processes in the clay deposits of the Malyy Balkhan (Turkmenia).

Another major department of the study of exogenic relief-forming factors, in which important research was done by Russian scholars, is devoted to the relief of areas of ancient continental glaciation. As early as 1871, i.e., a year before the publication of the work by the Swedish scholar Otto Torell which gained world renown after its translation into German (1875), P. A. Kropotkin and F. B. Shmidt formulated the basic propositions of the problem of ancient glaciation which are now shared by almost all naturalists. And a short time later, in 1876, there appeared the generalizing work by P. A. Kropotkin which, in particular, gave a thorough treatment of the geological geomorphological methods of analyzing the traces of ancient ice caps.

Great attention was paid in Russia to the study of eolian processes. Let us recall the classic monograph by N. A. Sokolov, "Dunes, Their Formation, Development, and Internal Structure" [*Dyuny, ikh Obrazovaniye, Razvitiye i Vnutrenneye Stroyeniye*] (1884; the German translation was published in 1894), and the investigations made in the deserts of Middle Asia in the 1880's in connection with the tasks of fixing the sands (A. F. Middendorf, V. A. Nalivkin, V. A. Obruchev, and others). Let us note that Russian investigators have never taken such extreme stands in the evaluation of the action of the eolian factor upon desert relief as became very widespread in connection with Johannes Walther's well-known investigations.

Russian scholars joined rather late in the investigation of the morphology of seashores. But then, neither did these investigations lead to more or less considerable theoretical constructions in foreign countries during the 19th and early 20th centuries.

In discussing the study of exogenic factors and the relief forms caused by them it is necessary to mention the creation of the study of natural zones by V. V. Dokuchayev, around the beginning of the 20th century. It is this major scientific generalization that became the fundamental basis of investigations into questions of climatic (perhaps more correctly landscape) geomorphology, which has evolved so broadly in our days.

Finally, let us mention the work on geomorphological regionalization done in our country in the pre-Revolutionary years. The series of proposed systems of regionalization may be united into two main groups, differing sharply in their approach to the solution of the problem. One of them includes schemes for division of the territory based chiefly on the differences in the occurrence of relief-forming processes in the Quaternary (Nikitin, 1886; Semenov-Tyan-Shanskiy, 1915; and Laskarev, 1916). The other group of regionalization schemes is based on a division of the territory into morphotectonic areas; such, for example, is the regionalization of Asiatic Russia proposed by L. S. Berg (1913).

The above survey of geomorphological investigations made in Russia before the Revolution is, of course, not complete; it gives only a most general characterization of the main trends and the names of only a few scholars — chiefly those whose scientific activity led to the creation of the trends mentioned. The circle of investigators actively working in the field of geomorphology was incomparably broader (Markov, 1948; Tikhomirov and Khain, 1956; Nikolayev, 1958). However, it is obvious from the foregoing that Russian scholars have made a large contribution to the development of this science. They created and successfully developed most important trends in it. One may speak of a wholly independent Russian geomorphological school with no less basis than, for example, of an American, a German or a French school. Entirely ungrounded, of course, are the attempts to affirm that geomorphology was founded in the Soviet Union on a nearly empty spot; it has developed in possession of a great scientific heritage.

After 1917, there was a radical shift in our country in the approach to the study of natural conditions and natural resources. With the establishment of Soviet rule, the organization and conduct of these investigations became an important state concern. This naturally led to the introduction of the planning principle into science, and to the organization of systematic investigations by large scientific collectives, which supplanted the scattered and sometimes casual work performed by individual scholars.

First of all, geomorphology in young Soviet Russia had to accumulate concrete factual material characterizing the relief of the country as a whole. The extent to which it had been studied in this respect was extremely inadequate. For vast territories of Siberia, Kazakhstan, Middle Asia, and the northern part of European Russia the necessary data were lacking even for compiling hypsometric survey maps, to say nothing of special-purpose, properly geomorphological materials. The results of the study of the country's relief made during a number of decades have been set forth in a summary by G. I. Tanfil'yev (1922-1923).

The evolution of the geomorphological study of the vast territory of our country required from the very beginning preparation of special corps of researchers. As early as 1918 the first geographic higher educational institution in the world, the Geographic Institute, was created in our country, and soon a geomorphological department was organized in it with a broad program of instruction, including, in addition to the general geographic and general geologic disciplines, a number of special subjects — the geology of Quaternary deposits, geochemistry, volcanology, and so forth. Major scholars were engaged to give lectures: L. S. Berg, A. P. Gerasimov, V. G. Glushkov, A. A. Grigor'yev,

I. D. Lukashevich, N. I. Kuznetsov, D. V. Nalivkin, S. S. Neustroyev, V. N. Sukachev, M. M. Tetyayev, A. Ye. Fersman, Yu. M. Shokal'skiy, and Ya. S. Edel'shteyn. The geomorphology course was originally given by I. D. Lukashevich, and later by M. M. Tetyayev and Ya. S. Edel'shteyn. Especially fruitful was the activity over many years of Ya. S. Edel'shteyn, whose pupils include many Soviet geomorphologists. Under the direction of A. A. Borzov, B. F. Dobrynin, and I. S. Shchukin, geomorphology began in these same years to be actively developed also at Moscow State University, where a large university geomorphological school was soon created. At present, geomorphology courses are given in dozens of the higher educational institutions of the country. The largest geomorphology chairs are in the geographic faculties of Moscow, Leningrad, and Kiyev universities.

The teaching of geomorphology in the higher schools was at first complicated by the lack of textbooks and teaching aids. The first short course was a book by Ya. S. Edel'shteyn issued in 1932 in lithographed form; considerably enlarged and revised, it has been twice re-published, in 1938 and in 1947. In 1934-1938, I. S. Shchukin's fundamental university textbook was published; in 1945 appeared the Russian translation of the corresponding section of Emmanuel de Martonne's "Physical Geography" *(Traité de Géographie Physique)*; in 1948, K. K. Markov's "Basic Problems of Geomorphology" [*Osnovnyye Problemy Geomorfologii*]; and in 1949, V. G. Bondarchuk's book, "Fundamentals of Geomorphology" [*Osnovy Geomorfologii*]. The publication of these books has greatly facilitated the taking of the geomorphology course, and has also contributed to the considerable spread of basic knowledge about this branch of natural science.

Investigations to ascertain the general character of the relief of vast, almost unexplored territories, which have been widely conducted since the middle 20's, have, in the space of about fifteen years, covered millions of square kilometers, principally in the Far East, in Eastern, Middle, and Western Siberia, Kazakhstan, Middle Asia, and the north of the European part of the USSR. Of the greatest significance have been the great integrated expeditions of the Academy of Sciences of the USSR, the expeditions of the All-Russian Geologic Institute (former Geologic Committee), of the State Hydrologic Institute, of Leningrad and Moscow universities, and of the territorial geologic administrations.

The clarification of the main features of the relief of the Soviet Union has been greatly promoted by the extensive surveying and map-compiling work of the Chief Administration of Geodesy and Cartography, which in the early 30's began to make wide use of aerial photogrammetry in practical field work.

As a result of this expeditionary and office work, in which hundreds of researchers participated, the accumulation of primary factual material for the characterization of the relief of the Soviet Union had been mainly completed in the pre-War years. Comparatively large "blank spots" were left only in the extreme north and northeast of the country.

One of the generalizations of all the work performed was the geomorphological regionalization worked out not long before the War by a large group of investigators united by the Institute of Geography of the Academy of Sciences of the USSR under the general guidance of A. A. Grigor'yev and K. K. Markov. The War, however, interfered with the due publication of this collective monograph, which did not come out until 1947. Another major scientific generalizing work was that of I. P. Gerasimov and K. K. Markov on the glacial epoch on the territory of the USSR (1939), in which much attention was paid to the development of the relief in the Quaternary.

The preliminary results of the geomorphological study of individual large territories of the country were reflected in brief summaries, published in the 30's, on the relief of the West-Siberian Lowland, the Minusinsk Basin, the Middle-Siberian Plateau, the Kyzylkum, the Karakums, the Pamir, and certain other regions. Considerably later, after the Great Patriotic War, began the publication of generalizing scientific monographs on the relief of certain major territories of the Soviet Union (the Urals, the Tyan'-Shan', and the Northeast of Siberia), in which the results of the investigations made chiefly in the twenty years before the War are summarized.

Alongside the execution of the great work program of a survey character, scientific methodological large-scale geomorphological investigations were conducted in the 20's and 30's, though only to a comparatively small extent, into certain comparatively limited territories, for example the Leningrad oblast (Yakovlev, 1925; Markov, 1931), in the Mari ASSR (Dobrynin, 1933), in the basin of the Dnepr (a number of works by B. L. Lichkov, published from 1926 on), in the Caucasus (investigations by A. L. Reyngard, V. P. Rengarten, S. S. Kuznetsov, L. A. Vardanyanets, and others), and in other areas.

Of incomparably larger scope was the detailed morphologic work performed under assignments from economic organizations in conjunction with the solution of concrete practical problems.

Already in 1919, geomorphologists were being engaged to take part in surveying for northern railroads. Almost from the very beginning of the evolution of the great program of surveying and cartographic work, in the 20's, geomorphologists under the general direction of A. A. Borzov also took an active part in them. Soon, specialists with these qualifications were being consulted in connection with the exploring and projecting work for the erection of the Volkhov Hydroelectric Station. This first positive experience in close collaboration by geomorphologists with surveyors and planners was later widely used in similar work connected with the erection of the hydroelectric plants on the Svir', the Dnepr, the Volga, and other rivers of the Soviet Union. Around the beginning of the 30's, the participation of geomorphologists in railroad surveying (the Turkestan-Siberian and Baykal-Amur trunklines, and others) was expanded. At about this same time geomorphologists joined in work connected with the preparations for building navigation and irrigation canals. In the 30's, there was a considerable expansion of geomorphological work connected with working out measures to combat soil erosion, with questions of seashore reinforcement and port construction, with prospecting and exploration for placers, with exploration for ground waters, etc.

However, one must not draw a more or less sharp line between the work of a survey character and the detailed investigations executed by assignment from various economic organizations: theoretically, they have supplemented one another. Broader structures (broader with respect to the territory covered) have been controlled by a detailed study of limited regions, and the conclusions reached on the basis of detailed investigations have gained wide scientific currency soon after comparison with the data on the study of extensive areas. This is what happened, for example, with the investigations made for the Volkhovstroy project by N. N. Sokolov (1926), whose conclusions were widely reflected in the further study of glacial geomorphology over vast areas of the northern half of the European part of the USSR. The investigations of the movement of alluvial deposits made on the Black Sea by P. K. Bozhich (1927) substantially determined the direction of the further development of the theory of the formation of seashores, the detailed studies of placer deposits led to the elaboration of the general theory of placers (Bilibin, 1938), and so forth. Still, geomorphological work of a survey nature has not been confined to scientific-research tasks. As a rule, such investigations were to give a characterization and evaluation of the relief for the purpose of harnessing the productive forces of major territories.

The close relation to practical questions has thus, from the very beginning, been an important feature of Soviet geomorphology. This relation is clearest in the work of the geologic organizations, which are introducing geomorphology more and more widely into the practice of surveying, prospecting, and exploring work. This is entirely understandable, inasmuch as geomorphology is a geologic-geographic science. Let us note incidentally that the position of geomorphology in the system of natural sciences has, in the USSR, never been the subject of sharp discussion, as is the case, for instance, in the United States of America, where certain investigators even attempt to divide a single science into geographic and geologic geomorphology. This, however, does not mean that there are among Soviet geomorphologists no individual investigators who are inclined to assign geomorphology either to geography alone or to geology alone.

The bonds between geomorphology and geology in the Soviet Union have been especially strengthened in recent years. One of the indications of this strengthening of the contacts between the two allied scientific disciplines is the fact that the geomorphological work embracing the most territory is being conducted in the system of the Ministry of Geology and Conservation of the Mineral Resources of the USSR by the All-Union Aerogeologic Trust and by the territorial geologic administrations. The instructions on the state geologic survey to a scale of 1:200,000 provide for the obligatory making of geomorphological observations "to elucidate the origin and development of relief, as well as to evaluate the prospects for a search for minerals connected with the processes of relief formation." The instructions also provide that "in regions of development of placers the geomorphological observations will be intensified in the search for placer deposits by geomorphological prospecting and surveying work (special geomorphological parties under special instructions)." The questions of the application of geomorphology in practice are dealt with in a book by T. V. Zvonkova (1959), in which this topic is discussed chiefly on the basis of work experience in the USSR.

The central theoretical question of geomorphology — the relationship between the endogenic and the exogenic factors in the formation of the face of the earth — have long since ceased to present a problem in its general form. The definite correspondence between the basic features of orography and the chief tectonic subdivisions of the globe was already established beyond a doubt many years ago. However, the degree of this correspondence, largely reflecting the character of the interaction between the endogenic and the exogenic factors in the process of relief development, has still been very poorly studied for major territories even in its general features. From this viewpoint, the recently published works of I. P. Gerasimov (1958, 1959), giving an analysis of the relationships between the features of the morphology of the USSR and its major structural elements, presents substantial interest. These relationships are examined in the light of the data on the age of the principal tectonic movements for this or that territory. The results of the comparison made by I. P. Gerasimov have shown that in a number of major regions like-type tectonic movements and structures are not reflected alike in the relief when there is a difference in their ages. It may be supposed that further investigations in this direction — the study of the development of the relief of a territory in conjunction with the history of its tectonic regime and the formation of various tectonic structures in different stages — will furnish important material for judging the concrete relationships between the roles of the endogenic and exogenic factors in the formation of relief and accordingly will substantially enhance the significance of geomorphological methods in the search for minerals, taking into account the connectons, long since noted by A. Ye. Fersman (1932, 1934), between the distribution of geochemical concentrations, on the one hand, and the tectonic structure and denudational processes, on the other.

As early as the 1920's, considerably increased attention was paid in the USSR to the study of the connections between relief and tectonics, particularly tectonic movements in Recent time, in the establishment of which a leading role often went precisely to the geomorphological method. Of great significance for the evolution of these investigations were the works of V. A. Obruchev, who in 1914-1915 established the fact that the main features of the contemporaneous relief of Transbaykalia and the Altay were created by Recent vertical movements accompanied by disjunctive dislocations on an immense scale. This outstanding geologist and geographer devoted to the problem of Recent movements a large number of works, published in the course of more than four decades — down to the end of his scientific activity (he died in 1956). His ideas about the great significance of these movements in the formation of the contemporaneous relief of Siberia have long since become widely known abroad, following the publication in German of Obruchev's monograph, "The Geology of Siberia" (1926). Ten years later his article "The Youth of the Relief of Siberia" [*Molodost' rel'yefa Sibiri*], appeared, and in 1948 Obruchev emphasized that "...neotectonics fully explains all the characteristics of the contemporaneous relief of the land surface of the entire globe...," meaning by neotectonics [*neotektonika*] (Obruchev's term) "...structures of the earth's crust created by the youngest movements, which occurred at the end of the Tertiary and in the first half of the Quaternary period." Thus, according to Obruchev, Recent tectonic movements are characterized by two features: the definite time of their occurrence and their leading role in the creation of present-day relief.

This conception, though widely shared, has not become generally accepted among Soviet geomorphologists and geologists. A number of investigators assign to the Recent only the movements of the Quaternary period; others, those of the Neogene-Quaternary. Moreover, not a few geologists and geomorphologists follow S. S. Shul'ts (1937, 1948, 1958) and regard as Recent only those movements which actively create the main features of contemporaneous relief, essentially renouncing a chronological interpretation of these movements. This is motivated by the fact that "...the age of young tectonic movements, often inherited from older ones, is very difficult to determine..." Such an interpretation, moreover, does not, as a rule, introduce any fundamental distinctions into the practice of investigation by comparison with a study conducted on the basis of the definition formulated by V. A. Obruchev, as in these investigations the Recent movements are usually confined to the Neogene-Quaternary. This is confirmed, in particular, by one of the best Soviet works in the field of regional geomorphology, the monograph by S. S. Shul'ts (1948), in which the abundant material on the Recent tectonics of the Tyan'-Shan' is limited to the Neogene-Quaternary.

Among the mountain areas of the Soviet Union, those that have been studied in most detail with respect to neotectonics are the Tyan'-Shan' (Kaletskaya, Avsyuk, and Matveyev, 1945, 1953) and the Altay, as well as the Caucasus and the Urals (Varsanof'yeva, 1932, etc., "Materials on the Geomorphology of the Urals," 1948; Bashenina, 1948). These territories are the subjects of a considerable number of investigations which have reliably substantiated the concept of the great range of the neotectonic movements that played a leading role in the formation of the relief of these mountain areas. Only for the Urals does the relief-forming role of neotectonic movements still remain an object of lively discussion, substantially reflecting the inadequate elaboration of the theoretical and methodological approaches to the study of the so-called mountain denudational levels or planation surfaces. This manifests itself in the various interpretations of the origin of the latter, in the choice of criteria for establishing their age and accordingly the identification of the planation surfaces of the same age situated at different altitudes and having definite differences in their geologic and geomorphological structure. However, in many cases detailed integrated investigations for individual small territories have led to indisputable conclusions permitting a correct orientation of prospecting work, for example in the Urals, in the southern Tyan'-Shan', and in other regions.

Alongside investigations of Recent tectonic movements in mountain areas, where these movements naturally manifest themselves with especial clarity, the study of them has also been widely developed on the vast plains expanses of the USSR. These investigations have been most extensive on the Russian Plain, being stimulated to a considerable extent by the great scope of hydro-power construction and the search for oil and gas. Among the numerous works devoted to clarification of the Recent tectonics in the Russian Plain, which to a very substantial extent repose upon geographic methods, the most important are B. L. Lichkov (1927, 1931, 1933, 1941), and others, V. P. Vyrzhikovskiy (1936), S. S. Sobolev (1939), Ya. D. Zekkel' (1945), V. V. Lomakin (1945), N. I. Nikolayev (1947, 1948, 1949, and others), K. I. Gerenchuk (1948, 1950, 1955, and others), P. K. Zamoriy (1950), Yu. A. Meshcheryakov (1950, 1951, 1953, 1954 and others), B. V. Selivanovskiy (1950, 1952), G. V. Vakhrushev and A. P. Rozhdestvenskiy (1953), and others.

The study of the longitudinal profiles of river terraces and channels, the so-called spectrum of river terraces, the configuration of the hydrographic network, the ravine-and-gulch relief, as well as detailed investigations of the alluvial strata, with the distinction of channel and floodplain facies in them, are becoming important methods for establishing the regions of Recent tectonic movements, their algebraic sign and, in some cases, also the amplitudes of the fluctuations. These methods are now beginning to be widely applied also to reveal local tectonic structures and, as shown by the regional conferences held in 1959 at Novosibirsk and Ufa, they are being used more and more intensively in prospecting practice. Especially promising is the application of geomorphological methods, in combination with geologic, geophysic, cartographic, and sometimes geodetic methods (repeated levelings), to discover active structures in oil and gas bearing regions.

The first generalizing summary on the Recent tectonics of the territory of the USSR was published by N. I. Nikolayev in 1949. The results of the treatment of this problem, including also a considerable part of the results of the investigations during the last decade, are reflected in the map of the Recent tectonics of the USSR prepared to scale of 1:5,000,000 by a large group of structural geologists and geomorphologists under the general direction of N. I. Nikolayev and S. S. Shul'ts.

Closely connected with the study of the Recent tectonic movements are the investigations, begun in the last few years, into the youngest, so-called contemporaneous tectonic movements. These investigations, conducted jointly by the Institute of Geography of the Academy of Sciences of the USSR, the Main Administration of Geodesy and Cartography, and the Main Hydrographic Administration, repose on geomorphological, geodetic, and sea-level observations. Of very great significance is the making of repeated high-precision levelings, the results of which are accompanied by a geologic geomorphological interpretation. An important element of this work is the geologic geomorphological evaluation of the conditions under which bench marks are placed. The preliminary results of these investigations over a considerable part of the European territory of the USSR and the shores of the seas surrounding it are summarized in a collection of articles published under the editorship of I. P. Gerasimov and Yu. V. Filippov (1958), and giving in particular the magnitudes of the uplifts and subsidence and the areas of their occurrence, as ascertained on the basis of work on a number of profiles, as well as on the shores of the Black and Baltic Seas.

The study of contemporaneous vertical movements is not only of great scientific interest, but also has an immediate practical outlet, permitting the markers of the supporting geodetic network to be located correctly. In combination with the extensive complex of work on neotectonics, the ascertainment of the rates and algebraic signs of contemporaneous movements permits a more precise contouring both of major territories with young movements of similar character and of individual local structures, and consequently it may become one of the real methods of exploration for minerals, particularly oil and gas.

We shall begin our survey of the studies made in the USSR of the activity of the exogenic relief-forming factors with the works devoted to water erosion and accumulation, one of the most important topics and one of the most favored by geomorphologists. It goes without saying that we shall have to confine ourselves to a brief discussion of only a few questions.

First of all, let us make some general remarks. In our country, the division of geomorphology which studies erosion and deposition processes by water is especially closely connected with practice. All the major investigations have been conducted and are being conducted to solve entirely concrete economic problems: the erection of hydroelectric stations and the digging of canals, the exploitation of river systems for transportation purposes, the control of ravine erosion and sheet erosion of the soil, the working out of measures to combat flash floods, the establishment of prospecting signs for alluvial placers, etc.

Secondly, since the very beginning of the evolution of these investigations, the most important have been made jointly by geomorphologists and hydrologists. It is characteristic that it was in the State Hydrologic Institute (Leningrad), created in 1919 under the direction of the outstanding hydrologist V. G. Glushkov, that the largest scientific center in the country at that time for the investigation of the morphology of river channels arose shortly after the organization of that institute. At present, however, the largest investigations of river-bed relief are made by the hydrotechnical designing institutes. Perhaps not a single one of the divisions of geomorphology has come so close to apparently purely engineering questions as the study of the relief-forming activity of running water, and it is not surprising that a number of investigations made in this field are engineering-geomorphological in character. The combination of geomorphologic and hydrologic methods in studying water erosional and depositional processes is also acquiring ever-greater significance in the works of French geomorphologists, who rely extensively upon the laws established in hydrology (see the works of Pierre Birot, André Cailleux, Jean Tricart, etc., as well as the work done in the United States of America by Luna B. Leopold and others).

The study of the processes of water erosion and deposition is made under the very wide range of physical geographic conditions represented on the territory of the Soviet Union. This circumstance is of great importance, since, along with the ascertainment of the general laws, it permits the establishment of substantial deviations from them due to the specific nature of this or that landscape.

To characterize the geomorphologic-hydrologic approach predominant among us in the study of water erosion and deposition processes, let us dwell upon the monograph by N. I. Makkaveyev (1955), which summarizes the results of a large number of investigations in this area. The analysis of the processes of river-bed formation is based by this investigator upon an integrated study, the leading elements of which are to an equal extent both geomorphology and hydrology. Makkaveyev formulates his most general conclusion in the following manner: "...the magnitude and the regime of the runoff directly affect the relief form of the bed, and inasmuch as the runoff is the 'product' of the landscape of the drainage basin, this 'product' is, in the last analysis, also the relief of the bed." The idea embodied in this formulation is essentially not a new one. But it is precisely this idea, advanced in its general form by V. V. Dokuchayev, that afforded the fundamental basis for numerous investigations, the results of which imparted considerable concreteness to this formulation. The generalization of the immense volume of material enabled Makkaveyev to give a thorough analysis of the formation of the basic elements of the relief of the bed—its longitudinal profile, floodplain, bends, and rapids. The results of this analysis, based on a consideration of the various combinations of the natural and, to a certain extent, on the anthropogenic factors of the river-bed process, have gained substantial forecasting significance and have been widely admitted into the practice of channel-rectifying work on streams and navigable canals.

The geomorphological-hydrologic approach also determines to a substantial extent the character of the investigations made during a number of years in conjunction with the elaboration of measures for combating soil and ravine erosion. In these investigations, the study of the soil and vegetation conditions is also acquiring a large role (investigations by D. L. Armand, I. P. Gerasimov, G. V. Zanin, A. S. Kes', A. S. Kozmenko, S. S. Sobolev, and others).

In contrast to this trend, which pays main attention to the study of water-erosion processes, a considerable number of investigations are devoted to the structure and origin of fluvial deposits, as well as the relief forms produced by them. These investigations are based to a considerably higher degree on methods of facies analysis.

The division into the above aspects is, of course, conventional to a certain extent and mainly reflects the content of the numerous investigations on comparatively specialized questions. The decision of general problems, as a rule, reposes on a broader methodological foundation. Thus, in the above mentioned monograph by N. I. Makkaveyev, considerable attention is also paid to to the facies characteristics of the alluvial strata, and in the investigation by Ye. V. Shantser (1951), the basis of which is precisely facies analysis, considerable space is assigned to an examination of the relations between the chief subdivisions of the alluvium (channel and floodplain) and the various conditions of the hydrologic regime. On the whole, however, no sufficiently complete combination of the various methodological procedures has as yet been attained in the study of the single fluvial process and the erosional and depositional forms created by it.

The combination of geomorphological and facies investigations has had wide practical application in prospecting work on alluvial placer deposits. The important role of the geomorphological method in the practice of this work has long since been recognized. But the profound theoretical basis for the necessity of this method as the foundation for prospecting and exploring for placers was first set forth in 1938 by Yu. A. Bilibin. His book showed, in particular, the significance of W. M. Davis's theory of the erosional cycle in determining the main ways of searching for placer deposits. Of essential significance in prospecting work are the ideas worked out by V. V. Lamakin (1943, 1944, 1947, 1948, 1950) about the so-called dynamic phases of river valleys and alluvial deposits. According to Lamakin, placers essentially form an integral part of residual deposits (perluvium) [perlyuviy]. Lately, much attention has been paid to the study of the relation between the natural enrichment of placers and the character of the equilibrium profile (I. P. Kartashov, M. V. Piotrovskiy, Ye. Ya. Sinyugin), and to the relation of placer deposits to neotectonics (A. I. Grigor'yev, Yu. P. Kazakevich).

In connection with the exploitation of mineral placers, great importance attaches to the further development of paleogeomorphological investigations, which have already led to a number of interesting conclusions, chiefly in the study of the fossil hydrographic network. The most substantial results, in our opinion, have been yielded by the investigations of B. L. Lichkov (1933, 1936) and G. I. Goretskiy (1947), and others.

Based on a detailed study of the geologic materials on the Dnepr region and on a comparison of them with the materials on the Russian Plain, Lichkov has come to the conclusion that the main features of its surface hydrography are very old, a number of its elements having been laid down in the Paleozoic. It is very probable that the ancient deposition of the basic elements of the hydrographic network represents a general law for platforms and possibly for shields. And if the formation of oil and gas deposits is connected with paleo-rivers, particularly with their deltas, it is obviously advisable to regard the present-day river valleys as inherited and to study the laws of the present surface hydrography in connection with the problem of oil and gas bearing. It is not out of the question that such investigations will lead to the establishment of still another prospecting indicator of these minerals.

The investigations by G. I. Goretskiy, based on extensive materials gathered during detailed surveys for the erection of hydroelectric stations, are devoted mainly to the establishment of a plan of the pre-Quaternary hydrographic network over considerable expanses of the Russian Plain. These investigations have led to important practical conclusions permitting an evaluation of the conditions for the construction of hydrotechnical works depending upon the character of the relationships in the patterns of contemporaneous and ancient valleys. Especially important are such relationships in karst regions, where favorable conditions for the building of dams and canals are created only in the case of a definite arrangement in the plan of contemporaneous and ancient valleys.

Since the War, the study of karst processes, as well as suffosion processes, has been substantially expanded, chiefly in connection with hydrotechnical, urban, and road construction. In 1950, "Karst" was published by N. A. Gvozdetskiy, devoted to questions of general karst science [karstovedeniye]. The Commission for the Study of Karst was organized in 1958 under the Division of Geologic-Geographic Sciences of the Academy of Sciences of the USSR to coordinate the investigations being made by the various institutions and the general scientific-methodological direction of them.

A considerable number of works are being published on the questions of the genesis of glacial relief. A great amount of material has been accumulated on the geologic structure of the various glacial forms, but much is still unclear as to the mechanism of their formation. The work by K. K. Markov (1931) still remains the most important investigation in this field.

Mention should be made of the development, in the last few years, of investigations into the geomorphology of regions with permafrost (works by S. P. Kachurin, A. I. Popov, and others). Main attention is being paid to questions of the genesis of the various elements of micro-relief.

Study of the relief forms of sand formations has been conducted principally in the deserts of Middle Asia and Kazakhstan. A large number of data have been gathered to illustrate the character of the eolian transfer of sandy material, the forms of primary sandy eolian accumulations, and also, in part, the composition of deposits making up the individual elements of the relief of sandy deserts. However, a generally recognized scheme of the formation and development of sand relief is still lacking. Most widespread among us is the concept worked out by B. A. Fedorovich (1940, 1946, 1948), and others, according to which the various forms of sand relief distinguished by this investigator correspond to wind-regime conditions specific for them. The origin of the most widespread type of continental sand formations—the ridge sands—is explained by B. A. Fedorovich from a standpoint close to that once set forth in explaining the origin of similar formations in the Thar Desert (Thomas Oldham), the Sahara (L. Aufrère), and Australia (C. T. Madigan).

We shall dwell in somewhat greater detail on the investigations of the morphology of seashores. An increase in the attention to this problem in conjunction with port-construction questions was noted in the 1920's, but these investigations were not widely developed until after the War. In the Institute of Oceanology of the Academy of Sciences of the USSR a special scientific center has arisen—the Laboratory for the Study of the Morphology of Seashores. The geomorphologists of the Geography Faculty of Moscow University have participated actively in working out the problem. The work done by local organizations, especially on the Black Sea coast, has gained wide scope and a study of the shores of major reservoirs has also been developed. At present, the numerous investigations of this problem are coordinated by a special subcommission forming a part of the Oceanologic Commission of the Academy of Sciences of the USSR.

The development of this field of geomorphology is determined, however, not so much by the rapid growth of the number of investigations as by the achievements in the treatment of theoretical and methodological questions. The trend which is developing in this country is based on the proposition that the development of the shore is due primarily to the relief of its underwater part as well as to the regime of the alluvial deposits entering a given section. Naturally, this proposition has necessitated a radical revision of the methods of studying seashores. Unlike the ideas developed by William Morris Davis and especially Douglas W. Johnson, which have prevailed until recently, the decisive role is assigned to processes occurring in the coastal strip of the sea floor. It is to a detailed study of this part of the shore profile that the special attention of investigators has been addressed.

This proposition was first based in detail in the monograph by V. P. Zenkovich (1946). Further investigation has shown that under various conditions of formation of seashores these processes take different courses. The results and generalization of the work of many investigators in in this direction have been set forth in the books by O. K. Leont'yev (1955) and V. P. Zenkovich (1958). In the last few years great significance in the practice of seashore investigation has been attached to the application of hydrodynamic methods, which have led to interesting theoretical conclusions. These, it is true, have not yet been carried to the point where it is possible to obtain estimate data (Longinov, 1956, 1957).

The results of the investigations of seashores are also being widely used in studying the reservoirs built on USSR territory. In particular, the results have acquired substantial significance in evaluating the trends in the reshaping of reservoir shores.

The questions of the methods of compiling geomorphological maps, which synthesize the theoretical ideas to a considerable extent and reflect the degree to which the relief of a territory has been studied, were treated in detail some years ago in a book by A. I. Spiridonov (1952). These questions, especially in the last few years, have become the object of lively discussion. A specially created interdepartmental commission has concerned itself with them for several years. One result of the work in this direction is the geomorphological map of the USSR to a scale of 1:4,000,000, recently compiled by a large group under the direction of I. P. Gerasimov, B. A. Fedorovich, and I. P. Zarutskaya. This map, constructed on the morphogenetic principle, represents a definite basis for an understanding of the character and origin of the main features of the relief of the country's territory, as well as for further investigations into questions of the methods of compiling geomorphological maps. At the same time, its contents show beyond a doubt that taking into account the multiplicity of relief forms and relief-forming factors on one map, even a large-scale one, is a task that is hardly solvable in practice. At the present time, along with the improvement of the contents of the synthetic maps, clear-cut criteria are being ascertained which are needed to reflect, on special-purpose geomorphological maps, the particular geomorphological characteristics and laws.

In appraising the development of Soviet geomorphology as a whole, it is possible to note very substantial achievements, both in the treatment of a number of theoretical propositions and in the establishment of close ties with practice. Specific organizational measures have played an important role in this respect: (a) the creation of large scientific centers in the individual research institutes and universities (in the Institutes of Geography and Oceanology of the Academy of Sciences of the USSR, in the institutions of the Ministry of Geology and Conservation of the Mineral Wealth of the USSR— the All-Union Geologic Institute and the Institute of the Geology of the Arctic—, in the geographic faculties of Moscow, Leningrad, and Kiyev universities, etc.); (b) the creation of an extensive network of specialized scientific collectives in the individual localities—as a part of the republic academies of sciences, in the territorial geological adminstrations, in the higher educational institutions; (c) the holding of a number of conferences on both general and particular questions of geomorphology.

The achievements would be still more appreciable if it were not for the definite lag in the publication of the results of investigations, which naturally hampers the development of the science and the practical application of new theoretical propositions. Despite the fact that no fewer generalizing monographs have been published during the last ten to twelve years than during the whole preceding thirty years, the number of such publications is still not sufficient. This fact reveals a certain underestimation of the role of digests summarizing the investigations, in the light of which one is able to determine the next tasks with considerably greater accuracy, to establish new forms of relationship to allied disciplines, and to eliminate duplication.

Such is the situation in the field of both topical and regional investigations. Thus far, an enormous amount of material gathered in the process of studying the relief of the USSR has not yet been generalized for a number of major territories. In addition to those mentioned, only a few large regional digests have been published in the last few years: on the Baykal mountain area (Dumitrashko, 1952), the European part of the USSR (Karandeyev, 1957), and Azerbaydzhan (1959).

The creation of a fundamental monograph on the geomorphology of the USSR should be regarded as one of the most important first-priority tasks of Soviet geomorphologists. The solution of this task is now unquestionably facilitated by the organization, in 1959, of the Geomorphological Commission under the Division of Geologic-Geographic Sciences of the Academy of Sciences of the USSR, under whose jurisdiction is the general coordination of the geomorphological investigations conducted in the Soviet Union and the scientific-methodical supervision of these investigations.

BASIC LITERATURE

Bashenina, N. V. The Origin of the Relief of the Southern Urals *(Proiskhozhdeniye Rel'yefa Yuzhnogo Urala).* Moscow, Geografgiz, 1948.

Bilibin, Yu. A. Fundamentals of the Geology of Placers *(Osnovy Geologii Rossypey).* 2nd ed., Moscow, AN SSSR, 1955.

Bondarchuk, V. G. Fundamentals of Geomorphology *(Osnovy Geomorfologii).* Moscow, Uchpedgiz, 1949.

Gvozdetskiy, N. A. *Karst.* 2nd ed., Moscow, Geografgiz, 1954.

Geomorfologicheskoye Rayonirovaniye SSSR (Geomorphologic Regionalization of the USSR) (under the editorship of A. A. Grigor'yev and K. K. Markov). *Tr. Komissii po Yestestv.-istor. Rayonirovaniyu SSSR,* vol. II, issue I, Moscow-Leningrad, izd-vo AN SSSR, 1947.

Geomorfologiya Azerbaydzhanskoy SSR (Geomorphology of the Azerbaydzhan SSR) (chief. ed. M. M. Kashkay). Baku, AN Azerb. SSR, 1959.

Gerasimov, I. P. The structural features of the relief of the Earth's crust on the territory of the USSR and their origin (Strukturnyye cherty rel'yefa zemnoy poverkhnosti na territorii SSSR i ikh proiskhozhdeniye). Moscow, Izd-vo AN SSSR, 1959.

Dumitrashko, N. V. The Geomorphology and Paleogeography of the Baykal Mountain Area *(Geomorfologiya i Paleogeografiya Baykal'skoy Gornoy Oblasti).* Moscow, Izd-vo AN SSSR, 1952.

Zvonkova, T. V. The Study of Relief for Practical Purposes *(Izucheniye Rel'yefa v Prakticheskikh TSelyakh).* Moscow, Geografgiz, 1959.

Zenkovich, V. P. The Dynamics and Morphology of Seashores *(Dinamika i Morfologiya Morskikh Beregov).* Moscow-Leningrad, izd-vo "Morskoy transport," 1946.

Zenkovich, V. P. The Morphology and Dynamics of the Soviet Shores of the Black Sea *(Morfologiya i Dinamika Sovetskikh Beregov Chernogo Morya).* Moscow, izd-vo AN SSSR, 1958.

Kaletskaya, M. S., Avsyuk, G. A., and Matveyev, S. N. The Mountains of Southeastern Kazakhstan *(Gory Yugo-vostochnogo Kazakhstana).* Alma-Ata, AN KazSSR, 1945.

Karandeyeva, M. V. The Geomorphology of the European Part of the USSR *(Geomorfologiya Yevropeyskoy Chasti SSSR).* (izd-vo-MGU Moscow State Univ.), 1959.

Leont'yev, O. K. The Geomorphology of the Sea Shores and Bottom *(Geomorfologiya Morskikh Beregov i Dna),* izd-vo MGU (Moscow State University), 1955.

Lichkov, B. L. "Some Features of the Geomorphology of the European Part of the USSR." *"Tr. Geol. In-ta AN SSSR,"* no. I, Leningrad, 1931.

Makkaveyev, N. I. The Bed of a River and the Erosion in its Basin *(Ruslo Reki i Eroziya v yeye Basseyne).* Moscow, AN SSSR, 1955.

Markov, K. K. "The Development of the Relief of the Northwestern Part of Leningrad Oblast" (Razvitiye Rel'yefa Severo-zapadnoy Chasti Leningradskoy Oblasti). *Tr. GGRU,* no. 117, 1931.

Markov, K. K. Basic Problems of Geomorphology *(Osnovnyye Problemy Geomorfologii).* Moscow, Geografgiz, 1948.

Materialy po Geomorfologii Urala (Materials on the Geomorphology of the Urals), no. I (under the editorship of Ya. S. Edel'shteyn and I. P. Gerasimov), Moscow-Leningrad, Gosgeolizdat, 1948.

Nikolayev, N. I. "Recent Tectonics of the USSR" (Noveyshaya Tektonika SSSR), *Trudy Komissii po Izucheniyu Chetvertichnogo Perioda,* vol. 8, Moscow-Leningrad, AN SSSR, 1949.

Nikolayev, N. I. The History of the Development of the Basic Ideas in Geomorphology (first essay). *Ocherki po Istorii Geologicheskikh Znaniy,* no. 6, Moscow, AN SSSR, 1958.

Sovremennyye Vertikal'nyye Dvizheniya Zemnoy Kory na Territorii Zapadnoy Poloviny Yevropeyskoy Chasti SSSR (Contemporaneous Vertical Movements of the Earth's Crust on the Territory of the Western Half of the European Part of the USSR) (under the editorship of I. P. Gerasimov and Yu. V. Filippov). *Tr. TsNIIGAiK,* no. 123, 1958.

Sokolov, N. N. "A Geomorphological Sketch of the Region of the Volkhov River and Lake Il'men'." *Materialy po Issledovaniyu Reki Volkhova i yego Basseyna,"* vol. VII, 1926.

Spiridonov, A. I. Geomorphological Mapping *(Geomorfologicheskoye Kartirovaniye).* Moscow, Geografgiz, 1952.

Tanfil'yev, G. I. "Geography of Russia, the Ukraine, and the Territories Adjacent to them on the West within the Russia of 1914" *(Geografiya Rossii, Ukrainy i Primykayushchikh k nim s Zapada Territoriy v Predelakh Rossii 1914 goda),* part II, issues 1 and 2, Odessa, 1922-1923.

Tikhomirov, V. V. and Khain, V. Ye. Brief Sketch of the History of Geology *(Kratkiy Ocherk Istorii Geologii).* Moscow, Gos. izd. lit. po geologii i okhrane nedr, 1956.

Trudy Vsesoyuznogo Rabochego Soveshchaniya po Itogam Izucheniya Chetvertichnogo Perioda (Transactions of the All-Union Workers' Conference on the Results of the Study of the Quaternary Period) (ed. Yu. A. Skvortsov). Tashkent, AN Uz. SSR, 1953.

Shantser, Ye. V. "The Alluvium of Plains Rivers of the Temperate Zone and its Significance for a Knowledge of the Laws of the Structure and Formation of Alluvial Series," *Trudy instituta geologicheskikh nauk AN SSSR,* no. 135; *seriya geol.* no. 55, 1931.

Shul'ts, S. S. "Analysis of the Recent Tectonics and Relief of the Tyan'-Shan', *"Zapiski VGO,"* novaya seriya, vol. 3, Moscow, 1948.

Shchukin, I. S. General Morphology of the Land *(Obshchaya Morfologiya Sushi),* vols. 1-2, ONTI, Moscow, 1934-1938.

Edel'shteyn, Ya. S. Fundamentals of Geomorphology *(Osnovy Geomorfologii),* 2nd ed., Moscow, Gosgeolizdat, 1949.

A. A. Borzov (1874-1939)

S. S. Neustruyev (1874-1928)

L. I. Prasolov (1875-1954)

V. L. Komarov (1869-1945)

V. N. Sukachev (born 1880)

P. P. Sushkin (1868-1928)

A. V. Martynov (1879-1938)

V. A. Obruchev (1863-1956)

CHAPTER 14

GEOGRAPHIC SOIL SCIENCE

I. P. Gerasimov

The present essay should begin by pointing out that the term "geographic soil science" [*geograficheskoye pochvovedeniye*] is not generally accepted. It may be understood in two different senses. In the narrower sense it is taken to mean only one section of general soil science, namely that devoted to the study of the laws of the spatial (geographic) distribution of different soils (the so-called geography of soils). However, such a limitation of the subject of geographic soil science as an independent science appears to us to be artificial and not to correspond to the definition of the subject of the other physical geographic sciences. If one proceeds from the latter, one must understand by geographic soil science the scientific discipline studying the soil as a component of the natural geographic environment or of the natural landscape. But, as is well known, the great Russian scholar V. V. Dokuchayev established that any soil is not only a component of the natural landscape, but is also a function or product of it. The Dokuchayev tenet that all soils on the earth's surface are formed by the "extraordinarily complex interaction of local climate, plant and animal organisms, composition and structure of the mother rocks, relief and, finally, age of the country"* serves as the basis for all modern scientific soil science. Moreover, in advancing the doctrine of the natural soil-forming factors and establishing that the whole complex of these factors (above all, the climatic and biologic ones) undergoes regular and interrelated spatial changes on the earth's surface, V. V. Dokuchayev showed that the geographic distribution of soils is indissolubly connected with their genesis and properties. In their theoretical form, these ideas of Dokuchayev's are expressed most vividly in the doctrine of natural zones and the corresponding genetic types of soils. Methodologically, they have been used in the field investigation of soils, which, as is known, is always conducted in uninterrupted relation to the natural factors of soil formation (mother rock, vegetation, climate, and relief). All this, taken together, has long since given a pronouncedly geographic character to all Dokuchayev soil science and has, as a matter of fact, made all soil science one of the main physical geographic disciplines.

In relation to the remarks made in the present essay, the term "geographic soil science" is interpreted in a more or less broad manner. It is understood to mean that aspect of scientific work in soil science which investigates soils in close mutual relation to the other components of the natural geographic landscapes and, precisely on the basis of an analysis of such interrelationships, works out the basic questions of the genesis and geography of soils, as well as their agricultural use.

Soviet geographic soil science, interpreted above, is the direct heir of the Dokuchayev orientation in soil science. All the principal teachings of the latter have come to be points of departure for the development of the theory of this scientific discipline in Soviet times. The socialist reconstruction of the USSR national economy, particularly the collectivization of agriculture and its further development, has confronted geographic soil science with great and responsible practical tasks. To solve these tasks, extensive practical scientific work was instituted. In performing it, new factual material has been gathered and the theory of geographic soil science has been developed.

Two trends in practical scientific soil investigations have been of chief significance in the development of Soviet geographic soil science. The first served the land organization of kolkhozes and sovkhozes, as well as the development of advanced, scientifically based agrotechnology and

---

*V. V. Dokuchayev, "Russkiy Chernozem," in the book, "V. V. Dokuchayev, Selected Writings" [*Izbrannyye Sochineniya*], vol. 1, 1948, p. 27.

mechanization in them. The second had the task of ascertaining and characterizing the virgin lands in the regions of new economic conquest. Investigations of the first sort have been conducted mainly in the old farming areas of the country: in the west, the center, and the south of the European territory of the USSR, as well as in the chernozem belt of Western Siberia; the work in the second direction has had a very wide geographic distribution—from the irrigated regions of Middle Asia to the steppe and tayga areas of Kazakhstan, Eastern Siberia, and the Far East.

For the purpose of correct land organization and the introduction of the new agrotechnology, it has been necessary to have detailed soil maps of all agricultural areas exploited by kolkhozes and sovkhozes. With the use of such maps—compiled chiefly to scales from 1:10,000 to 1:25,000—lands have been graded as to potential productivity [*bonitorovka*], a differentiated agrotechnology has been introduced, and reclamation measures have been carried out (chemical fertilization, liming, draining, etc.). During the Soviet period alone soil surveys for the above-mentioned purpose have embraced the immense territory of 200 million hectares.

To carry out practical scientific work on such a large scale, several thousand soil-science specialists with geographic qualifications were required. The general scheme of work has been as follows. On the basis of the land-organization plan of a farm and with partial use of aerial photogrammetry, a detailed soil map was compiled, showing the genetic varieties of soils and their granulometric composition. To the map were attached an explanatory note and cartograms describing the natural conditions of soil formation (i.e., climate, relief, soil-forming rocks, and vegetation) and characterizing the soils by their basic genetic and agronomic properties; the agricultural grade of the lands; and the recommended reclamation measures.

The organization and carrying out of practical scientific work on the detailed soil survey were entrusted to the local and central land organs of the Ministry of Agriculture; the soil scientific-research institutions and the soil-science chairs of the universities and agricultural institutes have been systematically enlisted for this great undertaking. Owing to the constant increase in the lands used in agriculture, as well as the continuing progress of agrotechnology, work in soil geography of this type has not yet been completed and is still continuing at the present time.

There is no need to stress what an enormous amount of new detailed geographic materials has been obtained in the process of this large-scale practical scientific work. These materials have, indeed, covered all the chief physical geographic characteristics of the main agricultural regions of our country, although they have, of course, differed in their scientific quality. Unfortunately, only a part of these materials has been more or less systematically worked up and generalized in regional summaries of soil geography and in general soil maps of the republics and oblasts. A considerable number of manuscript reports and maps still await further scientific utilization.

An examination and study of the soils of virgin lands scheduled for new agricultural exploitation have been made in various regions of the Soviet Union, to varied scales and for different practical purposes. A considerable place in such work has been occupied by soil-reclamation investigations in the arid, steppe, and desert regions of the south and southeast of the European part of the USSR, in Transcaucasia, and in Middle Asia. These investigations have been mainly connected with the construction of new irrigation systems and with the expansion of old irrigated oases and the creation of new ones. For such reclamation work, detailed soil surveys have been made to scales of from 1:5,000 to 1:10,000, along, of course, with smaller-scale ones to be used in the first stages of hydrotechnical designing. Another important trend in these investigations has been the participation of soil geographers in the major integrated expeditions, working chiefly in the eastern regions of the country (Siberia and the Far East) and having the task of making scientific investigations for the creation of new industrial centers, means of communication, and agricultural regions. While the main work in the detailed soil-reclamation investigations for irrigation-construction purposes has been done by specially created soil groups under the designing and surveying institutes, the soil investigations in the regions of new economic conquest have been carried out principally by collectives of the workers of scientific institutions and by the chairs of the higher educational institutions.

Alongside the above-characterized trends in practical scientific research in soil geography, great importance in the development of geographic soil science has also attached to soil work done in the study of the fodder, forest, and peat resources of the Soviet Union.

Like the detailed soil surveys in the old farming regions, for the purposes of land organization, all the soil-geographic work done in the regions of new agricultural conquest has created an enormous flow of new factual data on the physical geography of the territories studied. This flow has exceeded by many times the pre-revolutionary geographic materials, obtained chiefly during soil-botanical exploration for resettlement purposes. A large part of the new concrete material, in the process of the work, has been prepared and published (chiefly in the *Trudy* of the integrated expeditions), and also generalized in summary maps. Thus, the performance of the whole system of work under discussion was a most important stage in the general geographic study of our country's territory.

As has been noted, the broad development of detailed soil surveys in the old farming regions, as well as the extensive soil-geographic work in the new regions of agricultural conquest, have created powerful impulses for the development of the theory of geographic soil science. The main theoretical questions connected with the making of detailed soil surveys for kolkhoz and sovkhoz land organization and with the introduction of differentiated agrotechnology have been the questions of the rational detailed classification and nomenclature of soils and their agronomic and reclamational characterization. In the first stages of the development of mass soil-survey investigations, the lack of elaborated and generally accepted schemes of detailed soil classifications and the principles of agro-reclamational characterization naturally led to discrepancies in the results of all the work and to a reduction of its practical significance. Hence, one of the most urgent and responsible tasks of theoretical investigations in the field of geographic soil science in the USSR has been the elaboration of a single scientific systematization of the soils for the whole country, reduced to those taxonomic subdivisions which are used in detailed soil surveys. This task of elaboration was begun before the War and has in the main been solved since the War.

The elaboration of a single systematization of soils in the USSR has been based on a careful scientific analysis of the materials from the detailed soil-geographic work. This analysis, which included a scientific generalization of the factual materials, was organized in the V. V. Dokuchayev Soil Institute of the Academy of Sciences of the USSR after the publication of the sheets of the 1:1,000,000 state soil map of the USSR. This map was compiled from a digest of local materials and executed according to a unified method, on the basis of a common system of subdivision and soil nomenclature. The editor-in-chief of this map was L. I. Prasolov, and later I. P. Gerasimov. This mode of working out a unified soil systematization for the whole country was a most rational one. Basing the work on general theoretical principles permitted a thorough use of the immense amount of factual materials from the regional investigations and a systematic verification of the elaborated propositions from local experience. Inasmuch as the regional soil-geographic investigations continued without interruption, it was necessary to work out a system of soil division and nomenclature that would be flexible and dynamic enough to possess long-term validity and to assimilate new factual materials without basic revisions.

This task was successfully solved by establishing a system of taxonomic units of soil systematization on the basis of the Dokuchayev concept of genetic soil types. These units included the categories of subtype [*podtip*], genus [*rod*], and species [*vid*] of soils, based on the chief genetic features of the soils, as well as the categories [*kategorii*] and varieties [*raznovidnosti*] of soil differ-ence, based on the mechanical composition and the lithologic characteristics of the parent material. These systematic units were all basic subdivisions in the legend of the state soil map of the USSR.

A large number of separate sheets of the state soil map of the USSR have now been published for all the chief farming regions of the country. This great soil-cartographic achievement is being supplemented by smaller-scale general soil maps embracing the whole territory of the USSR (to a scale of 1:4,000,000) and of the European part of the USSR (to a scale of 1:2,500,000). All the general soil maps in this country are constructed on a single system of soil division and nomenclature, representing the general classification of the soils of the Soviet Union.

The single systematization of the soils of the Soviet Union used at the present time is based on the scientific principles laid down by V. V. Dokuchayev and N. M. Sibirtsev. The genetic type of soil, subdivided into subtypes, genera, species, subspecies [*podvidy*], and varieties, has been adopted as the chief taxonomic unit of Soviet classification. All these taxonomic categories are genetic in character; their distinction is founded on an analysis of the genetic nature of the soil-forming process. All the diagnostic criteria used in identifying this or that systematic unit are regarded as external (morphologic) signs of the development of a definite aggregate of biologic and physical geographic phenomena constituting the soil-forming process peculiar to a given genetic type of soils.

As an illustration of these principles, one may point out the characteristic morphologic features of the profile of podzol soils, as expressed in the development of a definite system of paragenetic horizons (podzol-eluvial and illuvial). All soils possessing a morphologic profile of similar structure are united under the single genetic type of podzol soils. The presence, in the podzol soil profile, of additional genetic horizons (for example, an upper turf or gley horizon) gives grounds for distinguishing still other subtypes of these soils—for example, turf-podzol or gley-podzol—alongside the typical *podzol soils*. Certain specific features in the character of the main genetic horizons (for example, increased content of humus substances or iron compounds in the illuvial horizon) make it possible to distinguish various genera of podzol soils (for example, illuvial-humus or illuvial-iron). The degree of development of the podzol process, as expressed in this or that stratum of genetic horizons, serves as the basis for dividing the soil type (subtype, genus) into species, for example slightly, medium, and strongly podzolic soils and podzols. The difference in mechanical composition is taken into account in distinguishing soil varieties, as are other characteristics of the parent material in distinguishing differences of soils.

The above-characterized system of taxonomic subdivisions makes it possible to give sufficiently full consideration to the chief genetic properties of soil types. At present, the total number of genetic soil types distinguished on the territory of the USSR reaches several dozens; it has grown considerably since the time of Dokychayev's classic works, when only the following types were known: the podzol soils of the tayga, the gray forest soils of the forest-steppe, the chernozems (black-earths) of the steppes, the chestnut soils of the dry steppes, the red-earths and yellow-earths of the subtropics, the solonetz and solonchak soils, and swampy and alluvial soils. This considerable enlargement of the number of genetic soil types on the territory of the USSR was due to two main causes: (1) the thorough study of the genesis and dynamics of soil types and the resulting breakdown of several aggregate concepts (for example, the soils of the tundras, the soils of the deserts, etc.), and (2) the discovery of new genetic soil types in soil field investigations.

A thorough study of the combinations of various properties in the most widespread genetic soil types (for example, podzol soils, chernozems, chestnut soils, solonetz soils, etc.), made from the dynamic angle (i.e., with a study of the seasonal changes in the heat and water regime), is regarded as one of the most important tasks of modern geographic soil science. Such a study is necessary for a scientifically based agronomic evaluation of soils and a differentiated (by soils) agrotechnology, as well as for the choice of the requisite reclamation measures aimed at increasing the fertility of the soil. The achievements of Soviet science in this field of soil science are very considerable. It suffices to point out, for example, the works by A. A. Rode, K. K. Gedroyts, V. R. Vil'yams, Ye. N. Ivanova, N. L. Blagovidov, and others on the study of the genetic nature of the processes of podzol formation; by I. V. Tyurin on the investigation of gray forest soils; by L. I. Prasolov, K. P. Gorshenin, and Ye. A. Afanas'yeva on the study of chernozems; by I. N. Antipov-Karatayev, Ye. N. Ivanova, and A. F. Bol'shakov on the investigation of the chestnut and brown soils of the dry steppes; by S. S. Neustruyev, N. A. Dimo and A. N. Rozanov on serozems; by B. B. Polynov, S. A. Zakharov, and M. N. Sabashvili on red-earths and yellow-earths; the investigations of K. K. Gedroyts, B. B. Polynov, V. A. Kovda, Ye. N. Ivanova, A. N. Rozanov, and others on the study of salinified soils (solonchak and solonetz), especially valuable for reclamation practice; the works of I. V. Tyurin, M. M. Kononova, Ye. N. Mishustin, and others on the dynamics of humus accumulation in microbiologic phenomena in the various genetic soil types; of I. N. Antipov-Karatayev, N. P. Gorbunov, I. D. Sedletskiy, and others on the study of the mineral part of soils; of N. A. Kachinskiy, A. A. Rode, and others on hydrophysical properties; of A. V. Sokolov and others on agrochemical characteristics, etc. As a result of all these investigations there has been a substantial refinement and development of the scientific concepts of the genetic nature of the earlier established soil types, many of which have appeared in an entirely new light.

During the Soviet period, the following new genetic soil types have been described and studied on the territory of the USSR: the mountain-meadow soils of the alpine and subalpine meadows (S. A. Zakharov, O. A. Mikhaylovskaya, and others); the brown forest soils of the broadleaf forests (L. I. Prasolov, S. V. Zonn, Yu. A. Liverovskiy, and others); the serozems of the desert steppes (S. S. Neustruyev, N. A. Dimo, A. N. Rozanov, S. A. Shuvalov, and others); the serozems of the deserts (S. S. Neustruyev, Ye. V. Lobova, and others); the brown soils of the dry forests and scrub (S. A. Zakharov, I. P. Gerasimov, and others); the gray-brown soils (A. N. Rozanov); the meadow-chernozem soils (I. P. Gerasimov, Ye. N. Ivanova, and others); the frozen tayga soils (Ye. N. Ivanova, N. A. Nogina, and others) and a number of other types.

Quite naturally, if the thorough study (especially from the dynamic angle) has opened up many new aspects of soil processes in the classical genetic soil types (podzols, chernozems, etc.), the investigation of new genetic soil types has especially enriched the general theory of Soviet genetic soil science. As an example, one may cite the entirely new treatment of the serozems of Middle Asia as soils of the subtropical semideserts, as given by A. N. Rozanov; and the establishment of the zonal type of brown forests soils for the southern mountain regions of the USSR, by L. I. Prasolov, Yu. A. Liverovskiy, and others.

It should be noted that the discovery and establishment of new genetic soil types in the USSR, as a rule, has been closely connected with the earlier mentioned soil-geographic investigations in the regions of new economic conquest. Such regions usually possess special physical geographic conditions, differing from those peculiar to the regions of development of the classical soil types established by V. V. Dokuchayev and his collaborators. Examples of this sort are the perpetually frozen tayga soils of Eastern Siberia, the brown forest soils of the broadleaf forests of the Far East, the brown soils of the dry subtropics of Transcaucasia, and others. Inasmuch as the soil-geographic study of a number of marginal regions of the USSR (for example the Extreme North and the northeast of Siberia) has not been completed, it is to be expected that further investigations will establish here other new, thus far unknown, soil formations. Thus, it may be stated that the period of geographic discoveries in the field of soil science is not yet over.

In association with the elaboration of a single soil systematization and the establishment and study of new genetic soil types, much attention has been paid in Soviet geographic soil science to the clarification of the general laws of the spatial distribution of soils. The solution of such theoretical questions, like the work on the systematization of soils, has been closely connected with the compilation and scientific analysis of general soil maps. Thus, for example, Soviet soil scientists, following the classical tradition of our native science, as already established by V. V. Dokuchayev and K. D. Glinka, are working systematically on the compilation of world soil maps. In 1937-1940, on the basis of a world soil map which he compiled, L. I. Prasolov effected a very important revision of the general concepts about the soil belts and zones of the world, and this revision has been continued subsequently by I. P. Gerasimov and V. R. Volobuyev. In this work, especially in the investigations by V. R. Volobuyev, the problems of the relation of the basic characteristics of soil to the zonal climatic conditions have been subjected to an all-around examination. In them, use has been made of certain procedures of mathematical analysis, supplemented lately by an analysis of the energy expenditures in soil formation. Ye. N. Ivanova and N. N. Rozov, on the basis of survey soil maps, have worked out a system of soil-geographic regionalization of the USSR. They have made wide use not only of the scientific principles of the Dokuchayev doctrine of natural zones, but also of more recent concepts of the so-called soil facies or provinces reflecting the local, regional peculiarities in the character of the soils. Special attention has been paid to the scientific analysis of the phenomena of vertical zonality of soils in the works of S. A. Zakharov, Yu. A. Liverovskiy, V. M. Fridland, and others. Without doubt, all these research trends in the field of soil science are of great importance for physical geography.

Because of the establishment of the general laws governing the spatial distribution of soils, as reflected in the development of world-wide soil belts, complex systems of zones, facies, and provinces, much attention is paid in Soviet geographic soil science to the study of local or regional peculiarities in the structure of the soil cover, or the geography of soils. We have in mind, in particular, those regular complexes and combinations of soils of different genetic character which are usually connected with changes in relief forms and cause some degree of heterogeneity in the structure of the soil cover of a locality. As concrete examples of such soil complexes and combinations, one may point out the solonetz microcomplexes on the undrained steppe plains of the south of our country, and the constant alternation of podzolic, podzolic-swampy, and swampy soils in the northern tayga areas. A detailed study and comparison of all such types of soil complexes and combinations represents an important prospective scientific task. Its solution will lead to discovery of definite pristine types of soil complexes peculiar to this or that combination of natural conditions of soil formation. Apparently, in working out this task, the aims of several general geographic (landscape-science) and soil-geographic scientific investigations will blend into one. At present, great significance is being attached to the study and scientific typing of soil complexes and combinations, not only in the USSR but also in foreign soil science (for example, in the United States of America).

A separate series of scientific questions in Soviet geographic soil science is connected with the problem of the evolution of the types of soil formation and the development of soil cover.
V. V. Dokuchayev, in a very general form, to be sure, emphasized the role of the time factor in the formation of soils. Later, the main attention in this problem was addressed to the processes of the development of soil cover in relation to the dynamics of the relief and the change in plant formations and climatic conditions. The general scheme of the gradual transformation of the soil cover of alluvial plains and floodplain terraces in pace with their geomorphologic development, the improvement of drainage, and the change from meadows and solonchak complexes to solonetz and steppe complexes has been worked out by S. S. Neustruyev, B. B. Polynov, V. A. Kovda, and others. A problem for discussion has been the question of the genesis of the gray forest soils of the forest-steppe as a product of the transformation of steppe (chernozem) soils under the influence of the transgression of the forest. This problem was posed in the works of S. I. Korzhinskiy; more recently, I. V. Tyurin, A. A. Zavalishin, and other Soviet soil scientists have concerned themselves with it.

A broader posing of the problem of the evolution of soil-formation types is that by V. R. Vil'yams. This scholar's well-known doctrine of a single soil-forming process gave a paleogeographic treatment to this problem, closely relating the development of the contemporaneous types of soil formation to the history of the formation of the plant cover. Despite a number of debatable and here-and-there erroneous (from the paleogeographic viewpoint) propositions, Vil'yams' concept has given a new aspect to the evolution problem in soil science and has created a point of departure for its further fruitful elaboration (see the works by I. P. Gerasimov, S. A. Kalyago, and others).

Among other major scientific problems of Soviet soil science it is necessary to single out also the problem of the transformation of the natural forms of soil formation as a result of man's agricultural activity. There now remain on the earth's surface almost no natural soils that have not undergone cultivation to some degree. In this connection, the overwhelming majority of natural soil formations usable for farming is found to be an important means of agricultural production and, having been to some degree transformed under the influence of cultivation and agro-reclamation, has also become an object (product) of labor. Man's farming activity exercises a profound effect upon the soil and strongly affects the main factors of soil formation (above all the natural vegetation), which lends this effect an especially radical character.

The study of the influence of cultivation upon the natural properties of the soil is one of the pressing scientific-research problems of Soviet soil science. It is a problem which embraces many complex questions thus far not sufficiently treated. However, intensive work is being done toward their solution (see the works of K. L. Blagovidov, N. P. Karpinskiy, V. A. Frantsesson, and others).
In particular, in the study and mapping of soils, especially on a large scale, all the soil features and properties formed as a result of cultivation are being carefully recorded. Using as a basis the systematic subdivisions established for natural soils, it is considered indispensable to ascertain in addition the general character and degree of cultivation of the various soils. Here, special attention is addressed to soils which are subjected to radical reclamation (drainage, irrigation, liming, etc.).

BASIC LITERATURE

Vilenskiy, D. G. The Russian Soil-cartographic School (Russkaya Pochvenno-kartograficheskaya Shkola), 1949.
Vil'yams, V. P. The Development of the Primary Soil-formation Process (Razvitiye Pervichnogo Pochvoobrazovatel'nogo Protsessa), Izbr. soch. (Selected Works), vol. II, 1949.
Volobuyev, V. R. Soils and Climate (Pochvy i Klimat), Baku, 1958.
Vysotskiy, G. N. "Essays on Soils and the Regime of Ground Waters." Byulleten' Pochvovedeniya, 1927, Nos. 5-8.
Gerasimov, I. P. "The Paleogeographic Significance of V. R. Vil'yams's Teachings." Probl. Fiz. Geogr., No. 16, 1951.
Gerasimov, I. P. "The Scientific Foundations of Soil Systematization." Pochvovedeniye, 1952, No. 11.
Gerasimov, I. P., and Glazovskaya, M. A. Soil Science and the Geography of Soils (Pochvovedeniye i Geografiya Pochv), 1960.
Ivanova, Ye. N., and Rozov, N. N. "On the State and Development of the Classification Problem in Soil Science." Pochvovedeniye, 1958, No. 10.

Kovda, V. A. The Origin and Regime of Salinified Soils *(Proiskhozhdeniye i Rezhim Zasolenykh Pochv)*, Moscow-Leningrad, 1946.

Neustruyev, S. S. "Soils and Cycles of Erosion." *Geogr. Vestn.*, vol. I, 1922.

Neustruyev, S. S. Elements of the Geography of Soils *(Elementy Geografii Pochv)*, 1930.

Polynov, B. B. The Crust of Weathering *(Kora Vyvetrivaniya)*, 1934.

Polynov, B. B. "The Guiding Ideas of the Modern Doctrine of the Formation and Development of Soils." *Vestn. AN SSSR,* 1947.

Pochvennaya s"yemka (Soil Survey), izd-vo AN SSSR, 1958.

Pochvy SSSR (Soils of the USSR), vols. I, II and III, izd-vo AN SSSR, 1940.

Prasolov, L. I. "The Brown-earths of the Crimea and the Caucasus." *Priroda*, 1929, No. 5.

Prasolov, L. I. "On the Unified Nomenclature and Principles of Genetic Soil Classification." *Pochvovedeniye,* 1937, No. 6.

Rode, A. A. The Podzol-forming Process *(Podzoloobrazovatel'nyy Protsess)*, Moscow-Leningrad, 1937.

Rode, A. A. Soil Science *(Pochvovedeniye)*, 1958.

Rozov, N. N. "The Development of V. V. Dokuchayev's Doctrine of the Zonality of Soils in the Present Period." *Izv. AN SSSR, seriya geogr.,* 1954, No. 4.

SOIL MAPS

Pochvennaya Karta SSSR (Soil Map of the USSR). Scale: 1:4,000,000. Compiled in 1954 by N. N. Rozov with the participation of Ye. V. Lobova, under the general scientific editorship of Academician I. P. Gerasimov.

Pochvennaya Karta Mira (Soil Map of the World). Scale: 1:20,000,000. Compiled by a group of authors under the direction of Academician I. P. Gerasimov (published in reduced and generalized form in the journal *Priroda,* 1956, No. 10).

CHAPTER 15

PLANT GEOGRAPHY (GEOBOTANY)

Ye. M. Lavrenko

Plant geography studies the plant cover of the earth in relation to the conditions of the environment or, in other words, in its mutual relation to the other components of the physical geographic envelope of the earth. The plant cover is made up of plant communities [*soobshchestva*] (phytocoenoses) which, on land, always represent combinations of several or many species of higher and lower plants; in bodies of water, plant communities consist more often of combinations of several or many species of lower plants, principally algae. Genuine one-species communities can be created only artificially in a sterile medium.

Plant geography, like any other science, has always developed in conjunction with the solution of practical tasks. At the end of the last, and the beginning of the current, century, the plant geographers of Russia took an energetic part in expeditions for the investigation of soils in connection with grading them as to potential productivity [*bonitirovka:* classification of their *bonitet* (index or class or valuation of "goodness" = "potential productivity" as a Russian agricultural and forestry term)]. These expeditions were organized by the *zemstvo* [provincial council] institutions. An especially big role in the development of both soil science and plant geography was played by the well-known expeditions headed by V. V. Dokuchayev for the study of the soils (and of the natural conditions in general) in the Nizhniy Novgorod and Poltava guberniyas, as well as for the study of ways to combat drought in the south of European Russia. The classicists of our native plant geography, A. N. Krasnov, G. I. Tanfil'yev, and G. N. Vysotskiy, took part in these expeditions. Plant geography was also developed in connection with the solution of forestry questions (G. F. Morozov, G. N. Vysotskiy, V. N. Sukachev, and others). At the beginning of the 20th century a great deal of geobotanical and soil work was done in Middle Asia, Kazakhstan, Siberia, and the Far East for the purpose of clarifying the natural conditions of the colonization reserves (expeditions of the Resettlement Administration), etc.

After the Great October Socialist Revolution, geobotanical investigations, usually in conjunction with soil investigations, were conducted in the 1920's and 1930's over immense territories of Middle Asia, Kazakhstan, Siberia, the Far East, and the Extreme North of our country to ascertain the possibilities for the agricultural conquest of the territory and for the purpose of land organization. Among these must be noted the work by B. N. Gorodkov and his pupils and collaborators in the Extreme North; V. V. Reverdatto and his pupils and collaborators in Siberia; V. L. Komarov, V. N. Vasil'yev, N. Ye. Kabanov, N. V. Pavlov, A. S. Poretskiy, and others in the Far East; and R. I. Abolin, M. M. Il'in, I. M. Krasheninnikov, I. V. Larin, N. V. Pavlov, A. V. Prozorovskiy, and his collaborators in Kazakhstan and Middle Asia. These investigations obtained a vast amount of material for a cartographic survey of the plant cover, and regional plant geography monographs were published.

From the 1920's down to the present time Soviet plant geographers have done a very great deal of itinerant, semistationary, and stationary work in all parts of the Soviet Union directed toward the improvement of the natural fodder area (hayfields and pasture lands), which still plays a main role in our country in the production of fodder. As a result of these investigations, it was possible to calculate how the areas of natural pasture lands and hayfields are distributed over the individual natural regions, how much fodder is harvested from them, and how productive and seasonal the different types of natural pasture lands and hayfields are. Ways were worked out for the rational utilization and improvement of these lands. The leading role in the investigations of pasture lands and hayfields belongs to I. V. Larin, L. G. Ramenskiy, and A. P. Shennikov. These extensive investigations are summed up to a certain extent in the monographs by A. P. Shennikov, "Meadow Science" [*Lugovedeniye*] (1941) and I. V. Larin, "Meadow and Pasture Management" [*Lugovodstvo i Pastbishchnoye Khozyaystvo*] (1956).

The geobotanist-foresters have also taken an inventory, worked out a typology, and assessed and mapped (by aerial photogrammetry) the forests of the USSR. A "Map of the Forests of the USSR" to a scale of 1:2,500,000 has been published under the general editorship of F. M. Kozlov and V. P. Tseplyayev (1955). Unfortunately, a generalizing monograph on the forests of the USSR is thus far lacking in this country.

The swamp-science plant geographers have also conducted extensive investigations of the vegetation of swamps and related peat bogs throughout the USSR from the Baltic lands to Kamchatka. As is known, the larger part of the world's peat reserve is located in our country. The study of swamps has been conducted in connection with their use for agriculture (after drainage) and for the production of peat. The investigations into the swamps of the USSR have been summed up in a number of monographs and generalizing works by V. S. Dokturovskiy (1935), N. Ya. Kats (1941, 1948), M. I. Neyshtadt (1938), V. N. Sukachev (1926), S. N. Tyuremnov (1949), and Yu. D. Tsinzerling (1938).

Lately, plant geographers have taken an active part in geologic and hydrologic explorations (Viktorov, 1955), especially with aerial photogrammetry. Here, the plant cover is used as an indicator of the ground-water level or the soil-forming rocks having a definite lithology. Geobotanical investigations have also been made to ascertain the water-conserving and soil-protecting significance of vegetation, as well as in connection with the designing of reclamation measures (irrigation, drainage, the construction of reservoirs, etc.).

The greatest influence upon the development of the theory of our native plant geography in almost all its departments has been exerted by the "Dokuchayev school" of the study of nature, founded by the talented Russian soil-scientist and geographer V. V. Dokuchayev (1846-1903) and continued by his gifted pupils and collaborators: G. N. Vysotskiy (1865-1940), A. N. Krasnov (1862-1914), G. F. Morozov (1867-1920), and G. I. Tanfil'yev (1857-1928). In the last few decades a large role has been played by the doctrine of the biosphere created by V. I. Vernadskiy (1863-1945), who was also one of the pupils and collaborators of V. V. Dokuchayev. It is due to this influence that the study of the plant cover has been conducted in the USSR in close association with the other components of the physical geographic complex.

Great influence upon the development of our native plant geography was also exercised by S. I. Korzhinskiy (1861-1900) and I. K. Pachoskiy (1864-1942), who directed special attention to the interrelationships between plants and plant communities. These ideas were further developed by V. N. Sukachev, A. P. Shennikov and others.

Let us dwell briefly upon the understanding by Soviet botanists of the nature of the plant cover. Of immense significance in clarifying the role of the plant cover in the life of the earth is V. I. Vernadskiy's doctrine of the biosphere, which embraces the troposphere, the hydrosphere, and the stratosphere [*stratisfera*]. The stratosphere is the part of the lithosphere composed of sedimentary rocks, sometimes metamorphosed. Organisms play an immense role in the formation of sedimentary rocks. Thus, Vernadskiy's biosphere and the physical geographic envelope of the earth (or geographic environment) of present-day geographers are essentially synonymous. The biosphere, according to Vernadskiy, is not only the sphere of concentration of contemporaneous living substances, but also the result of the vital activity of the latter from the moment of the appearance of life on the earth. From this point of view, the plant cover, in the composition of which green autotrophic plants fixing the energy of the sun on the earth predominate, serves, as it were, as the powerhouse for the biosphere.

Ye. M. Lavrenko (1949) has proposed that the name "phytogeosphere" be given to those parts (Vernadskiy's "life films" [*plenki zhizni*]) of the biosphere in which living substances are concentrated, usually with a preponderance of plants over animals. The term "phytogeosphere" includes also the medium (solid, liquid, or gaseous) in which the organisms live. Three basic types of phytogeosphere are distinguished: (1) terrestrial (on the surface of the dry land), (2) aquatic, illuminated by the sun (in the seas, lakes, and rivers), and (3) benthic (on the bottoms of deep bodies of water, to which sunlight does not penetrate).

The biogeocoenoses, the concept of which has been worked out by V. N. Sukachev (1942, 1945, 1947, 1957), should be taken as the unit of breakdown of the phytogeosphere on the dry land. The plant part of the biogeocoenosis represents a phytocoenosis or plant community, which may be defined as a combination of autotrophic and heterotrophic plants, among which definite interrelationships operate. The latter may be direct or (in most cases) indirect, through the medium acted upon by the plants making up the phytocoenosis. V. N. Sukachev and A. P. Shennikov have repeatedly directed attention to the importance of studying the interrelationships between the plants in plant associations.

In studying the structure of plant communities, one must distinguish between species populations and the society, and, in the case of mosaic phytocoenoses, micro-groupings. T. A. Rabotnov (1950) has pointed out the great significance of the phenotypic (age) study of species populations in communities. By "society" is meant the parts of the phytocoenosis in which definite life forms of plants predominate. The simplest manifestation of a society is the layer, but in a number of cases the layer may consist of several societies. Every society in a phytocoenosis exists in a separate medium, differing more or less from the medium of other societies in the same community. A definite stratification of the conditions of the medium usually exists in the biogeocoenosis with which a phytocoenosis is connected.

Not infrequently, plant communities have a more or less patchy or mosaic make-up, i.e., they fall in a horizontal direction into micro-groupings (microphytocoenoses) marked by certain changes in the structure of the society (Yaroshenko, 1950, 1953, 1958). But definite interrelationships operate, most often through the medium, among the plants making up the individual patches, in the above-ground and underground parts of the community.

In the structure of the plant community, it is necessary to distinguish a principal (edificatory) [edifikatornyy] society and subordinate societies. The principal, or edificatory, society, as a result of the vital activity of the plant species which form it, exercises an especially great influence on the environment of the community, the phytoclimate, the soil, etc. The other societies, which also exercise some influence on the environment, usually occupy "ecologic niches" under conditions of existence created largely by the edificatory society. The dominant species, singular or plural (A. Ya. Gordyagin's "dominants"), of the edificatory society is usually called the edificator [edifikator] (or edificators, if there are two or three) of the plant association.

Under the conditions of the environment of plant communities (or ecotope) [ekotop], L. G. Ramenskiy (1924, 1938) proposed the distinction between entopic [entopicheskiy] factors and their entirety ("entopy" [entopiya]), indirectly acting upon the plant association, and physiologically acting regimes, i.e., directly acting factors. This proposal is shared by a majority of Soviet plant geographers.

The plant communities (phytocoenosis) represents a certain integrality, but of much lower rank than that of the organism (Aleksandrova, 1958). Hence, it is wrong to liken the plant community to the organism, as is done by some foreign plant geographers. The integrality of the plant community is maintained by the renewal of its components. This produces not only a definite structure of the community (its species composition, the make-up of its societies, etc.), but also a definite age composition of the populations of the species entering into it. Of course, this integrality of the community is preserved only when there is a certain constancy in the conditions of the environment (physiologically acting regimes). If the conditions of the environment change as a result of the more-or-less considerable action by the plant community upon the environment or by any external influences, a replacement (succession) [suktsessiya] of one community by another is observed.

In the classification of plant communities, the biologic-ecologic properties of the edificators of the basic (edificatory) society are mainly taken into account in distinguishing the larger units (types of vegetation, etc.). In distinguishing the units of middle rank (formation) [formatsiya] account is taken of the species composition of the edificators, and in distinguishing the basic units of classification— the associations [assotsiatsii]—the species composition that is the dominant of all the more or less well distinguished societies.

Such in the most general outlines is the notion of the nature of plant communities [*soobshchestva*] held by the majority of Soviet plant geographers. General reviews of the main questions of phytocoenology have been published by V. N. Sukachev (1928, 1954), P. D. Yaroshenko (1950, 1953), and B. A. Bykov (1953, 1957).

Now let us dwell in somewhat fuller detail on questions concerning the geography and history of the plant cover.

One important method of studying the geography of the plant cover is to map it. Before the October Revolution the following vegetation maps were the most detailed and, indeed, almost the only ones in Russia: the "Botanico-geographic Map of the Russian Empire" by G. I. Tanfil'yev, to a scale of 1:25,200,000 (1900-1902) for the whole territory of Russia, and the "Map of the Vegetation of Asiatic Russia" by B. A. Fedchenko, to a scale of 1:12,600,000 (1914), published in the "Atlas of Asiatic Russia."

After 1917, the well-known Soviet botanist N. I. Kuznetsov, who founded the Geobotany Department in the Main Botanical Garden and later in the Botanical Institute of the Academy of Sciences of the USSR, performed, from 1923 on, extensive work on the compilation of a map of the vegetation of the European part of the USSR to a scale of 1:1,050,000. This scholar laid the foundation of Soviet botanical cartography. After his death (1932), the work of compiling this map, at first to the same scale, but later to a scale of 1:1,000,000, was continued by a large group of plant geographers under the direction of Kuznetsov's successors, Yu. D. Tsinzerling and Ye. V. Shiffers. These maps show both the reconstructed and the present-day plant cover, although not always consistently enough. The eight sheets of the "Geobotanical Map of the European Part of the USSR," to a scale of 1:1,050,000, published under the editorship of N. I. Kuznetsov have rightly been called by L. S. Berg (1948) "a remarkable achievement of botanical geography."

In the first half of the 1930's there appeared a number of small-scale and some medium-scale maps of the vegetation of individual more-or-less large regions of the USSR, including union and autonomous republics, krays, and oblasts; for example, that of Middle Asia to a scale of 1:3,000,000, by Ye. P. Korovin (1932); the Kazakh SSR, 1:2,000,000, by A. V. Prozorovskiy and others (1933); Transcaucasia, 1:420,000, by A. A. Grossgeym (1930); the Georgian SSR, 1:400,000, by N. N. Ketskhoveli (1935); the Dagestan SSR, 1:500,000, by S. I. Vinogradov and G. A. Tolchain (1932); the Gor'kiy kray, 1:500,000, by V. V. Alekhin (1934); Moscow oblast, 1:1,500,000, by V. V. Alekhin (1933); and others. Most of these maps give an idea of the original (reconstructed) plant cover. Among these maps, the "Geobotanical Map of Kazakhstan" (1:2,000,000), compiled by A. V. Prozorovskiy, N. I. Rubtsov, A. A. Dmitriyeva, and M. N. Avramchik, possesses especially high scientific merit.

In the 1930's there also appeared a number of small-scale vegetation maps embracing the whole territory of the USSR or the European or Asiatic part separately. Such maps were published in the "Atlas of the Industry of the USSR" (1930) and in the "Great Soviet Atlas of the World" (1937).

In the second half of the 1930's the Department of Geobotany of the Botanical Institute of the Academy of Sciences of the USSR proceeded to compile survey geobotanical wall maps, also to a small scale, but much larger than those cited above. Among these maps, which came out in separate editions, are the "Map of the Vegetation of the USSR," to a scale of 1:5,000,000, compiled at first under the editorship of Yu. D. Tsinzerling, and later Ye. M. Lavrenko (1939); the "Map of the Vegetation of the European Part of the USSR," 1:2,500,000 (1949); and the "Geobotanical Map of the USSR," 1:4,000,000 (1956). (The 1:2,500,000 map was published in 1949, but is dated 1948 on the cardboard case; the explanatory text to it came out in 1950.) The last two maps were published under the editorship of V. B. Sochava and Ye. M. Lavrenko. All these maps were accompanied by detailed explanatory texts, the text to the last map ("The Plant Cover of the USSR," 1956) consisting of two volumes.

After the Great Patriotic War, work was resumed on the compilation of maps of the vegetation of individual regions of the USSR to a scale of 1:1,000,000 or thereabouts. Under the general direction of V. B. Sochava, a geobotanical map of the Baltic union republics and of Pskov and Leningrad oblasts was compiled. Similar cartographic work is being done on the Altay, the southern part of the Far East, and so forth. A map of the vegetation of Middle Asia and southern Kazakhstan to a scale of 1:1,000,000 in 17 sheets has now been published.

In the compilation of this last-named map, which was done under the immediate supervision and editorship of L. Ye. Rodin, there participated the workers of the botanical scientific-research institutions of the six academies of sciences of the USSR, the Kazakh SSR, the Kirgiz SSR, the Tadzhik SSR, the Turkmen SSR, and the Uzbek SSR, including such experts on the vegetation of Middle Asia as I. V. Vykhodtsev, Ye. P. Korovin, V. A. Nikitin, P. N. Ovchinnikov, M. P. Petrov, N. I. Rubtsov, K. V. Stanyukovich, and others. This is the largest block of a geobotanic map to a scale of 1:1,000,000 in world cartography.

Soviet plant geographers have also published original vegetation maps for certain foreign territories. Thus, A. A. Yunatov, who has worked for many years in the Mongolian People's Republic, has printed a vegetation map of that country to a scale of 1:8,000,000 (1954) and has also compiled much more detailed vegetation maps of the Mongolian People's Republic that have not been published, as yet. I. A. Linchevskiy and A. V. Prozorovskiy (1946) have published a vegetation map of Afghanistan to a scale of about 1:10,000,000. In the last few years, V. B. Sochava has conferred on the compilation of a vegetation map of the Rumanian People's Republic to a scale of 1:500,000. This map is now completed.

Thus, in the field of geobotanical cartography, Soviet science has undoubtedly assumed one of the first places in the world.

Another important section of the work of Soviet plant geographers has been the regionalization of the plant cover of the USSR. Very many projects have been published for the geobotanical regionalization of individual more-or-less large parts of the USSR—union and autonomous republics, krays, oblasts, and so forth.

The whole territory of the USSR is embraced by a geobotanical regionalization of the USSR worked out by the Department of Geobotany of the Botanical Institute of the Academy of Sciences of the USSR and published in the series, *Trudy,* of the Commission for the Natural-Historical Regionalization of the USSR, of the Council for the Study of the Productive Forces under the Academy of Sciences of the USSR (1947). The smallest unit adopted in this regionalization is the district [*okrug*]; altogether, 384 districts have been distinguished in the USSR and briefly described. The largest unit is the *oblast',* which is characterized by the predominance of a definite type of vegetation on the interfluves [*plakory*], i.e., under the conditions of drained plains or low mountains, and also by a definite system of belting in the mountains. Characteristic of each oblast, furthermore, is the systematic composition of the flora, particularly genus and species endemism. Differences are also noted in the history of the plant cover; in particular, the ages of the individual oblasts are distinguished. The oblasts extending in a latitudinal direction and, in this case, coinciding with the concept of soil-and-plant zones, are divided further into strips (subzones) [*polosy*]—in the latitudinal direction—and into provinces, principally in the meridional direction. The sectors [*sektory*] of provinces cut off by the strips are divided further into okrugs. The oblasts, principally oceanic in their location, which occupy relatively limited territories, are divided directly into okrugs. Altogether, eleven botanico-geographic oblasts have been distinguished in the USSR.

Despite certain defects, this regionalization, firstly, does not exaggerate the latitudinal zonality of the plant cover; secondly, it reflects equally both the zonal and the provincial regularities; and, thirdly, it does not sever the regularities of plant distribution in the mountains from the latitudinal-zonal phenomena, but regards them as conjugate.

The geobotanical maps embracing the whole territory of the USSR or parts of it reflect the basic regularities of the geographic distribution of the plant cover, depending upon a number of factors, primarily climate, conditions of relief (geomorphology), soil cover, and also the geologic history of the locality.

To what extent have the relations of the plant cover of the USSR to these factors been analyzed? This has been done in the most general form both by plant geographers G. I. Tanfil'yev, V. V. Alekhin, B. A. Keller, and others and by physical geographers L. S. Berg, A. A. Grigor'yev, S. P. Suslov, and others.

In their investigations, plant geographers examine primarily the relation of the vegetation to the relief. Thus, in the above-mentioned project for the geobotanical regionalization of the USSR (1947), much attention was paid to the relations of the vegetation to the geomorphologic breakdown of the country.

Inasmuch as the contemporaneous orography is closely related to the geotectonics, the latter also "shines through" to a certain extent in the contemporaneous plant cover. In the young (alpine) or renovated alpine orogenesis of the older mountain structures, this manifests itself in the vertical belting of the vegetation. On the borders between the old peneplained mountain systems and the surface strata of the folded foundation, latitudinal-zonal regularities are usually preserved in the distribution of the plant cover, but are complicated by combinations of various petrophytic associations and by some manifestations of vertical belting, usually only slightly pronounced. We observe such phenomena, for example, in the Kazakh Fold Land, the Donets Ridge, etc. The latitudinal-zonal regularities are most pronounced in uplifted, and therefore surface-drained, platforms with a more or less deep deposit of the folded foundation, for example on the Russian (Eastern European) Plain (Platform). On the other hand, on greatly depressed platforms having at present the character of lowland plains, for example, on the Western Siberian Lowland, the latitudinal zonality of the plant cover is complicated by the hydrogenic phenomena in the plant cover: by the wide distribution of swamps of various types, swampy forests, meadows, and so forth.

In the works of I. M. Krasheninnikov, much attention has been paid to the geomorphogenic **relations of the plant cover** with respect to their dynamics, using as illustrations the vegetation of the Southern Urals, Kazakhstan, and certain regions of Mongolia.

Soviet plant geographers, following the traditions of the V. V. Dokuchayev school in the field of soil science and plant geography, usually endeavor to relate the vegetation with the soils; in this respect, a great deal of material has been accumulated in our literature. However, many phenomena in the soil-and-plant relationships observed over vast expanses have not been sufficiently studied. I shall cite but one example.

In studying the relations of the steppe and desert vegetation to various subtypes of chernozem, chestnut, and brown soils as one moves from west to east along the respective soil zones, one is struck by one very interesting empirical law of regularity: the farther one goes toward the east, the more "northern" are the types of vegetation that appear on these soils. Thus, in the south of the European part of the USSR, on the southern chernozems, one observes principally dry feathergrass-and-fescue steppes, while in the south of the western Siberian Lowland and in northern Kazakhstan less xerophytic, i.e., more northern, variherbaceous-fescue-and-feathergrass* steppes are already associated with the southern chernozems. On the dark-chestnut soils of the northern part of Kazakhstan we encounter dry fescue-and-feathergrass steppes, while in the northern part of Mongolia, in the Khangay, on dark-chestnut soils (non-solonetz), we find special "mountain" steppes analogous to the variherbaceous-fescue-and-feathergrass steppes which in northern Kazakhstan are associated with southern chernozems. On brown soils in northern Kazakhstan one observes northern semishrub (wormwood and saltwort) deserts, while in Mongolia on analogous soils we encounter desert (semishrub-and-feathergrass and semishrub-and-bulb) steppes, the analogues of which in Kazakhstan are associated with light-chestnut soils. All such phenomena of soil-and-plant "inversions" demand close attention on the part of plant geographers and soil scientists.

The relations of the vegetation of the USSR to the climate require further study. In their general form they have been examined by geographers interested in the typology of climates and the climatic regionalization of the earth in conjunction with its landscape and botanico-geographic division (W. P. Köppen, L. S. Berg, and others).

V. B. Sochava has examined the relation of the vegetation of the USSR to the climate-forming processes and dynamic types of climate, on the basis of the works of Soviet climatologists, chiefly B. P. Alisov. On the basis of a study of these interrelationships, Sochava (1948) gives a scheme of regionalization of the plant cover of the USSR which may be called "climatico-geobotanical." He writes: "Of prime importance are the mutual relationships of the vegetation to the climate and the Earth's surface, which we call geographic relations of the first order" (p. 5).

---

*The components in such technical descriptions are customarily arranged in the order of their predominance or proportion.—Translator

Sochava distinguishes "geobotanical belts" [*geobotanicheskiye poyasa*] (within the borders of the USSR there are only three: arctic, humid, and arid), divided into "geobotanical fields" [*polya*], and the latter in turn into sections [*uchastki*] and massifs [*massivy*]. In addition, "geographic nodes" [*uzly*] are distinguished in large and complex mountain systems (in the USSR there are three: the Caucasian, the Middle Asiatic, and the Altay).

In the USSR, an ecologic trend is also developing in climatology, which is conceived in this country chiefly as agricultural climatology. Climate is studied as a condition for growing cultivated plants and artificial cultivated phytocoenoses (G. T. Selyaninov, P. I. Koloskov, S. A. Sapozhnikov, and F. F. Davitaya). These works present considerable interest for plant geographers as well. Still, it is to be regretted that there has been in this country almost no development of the geobotanical branch of ecologic climatology having as its purpose the study of climate as an environment for the natural plant cover.

I shall dwell briefly upon certain questions of the study of the general laws of the distribution of the vegetation in the extratropical countries of the Northern Hemisphere. It is necessary, first of all, to point out the treatment by M. G. Popov (1927, 1929 and 1950) of the concept of the "Area of the Ancient Midland" [*Oblast' Drevnego Sredizem'ya*], which on the continent of Eurasia extends from the Great Khingan in the east to the Strait of Gibraltar in the west and embraces desert, steppe, and some dry forest lands of Eurasia. Although this concept arose on the basis of the study of the flora, it also has a more general botanical geographic significance. M. G. Popov (1929) regards the Ancient Midland as being in a higher rank, like the "plant kingdom" of Western European authors or the "dominion" in A. P. Il'inskiy's sense (1937).

The concept of an "Ancient Midland" has been adopted by almost all USSR botanical geographers. I believe that the Ancient Midland within somewhat different limits (including the steppes of Eurasia) should be treated as a subdominion of Holarctica.

On the basis of a study of the geography of the plant cover of the USSR, as reflected in the survey maps of the vegetation of our country, the author of these lines (1950) has proposed a division of Palearctica into 10 botanical geographic areas [*oblasti*]. (If one distinguishes a separate area of polar [arctic] deserts, the number increases to eleven.) This division of Palearctica emphasizes the differences in the plant cover of the inner continental part of Eurasia, where the phenomena of latitudinal zonality are evolving in their classical form, so to speak, as well as in that of its western and eastern margins, with which the separate oceanic botanical areas of Palearctica are associated.

The work of Soviet plant geographers, cartographically recorded in the survey maps of the vegetation of the USSR, poses an important question: that of the types of belting of vegetation in mountains. The vegetation maps of the USSR to scales of 1:5,000,000 (1939) and 1:4,000,000 (1956) clearly show the main vegetation types of the high mountains of Eurasia, the formation of which has been examined by A. I. Tolmachev (1948): alpine, bald-top [*golets*], highland xerophytic, highland steppe, and high-mountain desert. As pointed out by A. I. Tolmachev, these high-mountain vegetation types were first recorded cartographically on the "Map of the Vegetation of the USSR" to 1:5,000,000 (1939).

The main authors of the "Map of the Vegetation of the USSR" to 1:5,000,000 (Vasil'yev, Gorodkov, Il'inskiy, Lavrenko, Prozorovskiy, and Shiffers, 1940) established five main types of belting in the mountains of the USSR: arctic (tundra), boreal (baldtop-tayga [*gol'tsovo-tayezhnyy*]), Kamchatkan (baldtop-birchwood), nemoral (alpine-broadleaf-forest), and arid (desert-steppe), the latter with three variants (Fore-Asiatic, Tyan'-Shan', and Northern Mongolian). Lately, K. V. Stanyukovich (1955) has given a more detailed typology of the vegetation belting in the mountains of the USSR. He establishes 13 types of belting, with a number of variants, and unites them into two main groups, maritime and continental. The next thing is to make a detailed climatologic interpretation of the types of vegetation belting in the mountains of the USSR.

Soviet plant geographers have carried on investigations not only in the USSR but also in some foreign countries. An especially large amount of work has been done in studying the vegetation of the Mongolian People's Republic (works by V. I. Baranov, A. V. Kalinina, Ye. M. Lavrenko, N. V. Pavlov, Ye. G. Pobedimova, I. A. Tsatsenkin, and A. A. Yunatov). A. A. Yunatov has published three monographs on the vegetation of the Mongolian People's Republic (1950, 1951, 1954).

Soviet botanists have also carried on great geobotanical investigations in some regions of the Chinese People's Republic, in the Syrian region of the United Arab Republic, and in some other countries of the world. Works have peen published on the forests of the subtropical and tropical parts of China (N. V. Dylis, V. N. Sukachev, and A. A. Fedorov), on the steppes and savannas of China (Ye. M. Lavrenko), on the vegetation of India (P. B. Vipper, V. N. Sukachev), Guinea (Ye. M. Lavrenko) and other countries.

Soviet botanists have devoted much attention in their works to questions of the history of the flora and vegetation of the USSR and adjacent countries. Interest in the history of the plant cover dates far back in our native science. F. Ruprekht's work on the origin of chernozem was published in 1866. At the end of the last century there appeared a number of classical works by A. N. Krasnov (1888, 1894) on the history of the flora of the Tyan'-Shan' and on the origin of the flora of the temperate lands of the Northern Hemisphere from the tropical and subtropical flora; by D. I. Litvinov (1891) on the genesis of the flora of the stony outcrops of the south of European Russia; by S. I. Korzhinskiy (1899) on the development of the plant cover of Russia since the Tertiary; by V. L. Komarov (1908) on the origin of certain genera of the flora of the temperate lands of the Northern Hemisphere in Eastern and Central Asia; by N. I. Kuznetsov (1909) on the history of the plant cover of the Caucasus; and others. These works expressed original and very promising ideas about questions of the history of the plant cover of the Northern Hemisphere.

In Soviet times, A. N. Krishtofovich and I. V. Palibin have concerned themselves to an especially great extent with the questions of the history of Tertiary floras. A number of summaries on the Tertiary floras of the USSR have been published by V. I. Baranov (1948, 1950, 1954). Widely known is A. N. Krishtofovich's concept (1936, 1957) regarding the "Turgay" and "Poltava" floras which occupied in the Paleogene the whole territory of the then-dry land within the USSR and adjacent countries. The boundary between these floras ran approximately along a line uniting the present mouths of the Vistula and Yangtze rivers. To the north of this line extended the area of temperate deciduous forest Turgay flora, with a smaller or larger participation of coniferous species; and to the south, the area of the subtropical, and still farther southward, even tropical, mainly evergreen forest Poltava flora. Later, in the Neogene, owing to the chilling of the climate over the larger part of Europe and Western Asia, the Poltava flora was replaced by Turgay flora, while in the Far East of Asia the boundary between the more northern deciduous and southern evergreen floras did not change substantially.

Soviet botanists have done a great deal to work out one of the most important problems of historical phytogeography, the origin of temperate floras. Asa Gray and A. Engler once proposed a high-latitude (Arcto-Tertiary) origin of the flora now inhabiting the middle latitudes with a more or less temperate climate. This viewpoint was shared by N. I. Kuznetsov (1920), M. G. Popov (1949), the author of these lines, and by others. A. N. Krasnov (1894), on the basis of his own investigations in the east of Asia (from Java to Sakhalin), proposed another solution: the tropico-subtropical origin of the temperate floras, particularly in the Far East. These ideas about the low-latitude origin of the temperate floras were also further developed with success by Soviet investigators, especially Ye. V. Vul'f (1944), who published a major survey on the history of the floras of the globe, as well as by An. A. Fedorov (1957) and A. L. Takhtadzhyan (1957). The latter believes that the native land of the angiosperms, which predominate in most of the plant associations of the dry land of the globe, was the subtropical area of Kathasia [*Kataziya*], i.e., the Chinese Platform of the geologists, principally its southern part, the Southern Chinese Massif, which became dry land at the end of the Triassic period. According to the views of A. L. Takhtadzhyan, the angiosperm plants in the Cretaceous spread in several directions from Kathasia, thus giving rise to the floras of the tropical and temperate zones on all the continents. That the primary (ancestral) representatives of the temperate flora were born in this same Kathasia, in the higher belts of the mountains, is very probable.

Ye. M. Lavrenko (1951) has made an attempt to establish the age of the main botanical areas of Palearctica, meaning by the age of the botanical area the time when, firstly, the plant cover on the interfluves [*plakory*] and in the lower belt of the mountains which is still characteristic of these positions assumed its main features; and, secondly, when the present composition of the edificators became defined in its general features on the level of the series of species and sections of species. What is had in mind here is the formation of the respective plant cover at least on the part of the territory occupied by a given botanical area. To the oldest areas originating already in the Paleogene, Ye. M. Lavrenko has assigned the Japanese-Chinese subtropical area of evergreen forests, the Far-Eastern coniferous-broadleaf forest area, extending from the basin of the Amur to the Yangtze, and the Macronesian subtropical area of evergreen forests. The first of these three areas is evidently the oldest. The Mediterranean Sea subtropical area of hemixerophytic evergreen forests originated later, not earlier than the end of the Miocene, as a result of a certain drying of the climate in the lands adjoining the Mediterranean Sea, in conjunction with the Alpine mountain formation. The age of the European broadleaf-forest area, having in mind its southern regions with forests of a richer composition, is also Neogene — Late Miocene or Pliocene. The Eurasian conifer-forest (tayga) area is the youngest forest area of Palearctica. The formation of forests of the tayga type on plains evidently began at the end of the Pliocene as a result of a strong cooling of the climate, but this area probably received the present forest composition in the Pleistocene. The tundra, as an interfluve (zonal) type, did not begin to take shape until the Pleistocene (A. I. Tolmachev and B. A. Tikhomirov).

The tayga and tundra in an interfluve location are undoubtedly younger than the mountain tayga and mountain tundra. Thus, with respect to the tayga, S. I. Korzhinskiy (1899) pointed out the mountains of Southern Siberia as foci of origination of the Siberian coniferous forests of the tayga type. This idea of the "primariness of the mountain tayga" has since been developed by A. I. Tolmachev (1943), and recently by An. A. Fedorov (1957).

Soviet botanists have paid much attention to the question of the origin of the desert vegetation of Eurasia (Ancient Midland), especially M. G. Popov (1927, 1931, 1938), M. M. Il'in (1937, 1946, 1958), and Ye. P. Korovin (1934, 1938, 1958).

M. G. Popov (1938) begins the history of the xerophytic flora of the deserts of Eurasia with the Cretaceous and Paleogene, but regards the period from the end of the Miocene to the beginning of the Pliocene as the main time of formation of the xerophytic flora of the Ancient Midland, including the flora of the deserts. M. M. Il'in (1946) also gives a similar periodization of the formation of the flora of the deserts of Middle Asia, but regards the flora of the deserts of [non-Soviet] Central Asia as very much younger than that of [Soviet] Middle Asia (Il'in, 1958). P. N. Ovchinnikov (1955) considers the desert semishrub vegetation of the Turanian plains, the plateaus of the Pamir, as well as those of Central Asia to be a young formation originating in the Quaternary. The author of these lines believes that the desert semishrub associations (of saltworts, but later also of wormwoods) may still have appeared in the Neogene under the plains conditions in the lands of the Ancient Midland, but that individual associations of the desert type could have been formed on saltmarshes and outcrops of salinified rocks at a much earlier time.

In general, it must be borne in mind that, in examining zonal types of vegetation, one must distinguish: (1) the time of origin of a given type of vegetation under special topologic conditions (in the middle or upper belts in the mountains or on special substrata, etc.); (2) the time of the spread of the respective type of vegetation on the plains or in the lower belt of mountains, under more or less interfluve conditions.

Of great significance among the concepts advanced by Soviet botanists concerning the history of flora and vegetation are those of I. M. Krasheninnikov (1933, 1946) regarding the "Pleistocene forest-steppe" and the "Pleistocene floristic complex," under the conditions of which occurred the process of cryoxerophytization of many more or less mesophile plants (including forest and meadow plants), which thus entered into the steppe communities.

During the last three decades, and particularly since the War, much work has been done by micropaleobotanists on the study of sedimentary rocks of different ages. The results obtained have been used for paleogeographic reconstructions. Among the investigations made on the basis of spore and pollen analysis, let us mention the works concerning the Tertiary by I. M. Pokrovskaya, Ye. D. Zaklinskaya, A. A. Chiguyayeva, Ye. N. Ananova, and others; and on the Pleistocene by

V. P. Grichuk and his collaborators. Special note should be taken of the summary based on the extensive material from the spore and pollen analysis of peat bogs, by M. I. Neyshtadt (1957), entitled "History of the Forests and the Paleogeography of the USSR in the Holocene" [*Istoriya Lesov i Paleogeografiya SSSR v Golotsene.*]

Only a few of the main problems of Soviet plant geography have been mentioned above. In a short survey it is impossible to deal fully with the immense volume of work on the study of the plant cover of the USSR performed by our native botanists since the Great October Socialist Revolution.

BASIC LITERATURE

Baranov, V. I. "Stages of the Development of the Flora and Vegetation of the USSR in the Tertiary Period," parts 1-3, *Uchen. zap. Kaz. gos. un-ta,* vol. 108, book 3; vol. 110, book 6; vol. 114, book 4. Kazan', 1948, 1950, 1954.

Bykov, B. A. Geobotany (*Geobotanika*). Alma-Ata, 1953, 2nd ed., 1957.

Viktorov, S. V. Use of the Geobotanical Method in Geologic and Hydrogeologic Investigations (*Ispol'zovaniye Geobotanicheskogo Metoda pri Geologicheskikh i Gidrogeologicheskikh Issledovaniyakh*). Moscow, 1955.

Vul'f, Ye. V. Historical Geography of Plants. History of the Floras of the Globe (*Istoricheskaya Geografiya Rasteniy. Istoriya Flor Zemnogo Shara*). Moscow-Leningrad, 1944.

Geobotanicheskoye Rayonirovaniye SSSR (Geobotanical Regionalization of the USSR). Under the editorship of Ye. M. Lavrenko.

Grossgeym, A. A. "Analysis of the Flora of the Caucasus." *Tr. Bot. in-ta,* vol. I, AN SSSR, Azerbaydzhanskiy filial, Baku, 1936.

Il'in, M. M. "Concerning the Origin of the Flora of the Deserts of Middle Asia." *Sov. Botanika,* 1937, No. 6, Moscow-Leningrad, 1933.

Il'inskiy, A. P. Vegetation of the Globe. Geography of Plants (*Rastitel'nost' Zemnogo Shara. Geografiya Rasteniy*), III, Moscow-Leningrad, 1937.

Kats, N. Ya. Types of Swamps of the USSR and Western Europe and their Geographic Distribution (*Tipy Bolot SSSR i Zapadnoy Yevropy i ikh Geograficheskoye Rasprostraneniye*), Moscow, 1948.

Korovin, Ye. P. Vegetation of Middle Asia and Southern Kazakhstan (*Rastitelnost' Sredney Azii i Yuzhnogo Kazakhstana*), Moscow-Tashkent, 1934.

Krasheninnikov, I. M. Geographic Works (*Geograficheskiye Raboty*), 2nd ed., Moscow, Geografgiz, 1954.

Krishtofovich, A. N. *Paleobotanika,* 4th ed., Leningrad, 1957.

Lavrenko, Ye. M. "The Age of the Botanical Areas of Extratropical Eurasia." *Izv. AN SSSR. Seriya geogr.,* vol. 2, 1951.

Lebedov, D. V. An Introduction to the Botanical Literature of the USSR. A Handbook for Geobotanists (*Vvedeniye v Botanicheskuyu Literaturu SSSR. Posobiye Dlya Geobotanikov*), Moscow-Leningrad, 1956.

Ovchinnikov, P. N. "Main Directions of Species Formation in Relation to the Origin of the Types of Vegetation of Middle Asia," *Tr. AN Tadzh. SSR,* XXI, Stalinabad, 1955.

Popov, M. G. Selected Works (*Izbrannyye Sochineniya*), AN Turkm. SSR, Ashkhabad, 1958.

Ramenskiy, L. G. Introduction to the Integrated Soil-botanical Investigation of Lands (*Vvedeniye v Kompleksnoye Pochvenno-geobotanicheskoye Issledovaniye Zemel'*), Moscow, 1938.

Rastitelnost' SSSR (Vegetation of the USSR), vols. I and II, Izd-vo AN SSSR, Moscow-Leningrad, 1938, 1940.

Rastitel'nyy Pokrov SSSR (The Plant Cover of the USSR), vols. I and II, izd-vo AN SSSR, Moscow-Leningrad, 1956.

Sochava, V. B. "The Geographic Relations of the Plant Cover on the Territory of the USSR," *Leningr. gos. ped. in-t im. A. I. Gertsena, Uchen. zap.* vol. 73. Chair of Physical Geography, Leningrad, 1948.

Sukachev, V. N. Plant Communities (Introduction to Phytosociology) (*Rastitel'nyye Soobshchestva* [*Vvedeniye v Fitosotsiologiyu*]), 4th ed., Leningrad-Moscow, 1928.

Sukachev, V. N. "Fundamentals of the Theory of Biogeocoenology." In the book: *Yubileynyy Sbornik, Posvyashchennyy 30-letiyu Velikoy Oktyabr'skoy Sotsialisticheskoy Revolyutsii,* part 2, Izd-vo AN SSSR, Moscow-Leningrad, 1947.

Takhtadzhyan, A. L. "Concerning the Question of the Origin of the Temperate Flora of Eurasia." *Bot. zh.,* No. 42, II, Moscow-Leningrad, 1957.

Tolmachev, A. I. "On the Origin of some Basic Elements of the High-mountain Floras of the Northern Hemisphere." *Materialy po Istorii Flory i Rastitel'nosti SSSR,* III, Moscow-Leningrad, 1958.

Trudy Komissii po Yestestvenno-istoricheskomu Rayonirovaniyu SSSR (Transactions of the Commission on the Natural-Historical Regionalization of the USSR), vol. II, issue 2, Moscow-Leningrad, 1947.

Tyuremnov, S. N. Peat Deposits and their Exploration (*Torfyanyye Mestorozhdeniya i ikh Razvedka*), 2nd ed., Moscow-Leningrad, 1949.

Fedorov, An. A. "The Flora of Southwestern China and its Significance for a Knowledge of the Plant World of Eurasia" (Flora Yugo-zapadnogo Kitaya i yeye Znacheniye dlya Poznaniya Rastitel'nogo Mira Yevrazii). *Komarovskiye chteniya,* X, Desyat' let so dnya smerti V. L. Komarova, Moscow-Leningrad, 1957.

Shennikov, A. P. "Theoretical Geobotany in the last 20 years." *Sov. botanika,* 1937, No. 5, Moscow-Leningrad, 1937.

Yunatov, A. A. "The Main Features of the Plant Cover of the Mongolian People's Republic." *Tr. mongol'skoy komissii AN SSSR,* no. 39, Moscow-Leningrad, 1950.

Yaroshenko, P. D. Fundamentals of the Study of the Plant Cover (*Osnovy Ucheniya o Rastitel'nom Pokrove*). Moscow, 1950; 2nd ed., Moscow, 1953.

CHAPTER 16

ZOOGEOGRAPHY OF THE LAND

Yu. A. Isakov and A. N. Formozov

The study of the geography of the animals of the Soviet Union and the countries adjoining it on the southeast has a great and glorious history. It is customary to consider that the scientific investigation of the animal world of Russia began with Daniel Messerschmidt (1685-1735), whom Peter I sent out in 1720 to study Siberia, and was soon brilliantly continued and developed by a whole galaxy of great scholars in the period of V. Bering's expeditions (1725-1743) and the famous "academic expeditions" which embraced almost the whole territory of Russia and the adjacent areas of the Caucasus and Iran. While giving due credit to the erudition, energy, self-denial and devotion to science of the participants in these expeditions, it may be confidently asserted that the fullness of the zoological information gathered by them was to a certain extent due to the fact that many species of animals, birds, and fish, especially those of economic significance, had long since been fairly familiar to the peoples of our country.

In the 15th and 16th centuries the regions of the European North were already perfectly well known as far as Spitsbergen and Novaya Zemlya, particularly the localities ranged over by walruses, seals, eider ducks, and the large hawks, especially the gerfalcons (Witsen Nicolaes, Amsterdam, 1692), which were of great value to hawk hunters. Moreover, gerfalcons were constantly being sent as gifts with various sorts of diplomatic missions dispatched by the Muscovite tsars to the countries of the Near East and Western Europe.

As Russian military servicemen and merchants advanced into Siberia in the 16th and 17th centuries, Moscow received from them reports containing brief descriptions of the new areas, their population and game, especially the reserves of valuable fur-bearing animals, since the furs ("soft stuff") [myagkaya rukhlyad'] were at that time the chief magnet attracting searchers for "new lands." The many documents that have come down to us from that epoch, for all their laconicism, are marked by a notably precise characterization of the faunal wealth of Siberia. The methods employed at that time in catching animals with different sorts of self-operating snares or by archery required an excellent knowledge of the distribution by biotypes, and the behavior, migrations, and other seasonal aspects of the life of game animals. Naturally, the gathering of information through the interrogation of both the aboriginal population and the old Russian settlers of Siberia occupied a large place in the work of P. S. Pallas, I. I. Lepekhin, S. P. Krasheninnikov, V. F. Zuyev, and other participants in the academic expeditions. This is why the materials on the distribution and biology of many animals which it was difficult for the travelers themselves to catch came to be so extensive in the investigations made by the scholars of the middle of the 18th century. Their accounts, with descriptions of the localities explored (Pallas, 1771-1776; Gmelin, 1771-1785; Georgi, 1786, 1787-1802; Zuyev, 1787; Lepekhin, 1771-1805; Krasheninnikov, 1755) and others, and especially the "Zoographia Rosso-Asiatica" of P. S. Pallas (1811-1812), contain much information about the natural conditions of the country and the distribution of the animals. As a result, by the end of the 18th century Russia was zoologically one of the best studied countries. But zoogeographic generalizations were still lacking in the works enumerated above.

In the first half of the 19th century the number of regional faunal investigations increased appreciably, a considerable part of them being carried out, not by workers of the Academy of Sciences but by provincial scholars, chiefly professors in universities; individual amateurs also began to appear among physicians, landowners, etc., and this was especially promoted by the rise of the first scientific associations in Russia, the Moscow Society of Nature Students [*Moskovskoye Obshchestvo Ispytateley Prirody*], founded in 1805, and the Free Economic Society [*Vol'noye Ekonomicheskoye Obshchestvo*]. One of the active members of the Society of Nature Students, K. F. Rul'ye, a professor in Moscow University, attached special significance to the study of animals in their manifold relations to environmental conditions, particularly the seasonal phenomena of their life, and laid in Russia the foundation of a science which subsequently came to be called ecology. His closest pupil, N. A. Severtsov, profoundly assimilated Rul'ye's research methods. In his very first independent work, "Periodic Phenomena in the Life of the Animals, Birds, and Reptiles of Voronezh Guberniya" (1855), Severtsov gave not only a fine regional description of the fauna, but also a detailed treatment of the seasonal phenomena in the life of land vertebrates in relation to the climatic, biotic, and topographic characteristics of the area investigated. This ecologic zoogeographic work by Severtsov, innovational in character and based on nine years of stationary observations, contained many valuable generalizations and had no equal in the world literature of the time.

The further investigations by Severtsov, which gained him the fame of an outstanding traveler, zoologist, and geographer, were made in the steppes, semideserts, and deserts of the Caspian Lowland and the Aral Sea region, in the mountain areas of the Tyan'-Shan' and Pamir, at that time still completely unknown to Europeans. Severtsov's twenty years of intensive expeditionary work in Middle Asia yielded a great wealth of zoological and zoogeographic results. In addition to describing many species formerly unknown to science, he ascertained the characteristics of the distribution of animals by vertical belts in the Tyan'-Shan' and made a successful attempt to analyze the genetic relations of the Turkestan fauna (Severtsov, 1878). His explorations, which embraced localities bordering on India and the Himalayas, joined up the territory studied by Russian geographers and biologists with the areas in which English scholars were successfully working. An untimely death prevented Severtsov from working up all the materials gathered. The main work published, which was actually nothing more than a preliminary account, was "The Vertical and Horizontal Distribution of Turkestan Animals." Soon after its publication, this work was translated into many Western European languages. In this book, Severtsov paid much attention to hypotheses of the formation of the "Turkestan fauna." The inadequacy of the paleogeographic data naturally made a number of Severtsov's propositions and conclusions erroneous, but since that time historicism has been an integral part of zoogeographic investigations by Russian scholars and for a certain period even thrust into the background the study of the influence of the present physical geographic conditions on the life and formation of the fauna, the fruitfulness of which Severtsov demonstrated in the 1855 work.

Still, by no means all of Severtsov's efforts to establish the history of palaearctic animals were unsuccessful. Concerning himself with the question of species formation and the geography of mountain sheep of the genus Ovis, and studying the characteristics of the Middle Asiatic, Siberian, and North American representatives of the group known at that time, Severtsov came to the conclusion that the forms which penetrated from Asia into North America, later spreading northward along the mountain chains and being modified in the course of this spread, finally reached the isthmus uniting the two continents in the region of Bering Strait and in geologically recent times populated the whole northeast of Siberia. Severtsov's interesting hypothesis of a recent dry-land connection between Asia and America, based on zoogeographic data, has since been confirmed by a number of geologic, zoogeographic, and paleogeographic investigations by Soviet scholars. (See, for example, P. P. Sushkin, 1925; and V. N. Saks, 1936, 1940, 1953.)

In a special zoogeographic analysis of the fauna of eastern Palaearctica ("On the Zoological, Principally Ornithological, Areas of the Extratropical Parts of our Continent," 1877), Severtsov proposed his division into sub-oblasts and okrugs, taking into account the data on the distribution of animals and the association of definite complexes of them with the natural geographic zones. Thus, the author of the doctrine of natural-geographic zonality, the outstanding Russian geographer and soil scientist V. V. Dokuchayev, had one of his predecessors in the person of N. A. Severtsov. A contemporary of Severtsov, Academician A. F. Middendorf, known for his remarkable many-volume account of his travels to the north and east of Siberia, which contains zoogeographic sections, was a great biogeographer and laid the foundations of our native ecology by concerning himself with the question of the influence of climatic conditions on the life and distribution of vertebrates. Both of these naturalists devoted much attention to the study of the migrations of animals, especially birds.

A survey of the development of zoogeography in the 19th century would be incomplete without the mention of the works of G. S. Karelin, E. A. Eversmann, M. N. Bogdanov, G. I. Radde, K. F. Kessler, and V. K. Tachanovskiy, to say nothing of a considerable number of others. The famous traveler, geographer, and naturalist N. M. Przheval'skiy holds a special place among the explorers of this period. Covering with the network of his itineraries an enormous expanse of Central Asia heretofore completely unknown to Europeans, he gathered exceptionally valuable data on the nature of the areas explored, their fauna, and the conditions of existence of the animals. The very rich collections delivered by him to the Zoological Museum of the Academy of Sciences served as material for a number of monographs written by many scholars. The blank spots on the map of Central Asia were erased by the labors of this universally known traveler, and zoogeographers received extensive material for generalization.

Thus, through the efforts of Russian scholars, the basic information on the fauna of a considerable part of Eurasia had been accumulated by the end of the 19th century and become the property of world science. The higher vertebrates and certain groups of insects had been studied, but the bulk of the invertebrates still remained unknown to science. The paltry number of specialists and the extreme lack of funds in the Academy of Sciences and the universities of tsarist Russia hampered not only zoological field research, but also the working-up of the collected materials. Many collections awaited study for decades. Only individual enthusiasts, deterred by no privations, like N. A. Zarudnyy, who with negligible means managed to study the fauna of the Orenburg steppes, the deserts and mountains of Turkmenistan, and a number of provinces of Iran, carried on successful work on the margins of the country. The closest pupils of the outstanding zoogeographers of this period, for example, M. A. Menzbir, professor in Moscow University and a great ornithologist and zoogeographer, and N. A. Severtsov's closest pupil, Academician P. P. Sushkin, and others, having begun their work at the end of the 19th century, continued their activity in the first half of the current century and transmitted the best traditions of our native zoogeographers to numerous pupils after the Great October Socialist Revolution.

The main characteristics of the development of zoogeography in Soviet Russia are connected with the appearance of numerous young specialists who have rapidly arisen alongside the scholars of an earlier generation, as well as with the immense expansion and planned character of special-purpose exploring expeditions, with the rise of a number of new republic and oblast scientific centers in formerly backward parts of the country, and with the execution of many scientific investigations aimed directly at the solution of most important tasks. Among the essential deficiencies of the earlier work of Soviet investigators must be counted their narrow zoological character and lack of geographic viewpoint.

How imperfectly even the mammals had been studied in pre-revolutionary Russia is evidenced by the following facts: in Soviet times, when an intensive faunal exploration of Siberia and Middle Asia was begun, not only were many species of insectivora, chiroptera, and rodents discovered that were new to science, but such genera were described as, for example, the remarkable jerboas [tushkanchiki] Eremodipus and Paradipus, the boyalych [the saltwort Salsola arbuscula], the dormouse genus Selevinia, and even a new subfamily, the Seleviniinae, having a single species, thus far known only from the Betpak-Dala Desert of Kazakhstan.

The study of individual faunal territories—a quite indispensable initial stage of any zoogeographic investigation—has not yet been entirely completed in USSR. Over its vast expanses there remain a good many sections that have clearly not been explored sufficiently. Nevertheless, at the beginning of this century the information on certain groups of animals had attained such a level that it had become possible to compile major faunal compendia for the territory of Russia as a whole. Their number has, of course, been sharply increased in the Soviet period.

A special place is occupied by the continuing, many-volume publication of the "Fauna of the USSR," issued by the Academy of Sciences of the USSR, representing a series of monographs devoted to the most varied groups of animals. Each one of them, in addition to a general characterization of the group as a whole, gives detailed information about the distribution and ecology of the individual species. A thorough study of the fish fauna of the fresh waters of the USSR and adjacent countries was prepared and pub'ished by L. S. Berg (1916, 1948-1949); on winged ticks, by V. B. Dubinin (1951); a monograph on bird fauna, by a group of workers of Moscow University under the general editorship of G. P. Dement'yev and N. A. Gladkov ("The Birds of the Soviet Union", vol. I-VI, 1951-1954); on mammals, by S. I. Ognev (1928-1950); on locusts, by G. Ya. Bey-Biyenko and A. I. Mishchenko (1950), and a number of others.

A somewhat different ecologic zoogeographic idea is another major publication, "The Animal World of the USSR" (vols. I-V, 1936-1958), characterizing the animal population of the various natural zones of our country. The appearance of these and some other summaries has made it possible for wide circles of specialists and amateurs to engage in research work. Faunal explorations have continued successfully in Central Asia; works containing valuable zoogeographic facts and generalizations have been published (Tugarinov, 1928; Formozov, 1928; Kozlova, 1930; Bannikov, 1954, on the animals of Mongolia; Kozlova, 1952, on the avifauna of the Tibetan Plateau). In the last few years, newly trained local national personnel have conducted joint work in Mongolia and the Chinese People's Republic in co-operation with Soviet explorers.

A number of territories have already been studied so fully with respect to fauna that it has proved possible to make a well-grounded zoogeographic regionalization of them on the basis of the data on the distribution of land vertebrates, fresh-water fish, certain groups of insects (butterflies, beetles, etc.), land molluscs, and so forth. The first attempts at such a generalization were made only by comparing the species composition of the fauna of individual sections, but substantial attention later came to be directed toward the origin of species, the association of them and of whole ecologic groups with various elements of the landscape and, finally, toward the abundance of certain background forms (Kurentsov, 1947-1958; Dal', 1954; Strautman, 1954; Medvedev, 1957 and others). Generalizing the accumulated materials, L. S. Berg (1923-1949) gave a scheme of detailed regionalization of the whole territory of the USSR, based on a study of fresh-water fish; and B. A. Kuznetsov (1950) filled out this work with respect to mammal fauna.

As is known, the general scheme of division of the land into main zoogeographic areas [oblasti] and subareas [podoblasti] was determined by the beginning of our century. Many great scholars of our country participated in working it out: N. A. Severtsov (1877) and M. A. Menzbir (1882, 1914, 1934), A. A. Byalynitskiy-Birulya (1917), V. L. Bianki (1905, 1918), P. P. Sushkin (1921, 1932), N. Ya. Kuznetsov (1929), L. S. Berg (1932, 1933, 1934), A. Bartenev (1933, 1935), A. P. Semenov-Tyan-Shanskiy (1935), and others. Questions of the subdivision of the Paleoarctic area attracted their special attention. However, the division of the territory into subareas and provinces [provintsii] was often made principally on the basis of a statistical analysis of the species composition of their fauna, without giving sufficient consideration to genesis. The "Mediterranean," "European-Siberian," and other faunas are very heterogeneous in their origin, so that these terms themselves have to some degree lost their significance. Hence, the notions about zoogeographic subareas are still far from perfection and require revision.

Let us note some interesting attempts made in the last few years to revise, on the basis of the accumulated new data, the notions about the genetic composition of the faunas and about the boundaries of the individual subareas and provinces. V. V. Kucheruk (1959), having studied the ranges [arealy] and biotic relations of the mammals of the steppe complex peculiar to the extratropical part of Eurasia, has come to the conclusion that "the steppe fauna complex represents one of the basic, wholly independent units..." The territory on which this complex predominates should be called the Steppe Zoogeographic Subarea of Palaearctica. In its outlines, it is very close to the botanical geographic Eurasian Steppe Area distinguished by Ye. M. Lavrenko (1950). V. E. Martino (1958) has examined the interrelations between the faunas of Fore-Asia and the Mediterranean; V. G. Geptner has ascertained important characteristics of the Fore-Asian fauna (1940) and the interrelations between the Mediterranean fauna and that of the whole desert-steppe zone of Paleoarctica (1945); and I. A. Dolgushin (1958) has analyzed the species composition of birds by the character of the distribution of those actually associated with the Mediterranean.

The investigations of P. P. Sushkin (1918-1922, 1925) were of great significance in their time for the development of the historical approach to these questions. On the basis of information about the present-day distribution of animals and with the use of geologic and paleogeographic data as well, he wrote an essay on the history of the formation of the fauna of Palaearctic Asia and especially Middle Siberia, establishing the connections of the latter with the fauna of the Asiatic highlands. A comparison of the faunas of the Old and New Worlds led him to the hypothesis of the existence, in the northern part of the Pacific Ocean in the recent geologic past, of the extensive land of Beringia, which served as a center for the distribution of a large number of tayga forms of animals common to both continents. He also expressed important ideas about the presence of separate foci of fauna formation in the Central Asiatic deserts and about the role of the glacial epoch in the re-distribution of faunas.

These ideas were adopted and successfully developed by a number of zoogeographers. B. K. Shtegman (1932, 1936, 1938) demonstrated, from the example of birds, the significance of Beringia as a bridge across which a lively exchange of the representatives of the faunas of Asia and America took place. Owing to the changes in the local climatic conditions, several waves of migration of representatives of the faunas of the tundra, tayga, and mixed forests passed over this bridge. However, the steppe birds were unable to make use of the continental connecting strip, so that species and genera common to both continents are missing among them (except for the horned lark, which penetrated from the tundra zone). Shtegman (1931) established that the center of formation of the tayga fauna was Eastern Siberia, from which representatives of the tayga biocoenoses spread far to the west and colonized Europe. However, the latter assumption meets with substantial objections. Apparently, on the territory of Europe and Western Siberia the tayga complex of species is composed of local Late-Tertiary forms, which retreated in the Ice Age into the mountains of Europe and, perhaps into those of the Southern Urals (Vorontsov, 1955). Historically and geographically, the zone of mixed forests represents a belt of interaction between the complexes of animals peculiar to the broadleaf and coniferous forests. The main core of its ornithofauna is composed of species connected with the first of these zones; it is joined by the inhabitants of the European tayga and only a small number of the representatives of the tayga of Eastern Siberia, the process of whose westward spread is continuing before our eyes (Vorontsov, 1954; Formozov, 1959).

A thorough analysis of the composition and origin of the Arctic fauna of Eurasia was made by N. Ya. Kuznetsov (1935, 1938), principally on the basis of materials on the lepidoptera. He succeeded in establishing that the present Arctic fauna is composed to a considerable extent of the relicts of the old autochthonous glacial and even preglacial fauna. All the so-called euarcts [evarktiki] are unquestionably endemic inhabitants of the Arctic which have survived the glacial conditions on the spot. The degree of their adaptation to the living conditions is so great that the assumption of their immigration in postglacial times is not very probable. The initial material for the formation of the fauna was apparently the animal population of the ancient Angara continent, and consequently the primordial (down to the early Quaternary) Beringian fauna has in turn an Angara origin. Kuznetsov considers that a natural and historically based zoogeographic division of Palaearctica can be achieved by studying the history of the geography of the refuges of the Ice Age and the disjunctive breaks in the preglacial habitat areas of species.

On the basis of a study of the mammal fauna of the deserts of Palaearctica, V. G. Geptner (1938, 1940, 1945, 1958) came to the conclusion that, in addition to the two main foci of desert form development (the Saharan and the Central-Asiatic, or, more precisely, the Mongolian-Kashgarian) there is, in the plains part of Turkestan, still another old and rather considerable focus of form development, attested by the high degree of endemism of the local fauna (four or five endemic genera). All the Turanian endemics are typical psammophytes, whereas the inhabitants of deserts with hard ground predominate among the central Asiatic ones. To a considerable extent, these ecologic complexes of desert animals have independent courses of development. This is evidenced by the presence of an Iranian-Afghan focus of form development of animals of the mountainous, as well as the gravel plains deserts and the Kazakhstan semidesert center, which are isolated from the Turanian ecologically, not geographically.

Important considerations regarding the history of the development of the alpine faunas, chiefly on the basis of a study of coleoptera, have been offered by A. P. Semenov-Tyan-Shanskiy (1928).

Interesting thoughts on this same question have been expressed by A. G. Bannikov (1958).

A. V. Martynov (1929) approached the revision of the scheme of zoogeographic division of Eurasia from a new standpoint. He called attention to the fact that the faunal composition of a very old group of insects, the caddis flies, in the largest zoogeographic units (areas, subareas, and some others) is distinctly affected by the Tertiary geologic history of the continents. However, within them both the horizontal and the vertical distribution of the species is governed by the characteristics of the ecology of the larval stage of these insects. The caddis flies are represented by two ecologic groups: limnophile forms, inhabiting the plains lakes and streams with a slow current, and the rheophiles, peculiar to the rapid streams of mountain lands. These groups of species are ecologically isolated from one another and often have a different history. They react differently to considerable changes in climate. The chilling characteristic of the Ice Age caused a southward displacement of the complex of species peculiar to the plains, and brought about the formation of the complex mixed fauna of the European part of the USSR and Western Siberia, the species of which possess extensive ranges. The fauna of the mountain regions survived this period on the spot, and retained its preglacial character to a considerable extent.

On the basis of a study of these biocomplexes, Martynov arranges in an entirely new manner the boundaries of the main zoogeographic areas. Bartenev (1930-1932) has also undertaken to subdivide Palaearctica into subareas on the basis of a grouping of dragonflies by their ecologic features.

Studying the present habitat areas of the species and genera of birds, B. K. Shtegman (1936, 1938) established that the ornithofauna of Palaearctica is composed of a limited number of types, the representatives of which are similar in origin, development, and ecologic characteristics. He notes seven such main types of fauna: Arctic, Siberian, European, Mediterranean, Mongolian, Tibetan, and Chinese. The first of these embraces the Arctic of the Old and New Worlds, and the territory occupied by it is distinguished as an independent area. No linear boundaries exist between the zones of distribution of the various types of fauna: there is interpenetration between them. The method proposed by Shtegman for the cartographic representation of the distribution of the various types of fauna by indicating with colored spots the presence of representatives of this or that complex graphically shows the localization of the centers of origin of the fauna, the dynamics of its spread (i.e., history), and its association with specific landscapes (i.e., features of ecology). This approach to the analysis of the distribution and mapping of genetically heterogeneous faunal groupings represents a considerable step forward.

The reality, correct understanding, and relative significance of certain types of fauna noted by Shtegman have been subjected to criticism by a number of investigators; for example, the Tibetan, by Kozlova, 1952; the Siberian, by Vorontsov, 1954, 1955; the Mediterranean, by Dolgushin, 1958. However, the approach adopted by Shtegman to the analysis of fauna has had great influence on the development of such investigations and has been widely used by Soviet and foreign scholars. Against the background of the main types of fauna, secondary daughter foci of their formation have been discovered, not less than eight of which have been counted by entomologists in the Far East alone (Kurentsov, 1958).

The next stage in the development of the doctrine of faunal types was marked by the investigations of G. V. Nikol'skiy (1947), who made a comparative analysis of the biologic characteristics of fish belonging to various faunal types or complexes. In the USSR, he counts 12 faunal complexes of fresh-water fishes whose origin is associated with territories differing substantially in their physical geographic conditions. The species making up one faunal complex develop jointly, under conditions of a definite geographic environment, so that similar features of adaptation to the abiotic conditions develop in them, and adaptive features are formed in their mutual relations to each other. Within each complex, the food competition between the various species is mitigated by the divergence of their food spectra, and the relations between predators and victims are co-adapted, which stabilizes the dynamics of the numerical strength of both. Inter-species competition within a complex fauna manifests itself with especial sharpness between species originating from different faunal complexes but occupying similar ecologic niches. Gradually, as a result of adaptation, a new complex is formed through the remodeling of old complexes under new conditions. Undoubtedly, the ascertainment and analysis of the main characteristics of faunal complexes are to become one of the most important tasks of modern zoogeographic research.

Lately, a considerable group of Soviet scholars (N. K. Vereshchagin and I. M. Gromov, I. G. Pidoplichko, M. A. Voinstvenskiy, G. V. Nikol'skiy, and V. D. Lebedev, and others) has been studying with success the Quaternary history of the mammal, bird, and fish faunas, using paleontologic materials obtained in excavations. This furnishes historical zoogeography with many new facts and firm points of support. The elaboration of techniques to be used in making special searches for burials of animal bone remnants, as well as close contact with archeologists, have insured an unusually rapid accumulation of materials from formerly entirely unstudied regions of our country. The work of this cycle has enriched science with many valuable facts, and also has permitted a number of interesting generalizations characterizing the changes in the fresh-water ichthyofaunas of the European part of the USSR and Western Siberia during the Quaternary period (Nikol'skiy, 1945; Lebedev, 1952, 1959), the elucidation of the history of the formation of the fauna of the European steppes (Pidoplichko, 1950) and the Caucasus (Vereshchagin, 1952, 1959), and the main features of the former distribution of a number of game animals (Tsalkin, 1951, 1956, 1958) and others.

Hydrobiologists have successfully developed investigations of the rich and peculiar fauna of Lake Baykal, the deepest lake in the world, as well as a number of neighboring lakes in which certain elements of the ancient Baykal fauna have been found. This work (Berg, 1922, 1940; Kozhov, 1937) furnishes a great deal of material for judging the stages of formation of the fauna of waters, beginning with the Mesozoic. Very valuable in this respect are the investigations of the fauna of underground waters by Ya. A. Birshteyn.

Still another very interesting trend in the field of the history of fauna is being successfully developed by S. V. Kirikov (1952-1958). As a result of a careful study of numerous and heterogeneous documents preserved in the archives, he has succeeded in reconstructing a picture of the change in landscapes and faunas, chiefly of the game animals of the forest zone, forest-steppe, and steppe of the USSR from the 13th to the 19th century.

In a series of investigations, L. S. Berg (1909, 1920, 1947) utilized paleoclimatic data to explain certain important laws of the present distribution of animals: the phenomena of bipolarity, amphiboreality, etc. These ideas have been developed by many Soviet zoogeographers and have been used by them in solving problems of the formation of regional faunas or the spread of individual systematic groups of animals (Dmitriyev, 1935; Kuznetsov, 1935; Martynov, 1929; Nikol'skiy, 1940; Sviridenko, 1937; Serebrovskiy, 1924; Stanchinskiy, 1922, 1926; Tugarinov, 1934; Turdakov, 1958; Formozov, 1929; Khazatskiy, 1949, 1957, 1958; Chernov, 1949; and others). The considerable progress in paleontologic and geologic research has made it possible to reconstruct the general picture of the formation of the fauna of the European part of the USSR (Menzbir, 1934), of individual landscape zones and, finally, of the country as a whole (Serebrovskiy, 1935; 1936; Pidoplichko, 1946-1956; and Lindberg, 1955).

Most original are the views of I. G. Pidoplichko, which have found no support either among geologists or among zoogeographers. On the basis of paleontologic data and a study of the biology and distribution of Quaternary land vertebrates, he subjected to sharp criticism the migration theory of the formation of present-day fauna, which is being developed by a number of major foreign (Wallace, Dawkins, Nehrung, Osborn, and others) and Russian scholars. In contrast to most of his predecessors, Pidoplichko believes that the glaciations in the southern half of eastern Europe did not exercise such an exceptional influence on the formation of the fauna as is usually ascribed to them. The Quaternary fauna of the steppe and forest-steppe, in his opinion, developed autochthonously, beginning with the Pliocene. No migrations leading to the mixture of faunas occurred in this zone, and the appearance of a certain number of northern species introduced no substantial changes into the basic aspect of the local fauna. Its present semblance is due chiefly to economic activity.

In a number of cases zoogeographic investigations and generalizations have been used to make broad paleogeographic reconstructions. On the basis of data on the present distribution of birds, V. V. Stanchinskiy (1926) has attempted to reconstruct the postglacial changes on the territory of the European part of the USSR, and I. G. Pidoplichko has come to the above-mentioned conclusions about the absence of a solid glaciation on the European Plain. Finally, G. U. Lindberg (1955), applying the biogeographic method of investigating the fresh-water fish fauna, has worked out a hypothesis of the hydrocratic fluctuations of the level of the World Ocean, which have caused not less than three successions of universal regressions and transgressions during the Quaternary period. The features of similarity, for example, in the fresh-water fish fauna of Sakhalin and Japan, on the one hand, and the eastern part of the Asiatic continent, on the other, the presence of distinct traces of stream valleys on the sea floor, and so forth, are most important arguments in favor of Lindberg's views.

A study of the ranges of individual species and of larger systematic categories is possible only if the regional faunas have been studied to a definite degree, and it is therefore one of the final stages of zoogeographic research. For this reason, much less work on ranges has been performed than faunal work. However, it is precisely this cycle of research that is directly related to practical demands, so its development has proved very fruitful. Primarily and most fully studied has been the distribution of species having great significance in the economy and life of the country: certain game animals and birds, agricultural pests, and also animals that carry and transmit infectious diseases. A period of summarization of the first results of the research in this question has now set in. Maps of ranges are included more and more frequently in regional and general faunal compendia. We note, for example, the monograph by S. I. Ognev (1928-1950), the guide to the mammals of the USSR (Bobrinskiy, Kuznetsov, Kuzyakin, 1944) and the collective work on the "Birds of the Soviet Union" (under the editorship of Dement'yev and Gladkov, 1951-1954).

Until quite recently, the attention of scholars had been turned only to the establishment of the boundaries of the ranges [*arealy*], i.e., the limits of the area [*oblast'*] of distribution of the species. But when the work was performed for the account of production organizations of various types, this proved far from adequate. Information was required about the distribution of the populations of a species within the range (solid, discontinuous, lace-like, or spotty) and about the distribution of the regions of high and low numerical strength. The solution of these tasks prompted serious efforts to work out methods for the quantitative inventory of animals and the mapping of their population. As a result, several procedures for counting animals and birds from airplanes were proposed and tested in practice (Freyman and Dorofeyev, 1928; Geptner, 1948; Rakov, 1957; Semenov, 1957; Shilov and Besedin, 1954; Petrov, Kasatkin, and others, 1956); from automobiles (Formozov, 1934, 1953; Varshavskiy and Shilov, 1954, and others) and in traverses on foot. The most practical and promising procedures are described in a special collection of articles ("Methods of Inventorying the Numerical Strength and Geographic Distribution of Land Vertebrates," 1952) and in a number of official instructions on inventorying game animals, rodents (transmitters of human diseases), insects (forest and agricultural pests), and other animals, as well as in a large number of separate articles. Further methodological research in this field is urgently necessary.

The study of the range has demonstrated the extreme dynamism of its internal structure and external boundaries. Naturally, much attention has been attracted by the problem of the pulsation of the boundaries of the ranges, usually due to the fluctuations of the climatic conditions, which manifest themselves most sharply under the conditions of the arid zone (Formozov, 1937, 1959; Chel'tsov, 1958; and others). A number of investigations have been devoted to ascertaining the influence of the present warming of the climate on the change in the boundaries of the ranges of animals in the north of Eurasia (L. S. Berg, 1947; V. Ya. Parovshchikov, 1959; E. V. Kumari, 1958; T. L. Ivanauskas, 1957; and others). During the last few years, a watch has been kept on the process of the settlement on the new sections of land exposed as a result of the large drop in the level of the Caspian Sea (Lavrovskiy, 1959). It has been shown from a number of examples that the cases of rapid displacement of the boundaries of the range of the most diverse animals are often due to the influence of the economic activity of human society (Deksbakh, 1935; Formozov, 1937, 1959; Kuzyakin, 1951; Babenyshev and Glushko, 1956; Korzina, 1957; and others).

Great complexities in the characterization of the distribution of the population [*populyatsiya*] of a species are caused by the uneven distribution of the population [*naseleniye*] and the fluctuation of the numerical strength of the individuals in various parts of the range. The elaboration of this circle of questions has led to the formulation of essentially important concepts about the zones of stable and unstable harmfulness (high number) of animal pests (Rubtsov, 1937-1938, and others) and about the zones of similar favorability of the environment (Formozov, 1935), as well as to attempts to produce maps which reflect the differences in the character and permanency of sojourn and the types of the dynamics of the numerical strength of the individual geographic populations of a species within its range (Isakov, 1950). Most fully studied from this angle are certain harmful insects: the migratory locust (Zakharov, 1946; and others), the *shistotserka* locust (Shcherbinovskiy, 1952), the corn moth (Kozhanchikov, 1938; Budanov, 1951; and others), the Siberian silkworm [*sibirskiy shelkopryad*] (Okunev, 1955), certain species of coleoptera (Dobrovol'skiy, 1947); rodents: the field mouse (Sviridenko, 1943), the water rat (Isakov, 1950; Maksimov, 1958), the big gerbil [*bol'shaya peschanka*] (Varshavskiy and Shilov, 1956) and others; certain fur-bearing animals: the squirrel, sable, and polar fox (Kiris, 1947; Nadeyev and Timofeyev, 1955; Chirkova, 1952), and ducks (Isakov, 1954). Further investigation in this direction is one of the urgent practical tasks of Soviet zoogeography.

The ascertainment of the environmental factors governing the present boundaries and causing a reduction in the area of distribution or else contributing to its expansion is an important aspect of this problem. Mention has already been made of the significance of a number of abiotic factors, including the air temperature, expressed by the isotherms of the individual months or seasons, the ice regime of water bodies, the maximum depth of the snow cover, the soil humidity, the geologic structure of the locality, etc., and, among the biotic factors, the role of the distribution of plant formations. As an example, we point out the article by V. N. Beklemishev and A. N. Zhelokhovtsev (1945) describing the distribution of the mosquitoes of the genus Anopheles in the USSR and comparing the character of the boundaries of the species ranges with the isotherms of the summer months and the duration of the warm period of the year, favorable to the propagation of these insects. A successful beginning has been made in the study of the role of the snow cover, to which several original investigations (Stanchinskiy, 1926; Nasimovich, 1955) and a small monograph by A. N. Formozov (1946) have been devoted. The question of the relation of the distribution of birds which are narrowly specialized in their feeding — the crossbills (*Loxia*) and nutcrackers (*Nucifraga*) — and to the distribution of their food plants — certain species of conifers — has been thoroughly elucidated in articles by S. V. Kirikov (1936, 1940). N. Ya. Kuznetsov (1930), A. K. Mordvilko (1935), and V. V. Popov have analyzed, on the basis of a number of examples, the lengthy interlinked evolution of certain species of butterflies, aphids, and bees and their food plants, which manifests itself in the present character of the distribution of these insects.

A number of investigations have shown that man's activity, simultaneously with the natural factors, has exercised immense influence upon the distribution of animals in the past, beginning with the Neolithic epoch, and continues to do so at present. The economic conquest of the territory, the extermination of some species, and the passive dispersion of others result in the transformation of the natural landscapes and the formation of a new "cultural" landscape. P. V. Serebrovskiy (1936) has given an evaluation of this process on the historical plane, and A. N. Formozov (1937) has systematized the available materials and characterized the multiplicity of forms of man's action upon the animal world. Among the extensive complex of works in this direction it is necessary to mention the investigation made by N. F. Kashchenko (1913) of the stages of settlement of Siberia by the gray rat as transportation improved and the railroad network grew; by V. N. Zryakovskiy (1926), P. A. Sviridenko (1927) and many other authors on the distribution of the little ground squirrel (*malyy suslik*) in the south of the European part of the USSR in connection with the pastoral degression of the steppe vegetation; by N. A. Gladkov (1938) and A. K. Rustamov (1956) on the formation of the fauna of the cultivated oases of Middle Asia; by I. B. Volchanetskiy and S. I. Medvedev (1950) on the rise of the animal world of the forest shelter belts; and a number of other investigations.

Special significance as a nature-transforming factor has been attached in the USSR to the construction of reservoirs, which radically alter the living conditions of aquatic animals and accordingly, also, the fauna of the streams. The study of the questions related therewith is being successfully pursued by a large number of scientific collectives, including the special Institute of the Biology of Reservoirs under the Academy of Sciences of the USSR. The work on the acclimatization and active dissemination of valuable species of mammals, birds, fish, and certain invertebrates has assumed enormous proportions and is rapidly altering the habitat areas of a number of species. These questions are engaging the special attention of Soviet zoogeographers and are being widely treated in the press.

Valuable investigations of the ways of formation of the species habitat areas have been carried out on parasitologic material. I. G. Ioff (1936, 1949) has explained the laws of the present distribution of ground-squirrel fleas, proceeding from the history of the spread of their hosts, and, in a monograph devoted to the fleas of Kirgizia, has made a thorough all-around analysis of the historical and ecologic causes of the vertical and horizontal distribution of these insects in the mountains and deserts. V. B. Dubinin (1953), on the basis of a study of the present distribution of winged ticks [per'yevyye kleshchi], parasitic on ducks, and a comparison of these data with the materials on the geography and paleontology of their hosts, has clarified the origin of this ectoparasite fauna in individual territories and has constructed original schemes outlining the paths of the spread of certain subfamilies of duck-family birds in the geologic past.

The present structure of the range of a species is a derivative of the historical development of the species population under the conditions of a definite geographic environment. Hence, the structure of the range reflects the history of its rise in the process of the evolution of the species. To understand the causes of the dynamism of a range it is necessary to know its history, as well as the basic laws governing the existence of the local populations, the degree of their permanency and relation to adjacent populations, attachment to the locality, mobility, and distribution over the territory (Arnol'di, 1957). Investigation in this field (bordering on the ecology of animals) has undergone broad development in our country. This has resulted in the elaboration of concepts about the primary populations of a species for fish, birds, mammals and insects (Lebedev, 1946; Isakov, 1948, 1957; Naumov, 1936, 1955; Gilyarov, 1954; Mazokhin-Porshnyakov, 1954 and others) and about the types of populations for animals (Formozov, 1947; Varshavskiy, 1952; Naumov, 1955 and others). These propositions, in addition to their significance for the solution of a number of theoretical questions, have found a wide outlet in practice and have served as a scientific foundation for the execution of a number of anti-epidemic measures and work on the acclimatization (resettlement) of animals.

Closely related to the problem of range are questions of migration. The study of seasonal flights of birds by the banding method has undergone wide development in the USSR since the creation of the Central Banding Bureau in 1934, which has become the organizing and methodological center for research in this field. The rich factual materials accumulated during these years have permitted the establishment of the laws of the seasonal distribution of the populations of certain species of birds of our fauna. The results of the investigations have been published in nine issues of the Transactions [Trudy] of the Banding Bureau (1937-1957) and in numerous articles. For the purpose of making a thorough study of the problem of seasonal migrations, seven special ornithologic stations have been created, which make observations in accordance with an extensive program. The theoretical elaboration of the collected materials has enabled A. Ya. Tugarinov (1936, 1950) to compile a general scheme of the main directions of the flights of birds in the USSR and to express general considerations about the origin of their migrations in Palaearctica.

The marking of a number of species of mammals with bands began in this country in the 1930's, and in some cases very interesting data have been obtained about the direction and distance of the migrations (squirrels—Salmin, 1938; polar foxes—Sdobnikov, 1940; flying mice—Lavrov, 1958). The seasonal migrations of ungulates (Nasimovich, 1955 and others), seals, and cetaceans have been studied rather thoroughly, but this has thus far been done quite insufficiently for all the other mammals, fresh-water fish, and insects.

The problem of the non-periodic migrations of animals, their mass movements out of their habitat area, and their times of arrival has attracted much attention from Soviet scholars. Studies have been made of the climatic conditions determining locust attacks (Zakharov, 1946; Shcherbinovskiy, 1952, and others), the mass emigrations of the sand grouse [sadzha, Syrrhaptes] and the flamingo (Sudilovskaya, 1933; Isakov and Formozov, 1946), as well as the influence of the yields of the main kinds of food on the migrations of squirrels and the invasions of Europe by crossbills and nutcrackers (Formozov, 1935). One such migration in northeast Siberia has resulted in the successful settlement of the squirrel in the forests of Kamchatka.

Soviet scholars have devoted an immense number of works to the questions of the geographic variability of animals, but the overwhelming majority of them are specialized in character and relate rather to the field of systematization than to zoogeography. The geographic aspect of this phenomenon, formulated by L. S. Berg (1922, 1924) in the sense that the action of the geographic landscape on organisms forces them to change in a definite direction, insofar as the organization of the species permits, is largely confirmed by subsequent authors, for example, S. V. Kirikov (1956) from the example of the distribution of melanism in mammals, and by P. V. Serebrovskiy (1925) from the geographic changes of coloring in birds. The direct action of climatic conditions on the coloring and structure of the fur cover has been confirmed by the results of the acclimatization of fur-bearing animals under landscape conditions new to them (Lavrov, 1957; Gerasimova, 1958). Especially clear is the action of the geographic environment in the variability of ecologic features such as the seasonal life rhythms, certain reproduction characteristics, the dynamics of numerical strength, and so forth (Stanchinskiy, 1922, 1927; Naumov, 1954; Mal'chevskiy (1958), as well as in the rise of local populations distinguished by physiological features (Kalabukhov, 1935, and others; Bashenina, 1958). Interesting considerations regarding the geographic variability of the metabolism in plants and animals, which may result in the rise of new physiological races, have been expressed by V. V. Koval'skiy (1957) on the basis of a study of the biogeochemical provinces. The elaboration of these questions has had a direct outlet in national-economic practice, especially in the field of animal husbandry.

The employment of methods of mathematical statistics in testing the so-called basic rules of geographic variability (of Bergman and Allen) has made it possible to establish the inapplicability of the latter with respect to warm-blooded animals. It has been proposed to replace both these rules by the "rule of the optimum," since each species will grow to the maximum size under the optimal temperature conditions of the environment that are specific for it, whereas lower or higher temperatures cause a reduction in size. The same is true of the development of appendages to the body (Terent'yev, 1947; Baranova, 1957). Variation statistics have also been applied to the solution of other tasks, but they have not undergone wide distribution in zoogeographic research in the USSR (Terent'yev, 1946, 1958; Lyubishchev, 1958).

A weak side of a considerable number of present-day zoogeographic investigations is the lack of organic connection with other sciences. This fact has had the result that the rich factual materials accumulated by zoogeographers, and many interesting generalizations made on their basis, are being quite inadequately utilized by soil scientists, climatologists, hydrologists, and the scholars of other neighboring specialties.

A profound and promising generalization in the field of biogeography is V. N. Sukachev's doctrine of biogeocoenoses. Despite this, far from enough attention has thus far been paid in our country to the geography of zoocoenoses and biocoenoses of the land. In this respect, the geography of land animals has lagged far behind the biogeography of the sea. Considerable results have been achieved only in the field of the study of the geography of the natural foci of certain zoocoenoses. A powerful stimulus for the development of this research has been the doctrine, created by Ye. N. Pavlovskiy, of the natural focality of transmissible diseases. Inasmuch as the exciters of a number of diseases are members of definite biocoenoses, it has been possible to work out the problems of the geography and genesis of the natural foci of plague (Rall', 1958a, 1958b; Fenyuk, 1958; Petrov and Shmuter, 1958), of leishmaniasis (Latyshev and others, 1951), tularemia (Olsuf'yev, 1947; Kuzyakin, 1947; Maksimov, 1946, 1957), and certain other diseases.

In his classic work, "Periodical Phenomena in the Life of Wild Animals, Birds, and Reptiles of the Voronezh Guberniya," published more than a hundred years ago, N. A. Severtsov laid the groundwork for a special approach to the study of the animal world. He examined it in close connection with the concrete conditions of the local geographic environment. This original ecologic geographic orientation found in our country a number of followers, who produced characterizations of the animal world of the Karakums, the Kyzylkum, and the *syrts* [plateaus] of the Tyan'-Shan' (Kashkarov and Kurbatov, 1929; Kashkarov, Zhukov, Stanyukovich, 1938; Zakhidov, 1957, 1958), of the steppes and deserts of Middle Asia, Kazakhstan, Mongolia, and Siberia (Formozov, 1928, 1934, 1950, 1958), of the mountain tundra of the Khibiny (Fridolin, 1936), and others. In varying degrees of detail they reveal the results of the long action of a complex of natural conditions on the animal population. The set of biologic groups or life forms characteristic of this or that landscape, the morpho-physiologic and ecologic adaptations common to a number of species and the peculiarities of the seasonal phenomena are examined in close connection with the environmental factors. Among the above-enumerated questions, it is the problem of the rise and classification of life forms that has perhaps attracted the most attention (Formozov, 1929, 1956; Kashkarov, 1933; Bey-Biyenko, 1936; Sergeyev, 1940; Belopol'skiy, 1957; and others).

Zoogeographic research has undergone very wide development in the USSR, in keeping with its theoretic interest and the great significance attached to it in various fields of the national economy. The performance of such a large volume of work requires a considerable number of specialists, whose training is provided by the biologic and geographic faculties of the universities and pedagogic institutions, which have special zoogeography courses in their curriculums. A big role in the training of personnel and the popularization of the main tenets of zoogeography has been played by the instruction handbooks produced by I. I. Puzanov, N. A. Bobrinskiy, Ya. A. Birshteyn, and L. A. Zenkevich, especially the "General Zoogeography" by V. G. Geptner (1936), the first book of this type in world literature. There are long-established and successful zoogeographic centers in the Zoologic Institute of the Academy of Sciences of the USSR (Leningrad), in the Leningrad, Khar'kov, and Moscow universities, in the Institute of Geography of the Academy of Sciences of the USSR, and so forth. Active new groups have arisen in a number of union republics: in the Ukraine (F. I. Strautman and others), in Estonia (A. Khaberman and E. V. Kumari), in Kazakhstan (I. A. Dolgushin, V. S. Bazhanov, M. N. Korelov, S. N. Varshavskiy, and others), in Uzbekistan (T. Z. Zakhidov and R. N. Meklenburtsev), in Turkmenia (A. K. Rustamov), in Kirgizia (F. A. Turdakov and A. I. Yanushevich), and others. In 1957 two special conferences were held: at the Institute of Geography of the Academy of Sciences of the USSR on questions of the geography of the population of vertebrates, and at the L'vov State University on the problems of the zoogeography of the land. In addition, questions of animal geography have been included in the program of a number of zoologic conferences on different subjects. The reading of a large number of papers and the exchange of opinions on many scientific questions of zoogeography have contributed to the further development of research in this field.

Soviet zoogeographers are making good progress in working out the larger part of the problems mentioned in the present essay. One can have no doubt about the further flourishing of zoogeographic research in our country.

BASIC LITERATURE

Arnol'di, K. V. "On the Theory of the Range in Relation to Ecology and the Origin of Species Populations." *Zool. zhurn.*, vol. 36, no. 2, 1957.

Berg, L. S. Climate and Life *(Klimat i zhizn')*, 2nd ed., 1947; The Fish of the Fresh Waters of the USSR and Neighboring Countries *(Ryby Presnykh Vod SSSR i Sopredel'nykh Stran)*, 4th ed., vol. I, 1948; vol. II, 1948; vol. III, 1949.

Geptner, V. G. "The Desert-steppe Fauna of Palearctica and the Foci of its Development," *Byull. Mosk. obshch. ispyt. prir., otd. biol.*, vol. 9, nos. 1-2, 1945.

Gladkov, N. A. "Notes on the Ornithologic Fauna of the Cultivated Sections of Turkestan." *Byull. Mosk. obshch. ispyt. prir., otd. biol.*, vol. 47, nos. 5-6, 1938.

Dubinin, V. B. "Some Laws of the Geographic Distribution and Evolution of Winged Ticks in Relation to the Evolution of their Hosts." *Tr. Zool. in-ta AN SSSR*, vol. 13, 1953.

Ioff, I. G. "On the Geographic Distribution of Ground-squirrel Fleas in Relation to the History of the Spread of Ground Squirrels." *Parazitol.*, sbornik AN SSSR, no. 6, 1936; "Aphaniptera of Kirgizia," sb. *Ektoparazity*, no. 1, 1949.

Isakov, Yu. A. "Theory and Practice of the Migration of Birds of Passage," *Tr. Vtoroy Pribalt. ornitol. konfer.*, 1957; "Some Questions of the Study of the Fauna and Geographic Distribution of Birds," *ibidem*.

Kashkarov, D. N., and Kurbatov, P. V. "Ecologic Survey of the Vertebrate Fauna of the Central Kara-Kums." *Tr. Sr.-Az. gos. un-ta*, vol. 12a, no. 7, 1928.

Kaskharov, D. N., and Korovin, Ye. P. "Experiment in the Analysis of the Ecologic Paths of the Spread of the Flora and Fauna of Middle Asia." *Zhurn. ekol. i biotsenol.*, vol. I, no. 1, 1931.

Kaskharov, D. N., Zhukov, A. and Stanyukovich, K. V. The Cold Desert of the Central Tyan'-Shan' *(Kholodnaya Pustynya Tsentral'nogo Tyan'-Shanya)*, Leningrad State Univ., 1937.

Kirikov, S. V. "Historical Changes in the Animal World of our Country in the 13th-19th Centuries." *Izv. AN SSSR, Seriya geogr.*, 1952, No. 6; 1953, No. 4; 1955, No. 1; 1958, No. 1.

Kuznetsov, B. A. Essay on the Zoogeographic Regionalization of the USSR *(Ocherk Zoogeograficheskogo Rayonirovaniya SSSR)*, izd. MOIP, 1950.

Kuznetsov, N. Ya. "Zoogeographic Areas and their Subdivisions in Application to the Order of Coleoptera. The Fauna of the USSR and Adjacent Countries. Coleoptera, Introduction *(Zoogeograficheskiye Oblasti, ikh Podrazdeleniya v Primenenii k Otryadu Cheshuyekrylykh. Fauna SSSR i Sopredel'nykh Stran. Coleoptera, Vvedeniye)*, II, Izd-vo AN SSSR, 1929; "The Relation of the Geographic Distribution of *Belyanki* [butterflies of the genus Pieris] to the Distribution of their Food Plants and the Chemistry of the Latter." *Yezhegodn. Zool. muzeya AN SSSR*, vol. 31, 1930; "The Arctic Fauna of Eurasia and its Origin (Principally on the Basis of Material on Coleoptera)," *Tr. Zool. in-ta AN SSSR*, vol. 5, no. 1, 1938.

Lindberg, G. U. The Quaternary Period in the Light of the Biogeographic Data *(Chetvertichnyy Period v Svete Biogeograficheskikh Dannykh)*. Izd-vo AN SSSR, 1955.

Martynov, A. V. "Ecologic Premises for the Zoogeography of Fresh-water Animals." *Russk. zool. zhurn.*, vol. 9, 1930.

Nasimovich, A. A. The Role of the Regime of the Snow Cover in the Life of Ungulates on the Territory of the USSR *(Rol' Rezhima Snezhnogo Pokrova v Zhizni Kopytnykh Zhivotnykh na Territorii SSSR)*, 1955.

Nikol'skiy, G. V. "On the Biologic Specificity of the Faunal Complexes and the Significance of its Analysis for Zoogeography." *Russk. Zool. zhurn.*, vol. 26, no. 3, 1947.

Pidoplichko, I. G. On the Glacial Epoch *(O Lednikovom Periode)*, nos. 1-4, Kiyev, 1946-1956.

Rall', Yu. M. The Paleogenesis of the Natural Foci of Plague in Relation to the Geography of Carrier Rodents. Problems of Land Zoogeography *(Paleogenezis Prirodnykh Ochagov Chumy v Svyazi s Geografiyey Nositeley-gryzunov. Problemy zoogeografii sushi)*. L'vov, 1958.

Rubtsov, I. O. "On the Theoretical Basis of the Regionalization of Noxious Insects and the Forecasting of their Mass Propagation." *Zashchita rast.*, sb. 14, 1937; sb. 16, 1938.

Rustamov, A. K. "Concerning the Study of the Avifauna of the Cultural Landscapes of Middle Asia." *Tr. Turkmen. s-kh. in-ta*, vol. 8, 1956.

Semenov-Tyan-Shankiy, A. P. "The Limits and Zoogeographic Subdivisions of the Palearctic Area for Terrestrial Dry-land Animals on the Basis of the Geographic Distribution of Coleoptera." *Tr. Zool. in-ta AN SSSR*, vol. II, 1935; "Main Features of the History of the Development of the Alpine Faunas." *Tr. III Vseross. s"yezda zool., anat., gistol.*, 1928.

Serebrovskiy, P. V. "The Role of Climate in the Evolution of Birds." *Byull. Mosk. obshch. ispyt. prir.*, vol. 34, 1925; History of the Animal World of the USSR *(Istoriya Zhivotnogo Mira SSSR)*, Leningrad, 1939.

Stranchinskiy, V. V. "The Postglacial Changes in European Russia according to the Data on the Present Distribution of Birds." *Izv. In-ta geogr.*, no. 3, 1922; "On Certain Climatic Boundaries of the Distribution of Birds in Eastern Europe." *Tr. Smolensk. obshch. yestestvoisp. i vrachey*, vol. 1, 1926.

Sushkin, P. P. "The Zoologic Areas of Middle Siberia and the Nearest Parts of Highland Asia and an Experiment in the History of the Present Fauna of Palearctic Asia." *Byull. Mosk. obshch. ispyt. prir.*, 34, 1925.

Tugarinov, A. Ya. "Migrations of Birds on the Territory of the Union." *Zhivotnyy mir SSSR*, 1, 1936; "The Origin of the Migrations of the Birds of Palearctica." *Sbornik pamyati akademika P. P. Sushkina*, AN SSSR, 1950.

Fenyuk, B. K. "Questions of the geography of the natural foci of plague." "Probl. zoogeogr. sushi," L'vov, 1958.

Formozov, A. N. "The Lake Forest-steppe and Steppe of Western Siberia as Areas of Mass Habitation of Aquatic Birds." *Byull. Mosk. obshch. isp. prir.*, vol. 43, no. 2, 1934; "On the Acclimation of Land Vertebrate Fauna and the Questions of its Reconstruction," part I, "The Changing of Fauna by Man." *Zool. zhurn.*, vol. 16, no. 3, 1937; "The Snow Cover as a Factor of Environment, its Significance in the Life of Mammals and Birds of the USSR," *Materialy k poznaniyu fauny i flory SSSR, izd. Mosk. obshch. ispyt. prir., Otd. zool.* no. 5 (20) 1946; "The Animal World." In the book *Kazakhstan*, AN SSSR, 1950.

Fridolin, V. "Animal and Plant Societies of the Mountain Land Khibiny," 1. *Tr. Kol'sk. bazy AN SSSR*, 3, 1936.

Tsalkin, V. I. "Material for the History of Cattle Breeding and Hunting in Ancient Russia." *Materialy k issled. po arkheol. SSSR*, no. 51, 1956.

Shtegman, B. K. "Foundations of the Ornithogeographical Division of the Palearctic." *Fauna of the USSR, Birds*, vol. 1, no. 2, 1938.

CHAPTER 17

GEOGRAPHY OF POPULATION AND POPULATED POINTS

V. V. Pokshishevskiy

The geography of population is regarded by Soviet geographers as a special economic geographic discipline studying the composition and distribution of the population and its territorial organization (the character of the distribution, the features and forms of the populated points, and so forth), both in connection with the general socioeconomic and natural conditions of a country (or countries) and in connection with the concrete conditions in each given region or locality.

Before the October Revolution, not a few concrete investigations characterizing the population of individual localities were carried out in Russia. Especially outstanding among these were the rather numerous investigations having an ethnogeographic bent, due both to the multinationality of the country and to the attention that progressive Russian scholars paid to the fate of the small nationalities living in Russia. But they were executed from case to case and created no geography of population as a special geographic discipline. To be sure, attempts at broader generalizations were sometimes made; one example is the monograph by A. I. Voyeykov, "The Distribution of the Population of the Earth in Dependence Upon the Natural Conditions and Man's Activity" (*Izvestiya RGO,* 1906, nos. 2-3). This monograph became widely known abroad, since it was published in the same year in *Petermanns Geographische Mitteilungen* (1906, Nos. 11-12). Another example is the monograph by V. P. Semenov-Tyan-Shanskiy, "City and Country in European Russia" (*Zapiski RGO po otd. statistiki,* vol. 10, St. Petersburg, 1910). But such works, surpassing the scientific level of their time, were isolated. The formation of the geography of population as a special discipline belongs wholly to the Soviet period.

Under the conditions of a planned economy, wide opportunities have opened up in the course of socialist construction for the practical application of the results of research in the field of population geography and the geographic problems of the development of populated points of various types. This stimulates the general advance of this branch of geography and orients it toward the treatment of subjects connected with the practical requirements of a planned socialist economy. In the course of the development of the economy it has been necessary to solve a considerable number of diverse questions, sometimes of prime importance, relating to the distribution of population both over the country as a whole and its major regions and in individual centers. The geographic shifts in the population distribution of the USSR have had the result that the numerical strength of the population in the Far East increased by nearly 3.5 times in 1926-1959, by 89 per cent in Eastern Siberia, by 78 per cent in the Urals, by more than twice in Armenia, and so forth. The numerical strength of the urban population grew from 26 million to 100 million in 1926-1959, and the number of towns [*goroda,* including cities, for which Russian has no separate word] and settlements of the urban type grew from 1,925 to 4,616 during this time (Fig. 3). In 1926, the population in only three cities exceeded 500,000 and there were 100,000-500,000 each in 28 cities. In 1959, there were 25 cities of the first category and 123 of the second. In the course of the creation of new towns and the development of old ones, urban housing has quadrupled. With the enlargement of the collective farms, which necessitated changes in the forms of rural population distribution, the number of homesteads [*dvory*] of collective farmers grew from 18.7 million to 19.9 million in 1940-1956, while the number of collective farms was reduced from 235,000 to 83,000.

Each of these phenomena raised its own scientific-practical problems of the analysis of the regional differences in the makeup and utilization of labor resources, of the investigation of the geography of the

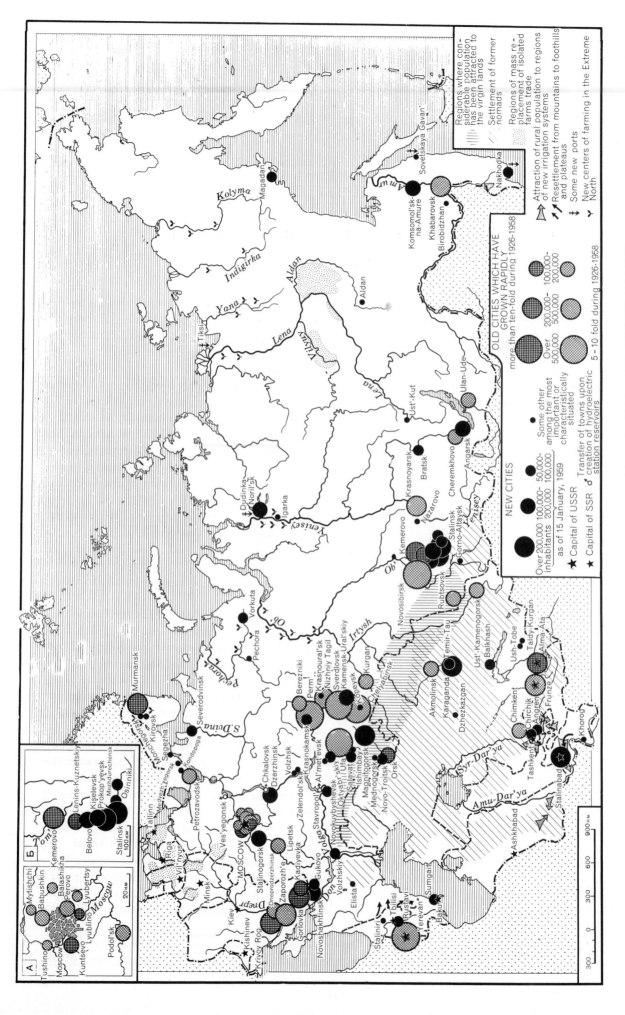

Fig. 3. CHANGES IN THE POPULATION GEOGRAPHY OF THE USSR DURING 1926-1959

migrations of population, and of the elaboration and realization (in application to the various concrete stages of the development of the country as a whole and of its individual regions) of the *material forms of population distribution most conformable to the socialist organization of production and way of life.* In order to judge the diversity of the problems arising here, we may recall, for example, the shifts of population due to the winning of new lands. During the last five years, on the virgin lands of Siberia and Kazakhstan, more than 35 million hectares alone have been plowed up, on only a few sovkhozes [state farms] many hundreds of new settlements have been created. Other examples of population shifts are the creation of new major industrial centers, with the rise of new forms of rural population distribution in the course of the settling down of formerly nomadic peoples (the total number of nomads who have changed to a sedentary way of life during the Soviet years amounts to several million persons); the transfer of populated points during the building of big hydrotechnical works; the establishment of new settlements in the course of great reclamation works such as the irrigation of the Golodnaya Step'; and the creation of kolkhoz settlements in a number of regions which formerly had a scattered homestead [*khutor*] distribution of the population, as in the Latvian SSR and in the Yakut ASSR. The historical causes of the predominance of a small-homestead distribution in these regions are, of course, quite different, but under the conditions of the change to large-scale collective agriculture these dispersed forms of population distribution proved to be an appreciable obstacle and this is why the course of rearranging the distribution was adopted.

The solution of practical questions relating to such processes largely falls to the lot of the land organizers and agronomists, architects, and engineer-economists, but for a full-valued solution it is also necessary to take into account the *geographic aspects of these problems.* The object of the practical investigations by geographers is the population itself (in its relations to production) and the material forms of its distribution. The *geographic specificity* of these investigations and their methodological orientation results in attention being concentrated primarily on territorial-spatial factors, and the discovery of the geographic relationships arising here. This necessitates an integrated examination of the questions, with consideration of many "local factors."

Soviet population geography proceeds from the fact that production factors are of leading importance for population distribution. The disposition of the population both over the country and within its regions is always determined by the character and geography of production, although changes in the distribution and in the material forms of the populated points frequently fail to keep pace with the changes in the geography of production. Hence, population geography under the conditions of a socialist economy strives to find those forms of population disposition and distribution which best conform to the requirements of production. Geographers must ascertain the necessary conditions for attracting population into regions where there is need for a labor force; analyze the disposition of the populated points with respect to raw-material sources, transportation routes, and so forth; note the "pattern" of rural population distribution which is most suitable from the viewpoint of relationship to the microgeography of farm lands; establish the material forms of towns favorable to the development of industrial and transportation functions and suitable for housing construction; and so forth. Here the natural environment, which will be discussed in more detail below, also affects the population distribution through production.

During the last decade the geographers of the USSR who study population and populated points have performed a great amount of work. As a result, population geography has now *fully taken shape as a separate branch of economic geography,* having its own distinctly defined range of subjects, its own practical tasks and its own methods.

Population geography in the USSR is being elaborated in close connection with economic geography and on the basis of its principles. While being, as it were, one of the branches of economic geography, population geography has occupied a somewhat different place than the geography of the individual branches of the economy (industry, transportation, etc.). Inasmuch as the population is the object of any economic activity, the characterization of its distribution thus acquires a synthetic, general economic-geographic significance. On the other hand, any cluster of population forms, as it were, a focal point of consumption. Hence, population geography reveals the place of a considerable circle of individual branches of the economy in the consumption "part" of the processes of social reproduction. In the course of consumption (understood in the broad sense, including, for example, the provision of housing, schooling and other forms of cultural service), the reproduction of the population itself is realized. This broadened understanding of the processes of social reproduction forms brings into the circle of interests of population geography many phenomena and functions usually assigned to the "non-productive sphere" and hence not attracting the attention of other branch economico-geographic disciplines which study comparatively clearly delimited areas of "productional" economy.

Still, it would be wrong to contrast population geography with economic geography or to place them side by side as equivalent disciplines. It would also be erroneous to regard economic geography as a part of population geography or as a department of that somewhat vague "geography of man" (human geography), a concept advanced by many geographic schools in capitalistic countries. Proceeding from the Marxist laws of the development of society, Soviet geographers criticize the bourgeois attempts to study the population "by itself," outside of its social organization and productional activity. Soviet geographers regard the concept of "geography of man" as unfitting for the simple reason that it is not oriented toward the study of the geography of human collectives, but opens the way to the metaphysical contemplation of the interrelations of the single man, as such, with the geographic environment. In reality, since primeval times the object of this interaction has been organized aggregates of persons performing a productional labor activity, i.e., not the abstract "man," but the population. Finally, the "geography of man" is rejected in the USSR because it is historically connected with anthropogeography in the spirit of Friedrich Ratzel, later developed by such foreign geographers as Ellen Churchill Semple and other environmentalists. This concept is also widely used by adherents who consider geography as the "ecology of man," bringing biologism into the realm of social relations. It has been demonstrated again and again that the concept of anthropo-geography and environmentalism go back to the philosophy of geographic determinism, and that viewing social phenomena from ecologic standpoints leads to a confusion of social and biologic laws.

In the course of its development, Soviet population geography has been obliged to solve important tasks, and this has required many discussions. Firstly, population greography had *to define more precisely its interrelations with the other scientific disciplines,* first drawing the line of demarcation with them and then fixing the lines of *interaction.* At the Second Congress of the Geographic Society of the USSR (1947) there were disputes over the boundaries separating population geography, for example, from ethnography, from historical geography, from demography, from the technico-economic disciplines serving urban construction, and also from the various other branches of economic geography itself (for example, from the geography of agriculture, which also has to deal with questions of rural population distribution in connection with the geographic characteristics of agricultural production). Not wholly clear, either, were the interrelations between population geography and all these disciplines in the joint practical solution of individual scientific tasks (i.e., the conditions for their cooperation). Sufficient clarity has now, in general, been brought into all these questions.

Secondly, it was necessary to *overcome the erroneous notions* still existing in the minds of some geographers (in the spirit of the views of the old Russian scholars of the pre-Marxist period, V. P. Semenov-Tyan-Shanskiy, for example) *that natural conditions exert a direct and determining influence on the forms of population distribution.* A fight also had to be waged against the general under-estimation of the significance of the study of population geography, against voluntaristic notions about the ease of remodeling this geography, against preoccupation with investigations of only the *geometric forms* of settlements, against the one-sided treatment of populated points merely as centers of production, without giving enough consideration to their other functions, and against the centering of investigations chiefly on the *externally visible features* of settlements, etc. This list of erroneous approaches inherited from the pre-Marxist past of geography in the USSR, or from errors committed in the first years of "searching"— approaches which needed to be overcome — shows how complex were the tasks of working out a correct methodology.

Thirdly, population geography has had to *establish basic concepts relating to the object of its investigation* (regarding the classification of types of settlements, etc.). Some of these concepts will be discussed below. Although this task cannot be regarded as fully solved, much has already been done here. The chief scientific lines of elaboration of population geography have also been traced, namely: (1) general questions of population geography on the scale of the whole country or of its major parts (laws of the distribution of population by regions in dependence upon the changes in the geography of production, the relationships between urban and rural population, population migrations, etc., (2) questions of urban geography, (3) questions of the geography of rural population distribution,

(4) the historical geography of population (investigations of an ethnogeographic character have proved to be closely related to the latter).

Fourthly and finally, it has been necessary *to work out methods of primary investigation:* field work (which required the creation of suitable programs and their testing in practice), *mapping* the results of the study of populated points, such as, for example, the dynamics of their population and the *cartographic representation* of their functions.

The chief scientific purpose of population geography in the USSR is the discovery, and application to the solution of practical tasks, of the *laws* governing:

(a) the *distribution of population* in its dynamics, including migrations (distribution should be studied in its relations to the geography of production)

(b) the formation of a network of populated points and, so to speak, the *"population-distribution pattern"* itself

(c) the development of the *material elements of populated points* of various types in their spatial interrelations, with consideration for the differences in economic and natural conditions.

Research in population geography in the USSR is directed not only toward the analysis and interpretation of phenomena, but also toward a constructive application of the laws to be established, toward practical recommendations.* Let us cite some examples of the laws which must be discovered and applied in the USSR by specialists in population geography.

1. TYPE OF ECONOMY AS A BASIC FACTOR DETERMINING THE CHARACTER OF POPULATION DISTRIBUTION AND ITS FORMS. The analysis of the population geography of any region shows graphically that the distribution depends directly upon the character and territorial organization of the economy. The big grain sovkhozes, extensive livestock raising, scattered mines, logging industry—each of these types of economy has its own appropriate forms of population distribution and definite types of populated points.

2. INFLUENCE OF THE NATURAL CONDITIONS ON POPULATION DISTRIBUTION AND ITS FORMS. This manifests itself only through an intermediate link—the distribution and territorial organization of *production.* Production is here the leading factor: its development is, as it were, "primary." It is the basis for an explanation of all the derivative elements of economic geography and only through it, intermediately, do the other influences, including the natural ones, manifest themselves. (However, since productional activity is effected by people, by the population, there sometimes also arise "secondary" laws, such as the development of production in already existing clusters of population.) When one goes on to examine the phenomena on a larger scale, the natural-geographic environment also emerges as a *technical factor,* and here one must sometimes consider its more "immediate" influence as well. Here belong, for example, the choice and the characteristics of grounds for housing and industrial construction, the technical conditions for dealing with them, etc. But production requirements are, in the last analysis, also at the bottom of such influences. Especially considerable is the difference in natural-productional preconditions in rural areas. Here, in analyzing population distribution within small areas, one has to give technical evaluations of plots of land, water-supply conditions, etc.

3. SOME CHARACTERISTICS OF AGRICULTURAL MIGRATIONS. On a relatively low level of productional culture (for example, in pre-Revolutionary Russia), the success of agricultural settlement has been promoted by the similarity between the natural-productional conditions of the places of origin and settlement of the colonists. As the productive forces develop, however, this situation (which had no absolute significance even in the past) is becoming less significant. The "familiarity" of the geographic environment for the settlers has an influence through the mechanism of the already constituted working habits necessary for economic activity in this environment. It is evident that, in creating new focal points of highly mechanized farming (for example, in the virgin lands in the USSR) the factor of "familiarity" retires into the background.

---

*Soviet geographers are rarely able to make independent detailed field investigations in foreign countries. The tasks of the population geography of these countries are most often confined to an analysis and interpretation of the available literary and statistical materials, which makes it possible to reflect questions of population geography in regional-geography characterizations from the standpoint of Soviet science. This much more modest task still presupposes a knowledge of the laws of population geography although, owing to the differences in the mode of production, they not infrequently are expressed differently than in the USSR.

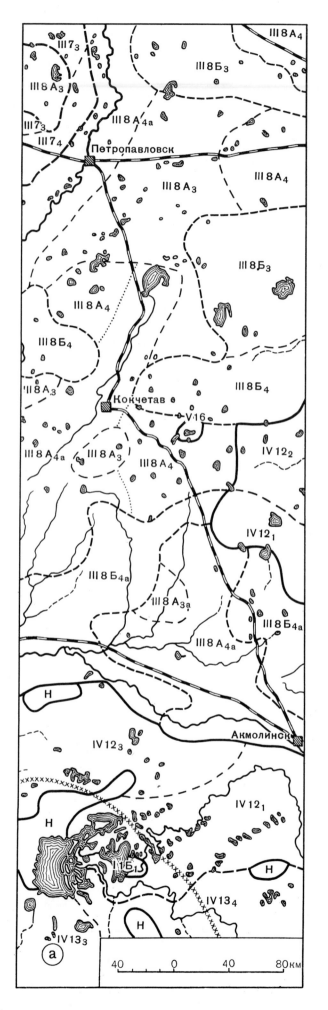

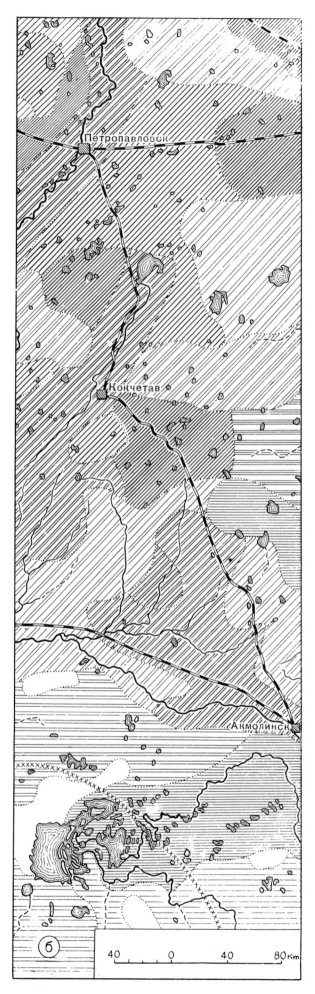

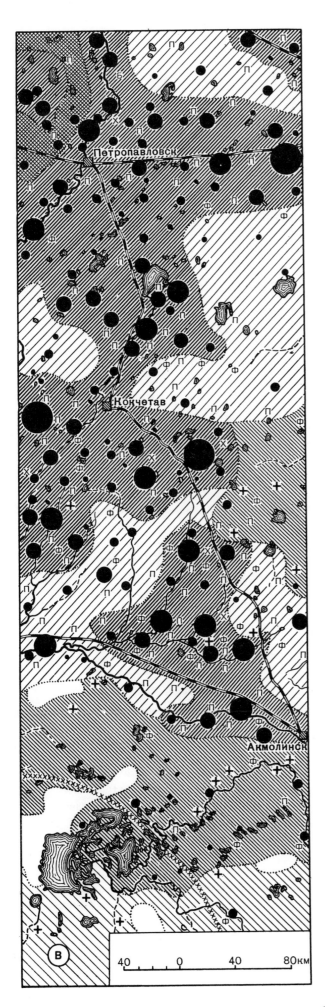

Fig. 4. FRAGMENTS OF DIFFERENT VARIANTS OF THE MAP OF RURAL POPULATION DISTRIBUTION OF THE USSR, compiled by V. S. Valev to a scale of 1:4,000,000. The purpose of the map is to show simultaneously the forms and productional types of population distribution.

[left] Areas distinguished by characteristics of population distribution are designated by letter-and-figure indices.

[middle] The same areas are hatched. For large territories, such as the whole USSR, a multi-coloring of the map is necessary because of the complexity of the legend.

[right] In order to make the map more graphic, the productional background has been simplified and symbols representing the character of the population have been entered. The black dots characterize the size of the population of permanent settlements; the letters characterize various kinds of scattered and temporarily inhabited dwellings such as field camps, animal raising points, industrial hunting and fishing bases, etc. Because of the small scale, only 10 per cent of the actual settlements of all categories are shown, the dots being placed at the points of greatest concentration. Maps were compiled according to all the variants before the winning of the virgin lands; the line of small crosses (in the lower left-hand corner) marks the southern boundary of the active remodeling of the network of rural settlements in connection with this winning. For details on the method of compiling the maps, see *Voprosy geografii*, no. 45, Moscow, 1959.

[See page 149 for text discussion of Fig. 4]

4. LAWS IN THE REALM OF THE ECONOMIC GEOGRAPHIC FUNCTIONS OF CITIES. Here a definite relation has been established between three factors: the integratedness [*kompleksnost'*] of the industrial structure of a town, a degree of development in it of diverse nonproductional functions (particularly cultural), and the size of its population. Towns whose development is based solely on a narrow circle of functions, for example, purely mining industry, attain considerable size only in rare cases. An analysis of the composition of the population leads to an understanding of the balances of labor in the branches of the economy concentrated in the town, helps to explain the total numerical strength of its population and its dynamics, and furnishes a scientific forecast of the growth of the town.

Material forms of populated places are often retained for a long time after their economic functions have radically changed. Especially "conservative" is the planning morphology of populated points, which sometimes reflects functions long since lost. This lag in the reshaping of material forms behind their economic content poses a number of practical tasks having to do with speeding the elimination of resulting inconsistencies, with the reconstruction of populated places, and with bringing them into conformity with the new functions.

5. INFLUENCE OF THE ECONOMIC GEOGRAPHIC LOCATION OF TOWNS on the concentration of one function or another in them. Elaboration of the concept of the economic geographic location is one of the important theoretical achievements of Soviet economic geography. This concept, which is widely applied in population geography and especially urban geography, includes the transportation situation of the town, the distance from fuel and raw-material bases, the density of the surrounding rural population, etc. Investigations have convincingly demonstrated the historicity of the concept of the economic geographic location of towns itself; it is a concept which changes in the course of the development of a region or of a whole country. It has been established from many examples that, when towns have grown to a considerable size, to use N. N. Baranskiy's expression, they "create a geographic location for themselves," developing and spatially organizing the productive forces on the territory gravitating toward them.

The above examples give an idea of the *character* of the laws with which population geography has to deal. They are particular laws of economic geography, reposing in turn on still more general economic laws peculiar to the given social formation, and on the tenets of dialectical materialism concerning the interrelations between society and the natural environment of its development. Although they are particular laws of economic geography, they must not be classed as secondary; they are essentially important as a concretization of more general laws. Let us recall the words of V. I. Lenin: "The general exists only in the individual, through the individual [*otdel'noye*]. Every individual is (in one way or another) general. Every general thing is (a particle or a side or essence) of the individual."*

It would be wrong to suppose that the laws of population geography have been included, so to speak, "in finished form" in more general socioeconomic laws. They can be deduced from them and developed, but only as a result of a special creative process. For this are needed both special methods and the utilization of data from many allied disciplines (for example, the various technical norms [*normativy*], etc.), which are required in connection with the tasks of investigation. For example, the geography of agriculture utilizes, let us say, agrotechnical norms. Thus, concrete research in urban geography is closely intertwined in its practical part with the work of town-building specialists in planning or regional planning.

The laws of population geography exist objectively, apart from the will of man, and this makes a knowledge of them especially important. A number of examples can be cited to show how these laws "take vengeance" on those who underestimate them. An example is attempts to construct population-distribution forms voluntaristically, without a scientific analysis of their objective causation.

As a result of discussions during the last decade, the above-enumerated theoretical standpoints have received fairly full recognition from Soviet scholars working in the field of population geography. This unity of views, however, does not prevent certain investigators from developing new trends in elaboration of their themes, and paying unequal attention to different aspects of them. For example, in the field of the study of towns, a number of geographers are less interested in their microgeography. Instead, they are giving an extensive and fruitful treatment to questions of geographic location and to the interrelations of towns (as well as their relationships to adjacent territories) and are analyzing the

---

*V. I. Lenin. *Works*, vol. 38, p. 359.

spatial functions of towns in the considerable areas gravitating toward them. This, for example, is the character of the work by N. N. Baranskiy, O. A. Konstantinov, I. M. Mayergoyz, and their pupils. In some works, the center of attention is transferred to the study of the historical formation of the network of towns and cities; for example, L. Ye. Iofa's investigation of the towns of the Urals and R. M. Kabo's investigation of the towns of Siberia. Other investigators concern themselves principally with the microgeography of towns, such as the work by Yu. G. Saushkin on Moscow, or with the large-scale study of population distribution in individual industrial nodes (V. G. Davidovich and others). O. A. Konstantinov and V. G. Davidovich have concerned themselves a great deal with the analysis of the dynamics of the network of towns and cities. Each of these trends also creates appropriate methodological equipment and "specializes" its scientific-research skills. In like manner, there is also specialization in the field of the study of rural population distribution (S. A. Kovalev and others), and so forth. The existence of such specialized trends is very helpful because it insures the deepening of research, aids in training new personnel, and yields more valuable practical results. All these trends are being developed in the USSR in a spirit of creative concord due to the unity of the basic theoretical views. Such concord insures a diversified treatment of the respective themes.

Alongside the specialized works, investigations of an integrated character on the population geography of individual regions are becoming more and more widespread (Fig. 4). Such integrated investigations usually form important chapters in all the regional economic geographic monographs devoted to the major regions of the USSR. As an example, one may point out the detailed characterizations of population and populated places in the monographs on Western Siberia, the republics of Middle Asia and Kazakhstan, published in recent years by the Institute of Geography of the Academy of Sciences of the USSR.

In addition to treating questions of population geography in regional economic geography monographs, topical collections of articles entitled "Questions of Geography" [*Voprosy geografii*], devoted entirely to population geography are published from time to time. (The collections which have been published are listed at the end of this chapter.) A number of articles and investigations on population geography are published in the scientific and scientific-methodological Soviet geographic journals and in numerous issues of the *Uchenyye Zapiski* and *Trudy* of the geographic faculties of various universities and pedagogic institutes (some are listed below). Many of these articles and investigations reflect work on dissertations by young economic geographers on population-geography subjects. Characterizations of individual towns, or groups of them, are often worked up as dissertations. A considerable number of monographs—geographic books and brochures about individual cities—have been published. (See, also, Chapter 49, "Publication of Geographic Literature.") A great deal of space is devoted to population geography in the four-volume *Kratkaya Geograficheskaya Entsiklopediya* ["Short Geographic Encyclopedia"], now being prepared for publication.

Of great significance is the work performed by Soviet geographers in the course of expeditions, research, and project work on the creation or reconstruction of populated places, and in regional planning. Many geographers specializing in population geography, for example, work in the State Institute for Urban Planning, in the designing organizations which solve population-distribution questions related to the creation of major hydrotechnical works and irrigation systems, in the organs supervising resettlement, and so on. The work performed by these geographers finds direct practical use.

BASIC LITERATURE

Baranskiy, N. N. "On the Economic Geographic Study of Towns." *Voprosy Geografii*, sbornik 2, Moscow, 1946. *Voprosy Geografii*, sbornik 5, Moscow, 1947; 14, Moscow, 1949; 38, Moscow, 1956; and 45, 1959. These four collections, containing about half a hundred articles, are devoted entirely to the geography of population and populated points.

Gorod i Rayon, kak Ob"yekty Geograficheskogo Izucheniya (Town and rayon, as Objects of Geographic Study). *Uchen. zap. MGPI*, vol. 54, Moscow, 1949 (collection of articles).

Iofa, L. Ye.. Towns of the Urals (*Goroda Urala*), Moscow, 1951.

Kabo, R. M. Towns of Western Siberia (*Goroda Zapadnoy Sibiri*), Moscow, 1949.

Knobel'sdorf, E. V. "Concerning the Question of the Types of Soviet Towns," *Geogr. sborn.*, 11, Moscow-Leningrad, 1957.

Kovalev, S. A. . "On the Economic Geographic Location of Rural Settlements and its Study." *Voprosy Geografii*, sb. 41, Moscow, 1957.

Kovalev, S. A. "Shifts in the Geography of the Population of the USSR in 40 Years." *Geografiya v Shkole*, 1957, No. 5.

Kovalev, S. A. "Types of Rural Settlements in the USSR." Collection of articles for the 18th International Geographic Congress. *Voprosy Geografii*, Izd-vo AN SSSR, Moscow-Leningrad, 1956.

Konstantinov, O. A. "An Experiment in the Study of the Influence of the Characteristics of a Region on the Character of Urban Settlements." *Tr. Leningr. In-ta Inzh. Kommun. Stroit.*, no. 3, Leningrad, 1936.

Konstantinov, O. A. "The Economic Geographic Location of the Big Cities of the USSR." *Izv. VGO*, 1946, No. 2.

Konstantinov, O. A. "On the Classification of Towns in Economic Geography." *Voprosy Geografii*, sb. 41, Moscow, 1957.

Lyalikov, N. I. "Essays on the Geography of Population of the USSR." *Geografiya v Shkole,* 1948, Nos. 3 and 5; 1949, Nos. 2 and 3.

Mayergoyz, I. M. "The Geographic Location of the City of Stalingrad." *Voprosy Geografii*, sb. 4, Moscow, 1946.

Pokshishevskiy, V. V. The Settlement of Siberia *(Zaseleniye Sibiri),* Irkutsk, 1951.

Pokshishevskiy, V. V. "On Certain Tasks of Integrated Physical Geographic Investigation of Towns" *Voprosy Geografii,* sb. 38, Moscow, 1952.

Pokshishevskiy, V. V. "Internal Migrations of Population as an Object of Geographic Study." Collection of articles for the 18th International Geographic Congress. *Voprosy Geografii*, AN SSSR, Moscow-Leningrad, 1956.

Pokshishevskiy, V. V. "Some Questions of the Microgeographic Study of the Towns of the USSR." *Geogr. sborn.*, XI, Moscow-Leningrad, 1957.

Pokshishevskiy, V. V. "Problems of Towns in the Present Economic Geographic Literature of the Chief Capitalist Countries." *Uchen. zap. MGPI,* vol. 120, Moscow, 1958.

Rashin, A. G. The Population of Russia during 100 years (1811-1913). *(Naseleniye Rossii za 100 let (1811-1913).* Moscow, 1956.

Spravochnik Puteshestvennika i Krayeveda (Handbook of the Traveler and Student of Local Studies), vol. II, Moscow, 1950 (programs of study of population and populated points, worked out by Yu. G. Saushkin).

Trube, L. D. Our Towns *(Nashi goroda).* Gor'kiy, 1954 (this book, in which an attempt was made to subordinate the classification of towns one-sidedly to the genetic feature, has aroused a lively polemic).

Yatsunskiy, V. K. "Changes in the Distribution of the Population of European Russia in 1724-1816." *Istoriya SSSR,* 1957, No. 1.

CHAPTER 18

GEOGRAPHY OF INDUSTRY

V. S. Klupt

The geography of industry, as a separate field of scientific knowledge, has taken shape in the USSR as a component part of economic geography. Soviet industrial geography is closely related to the requirements of socialist construction. Of course, various works treating the questions of the distribution of industry were published in pre-Revolutionary Russia, but their authors did not even attempt to pose the question of the radical transformation of the then-existing distribution, although it was irrational and retarded the country's economic development.

The capitalistic system with its private ownership of the means of production excludes outright the possibility of organizing a correct distribution of industry. In a socialist society, the situation is a fundamentally different one. Social ownership of the tools and means of production insures the possibility, and also generates the necessity of a planned development of the national economy. The correct distribution of industry has become all the more urgent a task in our country because an immense amount of construction of new enterprises is continuously going on in the USSR. Whole new branches of industry are being created and new industrial nodes are taking shape.

The elaboration of concrete questions of the distribution of industry has been participated in by the *Gosplan* [State Planning Commission] of the USSR and the *gosplans* of the union republics, by the institutes of economics in the system of the Academy of Sciences of the USSR and of the academies of sciences of the union republics, by the Institute of Geography of the Academy of Sciences of the USSR, by the designing organizations of many branches of industry and, finally, by the respective chairs of the higher educational institutions of the country.

The number of published works containing valuable material on the distribution of the industry of the USSR is fairly large. Among them should be mentioned two celebrated works which have played an exceptional role in the shaping of the modern geography of productive forces and in the development of economicogeographic science: (1) the Electrification Plan drawn up in 1920 under the direction of V. I. Lenin (the GOELRO plan), including a plan of distribution of industry by eight main economic regions, and (2) the First Five-Year Plan, in which the general theoretical propositions determining the tasks of the new distribution of industry in the USSR were worked out in great depth and detailed instructions were given on all branches and regions.

The successful elaboration of concrete questions concerning the correct distribution of industry in the USSR by numerous groups has become possible because they are armed with Marxist-Leninist theory, which reveals the objective laws of the distribution of socialist production taken as a whole. Reposing on the analysis and generalization of the experience in socialist construction in the USSR and the countries of the people's democracy, the Marxist-Leninist theory of the distribution of production is being continuously developed. The realization of the recognized objective laws in practice — in the work of the planning, designing, and scientific collectives — is insured in our country by the fact that at a definite moment new theoretical propositions are formulated as principles of distribution and become the directives of the Communist Party and Soviet Government for the planning organs and, most important of all, the property of the broad masses of workers who are building a communist society.

The correct distribution of industry in the USSR must contribute not only to its absolute growth, but also — and this is mandatory — to the growth of the productivity of the entire social labor of the Soviet people as the most important condition for the victory of the new social order. The distribution of socialist industry must also contribute to strengthening the friendship between the peoples inhabiting the Soviet Union and to strengthening the economic independence of our country and its defense capability.

Back in 1918 V. I. Lenin wrote about the necessity of distributing industry in Russia rationally "from the viewpoint of the nearness of raw materials and the possibility of the least waste of labor in passing from the treatment of the raw materials to all the successive stages of processing the semi-manufactures down to the finished product..." (V. I. Lenin, *Works,* vol. 27, p. 288). In the Electrification Plan this same thought is formulated thus: "...it cannot but be foreseen that the rationalization of our industry will be accompanied by a considerable geographic shift of it over the country for the purpose of bringing the manufacturing industry as near as possible to the main sources of raw materials and fuel..." *(Electrification Plan,* 2nd ed., 1955, p. 167). Ever since then, the location of industry *close to sources of raw materials and fuel and to regions of consumption* has been advanced as a principle of the distribution of socialist production in the resolutions of a number of congresses of the Communist Party of the Soviet Union and in the plans for the development of the national economy.

Closely related to this principle of the distribution of socialist industry is another principle, reflecting the essence of the national minority policy of the Communist Party. This policy provides for *lending all-around aid to the national minority regions for the liquidation of their former backwardness,* inherited from the past. The creation of numerous industrial enterprises and whole new branches in Transcaucasia, Middle Asia, Kazakhstan, and other once-backward regions was all the more rational because these territories are extraordinarily rich in natural resources. The very rapid industrial development of the national minority regions signifies at the same time also the location of industry close to sources of raw materials and to regions of consumption. Consequently, the interests of the USSR as a whole are happily combined with those of each individual republic.

The correct distribution of production in the USSR also means the necessity, in the interest of the strengthening of the country's defense capabilities, of *deconcentrating production over the territory* and moving a number of branches of industry into the heart of the country, and so forth. This third principle fully agrees and is intertwined with the two preceding ones. In the hard years of the Great Patriotic War against the fascist hordes, which temporarily succeeded in occupying a number of the most important industrial regions, supplying of the Soviet Army with weapons rested upon the reliable industrial base in the Urals and Siberia (the so-called Ural-Kuznetsk kombinat), as well as upon other regions in the east of the country, created by the Soviet people in accordance with the principles of the distribution of socialist production.

In the Soviet Union, the division of labor among the country's economic regions is organized on the basis of the *planned specialization of each region* in the leading branches of the economy which have therein the best natural and economic preconditions. However, the interests of the state have required that in each main economic region — with any specialization in the system of the whole national economy of the USSR — there should also be organization of the production of local fuel, building materials and glass, chemical fertilizers, and farm machinery, as well as a large assortment of articles of the light-manufacturing and food industries, upon which an incessant demand is made in the region. This ultimately diversified character of the industry of the main economic regions insures their growing independence of articles of universal consumption brought from long distances. It reduces long hauls of goods and rationalizes transportation operations. Such a development — we call it integrated development of the economy of each main economic region — creates still another important precondition for raising the labor productivity of the whole Soviet people.

The principle of the integrated development of the economy exercises a profound influence on the improvement of the distribution of industry. It requires a careful study of the natural wealth — and not only the principal riches but also the minor ones which have primarily local significance — a good knowledge of the objective laws of the distribution of each of the branches of the manufacturing industry, and an ability to use all the advantages resulting from the distribution of a complex group of interrelated lines of production on one and the same territory. Soviet science has great achievements in this respect. Reserves of various minerals in an immense number of deposits have been discovered, estimated, and published. A careful study has been made of the laws of the distribution of many branches of the manufacturing industry. Finally, the typical composition has been determined for the kinds of production to be grouped in line of planning in regions of cheap electric-power production, coal mining, and petroleum extraction, smelting of ferrous and non-ferrous metals, and so forth. Soviet economic geographers have well-known merits in this enterprise.

The practical use of the above-formulated principles leads, in the final analysis, to an even distribution of socialist industry over the whole territory of the USSR. This exhibits the radical difference between distribution under the conditions of capitalism (tendency to territorial concentration and the piling up of the manufacturing industry in a limited number of industrial nodes) and those under socialism (tendency to dispersion of the extractive and manufacturing industries, to location of them in all parts of the country).

The need for a socialist society to distribute its productive forces evenly in accordance with a single plan was brilliantly foreseen by Friedrich Engels. This idea of Engels has become forever a part of the golden fund of Marxism.

The objectively existing necessity of distributing our industry evenly does not, of course, manifest itself in an equal number of entirely like enterprises located on equal areas in all regions of the Soviet Union. That would be an absurdity. It does manifest itself in Soviet industry which is distributed more and more uniformly with each new stage of development, embracing ever-new territories and drawing into factories and plants ever-new strata of the population, bringing an ever-rising level of technical and general culture which liquidates the former patriarchality and seclusion of the marginal regions and creates the premises for ever-fuller satisfaction of the constantly growing material and cultural requirements of society. Of course, an ever-more uniform distribution of industry rests more and more upon the correct disposition of each separate branch on the territory of the USSR in conformity with the ascertained objective laws of their distribution. As early as 1931, progress in this direction had been so great that the Communist Party was able to set its course toward discontinuance of the construction of new industrial enterprises in the largest industrial centers of the country. This at first applied primarily to Moscow and Leningrad, but was later extended to certain other large cities (Khar'kov, Kiyev, Gor'kiy, etc.).

The Marxist-Leninist theory of the distribution of industry, tested by the practice of the development of the economy in the USSR, was created on the basis of overcoming various bourgeois theories, especially the location [*shtandortnyy* = German *Standort*] theory of Alfred Weber. An intense ideological struggle was required to prove the total unsoundness of Weber's general theoretical propositions and particularly their inapplicability under the conditions of socialist construction. In this struggle, the merits of Soviet economic geographers were also great, but victory was not won at once. Not a few authors of books and articles containing much factual material on the distribution of industry were under the influence of the location theory or, displaying total indifference to the theory, reduced the whole matter to a mere registration of the facts.

A combination of Marxist theory and the requirements of practice manifests itself most fully in those works in which the development and distribution of the individual branches (electric construction, fuel extraction, smelting of ferrous metals and machine manufacture) is treated in relation to and in conjunction with the development and distribution of all branches of industry. This integrated approach to the problem of the distribution of industry must be regarded as a great achievement of Soviet scientific thought in the field of the geography of industry.

★ ★ ★

Before the October Revolution the distribution of industrial production in Russia was extremely uneven. Almost half of all production was then furnished by the Central and Petrograd regions; the Ukraine also held a conspicuous place (more than 18 per cent), but the Urals were far behind (4 to 5 per cent), Baku and Groznyy stood as isolated industrial "islands," and in Siberia, Kazakhstan, and Middle Asia there was almost no factory or plant industry.

During the years of socialist industrialization the picture changed sharply. In 1958 the industrial production of the Soviet Union grew 36 times over 1913, the rate of growth of the eastern regions being much faster than that of the western regions, while the previously backward territories of Middle Asia and Transcaucasia became flourishing, industrially developed republics. Already in 1954, the regions of the East (i.e., the Urals, Western Siberia, Eastern Siberia, the Far East, Kazakhstan, and Middle Asia), taken together, furnished about a quarter of all the industrial product of the USSR (in 1912 their share was 8 per cent). The Middle and Lower Volga Region, Transcaucasia, the Belorussian SSR, and the Baltic Lands became mighty industrial regions. Now, all the main economic regions of the Soviet Union possess a large advanced industry.

The control figures for the development of the national economy for 1959-1965, ratified by the 21st Congress of the Communist Party of the Soviet Union, again provide for accelerated development of the economics of the eastern regions. In 1965, when coal mining will reach 600-612 million tons, oil extraction 230-240 million tons, electric-power production 500-520 billion kw-hrs, and steel production 86-91 million tons, the East's share in these will amount to 50, 30, 46, and 48 per cent, respectively.

An especially rapid development of coal mining will take place in Siberia (the coking coal of the Kuzbass, the steam coal of Irkutsk oblast and Krasnoyarsk kray), and in the Kazakh SSR the favorable mining-geology conditions for exploitation insure especially cheap coal. For this reason, a number of thermal electric stations with very great capacities are being built in Siberia.

In the East, a third ferrous-metallurgy base of the USSR will be created during the years of the seven-year plan. New plants will be built in the Kuzbass, Irkutsk oblast, and the Kazakh SSR. Enormous new deposits of iron ore will begin to be exploited in Kustanay oblast (Kazakh SSR), Krasnoyarsk kray, and Irkutsk oblast.

In Eastern Siberia, the largest hydroelectric stations in the world are being erected: the Bratsk GES and the Krasnoyarsk GES on the Yenisey. For this reason a number of electricity-consuming types of production (aluminum, electrochemistry, and others) are being sharply expanded.

Oil and gas extraction is undergoing preferential development in the European part of the country, on both banks of the Middle and Lower Volga and in the Bashkir ASSR, and, in addition, in the republics of Middle Asia. Oil refineries are being built in almost all the main regions of consumption of finished petroleum products.

In the so-called "old" industrial regions of the country, new and very large mineral deposits have also been discovered and are being put under exploitation. For example, the iron ore of the gigantic Kursk Magnetic Anomaly is beginning to be worked, and based on it, huge blast furnaces are being erected at Lipetsk. In the Ukrainian SSR, the Kremenchug iron-ore deposit is being newly exploited and ore-concentration combines are being built to use iron quartzites of the Krivoy Rog basin which were formerly disregarded. The growth of the raw-material base and the presence of coking coal in the Donbass make it possible to increase pig-iron and steel production in the Ukraine by about one and one-half times during the seven-year plan.

Such typical industries of the "old regions" as the machine-manufacturing and textiles continue their tempestuous development here. These regions remain the chief ones in the field of machine building, but there is now a decidedly large amount of it in all the economic regions of the country. A large manufacture of machine tools has arisen, for example, in the Belorussian SSR, and the electrotechnical industry in the Latvian, Armenian, and Azerbaydzhan republics. In addition to the Center, there is an automobile industry in the Belorussian SSR, the Ukrainian SSR, the Georgian SSR, in the Volga Region, and the Urals; a "heavy machine" building industry has been created in all the regions of coal and iron-ore mining and oil extraction; the farm-machinery industry is distributed over all the economic regions in conformity with the established specialization of agriculture, and so forth.

The Center and the Northwest, in which much more than half the population of the USSR is concentrated, continue to remain the chief producers of textiles. Still, enormous new textile factories have been built and are operating in the Volga Region, the Ukraine, Siberia, the Uzbek SSR, the Azerbaydzhan SSR, and so forth.

Thus, Soviet industry is becoming more and more uniformly distributed with each new stage of development, being at the same time brought closer to new rich sources of rew materials and fuel lying in the main regions of consumption. This insures the actual equality of the union republics in the field of economics and politics and enhances the defense capabilities of our Fatherland. By bringing into exploitation the rich mineral deposits with good mining-geology conditions and diminishing or even entirely eliminating the hauling of raw materials and finished products in opposite directions and to excessive distances, the correct distribution of Soviet industry contributes to the raising of the Soviet people's standard of living.

BASIC LITERATURE

See also the literature for Chapters 5, "Economic Geography," 28, "Economic Regionalization," and 29, "Investigations into the Integrated Development of the Productive Forces of the Economic Regions of the USSR."

F. Engels. "Anti-Düring" *(Anti-Dyuring)*, Moscow, 1951.

Atlas promyshlennosti SSSR (Atlas of the Industry of the USSR), publ. by the Presidium of the Supreme Council of National Economy of the USSR, Moscow, 1929-1931.

Atlas Energeticheskikh Resursov SSSR (Atlas of the Power Resources of the USSR), vols. I and II, Moscow, 1935.

Berezov, N. F. The Distribution of Ferrous Metallurgy in the USSR *(Razmeshcheniye Chernoy Metallurgii SSSR)*, Moscow, 1933.

Breyterman, A. D. Economic Geography of the USSR *(Ekonomicheskaya Geografiya SSSR)*, part. I. *Geografiya Tyazheloy Promyshlennosti,* Leningrad, 1958.

Vol'f, M. B. The Geographic Distribution of Russian Industry *(Geograficheskoye Razmeshcheniye Russkoy Promyshlennosti)*, Leningrad, 1927.

Genplan Elektrifikatsii (General Plan of Electrification), vols. 1-7. Materialy k Vsesoyuznoy Konferentsii, Moscow, 1932.

Dimanshteyn, Ya. B. "Problems of the Regionalization of the Metal Industry in Relation to the Conditions of Industrial Development of the Ukraine and the Union." *(Problemy Rayonirovaniya Metallopromyshlennosti v Svyazi s Usloviyami Promyshlennogo Razvitiya Ukrainy i Soyuza)*. Vyvody Raboty Komissii po Metallu pri Gosplane USSR, Khar'kov, 1927.

Kolosovskiy, N. N. The Future of the Ural-Kuznetsk Kombinat *(Budushcheye Uralo-Kuznetskogo Kombinata)*, Moscow, 1932.

Konstantinov, O. A. "Limitation of the Growth of Towns as a Factor in the Correct Distribution of Industry." *Voprosy geografii,* Collection of articles for the 18th International Geographic Congress, Moscow, 1956.

Lisichkin, S. M. Essays on the Development of the Oil-extracting Industry *(Ocherki Razvitiya Neftedobyvayushchey Promyshlennosti)*. In-t ekon. AN SSSR, Moscow, 1958.

Lifshits, R. S. Essays on the Distribution of the Industry of the USSR *(Ocherki po Razmeshcheniyu Promyshlennosti SSSR)*. In-t ekon. AN SSSR, Moscow, 1954.

Lifshits, R. S. The Distribution of Industry in Pre-Revolutionary Russia *(Razmeshcheniye Promyshlennosti v Dorevolyutsionnoy Rossii)*. In-t ekon. AN SSSR, Moscow, 1955.

Lifshits, R. S. The Distribution of Ferrous Metallurgy in the USSR *(Razmeshcheniye Chernoy Metallurgii SSSR)*. In-t ekon. AN SSSR, Moscow, 1958.

Opatskiy, L. V. The Distribution of the Food Industry in the USSR *(Razmeshcheniye Pishchevoy Promyshlennosti SSSR)*, Moscow, 1958.

Pokshishevskiy, V. V. Problems of the Distribution of Industry *(Problemy Razmeshcheniya Promyshlennosti)*, Moscow, 1932.

Probst, A. Ye. Basic Problems of the Geographic Distribution of the Fuel Economy of the USSR *(Osnovnyye Problemy Geograficheskogo Razmeshcheniya Toplivnogo Khozyaystva SSSR)*. Energet. in-t AN SSSR, Moscow, 1939.

Probst, A. Ye. The Socialist Distribution of the Extraction and Consumption of Fuel in the USSR *(Sotsialisticheskoye Razmeshcheniye Dobychi i Potrebleniya Topliva v SSSR)*, 1950.

Stepanov, P. N. Geography of Industry in the USSR *(Geografiya Promyshlennosti SSSR)*. Moscow, 1950. Same, 2nd ed., Moscow, 1955.

Tyazhelaya Industriya v SSSR (Heavy Industry in the USSR). *Ugol', Neft', Zhelezo,* Med' (Coal, petroleum, iron, copper). Under the editorship of V. E. Den, Leningrad, 1926.

Part III

INTEGRATED SCIENTIFIC
PROBLEMS AND TRENDS

B. B. Polynov (1877-1952)

N. N. Kolosovskiy (1891-1954)

A. Ye. Fersman (1883-1945)

Ye. N. Pavlovskiy (born 1884)

CHAPTER 19

PALEOGEOGRAPHY OF THE ICE AGE ON THE TERRITORY OF THE USSR

I. P. Gerasimov

Great theoretical and practical importance is attached to the scientific problems of the paleogeography of the Glacial (Quaternary) period in the USSR. This is due primarily to the fact that an extensive part of our country experienced very great and diverse geologic events during the Quaternary Period: extensive ancient continental glaciation, formation and accumulation of thick strata of various deposits, considerable changes in the shorelines of the sea basins (transgressions and regressions), radical reshaping of the hydrographic network, great climatic changes, profound transformations of the plant cover and the animal world, and gradual development of primitive human society.

The history of the Quaternary, or Glacial, period is being studied in the USSR by a large number of specialists working in different fields of science. A part of them are studying the Quaternary period (Quaternary deposits, fossil flora and fauna) from the *geologic* viewpoint, just as the Tertiary, Cretaceous, or any other period of the geologic past is studied. The chief aim of this study is to ascertain the course of geologic development of the earth's crust during the Quaternary period in order to work out the stratigraphy of the Quaternary deposits, to discover minerals, and to solve practical tasks from the field of hydrogeology and engineering geology. Another group of researchers is interested in the various events of the Glacial period from the *paleogeographic* viewpoint. They endeavor to ascertain the historical roots of present-day natural formations (relief forms, composition of vegetation and animals, the origin of man) for the purpose of working out the most rational ways of making practical use of them. Despite the difference in the scientific aims of these two groups, the objects, methods, and results of their investigations coincide and are closely related. Hence, the elaboration of the problems of the Glacial (Quaternary) period in the USSR is being conducted with the organized cooperation of specialists in a wide range of scientific fields—geologists, geographers, biologists, archeologists, etc. The special Commission on the Study of the Quaternary Period under the Academy of Sciences is organizing integrated scientific work on the problems of this period. It unites the specialists interested in these problems. Through the special National Committee (called the Soviet Section of the INQUA), Soviet Quaternary specialists form a part of the International Association for the Study of the Quaternary Period (INQUA). This international scientific association, as is known, was founded more than twenty years ago, the Soviet Union having been one of its organizers.

In 1957, the 5th International Congress of the INQUA was held in Spain (Madrid and Barcelona). Before this Congress, the All-Union Conference for the Study of the Quaternary Period had been held in the Soviet Union (in Moscow), having been organized by the Academy of Sciences of the USSR and the Ministry of Geology and Conservation. The scale of this Conference, in the work of which more than 500 specialists (geologists, geographers, paleontologists, anthropologists, and archeologists), representing 140 scientific and production institutions, took part, gives a certain idea of the scope of the study of the Quaternary period on the territory of the USSR.

The exact *definition* of the Quaternary period and the establishment of its lower limit, as well as the elaboration of the principles of its stratigraphic subdivision, should now be regarded as the central scientific tasks in the field of the study of the Quaternary period, equal in importance from both the geologic and the paleogeographic viewpoint.

The essence of the exact definition of the Quaternary period and the establishment of its lower limit consists in the following. Both of the existing definitions of this period, the Quaternary and the Diluvial (the latter definition is little used in the USSR), are archaic. They are supported only by priority and tradition, inasmuch as they have totally lost their original historical geologic significance (the Quaternary as contrasted to the Paleozoic and Mesozoic eras and the Tertiary period; the Diluvium as contrasted to the Alluvium and the Present period). Hence, the new definition of the Quaternary period should be more rational and be based on the establishment of those chief geologic or paleogeographic events which occurred during this period and caused its difference from the earlier ones. In Soviet scientific literature, two main proposals have, in fact, been advanced on this question: one proposal recommends the use of the definition "Anthropogene" (Anthropogenic period, system or era) by A. P. Pavlov, A. M. Zhirmunskiy, V. I. Gromov, and others; the other is "Glacial period" by I. P. Gerasimov and K. K. Markov, or "Cryogene period" by S. A. Kovalevskiy.

Let us dwell in somewhat greater detail on these proposals. The first is based on the generally known scientific proposition that the genus of man emerged from the animal world during the Quaternary period and attained its present shape through several intermediate forms.
The socio-economic life of human society originated in the same period. It is quite clear, therefore, that, from the viewpoint of man himself this series of events cannot but be regarded (without exception) as the most important among all of the geologic events of the Quaternary period. Hence it is natural that a brief symbol indicating this event, namely the "Anthropogene," should be fully entitled to substitution for the archaic definitions of "Quaternary," or "Diluvial," period.

The proposal to re-name the Quaternary period "Glacial" or "Cryogene" proceeded from the fact that the greatest general geologic event during the Quaternary (Diluvial) period was the grandiose world-wide and repeated *chilling* of the climate, under the influence of which huge mobile masses of continental ice were formed on all the continents of the earth. This concept gives us the right to define the corresponding time as the Glacial period. Although it is well known that the ancient continental ice did not form a solid cover on the land mass of the territory of the USSR and was absent from extensive plains in the southern (steppe and desert) part of the country, even here the influence of the cold glacial epoch (or epochs) was neverthless fairly strong. It manifested itself (a) in the climate: in the alternation of cold glacial and warmer interglacial epochs, in the areas of glaciation; or else in the alternation of "pluvial," or rainy, epochs with dry "xerothermic" ones in the extraglacial regions, (b) in the processes of the development of the relief and of the formation of continental deposits (moraines and fluvioglacial formations) in areas of ancient glaciation, and the formation of loess rocks and other sheet deposits in areas lying outside the ancient glaciation, (c) in the regular change in the *composition of vegetation and animals*, and (d) in the various modes of life of *primitive man*.

Thus, the cryogenic phenomena in the inorganic medium and in the development of life on the earth's surface, which occurred under the influence of repeated world-wide "cold waves" (epochs of ancient glaciation) represented an extremely powerful factor governing the gradual transformation of all nature, from its original Tertiary appearance to the present aspect of the nature surrounding us.
In the areas of ancient continental glaciation (i.e., on the larger northern part of the territory of the USSR), this transformation of the "preglacial" nature was very radical; practically the entire ancient preglacial nature over the whole territory of the glaciations was annihilated, and the present natural geographic landscapes were created—on the sheets of glacial deposits—almost entirely anew.
This applies to most of the forms of the present relief (moraine plains, zones of marginal formations), to the larger part of the hydrographic network, to the plant cover, and in large measure to the animal world. Moreover, in the extraglacial regions (i.e., in the south of the USSR) as well, the transformation of nature during the Quaternary period (of relief, deposits, vegetation, animals, etc.), although evolutionary in character, was very considerable.

For example, the vast zone of tundras in the north of the Soviet Union, with its peculiar relief, its characteristic vegetation and animal world, was obviously created entirely during the Quaternary period as a result of "cryogenesis." In pre-Quaternary times, the landscape of the present tundras apparently was wholly absent. Equally young (in the geologic sense) are the natural landscapes of swamps. Still not entirely ascertained are the genesis and age of the remarkable tayga forest landscapes of Siberia; there are grounds for believing that they also originated mainly in the Glacial period. Finally, there is no doubt that the ancient glaciation played an immense role in the formation of the present biocoenoses of the mixed forests and the steppes. It is interesting to note that the influence of the Glacial period also manifested itself very strongly in the evolution of primitive human society. Many Soviet archeologists and paleozoologists insistently advance the idea that the development of the paleolithic culture of man is closely connected with the epochs of glaciation (including the so-called Dnepr, or Riss, glaciation), and that the Neolithic does not appear until the period following the last, i.e., Valday (Würm) glaciation.

From all the foregoing it is clear that there certainly are grounds for the notion that the ancient great continental glaciation was a most important general geologic event of the Quaternary period. Hence, the term "Glacial period" or "Cryogene" to designate the Quaternary (Diluvial) period is, to a certain extent, fully justified. However, the majority of Soviet specialists on the Quaternary (Diluvial) period are inclined, at present, in favor of the term "Anthropogene." The proposal, at the All-Union Conference, for the gradual introduction of this term into geologo-geographic literature as a synonym for the "Quaternary" (Diluvial) period, in order to accustom people to it and prepare them for complete substitution, met with support.

As regards the term "Glacial period," or "Cryogene," the opinion of the majority was inclined not so much to use these *terms* as to use the *concepts* connected with them for the establishment of the lower limit of the Quaternary period (the Anthropogene). The essence of this proposal consists in drawing the stratigraphic boundary between the Quaternary and Tertiary periods according to the clearest traces (in the character of the deposits and the composition of the fossil flora and fauna) of the first great, world-wide climatic cold wave.

The second task, i.e., the stratigraphic subdivision of the Quaternary period (Anthropogene), is attracting much attention in the USSR. The task consists of establishing those scientific methods whereby it will be possible to divide the Quaternary period justifiably into smaller sections of time, and the objective indices that should be used in deciding to which of these sections this or that stratum of Quaternary deposits belongs in the different regions of the Soviet Union. The close interrelationship between these two tasks is quite clear. The division of the Quaternary period into more or less small sections of time should obviously be based on the natural stages in the development of the chief geologic (paleogeographic) events that took place during the Quaternary period and determined its peculiar character (i.e., definition). In so doing, the objective indices of the relative ages of the different layers of Quaternary deposits should be related to those traces of the past which testify in the clearest form to a definite stage in the geologic history of the Quaternary period.

As is known, the problem of the methods of stratigraphy and correlation for all the ancient deposits (Tertiary, Cretaceous, etc.) has long been solved on a traditional biologic (paleontologic) basis. However, for the Quaternary period (Anthropogene), the matter is considerably more complicated. The Quaternary fauna and flora are, as a rule, of continental origin and for this single reason alone they exhibit considerably more diversity and variability in space than do the fauna and flora of the seas, chiefly peculiar to the older deposits. This is to be explained by the great diversity in the conditions of the terrestrial medium, in comparison with the marine, a fact which causes very substantial difficulties in the synchronization of ecologically diversified forms and coenoses. But of still greater significance are the various time scales for the development of the Quaternary flora and fauna by comparison with the older ones. It must be remembered that the length of the Quaternary period (Anthropogene) is usually fixed at one million years, whereas all the other geologic periods lasted tens or hundreds of millions of years. It is quite natural that the Quaternary fauna and flora, while ecologically very diversified, should, as a rule, possess no such great systematic differences as the older ones. This applies above all to the lower animals (for example the very simple ones, molluscs, etc.), whose biostratigraphic significance is very important for all the ancient sediments. It may be stated that the Quaternary fauna and flora are made up in the main of only modern families, that modern genera are dominant, and that modern species of plants and animals predominate. Hence, relative systematic uniformity during considerable sections of time is characteristic of most of the Quaternary faunal and floral complexes, in contrast to the more ancient ones. Examples are the Mediterranean and Caspian complex of marine fauna or the so-called mammoth complex of land vertebrates, which existed for a very long time on the plains of Eurasia (V. I. Gromov, I. G. Pidoplichko, and others). All this makes it extremely difficult to apply biostratigraphic criteria to a detailed breakdown of the Quaternary strata.

From the foregoing, however, it does not follow that, in violation of the classical tradition of historical geology, doubts arise as to the possibility of applying the methods of biostratigraphy to Quaternary deposits. The following approach would obviously be more correct: taking into account the specific peculiarities of the fauna and flora of the Quaternary period (Anthropogene), the greater diversity of the geographic conditions of their existence, and the comparatively short absolute length of the period of their development, one should place the application of biostratigraphic methods in the study of Quaternary deposits under the control of a broader paleogeographic approach to the phenomena being studied. In particular, only on the basis of such an approach to, and consideration for, the paleoecologic conditions should the limits be fixed for applying this or that concrete biostratigraphic index (of species and coenoses) in breaking down and comparing Quaternary deposits.

To clarify this proposition let us dwell on one more scientific principle of the synchronism and metachronism of paleogeographic and paleobiologic phenomena. It is a principle which is common and very important to the study of the Quaternary period, and one which has been advanced in Soviet scientific literature on that period (Gerasimov and Markov, 1939). The essence of this principle may be very briefly formulated as follows: owing to the diversity of the local geographic circumstances over vast sections of the earth's surface, even a uniform earth-wide impulse (for example a world-wide change in the amount of solar radiation) must cause very multiform phenomena — consequences — in remote regions differing from one another in character (for example, climatic changes, glacial phenomena, transformations in the fauna and flora composition, etc.). To put it more briefly, basically synchronous impulses produce metachronous [non-simultaneous] consequences in the diversified natural geographic environment.

Here one should stress especially the great significance of the territory of the Soviet Union precisely for the elaboration of questions of the synchronism and metachronism of the events of the geologic past. Our country is large and very diversified in its modern physical geographic features. Hence, the above-mentioned theoretical principle (the diverse character of the reaction of the natural geographic environment to simple impulses) must have decisive significance in all paleogeographic reconstructions on Soviet territory.

To clarify still more this important geographic principle, let us examine the latest concepts about the character and number of ancient glaciations in different parts of the USSR.

Modern investigations outline for the territory of the western part of the USSR (the European part of the USSR or Russian Plain) a very complex, typically *polyglaciologic* picture of ancient glaciation. The works by G. F. Mirchink, S. A. Yakovlev, A. I. Moskvitin, V. P. Grichuk, N. N. Sokolov, M. M. Tsapenko, S. M. Shik, and others establish the development here of not less than three, four, or even more (up to 6-8) transgressive stages in the history of the continental sheet glaciation (glacial sheet or ice cap). Some of these stages are given the significance of independent glaciations (for example the Likhva, Dnepr, Moscow, and Valday stages), separated by large stages of regression of the glacial sheet (its total thawing). Others are regarded as non-independent stages [etapy or stadii], subordinate to the former. It should be noted that there are differing views of Soviet investigators as to the number of such independent glaciations or their stages. This is to be explained, in our opinion, by the still insufficiently exact and ununified content of the concepts "glacial" and "interglacial," "stadial," and "interstadial" epoch, phase or age. These concepts are treated differently by many investigators.

The polyglaciologic schemes of ancient glaciation evolvable for the Russian Plain are considerably simplified for the Urals and the West-Siberian Lowland. Here, according to the latest investigations (V. N. Saks, S. B. Shatskiy, and others), the development of a less sizable ancient glacial sheet is to be recognized than in the west of the USSR, with only two clearly pronounced transgressive epochs in its history: the Samara and the Zyryan'. The question of the independence of two other glaciations (the Tazovskiy and the Sartana) is indeed being discussed, but disagreements exist on this question.

For Eastern Siberia, which throughout the Quaternary period possessed an extremely rigorous, extracontinental climate, the latest investigations yield a still more simplified scheme.

Here, alongside forms of a mountain-glacier character, very peculiar forms of ancient glaciations (semi-sheet glaciers of the mountain foothills, extensive firn fields, etc.) have been established, but indisputable signs of interglacial epochs have not been discovered at all. Thus, for Eastern Siberia there is only one *monoglaciologic* scheme; at the same time, certain remarkable natural phenomena of a late glacial character (bald tops [*gol'tsy*], fossil ice, perpetual frost, thermokarst, etc.), found nowhere else in the world at corresponding latitudes, have been preserved here down to the present time.

Still farther east, in the coastal monsoon regions of the Far East — on the Chukot Peninsula and Kamchatka, on Sakhalin and in the Sikhote-Alin' (according to the latest data of G. F. Chemekov, G. S. Ganeshin, A. P. Vas'kovskiy and others), signs of rather extensive and repeated glaciations have been established. Some investigators discover in its history great features of similarity to the history of glaciation in the western part of the USSR, although on this territory quite unique formations are also observed. An example is the pyroclastic moraines of Kamchatka, formed by a capricious combination of present-day deep-seated volcanic heat (fire) with superficial climatic cold (firns and glaciers).

The foregoing suggests the need for a very cautious approach to the mutual comparison of even such major events as the ancient glaciations of the various regions of the USSR. While probably stimulated by a single common cause (the change in the heat balance of the earth's surface), the ancient glacial formations on the territory of the Soviet Union have possessed a very multiform character in space and a differently expressed rhythm in time (for example, the polyglacial phenomena in the West and the Far East and the monoglacial phenomena in the center of the continent). A no less realistic paleogeographic approach is also obviously obligatory for all those ecologic and systematic transformations in the composition of the flora and fauna which were effected under the influence of the great changes in the surrounding geographic environment (particularly the glaciations).

Precisely for this reason, in the study of the Quaternary period on the territory of the USSR, a very important (if not prime) role has always been assigned to the elaboration of so-called local, or relative, stratigraphic schemes based on an all-around consideration of the paleogeographic sequence of the chain of monotypic events which is peculiar to a limited territory; for example the Russian Plain, the Urals, Kazakhstan and middle Asia, and western Siberia. Of decisive significance in working out such schemes have been concrete biostratigraphic criteria, the limits of whose application, however, have not gone beyond the territory having a homogeneous course of paleogeographic development. For this reason, the makeup of the biostratigraphic indices could be very extensive (spore-and-pollen complexes, malacocoenoses, etc.), and their reliability adequate.

The chief difficulties arose in the correlation of the local stratigraphic subdivisions with each other and in the attempts to reduce them to a common, i.e., single stratigraphic scale for the territory of the whole USSR. The reliability of such comparisons, based chiefly on common biostratigraphic indices (spore-and-pollen spectra, mammologic complexes, archeologic finds), became more and more restricted as smaller and smaller stratigraphic subdivisions were compared with each other. Most specialists now acknowledge that a common system of subdivision of the Quaternary period (Anthropogene) for the whole territory of the USSR should be based only on the very principal stratigraphic units, i.e., on sections [*otdely*] and stages [*yarusy*, "tiers"]. Only within the framework of such major subdivisions, embracing considerable sections of time, is it correct to apply to the vast territory of the USSR the above-characterized principle of synchronism and metachronism in geologic development. Both a three-membered scheme (preglacial, glacial, and postglacial sections) and a four-membered scheme (ancient, middle, and recent Pleistocene and Holocene) are used as such subdivisions in the USSR.

Within the framework of the present chapter it is impossible to set forth the present state of many other important scientific problems of the Quaternary period (Anthropogene) which are being worked out in the USSR. Among them, the problem of the origin and age of the loesses and loess-like formations in the Ukraine, the northern Caucasus, Siberia, and middle Asia; the Quaternary history of the Black, Caspian and Aral seas; the questions of the Quaternary paleogeography of the steppe and desert territories; and particularly the problem of the genesis, age, and history of the sand deserts of Kazakhstan and middle Asia; the problem of the history of the formation of the profoundly unique bald-top [*golets*] landscapes of eastern Siberia; the recent and present-day volcanism of Kamchatka; and other major regional paleogeographic problems whose theoretical significance goes beyond the framework of the respective region. All enjoy the especial attention of Soviet paleogeographic researchers.

Alongside such problems of a regional character, Soviet paleogeographers have always treated the very complex, but especially important practical questions of the history of the formation of the valleys of the major rivers of the Soviet Union (the Volga, Dnepr, Don, Ural, the big Siberian rivers, etc.), as well as the ancient and present shoreline of the lakes, seas, and oceans touching the territory of the USSR. An immense amount of valuable materials has been accumulated on the first of these major lines of paleogeographic research (see the works by G. F. Mirchink, G. I. Goretskiy, Ye. I. Gerenchuk, etc.). As regards the study of the history of the lake and sea shorelines, as well as the paleogeography of the water basins themselves, new cycles of scientific paleogeographic investigations embracing not only the shores and coastal zones of our great bodies of water, but also the formerly unexplored deep-water regions have been recently executed in the USSR alongside the many classical works by N. I. Andrusov, A. D. Arkhangel'skiy, and N. M. Strakhov on the Black Sea, and by P. A. Pravoslavlev and L. S. Berg on the Caspian and Aral seas. On the basis of the latest works, an entirely new field of paleogeography, namely the Quaternary paleogeography of the oceans, has recently been under successful development in the USSR. The basic factual material for the development of this scientific trend is furnished by the all-around study of the columns of deep-water silt deposits obtained in the modern oceanologic work on the scientific-research vessels "Vityaz'," "M. V. Lomonosov," and others.

BASIC LITERATURE

Gerasimov, I. P. "The Origin of the Nature of the Present Geographic Zones." *Izv. AN SSSR, Seriya geogr.,* 1951, no. 2.

Gerasimov, I. P. and Markov, K. K. "The Glacial Period on the Territory of the USSR." *Tr. In-ta geogr. AN SSSR,* vol. 33, Moscow-Leningrad, 1939.

Grichuk, V.P. "The Vegetation of the Russian Plain in Lower and Middle Quaternary Times." *Tr. In-ta geogr. AN SSSR,* vol. 46, Moscow-Leningrad, 1950.

Gromov, V. I. "The Paleontologic and Archeologic Foundations of the Stratigraphy of the Continental Deposits of the Quaternary Period on the Territory of the USSR." *Tr. In-ta geogl. nauk,* vol. 64, no. 17, Moscow-Leningrad, 1948.

Gromov, V. I., Krasnov, I. I., and Nikiforova, K. V. "The Basic Principles of the Subdivision of the Quaternary System and its Lower Limit." *Izv. AN SSSR, Seriya geol.,* 1958, no. 5.

Kolosov, D. M. "Problems of the Ancient Glaciation of the Northeast of the USSR." Moscow-Leningrad, izd. Glavsevmorputi, 1947 *(Tr. gornogeol. upr.,* no. 30).

Lednikovyy Period na Yevropeyskoy Territorii SSSR i v Sibiri (The Glacial Period on the European Territory of the USSR and in Siberia). Sb. nauchnykh stat. izd. MGU (Moscow State University), 1959.

Materialy po Chetvertichnoy Geologii i Geomorfologii SSSR (Materials on the Quaternary Geology and Geomorphology of the USSR). Sbornik nauchnykh statey, VSEGEI, Gostoptekhizdat, 1959.

Markov, K. K. Paleogeography *(Paleogeografiya),* 1951-1960.

Mirchink, G. F. "On the Number of Glaciations of the Russian Plain." *Priroda,* 1928, nos. 7-8.

Moskvitin, A. I. "The Odintsovo Interglacial and the Position of the Moscow Glaciation among the other Glaciations of Europe." *Byull. MOIP, otd. geol.,* no. 21, 4, 1946.

Problemy Paleogeografii Chetvertichnogo Perioda (Problems of the Paleogeography of the Quaternary Period). Sbornik nauchnykh statey, izd. In-ta geogr. AN SSSR.

Saks, V. N. "An Experiment in the Reconstruction of the History of the Development of Siberia in the Quaternary Period." *Materialy po chetv. periodu SSSR,* 3, 1952.

Sokolov, N. N. "On the Location of the Limits of the Glaciations in the European Part of the USSR," *Tr. In-ta geogr., AN SSSR,* vol. 37, 1946.

Yakovlev, S. A. "Fundamentals of the Geology of the Quaternary Deposits of the Russian Plain," *Tr. VSEGEI,* 17, 1956.

CHAPTER 20

PALEOGEOGRAPHY OF POSTGLACIAL TIMES

M. I. Neyshtadt

The paleogeography of postglacial times, by which is meant the natural conditions in their development (dynamics) during the most recent geologic times (the Holocene), is the key to an understanding of the present natural setting of the various sections of the earth's surface. This problem is of both theoretical and practical interest because, despite the geologically short duration of the Holocene, diverse natural processes have evolved in this period on the territory of the USSR, the results of which represent an extensive field for the application of human labor. For example, one may point to Western Siberia, where heavy strata of organic sediments (up to 10 meters thick) were deposited during this interval of time over an expanse of tens of millions of hectares.

Characteristic traits have been manifested in the latest investigations of the paleogeography of the Holocene on USSR territory. The first of these is the *wide geographic range of the investigations.* In addition to the central areas of the European part of the USSR, numerous investigations have been conducted in Lithuania, Latvia, Estonia, Karelia, Belorussia, the Ukraine, the Caucasus, Western and Eastern Siberia, the Far East, Sakhalin, Kamchatka, and the Arctic. The second trait is the *integrated approach to the study of Holocene paleogeography,* the engagement of different trends of research: swamp-science, limnologic, geomorphologic, geologic, paleontologic, archeologic, and historical.

The third trait is the *study of the laws of the natural conditions of the Holocene in space and time,* both in the USSR as a whole and by separate regions of different sizes, and by the most interesting separate objects —"peat basins," major internal bodies of water, seacoasts, etc.

Finally, one should note the wide use by scientific institutions of the enormous amount of materials of the practical Soviet organizations. This may be illustrated, say, by the exploration of peat deposits, the study of which offers perhaps the most valuable material for paleogeographic purposes. In the RSFSR alone, for example, production organizations have now explored over 42,000 peat deposits, with a total area of 42,000,000 hectares. Plan materials, cadastral lists, and also specialized survey maps have been compiled for all these objects. Production work is being organized under constant consultation with scientific workers, and close ties thus exist between practice and science in this branch of geographic research.

A large amount of material for understanding the natural processes of the Holocene and their characteristics is furnished by the study of the sediments of this period, to which belong swamp, lake, delta, and eolian deposits of glaciers, and the like. The thickness of the Holocene deposits is at times very great: it reaches 16 meters in swamps, 25 meters in deltas and 40 meters in lakes. These deposits are widely distributed from the western border of the USSR in Belorussia and the Ukraine to the easternmost territories of the country (Kamchatka and Sakhalin) and from the Extreme North — the maritime lowlands of the Arctic Ocean — to the Colchidian Lowland in Transcaucasia. The Holocene autochthonous organic sediments have limited distribution only in the steppe zone, and are absent in the desert regions.

A study has been made in the USSR of the massive accumulations of Holocene deposits on individual sections of the forest zone. Thus, for example, in the West-Siberian Lowland the peat swamps or characteristic swamp-and-lake landscapes occupy as much as 80 per cent of the area on certain watersheds. In Western Kamchatka, swamps extend in an almost continuous line for over 500 kilometers, and so forth.

Integrated study of lake sediments — lithologic, chemical, and biologic — is being applied to the composition of the different groups of algae (especially diatoms), animals (including molluscs), pollens, etc. All this naturally creates very favorable points of departure for the study of Holocene paleogeography and the establishment of the general and particular laws of this period over the vast territory of the country.

A good many scientific questions exist, of course, in the problem of the Holocene. A certain amount of material has already been obtained on many of them; work has just begun on others, while still others are yet to be investigated.

One of these questions is the determination of the absolute age and length of the Holocene, which coincide for this latest geologic period of the earth. In the USSR, the duration of the Holocene has been determined by various methods. I. G. Pidoplichko, for example, has worked out a procedure for computing the age from the collagen content in calcined bones, and has estimated that the Holocene lasted 11,800 years. For the mountain regions (Terskey-Alatau Range in the Tyan'-Shan'), M. I. Iveronova has estimated the age of the Holocene at 10,000 years from the volume of talus and its rates of accumulation. A comparison by us of pollen diagrams, taking into account the determination of the absolute age from varved clays, has shown the length of the Holocene to be 12,000 years. According to A. V. Shnitnikov's historical-climatic data, the retreat of the glacier of the Würm glaciation began about 13,000-13,500 years ago. Thus, the duration of the Holocene is computed at a figure between 10,000 and 13,500 years, or an average of about 12,000 years.

The *lower limit of the Holocene* must be defined, from our point of view, by the time of the first deposits of organogenic sediments in the oldest of the present swamps and fresh-water lakes on territory which was under the last ice cap. This boundary can be established and then defined at many points by the pollen-analysis method. In particular, in the middle belt of the European part of the USSR the horizon with the lower maximum of fir pollen corresponds to it.

In comparison with the data of Swedish investigators, this will correspond to L. Post's 11th zone, which begins the Holocene in our understanding of the term. H. Gams arrives at a similar opinion.*

Investigation of the natural processes occurring in the Holocene requires an examination of their dynamics, which leads to a breakdown of the Holocene into separate sections of time. A comparison of the phenomena over the immense territory of the USSR can only be made with a relatively small number of divisions. Hence, the Holocene in the USSR has been broken up into four time sections: ancient [*drevnyy*], early [*ranniy*], middle [*sredniy*], and late [*pozdniy*], with absolute ages of 12,000-9,800, 9,800-7,700, 7,700-2,500, and 2,500 years, respectively. On the basis of a large amount of factual material, a proposition which is extremely important for investigators of paleogeography has been established concerning the possibility of correlating Holocene cross sections over the whole territory of the USSR. Investigations made by Soviet scientists have furnished a large amount of material and have permitted interesting conclusions on Holocene paleogeography.

First of all, one must note the research on the paleogeography of the natural zones and on the formation of botanico-geographic areas and provinces in their dynamics by separate periods of the Holocene. From the materials on the pollen diagrams of more than 500 cross sections of swamp and lake deposits, and with due consideration for the materials on the changes in the shorelines, paleogeographic maps of the USSR have been created for the ancient, early, middle, and late Holocene. These maps have graphically demonstrated the whole complexity of the natural setting and its constant changes in the Holocene (Fig. 5, page 168; Fig. 6, page 170).

These same basic materials were used to *regionalize the territory of the USSR with regard to the development of the plant cover.* Twenty-six regions were distinguished, each of which possesses its own special scheme of vegetation dynamics. A determination was made of the various initial compositions of the vegetation at the beginning of the Holocene in the separate sections of the territory of the USSR and its further differentiation in the process of the gradual development in dependence upon the climatic, orographic, and soil conditions, as well as upon the ecology and biology of the individual plants. In this way, the genetic causation of the present-day geobotanical regionalization of the USSR was demonstrated.

---

*H. Gams, "Fortschritte der quartären Vegetationsgeschichte des Ostens." Verhandl. d. 4 Internat. Tagung der Quartärtbotaniker 1957, *Verff. geobot. Inst. Rubel in Zürich*, H. 34.

The formation of the habitat areas [*arealy*] of many tree species, most of which substantially changed their habitat areas in the Holocene, was studied and represented cartographically. This made it possible, in a number of cases, to approach the questions of the explanation of the present distribution of trees in a manner quite different than was the case heretofore.

Investigations have begun into the *history of the Holocene fauna*, but great difficulties are being encountered in the solution of this question, chiefly for two reasons: the free migration of animals and the localization of their fossil remains. The latter are found principally at the abodes of man, more rarely in caves.

A study of the materials collected, especially the bone remains, enables one to affirm that certain changes occurred during the Holocene both in the composition of the fauna and in the limits of distribution of certain species. The biggest role here (aside from the influence of man, especially noticeable in the second half of the Holocene) was apparently played by the changes in the boundaries of the natural zones and botanico-geographic areas. For example, I. G. Podoplichko has shown that, at the beginning of the Holocene, mammoths and rhinoceroses still existed in the European part of the USSR. Certain animals narrowed their habitat areas; for example, the ground squirrel [*tushkanchik*], the *saygak* [*Saiga tatarica*, a sheeplike antelope], the steppe *pestrushki* [rodents of the genus Eremiomys], etc. Here and there forest faunal complexes have been replaced by forest-steppe ones, and forest-steppe complexes by steppe ones.

In the last few years, A. V. Tattar has discovered large accumulations of mammal and bird bones in the caves of the Zhiguli [hills in the Samara bend of the Volga] and the Upper Don, which were formed mainly through the hunting activity of many generations of the horned owl. The thickness of such deposits reaches 1.5 meters. The layer-by-layer study of these has made it possible to trace the change in the fauna in time and to compare it with different sections of the Holocene.

Widely evolved in the Holocene were the peat-forming processes, embracing vast expanses and substantially changing the natural aspect. The total area over which these processes are now taking place exceeds 71,000,000 hectares on the territory of the USSR. Sometimes peat formation solidly covers the watersheds and the stream valleys, leaving only the valley slopes free (Fig. 7, page 172).

The chief features of the types of peat bogs, by natural geographic zones, and the association of their development with definite conditions have now been established. Each geographic zone possesses its own types of peat bogs, peculiarities of development, and distribution (M. I. Neyshtadt, N. I. P'yavchenko, and S. N. Tyuremnov). Large peat basins are associated with bedrock sags (M. N. Nikonov) and with the present-day lowlands — up to a level of not over 200 meters absolute altitude.

The paleogeographic conditions of the second half of the Middle Holocene led to the formation, in the peat deposits of the upland type, of a so-called "border-line horizon" whose area of distribution is confined to a definite geographic region (see Fig. 5). To a certain degree, the fossil soils in the cross-sections of the floodplains of a number of rivers are similar to this horizon.

The principles of the regionalization of peat swamps have been worked out, principally on the basis of their paleogeography, with consideration for their present characteristics as well.

Numerous investigations have revealed an immense number of *paleo-lakes*, which existed for a fairly long time and ceased to exist in different periods of the Holocene. An especially large number of lakes, sometimes occupying considerable areas, ceased to exist in the upper half of the Middle Holocene, corresponding to a warmer and drier period. The lake beds in this period were largely filled with silt, and lowering of their level by gradual stages helped to turn them into swamps. The presence of paleo-lakes is attested by the strata of sapropel, reaching thicknesses of 5 to 8 meters and sometimes more. The time of the disappearance of the lakes is established by data from pollen analyses and by estimates of the annual layers, which in a number of cases (Lake Somino) are perfectly visible to the naked eye.

Considerable work has been done on the study of the Holocene history of present-day lakes (V. N. Sukachev, V. V. Kudryashev, M. I. Neyshtadt, N. V. Korde, V. P. Grichuk, L. L. Rossolimo, L. S. Kozlovskaya, and others). In many lakes, underwater terraces have been discovered and a detailed biologic and lithologic study of the silt has shown the presence of changes in the water and heat regime of the lakes.

The Holocene is also characterized by the formation of floodplain terraces and deltas, in which heavy thicknesses of alluvial deposits have accumulated. For example, the thickness of the flood-

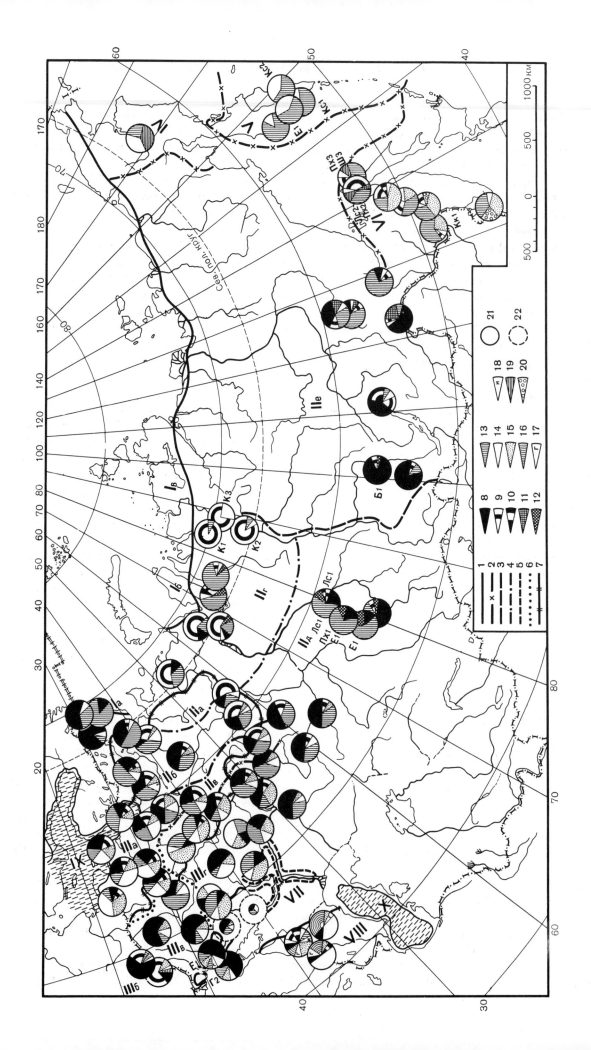

plain alluvium of the Kuban' River at Krasnodar reaches 15 meters, and that of the Holocene delta deposits of the Northern Dvina at Arkhangel'sk, 26 meters.

Of very great significance for the problem under discussion is the study of the paleogeography *of the seashores*. Such work has been done on the Baltic Sea by **K. K. Markov, E. F. Grinbergs,** and **V. K. Gudelis,** in whose studies the separate stages of development of the Baltic basin have been examined in detail. There are similar materials on the Black and Caspian seas and other basins. Interesting for the Black Sea coast, for example, are the facts obtained by various methods which indicate a subsidence of the shoreline of the Colchis in the Holocene. In this region, the lower layers of the present-day peat bogs, composed of sphagnum peat of the upland type, lie 6 meters below sea level. Most of the artificial hills [probably = man-made mounds] lying in the Colchidian Lowland have now sunk to a depth of 3 - 5 meters below sea level. Submerged towns and individual structures have been discovered here, as well as stream valleys whose original beds are filled out with deposits. From the data obtained by geomorphologic, archeologic, and swamp-science methods, the rate of subsidence in this region can be fixed at about 2 millimeters a year, on the average.

A study of *marine sediments* has been begun for paleogeographic reconstructions of the Holocenes. It has been established that the thickness of the Holocene sediments in the inland seas may reach 5 meters. In recent years, pollen and diatom analyses of a 27-meter core (taken in the Okhotsk Sea at a depth of 3,355 meters) have shown that the upper 2 meters formed by clay-and-diatom silt, belong to the Holocene sediments (A. P. Zhuze and Ye. V. Koreneva). The diatom and pollen analyses of these strata have yielded identical results, which on the whole also coincide with data obtained from analyses of the deposits of shoreside peat swamps. Thus, there arise alluring prospects for a wider use of the results of the investigation of marine sediments in studying the paleogeography of the Holocene.

Other methods have also been applied to the study of the paleogeography of the seas. From the phosphate and silicic-acid content, the minimum age of the present stage of the Black Sea has been fixed at 5,600 years (Ya. K. Gololobov). According to N. M. Strakhov, the beginning of the last stage of salinification of the Black Sea, which succeeded the stage of the Neo-Euxine Basin [*Novoevksinskiy Basseyn*], took place about 5,000 years ago (according to an estimate of the annual layers).

In studying the intricate complex of natural phenomena of the Holocene, one must not ignore *young tectonics,* which exercises great influence on the course and development of many natural processes. The amplitude of the vertical tectonic movements of the individual sections of the land reached a very great value in the Holocene; for example, the vertical movements of the shores of

Fig. 5. PALEOGEOGRAPHIC MAP OF THE MIDDLE HOLOCENE
(According to M. I. Neyshtadt)

I. Zone of the Tundra: Ia, Kola provinces; I б , Western Siberian; I в , Eastern Siberian.

II. Forest Zone: IIa, Eastern European province of the European-Siberian subarea of dark coniferous forests of the Eurasian conifer-forest (tayga) area; strip without broadleaf species; II б , Same; strip with participation of broadleaf species; II в , Same; strip with considerable participation of broadleaf species; II г , Western Siberian province of the same subarea; strip with predominance of fir; II д , Same; strip with considerable participation of Siberian pine [*Pinus sibirica*]; II e , Eastern Siberian subarea of clear conifer forests of the same area.

III. European Broadleaf Area: IIIa, Baltic subprovince; III б , Carpathian subprovince; III в , Polessian subprovince; III г , Middle Russian subprovince.

IV. Bering Shrub Forest-tundra Area.

V. Kamchatkan Herbaceous and Leaf-forest Area.

VI. Far Eastern Broadleaf-forest Area.

VII. Steppe zone.

VIII. Mediterranean Forest Area.

IX. Littorine Sea.

X. Caspian Sea (according to Leont'yev and Fedorov).

Boundaries:

1. Natural zones
2. Geobotanical areas
3. Subareas
4. Strips [*polosy*] of vegetation

5. Presumed natural zones
6. Subprovinces
7. Regions of distribution of peat bogs with horizon along the border

Symbols on pollen cyclograms:

8. pine; 9. fir; 10. spruce; 11. larch; 12. Siberian pine [*kedr*]; 13. birch; 14. alder; 15. oak + linden + elm; 16. hornbeam; 17. beech; 18. willow; 19. *kedrovyy slanik* [*Pinus pumila,* a pine of creeping, matted habit]; 20. Korean pine [*koreyskiy kedr*]; 21. spectra of the forest type; 22. spectra of the steppe (and forest-steppe) type.

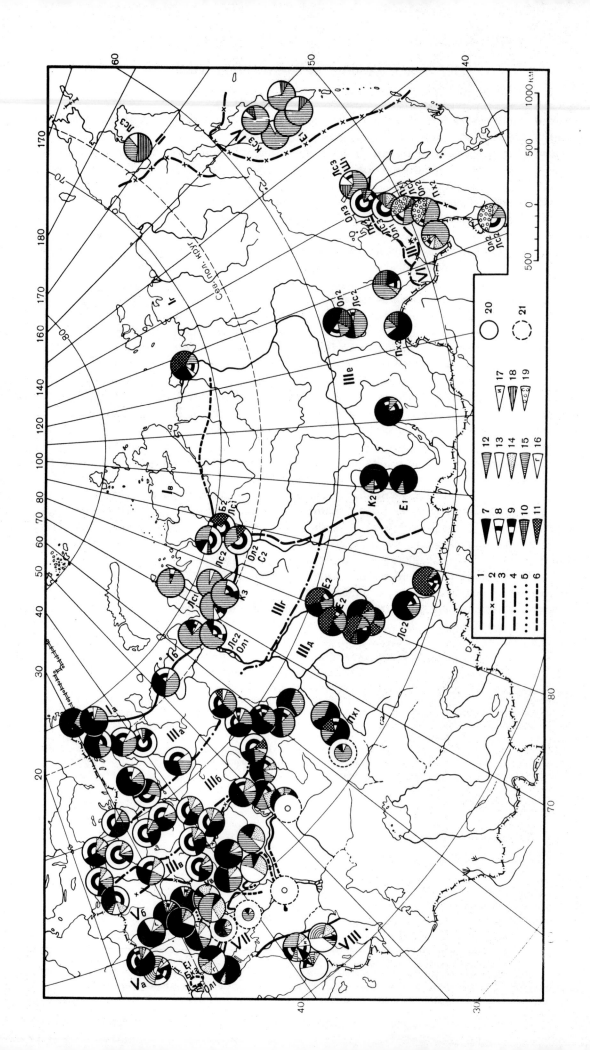

the Baltic Sea were as much as 70 meters. Movements having different [algebraic] signs and different magnitudes have been noted for the shoreline of Kamchatka and for many other regions.

V. B. Sochava has shown that the most recent vertical movements of the earth's crust exert an influence on the changes in the plant cover, although they act upon it through a multitude of other factors and simultaneously with other influences having a more direct ecologic significance. The reaction of the plant cover has its own peculiarities in the tundra, the tayga, and the steppe. A connection has been noted between the character of the tectonic structures and the laws of the structure of the floodplains of certain rivers (Yu. A. Meshcheryakov, S. K. Gorelov). Individual regions of uplift and subsidence have been established; for example, a conclusion has been drawn regarding the general tectonic subsidence of the Azov-Kuban' Plain and the uplift of the Stavropol' Upland in the Holocene.

Climatic changes in the Holocene, known earlier in their most general form, have lately been subjected to a more concrete and detailed study. It may be considered as established that the climate in this period has been subject to considerable secular fluctuations.

A large number of facts show that there have been five climatic periods, averaging about 2,000 years each, in the last 10,000 to 12,000 years. A. V. Shnitnikov, for example, has come to the conclusion that the Holocene had humidity rhythms lasting 1,800–1,900 years. I. Ye. Buchinskiy views the question of the past climate of the Russian Plain in a similar manner.

P. P. Predtechenskiy has compiled a table of climatic changes in the Holocene for the Russian Plain (see Table I, page 173).

Many other processes occurring in the Holocene are also being studied. The glaciation of a number of northern islands has continued, and glaciers have been preserved on the mountain ranges. In many regions of the volcanic-highland zone of the Minor Caucasus the latest massive effusions of andesite and dacite lavas have occurred, which have filled the valleys and formed hillocky covers, crowned by cinder cones. It has been demonstrated by the geomorphologic method (E. A. Rantsman) that the bottoms of the troughs of the last glaciation can have been cut through by young valleys in the Holocene to a depth of as much as 100 meters. The improvement of methods and instruments (G. B. Udintsev and A. P. Lisitsyn) have made it possible to observe the stratification of present-day marine deposits at a water depth of as great as 1,000 meters. The boundaries between the layers are marked by interlayers of volcanic sand, thus offering prospects for synchronizing these layers with the deposits of peat bogs and with soils in which such interlayers are also observed.

In the Holocene, especially in its second half, a big and ever more active role in the changing of nature has come to be played by man, who at the same time has lifted himself to higher levels of

---

Fig. 6. PALEOGEOGRAPHIC MAP OF THE LATE HOLOCENE
(According to M. I. Neyshtadt)

I. Zone of the Tundra: Ia, Kola province; I б , Eastern European; I в , Western Siberian; I г , Eastern Siberian
II. Bering Shrub (forest-tundra) Area
III. Forest Zone: IIIa, Eastern European province of the European-Siberian subarea of dark coniferous forests of the Eurasian conifer-forest (tayga) area; strip without broadleaf species; III б , Same; strip with participation of broadleaf species; III в , Same; strip with considerable participation of broadleaf species; III г , Western Siberian province of the same subarea; strip with predominance of fir; III д , Same, with predominance of Siberian pine; III е , Eastern Siberian subarea of clear conifer forests of the same area; III ж , Southern Okhotsk subarea of dark conifer forest.
IV. Kamchatkan Herbaceous and Leaf-forest Area
V. European Broadleaf-forest Area: Va, Carpathian subprovince; V б , Polessian subprovince; V в , Middle Russian subprovince
VI. Far Eastern Conifer and Broadleaf-forest Area
VII. Steppe Zone
VIII. Mediterranean Forest Area

Boundaries:

1. Natural zones
2. Botanical areas
3. Subareas
4. Strips of vegetation
5. Presumed natural zones
6. Subprovinces

Symbols on the pollen cyclograms:

7. pine; 8. fir; 9. spruce; 10. larch; 11. Siberian pine; 12. birch; 13. alder; 14. oak & linden & elm; 15. hornbeam; 16. beech; 17. willow; 18. kedrovyy slanik; 19. Korean pine; 20. spectra of the forest type; 21. spectra of the steppe (and forest-steppe) type

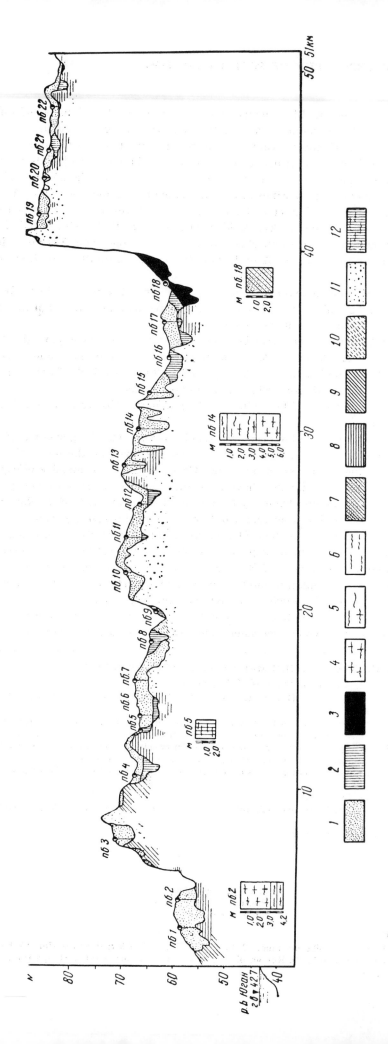

Fig. 7. PROFILE THROUGH HOLOCENE DEPOSITS (PEAT) ALONG THE LINE BOL'SHOY YUGAN - BOL'SHOY SALYM RIVERS. From materials of the *Rostorforazvedka* [Russian Peat Prospecting] Institute of the Main Administration of the Peat Reserves [*Torfyanoy Fond*] under the Council of Ministers of the RSFSR.

1. Holocene peat deposits of the upland type. 2. Holocene peat deposits of the transitional type, 3. Holocene peat deposits of the lowland type, 4. *fuscum* peat, 5. complex upland peat, 6. medium peat, 7. sedge peat, 8. clay, 9. loam, 10. clayey sand, 11. sand, 12. woody transitional peat; пб.19 [etc.], points where samples were taken.

TABLE I.

THE CHANGE IN CLIMATE IN THE HOLOCENE
(According to P. P. Predtechenskiy)

Period	Character of the Climate [Temperatures in Centigrade]
Lacustrine (Arctic) period, 11,900—9,600 B. C. 2,300 years	Temperature in maximum phase 1 to 1.5° lower than at present. Beginning of energetic thawing of margins of ice cap.
Neolacustrine [Novoozernyy] (Subarctic), 9,600—7,400 B. C. 2,200 years	Sharp intensification of general circulation and advection of heat. Thawing of bulk of Würm glacier. Temperature above present (in maximum phase) by 1.5 to 2° in north and up to 1° in south, in steppe zone.
Boreal, 7,400—5,100 B. C. 2,300 years	End of wormwood-and-goosefoot steppes at beginning of cycle. Beginning of advance of forest upon forest-steppe and tundra. Temperature 1 to 1.5° higher than present, beginning with maximum phase.
Oceanic (Atlantic), 5,100—2,800 B. C. 2,300 years	Considerable warming and assured moisture everywhere; climatic optimum. Advance of forest upon steppe and tundra. Temperature 2.8 to 4° higher than present. At end, slow drop in temperature.
Subboreal, 2,800—600 B. C. 2,200 years	Moderately warm and dry climate; at the end, a drop in temperature and an increase in humidity. At end of the cycle and in maximum phase, temperature as much as 2.5° higher than present. Chilling at end.
Suboceanic (Subatlantic), 600 B. C.—1,450 A. D. 2,050 years	Rapid termination of preceding cycle and commencement of this one. Three great fluctuations in maximum phase. Temperature 1 to 1.5° lower than present. Conclusion of cycle and commencement of following cycle very rapid. Cold.
Neoboreal [Novoboreal'nyy], 1,450—3,650 A. D. 2,200 years	Gradual rise in temperature after rapid and severe transitional period. Maximum phase will begin about 2,000 A. D. Fluctuation weaker than in preceding cycle. Temperature of maximum phase will exceed present by values up to 2.5°.

social development and has more and more subordinated the various forces of nature to himself.

The study of Holocene paleography is closely related to the practical tasks of the various branches of the national economy. This may be illustrated by one example. The change of the natural conditions in the Holocene has been reflected in the character of various formations, particularly in the peculiarities of the growth of swamps and the qualitative characteristics of the peat deposited in them. It has been established that, under the conditions of the Late Holocene, with its cool, moist climate, heavy masses of poorly disintegrated *Fuscum* or Medium peat have been deposited in swamps of the upland type. The peat is an excellent raw material for a number of chemical products and for cattle bedding, although little suited for use as fuel. On the other hand, the peat deposited in these same swamps under the conditions of the upper half of the Middle Holocene, characterized by a warm, dry climate, is very greatly disintegrated, has a high thermal value and contains the greatest amount of energy in the whole peat bog, is the best fuel material, but is entirely unsuited for cattle-bedding purposes, etc. These regular laws, discovered in the process of the study of Holocene paleogeography, are being widely exploited in practical swamp-prospecting work and in the evaluation of peat deposits. The paleogeographic investigations of the Holocene are also utilized for the stratigraphic breakdown of floodplain deposits, which is of practical importance in the construction of hydroelectric stations. Gold placers, etc., are not infrequently connected with the alluvial deposits of the present-day floodplain terrace.

BASIC LITERATURE

Buchinskiy, I. Ye. On the Climate of the Past of the Russian Plain *(O Klimate Proshlogo Russkoy Ravniny)*, 1957.

Gerasimov, I. P., and Markov, K. K. "The Glacial Period on the Territory of the USSR, The Physico-geographic Conditions of the Glacial Period." *Tr. In-ta geogr. AN SSSR*, no. 33, Moscow-Leningrad, AN SSSR, 1939.

Gorelov, S. K. "Laws of the Structure of Stream Floodplains of Ciscaucasia and their Significance for the Analysis of Young Tectonic Movements." *Dokl. AN SSSR*, 1958, vol. 123, no. 6.

Grinbergs, E. F. The Late Glacial and Post-glacial History of the Coast of the Latvian SSR. *(Pozdnelednikovaya i Poslelednikovaya Istoriya Poberezh'ya Latviyskoy SSR)*. AN Latv. SSR, Riga, 1957.

Gudelis, V. "The Main Features of the Stratigraphy and Paleogeography of the Holocene in Lithuania." *AN Litovsk. SSR, In-t geol. i geogr. Nauchnyye soobshcheniya*, vol. IV, Vil'nyus, 1957.

Zerov, D. K. The Swamps of the Ukrainian SSR, Vegetation and Stratigraphy *(Bolota USSR, Roslinnist' i Stratigrafiya)* [in Ukrainian]. Kiyev, 1938.

Kats, N. Ya. Swamps and Peat bogs *(Bolota i Torfyaniki)*. Textbook for Universities, Moscow, 1941.

Kemkhadze, M. V. "Concerning the Question of the Formation of the Colchidian Lowland in the Historical Epoch." *Soobshch. AN Gruz. SSR*, 1957, vol. 19, no. 1.

Koreneva, Ye. V. "Spore-and-pollen Analysis of the Bottom Deposits of the Okhotsk Sea." *Tr. In-ta okeanol.*, vol. 22, Moscow, 1957.

Markov, K. K. "The Late-glacial and Post-glacial History of the Environs of Leningrad against the Background of the Late-glacial and Post-glacial History of the Baltic Lands." *Tr. Komis. po izuch. chetvert. perioda*, vol. 4, no. 1, 1934.

Neyshtadt, M. I. The History of the Forests and the Paleogeography of the USSR in the Holocene. *(Istoriya Lesov i Paleogeografiya SSSR v Golotsene)*. AN SSSR, In-t geogr., 1957.

Pidoplichko, I. G. "On the Determination of the Geologic Age of the Bones of Anthropogenic Vertebrates and its Significance for Geochronology." *Tr. Komis. po izuch. chetvert. perioda*, vol. 13, Moscow, 1957.

Predtechenskiy, P. P. "Essay on the Late-glacial and Post-glacial History of the Climate of the USSR." *Tr. Labor. ozerovedeniya AN SSSR*, 1957, vol. 5.

P'yavchenko, N. I. Mound Peat bogs *(Bugristyye Torfyaniki)*. 1955.

Rantsman, E. Ya. "Concerning the Question of the Neotectonics of the Issyk-kul' Basin and the Mountains framing it in." *Izv. AN SSSR, seriya geogr.*, 1954, no. 4.

Sochava, V. B. "The most recent Vertical Movements of the Earth's Crust and the Plant Cover." *Zemlevedeniye*, 1950, vol. III.

Sukachev, V. N. and Poplavskaya, G. I. "Essay on the History of the Lakes and Vegetation of the Middle Urals during the Holocene according to the Data from the Study of Sapropel Deposits." *"Byull. Komis. po izuch. chetvert. perioda,"* no. 8, 1946.

Tattar, A. V. "The Mammal and Bird Fauna from the Upper Quaternary Deposits of the Caves of the Upper Don and Zhiguli and the Conditions of their Existence." *Uchen. zap. Leningr. ped. in-ta*, vol. 179, 1958.

Tyuremnov, S. N. Peat Deposits and their Exploration *(Torfyanyye Mestorozhdeniya i ikh Razvedka)*, 2nd ed., 1949.

Udintsev, G. B. and Lisitsyn, A. P. "The Study of the Stratification of the Present Marine Deposits with the Aid of Sonar." *Dokl. AN SSSR*, 1953, vol. 88, no. 5.

Shnitnikov, A. V. "The Variability of the Total Moisture of the Continents of the Northern Hemisphere." *Zap. Geogr. ob-va SSSR*, vol. 16, nov. seriya AN SSSR, 1957.

CHAPTER 21

THE HEAT AND WATER REGIME OF THE EARTH'S SURFACE

M. I. Budyko

Beginning with the end of the 19th century, physical geography began, to an ever-increasing degree, to become a complex or system of geographic sciences. The differentiation of the geographic sciences had a positive significance, inasmuch as it contributed to the rapid accumulation of empirical data and to the development of new methods of research, connected in a number of cases with the wide employment of materials from the physico-mathematical disciplines (especially in the hydrometeorologic sciences). But with the isolation of the particular geographic sciences there arose considerable difficulties in view of the necessity of generalizing the materials of the various divisions of physical geography for the solution of integrated problems.

In the middle 1930's, the works of A. A. Grigor'yev posed the question of the creation of a method of investigating the general physical geographic laws which would be suitable for the study of the whole complex of interrelated processes evolving in the external geographic envelope. Grigor'yev proposed that this method be based on the investigation of the systems of the balances of matter and energy characteristic of each typical physical geographic province (zone). Note was here taken of the leading significance of the balance of radiant energy and the moisture balance as factors determining the dynamics of the whole complex of natural surface processes. In the subsequent investigations by Grigor'yev and by other authors, the materials on the heat and water regime were used to explain the laws of geographic zonality and to work out other general problems of physical geography.

In 1954, the Presidium of the Academy of Sciences of the USSR included among the most important problems of Soviet science that of the "heat and water regime of the earth's surface, its role in the dynamics of natural processes and the methods of its transformation for practical purposes." Work programs concerning this problem were drawn up by a team of specialists under the direction of I. P. Gerasimov (Gerasimov and others, 1956).

In recent years, geographic investigations of the heat and water regime have been considerably expanded in a number of institutes of the Academy of Sciences of the USSR, the Hydrometeorologic Service, and other institutions. Let us set forth briefly the principal results of these investigations.

Radiation Regime. Measurements of the receipt of solar energy on the earth's surface were commenced over a hundred years ago, when the first actinometric instruments were created. In the 20th century, a world-wide network of actinometric stations has arisen, the number of which now exceeds 700, about 200 of them being in the USSR. At the larger part of these stations, the indices of short-wave solar radiation are measured.

In recent years, measurements of the radiation balance, i.e., the difference between the saturated short-wave radiation [*radiatsii*] and the effective long-wave eradiation [*izlucheniya*] from the earth's surface, have been commenced at a number of stations in the Soviet Union.

Inasmuch as the available observation data on radiation give information only about certain indices of the radiation regime, while there are no such data at all for the larger part of the earth's surface (especially for the oceans), methods for calculating the values of the flows of short-wave and long-wave radiation acquire special significance for the study of the geographic laws of the radiation regime. Such methods have been worked out in a number of meteorologic investigations. Improvement of these methods has made it possible, in the work done at the Main Geophysical Observatory, to construct world maps of the mean values of total radiation and of the radiation balance for each month and year ("Atlas of the Heat Balance," 1955). More detailed maps have been constructed for the USSR (Berlyand and Yefimova, 1955). Along with this, characterizations of the radiation regime for various areas and points of the Soviet Union have been obtained in a large number of works by Soviet authors, on the basis of the employment of calculating methods and generalization of the observation data (Berlyand, 1948; Orlova, 1954; Sapozhnikova, 1958; and others), and it has now become possible to ascertain the basic laws of the radiation climate of the globe, with the best study of the radiation regime having been made on the territory of the USSR. With the summarization of the observations made in accordance with the program of the International Geophysical Year it obviously will be possible to make considerably more precise and detailed the existing notions of the radiation regime on the earth's surface.

Heat Balance. Estimates of the basic components of the balance of thermal energy on the earth's surface were begun in the first decade of our century. Owing to the great difficulties of direct measurement of such components of the heat balance as the loss of heat in evaporation and the turbulent heat exchange of the earth's surface with the atmosphere, the respective systematic observations at the network of stations could only be organized in the last few years. Observations of the heat balance in the USSR are now being made at approximately 40 stations.

Owing to the lack of sufficiently complete materials on systematic observations, the geographic laws of the heat balance are being studied chiefly on the basis of a generalization of the results of indirect estimates. Improvement of the methods of such estimates in the work of the Main Geophysical Observatory has permitted the construction of the first maps of the heat-balance components for a definite land territory (Budyko, 1947), for the European part of the USSR (Berlyand, 1948) and a series of world maps ("Atlas of the Heat Balance," 1955; "Marine Atlas," 1953). The construction of world maps of the heat-balance components, despite their schematism and incompleteness, has made it possible to explain certain laws of the genesis of climate and has had significance for working out a number of general questions of physical geography.

In the experimental investigations of the heat balance made at stationary points and on a whole series of expeditions, valuable materials characterizing the regime of the heat-balance components in individual regions have been obtained.

Thermal Regime. Investigations of the thermal regime over many years have been confined mainly to the study of the air temperature, measured in a meteorologic screen. Major work devoted to the air-temperature regime has been performed by Ye. S. Rubinshteyn. In recent years, a series of world maps of air temperatures has been compiled under her direction ("Marine Atlas," 1953) and detailed maps of air temperatures for the USSR have been prepared ("Climatic Atlas of the USSR," 1959).

Of considerable interest for the study of the processes of soil formation are the materials on soil temperatures. Although observations of soil temperatures at different depths have long been conducted, only relatively recently has it been possible to overcome the methodological difficulties connected with the preparation of soil-temperature maps and to construct the respective maps for the territory of the USSR ("Climatic Atlas of the USSR," 1959).

Of substantial significance in the study of many geographic processes are the data on the temperature of the active surface, which, in particular, characterizes the temperature of the surfaces of leaves of terrestrial plants. The measurement of the temperature of the active surface is attended by very great difficulties and hence the study of the regime of this temperature is possible chiefly with the application of calculating methods for determining it. The use of the calculating method based on the solution of the heat-balance equation has made it possible to obtain a mass of data on the temperature of the active surface and to construct maps of this index (Budyko, 1958).

Precipitation Regime. Data on the precipitation regime are necessary in studying the water balance. The amount of precipitation has been measured at numerous meteorologic stations for a long time, which permits the construction of detailed precipitation maps on the basis of a direct generalization of the observation materials. Among the investigations devoted to the compilation of precipitation maps, the works of O. A. Drozdov merit special attention, particularly the world map of annual total precipitation prepared under his direction ("Marine Atlas," 1953) and the considerably more detailed maps (annual and monthly) for the USSR ("Climatic Atlas of the USSR," 1959). In constructing these maps, it was taken into account that the measurement of the amount of precipitation is done in a number of cases with perceptible systematic errors. Especially complex are the questions of the consideration of the amount of solid precipitation which is often blown out of the rain gauges, and of the measurement of horizontal precipitation in mountains and precipitation on the seas and oceans. Hence, the precipitation maps for a number of regions have to be refined by calculating methods on the basis of consideration for the general geographic laws. However, precipitation maps for high latitudes, mountain areas, and oceans are still not entirely reliable, which fact makes it difficult, in particular, to determine precisely the total annual precipitation average for the whole globe.

Evaporation Regime. Direct determination of evaporation both from the land surface and from the surface of bodies of water presents considerable difficulties. There are at present in the USSR about 40 stations at which evaporation from the soil is determined by measurement of the gradients of the meteorologic elements, and about 60 stations at which observations of evaporation are made with the aid of evaporators. Generalization of the observation data on evaporation is a rather complicated matter. Existing methods of determining evaporation from special observation data are not free from the influence of accidental and systematic errors. Owing to the great spatial variability of evaporation, it is not always easy to draw a conclusion about the representative nature of evaporation observations.

Inasmuch as no really massive observations of evaporation from the land are being made abroad, nor are such observations being conducted on the oceans, calculating methods are of basic significance for the study of the geographic laws of distribution of evaporation over the globe.

Beginning with the work of D. I. Kocherin published in 1929, a number of maps of mean annual values of the precipitation on the land surface were constructed from data on the water balance (as the difference between precipitation and runoff). To determine the mean monthly values of evaporation, use had to be made of considerably more complex methods, so that the first maps of evaporation from the land for individual months was not constructed until the 1950's. In 1954, the first world map of annual values of precipitation on the surface of the land and the oceans was published, prepared by the collaborators of the Main Geophysical Observatory (Budyko and others, 1954).

In the last few years there have been a large number of investigations devoted to the study of the space-and-time distribution of evaporation from the surface of the land and bodies of water in the USSR (The Agroclimatic and Water Resources of the Regions of Reclamation of Virgin and Idle Lands, 1955; Braslavskiy and Vikulina, 1954; Budagovskiy, 1956; Ogneva, 1958; Timofeyev, 1958; Troitskiy, 1948).

Runoff Regime. Existing methods permit the measurement of the magnitude of the runoff with rather high precision. Since the beginning of the 19th century these methods have been widely used in runoff observations at hydrologic stations. However, the world network of hydrologic stations is marked by a great lack of uniformity. While runoff observations in the USSR are now made at 7,000 points, no such operations whatsoever are being made in many extensive areas of the less developed countries. The first map of the mean yearly runoff for the European territory of the USSR was constructed by D. I. Kocherin at the end of the 1920's. Considerably more detailed runoff maps for the USSR have since been compiled by V. D. Zaykov and V. A. Troitskiy (Zaykov, 1944, 1946; Troitskiy, 1948). In the 1940's, M. I. L'vovich prepared the first and thus far only schematic map of world runoff (L'vovich, 1945), constructed largely from indirect estimate materials.

In the last few years, a large number of maps of different runoff indices (mean maximum and minimum runoff, etc.) have been published in monographic investigations of the hydrologic regime of individual parts of the USSR. The general digest of all the hydrologic observations published in the form of a multi-volume edition, the "Water Cadaster of the USSR," furnishes a wealth of material for the study of the laws of stream runoff in our country. In other countries there are, as a rule, no such detailed data on the hydrologic regime nor are there runoff maps.

Of substantial significance in the study of the geographic laws of the water balance are the materials on the moisture circulation in the upper layers of the soil. Lately, mass observations of the moisture content of the upper meter of the soil layer have been organized at numerous agro-meteorologic stations in the USSR. Although these observations are made only in agricultural fields, they permit a general idea to be obtained about the water regime of the soil of the various geographic regions. In this connection, the maps of soil humidity constructed by a number of specialists of the Central Forecasting Institute deserve mention (The Agroclimatic and Water Resources of the

Regions of Reclamation of Virgin and Idle Lands, 1955; Verigo, 1948).

Thus, extensive materials have now been gathered on the heat and water regime of the earth's surface, which can be used to work out various theoretical and practical problems. Let us dwell briefly upon the principal trends of research based on the use of materials on the heat and water balances.

Hydrometeorologic Sciences. In climatology, data on the heat and water balance are being used to work out general questions of the theory of climate (Gal'tsov, 1957; Rakipova, 1952, 1953, 1957), in the study of moisture circulation (Budyko and Drozdov, 1950, 1953; Drozdov, 1956; Kashin and Pogosyan, 1950), in the comparative analysis of the climate of different territories (Alisov, 1956; Bagdasaryan, 1958; Lebedev, 1958; Orlova, 1954; Sapozhnikova, 1948).

In agrometeorologic investigations, the materials on the radiation regime and the heat balance are important for the study of the meteorologic conditions for the development of agricultural plants (Budyko, 1956; Davitaya, 1958; Kirillova, 1955; Rusin, 1957; Sapozhnikova, 1948). The water-balance method in this field of meteorology plays an important role in the investigation of the moisture supply of plants.

In work on the hydrology of the land, data on the heat balance are widely employed for estimates and forecasts of the snow-thaw regime (Kuz'min, 1948), for the study of the thermal regime of water bodies, including forecasts of the freezing and thawing of ice (Timofeyev, 1958), and for the study of the hydrologic regime of swamps (Romanov, 1953). Estimates of the heat balance are of great significance in determining evaporation both from the existing water bodies and from projected reservoirs (Braslavskiy, 1954; Ogneva, 1958; Timofeyev, 1958). Working out the question of the relation between the heat and water balances of the land has resulted in clarifying the possibility of using the materials on the heat balance in determining the mean values of the runoff and evaporation from the land (Budyko, 1956). The water-balance method is basic in working out most of the problems of land hydrology. Finally, in investigations of the hydrometeorologic regime of the seas and oceans, estimates of the heat balance are used to study the laws of the regime of currents, salinity, evaporation, etc. Lately, attempts have been made to use the data on the heat balance of oceans in working out methods of hydrometeorologic forecasting (The Agroclimatic and Water Resources of the Regions of Reclamation of Virgin and Idle Lands, 1955; Kolesnikov, 1954; Skriptunova, 1957).

General Questions of Physical Geography. The series of works by A. A. Grigor'yev, mentioned at the beginning of this article (Grigor'yev, 1946, 1954, 1958), established the laws connecting the characteristics of the heat and water balances with the intensity of the main physical geographic processes. These works devote special attention to the study of the conditions contributing to the highest intensity of the natural biologic processes, particularly the highest productivity of the natural plant cover.

Allied to this research trend are the works of many authors which compare the characteristics of the heat and water regime with the indices of the geobotanical, soil, and certain other natural processes. The works of D. L. Armand (1949, 1950) are devoted to the relation of geobotanical zonality to the radiation factors in the application of mathematical-statistical methods. The investigations by V. R. Volobuyev (1953, 1958) have furnished a large amount of material characterizing the dependence of soil zonality upon the heat and moisture regime. N. N. Ivanov (1948) and other authors have compared the distribution of geographic zones with the distribution of the various moisture indices.

The work done at the Main Geophysical Observatory (Budyko, 1956) has attempted to apply the data on the balances of thermal energy and moisture to the study of the general physical geographic laws by the deductive method, on the basis of physical laws. These investigations have examined questions of physical geographic zonality, questions of the influence of the energy balance on the development of vegetation, etc.

Quite recently, works by A. A. Grigor'yev and the author (1956, 1959) have proposed a "periodic law of geographic zonality" (see Chapter 3, "Physical Geography of the Land"), governing the regular relationship of the conditions of the heat and water balance to the geographic zones. This law has been used to construct a scheme of climatic classification of the USSR.

Transformation of Natural Processes. Materials on the heat and water balances are widely employed in substantiating the efficiency and the planning of many reclamation measures. In particular, the water-balance method underlies the existing procedures for standardizing irrigation

(Kostyakov, 1951). Estimates of the heat balance can be used in determining irrigation norms and in evaluating the influence of irrigation on the meteorologic regime of the surface layer of the air (Budyko and others, 1956; Gracheva and others, 1957; Seryakova, 1957). Investigations of the heat balance of the earth's surface have made it possible to work out the physical theory of the hydrometeorologic efficiency of shelterbelt planting. The conclusions drawn from this theory have had definite significance for the basis of the most suitable designs of forest belts under various climatic conditions (Budyko and others, 1956).

Very wide use is being made of estimates of the water and heat balances in projecting reclamation measures in areas of excess moisture, particularly in planning the drainage of swamps. Here, information about the heat balance is used both in determining the evaporation from swamps and in evaluating the influence of drainage on the meteorologic regime of the surface layer of the air. Observations of the heat balance are used in ascertaining the influence of echeloned plantings on the thermal regime in regions with insufficient heat, in evaluating the efficiency of various methods of protecting plants from frost (Berlyand and Krasikov, 1953), and in solving a number of similar agrometeorologic questions. Materials on the heat balance acquire special significance in estimating the efficiency of measures for thawing out frozen subsoils.

Without dwelling on the many other problems of the local changes in the natural conditions requiring the use of materials on the heat and water balances for their solution, let us note that it is now possible to raise the question of the projecting of measures for changing natural conditions on a wide scale, with relation to vigorous action upon the climate and hydrologic regime of large territories. The projecting of such measures in all cases makes wide use of materials on the water and heat balances. For example, great interest is now offered by the question of the artificial enlargement of the quantity of precipitation in areas of insufficient moisture by means of sowing special reagents in the air. To evaluate the efficiency of such measures, detailed estimates of the water balance of the earth's surface and atmosphere are necessary. The considerable success attained in recent years in the investigation of the moisture circulation permits one to believe that such estimates can be made with sufficient precision for practical purposes.

A second example: Specialists have long been interested in the question of the possibility of acting upon glaciers and the ice cover of the Arctic Ocean. The energy possibilities now available are insufficient to realize major projects of this sort. It may, however, be assumed that in the comparatively near future such projects will be fully realizable owing to the rapid progress in the field of the development of atomic energy. Their justification will be largely a matter of estimating the heat balance of the object under study in the existing state, and under this or that artificial action.

Thus, the heat and water balance methods are widely employed in the hydrometeorologic sciences to solve major theoretical and practical tasks. With the further development of the use of these methods in the hydrometeorologic disciplines, they will find considerably wider employment in working out the general problems of physical geography connected with the study of complex geographic phenomena and processes. The development of research in this direction will, on the one hand, contribute to bringing the particular geographic disciplines closer together and, on the other hand, aid in the gradual conversion of physical geography from a largely descriptive science into one using principally quantitative methods of investigation.

BASIC LITERATURE

Agroklimaticheskiye i Vodnyye Resursy Rayonov Osvoyeniya Tselinnykh i Zalezhnykh Zemel' (The Agroclimatic and Water resources of the Regions of Reclamation of Virgin and Idle Lands). Under the editorship of F. F. Davitaya, Gidrometeoizdat, Leningrad, 1955.

Alpat'yev, M. A. The Moisture Circulation of Cultivated Plants *(Vlagooborot Kul'turnykh Rasteniy).* Gidrometeoizdat, Leningrad, 1954.

Armand, D. L. "On the Functional and Correlative Connections in Physical Geography," *Izv. VGO,* 1949, No. 1.

Armand, D. L. "An Experiment in the Mathematical Analysis of the Relation between the Type of Vegetation and Climate," *Izv. VGO,* 1950, No. 1.

Atlas Teplogo Balansa (Atlas of the Heat Balance). Under the editorship of M. I. Budyko, Leningrad, 1955.

Belinskiy, N. A. "Concerning the Question of the Interaction between the Ocean and the Atmosphere," *Meteorol. i gidrol.,* 1953, No. 8.

Benashvili, I. A. "Concerning the Question of the Annual Fluctuations of the Temperature on the Surface of the Northern Part of the Pacific Ocean in Relation to its Energy Balance," *Tr. GOIN*, no. 8, 1948.

Berlyand, T. G. "The Radiation and Heat Balance of the European Part of the USSR," *Tr. GGO*, no. 10 (72), 1948.

Berlyand, T. G., and Yefimova, N. A. "Monthly Maps of Total Solar Radiation and the Radiation Balance on the Territory of the Soviet Union," *Tr. Glav. geof. observ.*, no. 50 (112), 1955.

Berlyand, M. Ye. Prediction and Regulation of the Heat Regime of the Surface Layer of the Atmosphere *(Predskazaniye i Regulirovaniye Teplogo Rezhima Prizemnogo Sloya Atmosfery)*, Gidrometeoizdat, 1956.

Braslavskiy, A. P., and Vikulina, Z. A. Norms of Evaporation from the Surfaces of Reservoirs. *(Normy Ispareniya s Poverkhnosti Vodokhranilishch)*, Gidrometeoizdat, Leningrad, 1954.

Budagovskiy, A. I. "Basic Laws of Evaporation in the Steppe Zone," *Izv. AN SSSR, seriya geogr.*, 1956, No. 3.

Budyko, M. I. "On the Water and Heat Balances of the Land Surface," *Meteorol. i gidrol.*, 1947, No. 5.

Budyko, M. I. The Heat Balance of the Earth's Surface *(Teplovoy Balans Zemnoy Poverkhnosti)*, Gidrometeoizdat, Leningrad, 1956. [Available in English as *The Heat Balance of the Earth's Surface* by M. I. Budyko. Translated by Nina A. Stepanova (Washington, D.C.: U.S. Weather Bureau, 1958), 259 pp. Available from the Office of Technical Services, U.S. Department of Commerce, Washington 25, D.C. as translation PB 131692. Price $4.00.—Ed.]

Budyko, M. I. "The Temperature of the Active Surface and its Bioclimatic Significance," Sb. *Sovremennyye Problemy Meteorologii Prizemnogo Sloya Vozdukha*, Gidrometeoizdat, 1958.

Budyko, M. I., Berlyand, T. G., and Zubenok, L. I. "The Heat Balance of the Earth's Surface," *Izv. AN SSSR, seriya geogr.*, No. 3, 1954.

Budyko, M. I., and Drozdov, O. A. "On the Moisture Circulation on a Limited Land Territory," Sb. *Voprosy Gidrometeorologicheskoy Effektivnosti Polezashchitnogo Lesorazvedeniya* (Questions of the Hydrometeorologic Efficiency of Shelter-belt Planting), Gidrometeoizdat, Leningrad, 1950.

Budyko, M. I., and Drozdov, O. A. "The Laws of Moisture Circulation in the Atmosphere," *Izv. AN SSSR, seriya geogr.*, 1953, No. 4.

Budyko, M. I., Drozdov, O. A., L'vovich, M. I., Pogosyan, Kh. P., Sapozhnikova, S. A., and Yudin, M. I. Changes in Climate in Connection with the Plan for Transforming the Nature of the Arid Regions of the USSR *(Izmeneniye Klimata v Svyazi s Planom Preobrazovaniya Prirody Zasushlivykh Rayonov SSSR)*, Gidrometeoizdat, Leningrad, 1956.

Verigo, S. A. "The Dynamics of the Supplies of Soil Moisture on the Territory of the USSR," *Tr. po s.-kh. meteorol.*, XXVI, 1948.

Volobuyev, V. R. "Investigation of Soil-hydrologic Relationships." *Izv. AN SSSR, seriya geogr.*, 1948, No. 6.

Volobuyev, V. R. "Soils and Climate" *(Pochvy i Klimat)*. Izd. AN Azerb. SSR, Baku, 1953.

Gal'tsov, A. P. "Changes in Evaporability as Indices of the Process of Formation of the Dry Wind *(sukhovey)*," in Sb. *Sukhovei, ikh Proiskhozhdeniye i Bor'ba s Nimi* (Dry winds, their origin and control), AN SSSR, 1957.

Gerasimov, I. P., Armand, D. L., Budyko, M. I., Davitaya, F. F., Dzerdzeyevskiy, B. L., Kunin, V. N., L'vovich, M. I., Rikhter, G. D., and Shvetsov, P. F. "The Heat and Water Regime of the Earth's Surface, its Role in the Dynamics of the Natural Processes, Geographic Differences and Methods of Transformation for Practical Purposes," *Izv. AN SSSR, seriya geogr.*, 1956, No. 4.

Gracheva, V. P., Utina, Z. M., and Khineyko, N. P. "Irrigation Norms for Different Climatic Conditions," *Tr. GGO*, no. 69, 1957.

Grigor'yev, A. A. "Some Results of the Elaboration of New Ideas in Physical Geography," *Izv. AN SSSR, seriya geogr. i geof.*, 1946, No. 2.

Grigor'yev, A. A. "Geographic Zonality and Some of its Laws," *Izv. AN SSSR, seriya geogr.*, 1954, Nos. 5 and 6.

Grigor'yev, A. A. "On some Geographic Laws of Heat Exchange and Moisture Exchange," *Izv. AN SSSR, seriya geogr.*, 1948, No. 6.

Grigor'yev, A. A., and Budyko, M. I. "On the Periodic Law of Geographic Zonality," *Dokl. AN SSSR*, vol. 110, 1956, No. 1.

Grigor'yev, A. A., and Budyko, M. I. "Classification of the Climates of the USSR," *Izv. AN SSSR, seriya geogr.*, 1959, No. 3.

Davitaya, F. F. "Consideration of Microclimatic Characteristics in Distributing Cultivated Plants and in Specializing Agriculture." in Sbornik *Sovremennyye Problemy Meteorologii Prizemnogo Sloya Vozdukha*, Gidrometeoizdat, Leningrad, 1958.

Drozdov, O. A. "The Moisture Balance in the Atmosphere," in Sbornik *A. I. Voyeykov i Sovremennyye Problemy Klimatologii*, Gidrometeoizdat, Leningrad, 1956.

Zaykov, B. D. "The Intra-year Distribution of Stream Runoff on the Territory of Europe," *Tr. NIU*, seriya IV, no. 15, 1944.

Ivanov, N. N. "Landscape-climatic Zones of the Globe," *Zap. VGO*, new series, vol. I, 1948.

Kashin, K. I., and Pogosyan, Kh. P. "On the Moisture Circulation in the Atmosphere," in Sbornik *Voprosy Gidrometeorologicheskoy Effektivnosti Polezashchitnogo Lesorazvedeniya*," Gidrometeoizdat, Leningrad, 1950.

Kirillova, T. V. "The Heat Balance of a Wheat Field," *Meteorol. i gidrol.*, 1955, No. 2.

Klimaticheskiy atlas SSSR (Climatic Atlas of the USSR), vol. I, 1959.

Kolesnikov, A. G. "Computation of the Daily Variability of the Temperature of the Sea by Means of the Heat Balance of the Surface of the Sea," *Izv. AN SSSR, seriya geof.*, 1954, No. 2.

Kocherin, D. I. "Evaporation from the Surface of Basins and the Runoff Coefficient in their Variation Over the Territory of the European Part of the USSR." *Gidrotekhnicheskiy Sbornik Mosk. Vyssh. Tekhn. Uchilishcha*, No. 2, 1929.

Kuz'min, P. P. "Investigation and Calculation of Snow Thaw," *Tr. Gos. gidr. in-ta*, no. 7, 1948.

Mezentsev, V. S. "Zones of Moisture and Heat Supply of the West-Siberian Plain," *Tr. Tomsk. gos. un-ta, seriya geogr.*, V nauchnaya konferentsiya Tomsk. un-ta, 1957.

Morskoy Atlas (Marine Atlas), vol. II, 1953.

"New Program of Research in the Problem of the Heat and Water Regime of the Earth's Surface, its Role in the Dynamics of Natural Phenomena and Methods of Transformation for Practical Purposes," *Izv. AN SSSR, seriya geogr.*, 1958, No. 6.

Ogneva, T. A. "Experiment in Calculating Evaporation from the Surface of Lake Balkhash," *Tr. GGO*, vol. 78, 1958.

Pagava, S. T. and others. The Influence of the North Atlantic on the Development of Synoptic Processes *(Vliyaniye Severnoy Atlantiki na Razvitiye Sinopticheskikh Protsessov)*, Gidrometeoizdat, 1958.

Rakipova, L. R. "On the Mean Annual Zonal Distribution of the Temperature in the Earth's Atmosphere," *Tr. Glav. geof. observ.*, no. 33 (95), 1952.

Rakipova, L. R. "The Mean Annual Zonal Temperature of the Earth's Atmosphere and the Factors Determining it," *Tr. GGO*, no. 41 (103), 1953.

Rakipova, L. R. The Heat Regime of the Atmosphere *(Teplovoy Rezhim Atmosfery)*, Gidrometeoizdat, 1957.

Romanov, V. V. "Investigation of Evaporation from Sphagnum Swamps," *Tr. GGI*, no. 39, 1953.

Rusin, N. P. "Evaporation and the Heat Balance with Dry Winds (sukhovei)," in Sbornik *Sukhovei, ikh Proiskhozhdeniye i Bor'ba s Nimi*, AN SSSR, 1957.

Sapozhnikova, S. A. "The Heat Balance of the Active Surface in the Main Geographic Zones of the USSR," *Tr. II Vsesoyuzn. geogr. s"yezda*, vol. II, 1948.

Sapozhnikova, S. A. "Characterization of Certain Characteristics of the Heat Balance of a Wheat Field in Application to the Agricultural Evaluation of Climate," *Probl. fizich. geogr.*, no. 13, 1948.

Seryakova, L. P. "Determination of Evaporability and Calculation of Irrigation Norms," *Izv. AN SSSR, seriya geogr.*, 1957, No. 6.

Skriptunova, L. I. "On the Role of the Heat Balance of the Surface in the Regime of the Water Temperature in the Northern Part of the Atlantic Ocean," *Meteorol. i gidrol.*, 1957, No. 7.

Timofeyev, M. P. "On the Methods of Calculating the Temperature of Water Bodies," *Meteorol. i gidrol.*, 1958, No. 12.

Timofeyev, M. P. "The Heat Balance of Water Bodies and Methods of Determining their Evaporation," in Sbornik *Sovr. Problemy Meteorol. Prizemnogo Sloya Vozdukha*, Gidrometeoizdat, 1958.

Chudnovskiy, A. F. "The Energy Method of Studying Questions of the Irrigation of Agricultural Crops," in Sbornik *Sukhovei, ikh Proiskhozhdeniye i Bor'ba s Nimi*, AN SSSR, 1957.

CHAPTER 22

PRESENT STATE OF THE THEORY OF GEOGRAPHIC ZONALITY

A. A. Grigor'yev

The general theory of physical geography in its modern sense began to take shape around the beginning of the 20th century, when V. V. Dokuchayev established two basic physical geographic laws: (1) the *law of the integrity and continuity of the geographic environment* (the mutual causality of all its components: the lithosphere, the lower parts of the atmosphere, the hydrosphere, the plant and soil covers, and the animal world), and (2) the *law of geographic zonality*. Owing to the profound mutual causality of the structure and development of the components of the geographic environment (or envelope), all of them together form a single continuous whole — a special natural phenomenon possessing its own laws governing structure, composition, dynamics, and development.

Having been formed and continuing to develop on the surface of our planet, in the zone of its interaction with the rest of the universe, the geographic environment (or envelope) has a genetically continuous connection with the earth's surface which is irradiated by solar energy. Owing to the hydrothermal and geochemical conditions which prevailed here, the geographic envelope in time came to be an arena for the rise and development of life and was enriched by the plant and soil covers and animal life which entered into its composition. Later, the geographic environment was the scene of the rise and development of human society.

In establishing the integrity and continuity of the geographic environment, Dokuchayev did not touch upon the question of what concrete natural processes underlie the mutual causality of the development of its components. Many Soviet scholars have contributed their mite to the study of this basic theoretical problem of physical geography. The author of these lines has shown recently that the *foundation of the interrelation, interaction, and mutual causality of the components of the geographical envelope of the globe lies in the exchange of matter and energy* among the components, and also between this envelope and the "outside world" (the elements of the cosmos, primarily solar radiation, on one hand, and the subcrustal masses, on the other).

The interchange of matter and energy between the components of the geographic envelope is composed of the continuously interrelated, oppositely directed processes of the receipt and expenditure of matter and energy, their assimilation and dissemination. In the course of this interchange, a part of the matter and energy of one component is constantly passing over into the composition of others, and one form of energy is being converted into another. This is accompanied by a change in the composition of the components which are assimilated by other components and a change in the bulk of each component, under the prolonged action of the substances of the other components (in the course of chemical and physical and, in appropriate cases, biochemical and biophysical interactions also). In the course of our planet's development, these changes have, as a rule, led to a complication of the composition and structure of the components of the geographic envelope. And the complication of the composition and structure of the geographic envelope has inevitably entailed a complication of the processes of the exchange of matter and energy between its components, as well as between it and the outer world. This, in turn, has caused the rise in the geographic envelope of new geochemical or biochemical reactions and other natural processes which, as a rule, have led to a further complication of the composition and structure of the geographic envelope, and so forth.

The complication of the composition and structure of the geographic envelope in certain features has manifested itself in many forms during periods of time on a geologic scale. The geologic structure of the earth's crust has become more complex. New and ever more highly organized types of plants have appeared, and this has been accompanied by the evolution by the plant cover of new and more complex organic compounds. The same applies to the new and more highly organized types of animals, often connected in their life activity with new types of plants. There have arisen new types of soil cover connected with the entrance into the soil of organic and mineral-organic compounds which did not exist before and which are evolved by new species of plants. The appearance of new types of organisms and soil types has led to a complication of the chemical composition of the waters of the land and, consequently, also of the ocean, in which more highly organized marine organisms have also appeared. All these changes in the composition of the biotic components, as well as of the hydrosphere, have exerted a very strong influence on the composition of the atmosphere, again in the direction of complexity.

Alongside the processes of complication of the composition and structure, processes of an opposite character have also been effected in the geographic envelope, but they have not played a dominant role.

Thus, the process of the interchange of matter and energy between the components of the geographic envelope lead, as a rule, to the progressive complication of its composition and structure, causing the development of the envelope to be directed from the simple to the complex, from the lower to the higher, i.e., in accordance with one of the basic laws of materialistic dialectics. The interchange of matter and energy among the components of the geographic envelope and between the geographic envelope and the outer world underlies this development of the envelope. The moving force of the development of the geographic envelope is the unity of the continuously interrelated and opposite processes of the receipt and expenditure of matter and energy, their assimilation and dissimilation, as well as the processes accompanying them.

The law of geographic zonality underlies the very complex natural differentiation of the geographic envelope of the globe into separate natural territories, possessing specific natural characteristics, varying in accordance with law from one zone to another in dependence upon their geographic location on the surface of our planet. At the same time, these natural territories form a system of taxonomic geographic units. The units of highest rank (geographic belts [poyasa] and their provinces [provintsii], or sectors [sektory]) each include several geographic zones [zony]. Others represent a system of intrazonal natural territories differing from one another in the degree of similarity or difference in the structure of the geographic envelope of the given zone. They form a successive series of taxonomic territorial units lower than the zone, and are especially numerous in mountain regions of complex structure. Among these units may be distinguished intrazonal areas [oblasti], subzones, subareas [podoblasti], altitudinal belts [vysotnyye poyasa] (in the mountains), districts [okruga], subdistricts [podokruga], regions [rayony], subregions [podrayony], and landscapes [landshafty].

Where extensive lowlands or mountain uplifts traverse several geographic belts or horizontal zones, interbelt and interzonal "geographic lands" [geograficheskiye strany], embracing the whole of such a lowland or mountain uplift, are naturally distinguished. They consist of sections of several neighboring geographic belts or zones.

The comparative study of the geographic zones of the land masses of the globe has shown that they form a system which is regulated by laws, underlain by very closely interrelated territorial variations in the annual magnitudes of the radiation balance of the earth's surface (differing little from the magnitude of the radiation balance of the growing period) and of the annual precipitation, as well as in the relationship between the radiation balance and the annual precipitation, expressed in thermal units, i.e., in the amount of calories necessary to evaporate the annual precipitation. This ratio has been given the name of "radiation index of dryness" [radiatsionny indeks sukhosti].

Indeed, the above-enumerated factors exert a determining influence on the structure and development of the outer tier of the geographic envelope. After all, the annual radiation balance is the main source of energy for the majority of the natural processes taking place on the earth's surface. The annual precipitation and its relationship to the annual radiation balance of the earth's surface have decisive significance for the development of the whole complex of natural

TABLE I. GEOGRAPHIC ZONALITY
(according to A. A. Grigor'yev and M. I. Budyko)

Thermal energy base — radiation balance	Moisture conditions — radiation index of dryness								
	less than 0 (extremely excessive moisture)	from 0 to 1					from 1 to 2 (moderately insufficient moisture)	from 2 to 3 (insufficient moisture)	more than 3 (extremely insufficient moisture)
		excessive moisture				optimal moisture			
		0–1/5	1/5–2/5	2/5–3/5	3/5–4/5	4/5–1			
Less than 0 (high latitudes)	1. Perpetual snow	—	—	—	—	—	—	—	—
From 0 to 50 kcal/cm² per year (Southern Arctic, subarctic, and middle latitudes)	—	IIa Arctic desert	IIb Tundra (in south with small patches of sparse forest)	IIc Northern and middle tayga	IId Southern tayga and mixed forests	IIe Leaf forest and forest-steppe	III Steppe	IV Semi-steppe of temperate belt	V Desert of temperate belt
From 50 to 75 kcal/cm² per year (Subtropical latitudes)	—	VIa Regions with subtropical hemihylaea with considerable amount of swamps			VIb Subtropical rain forests		VIIb Subtropical steppe / VIIa Sclerophyllous subtropical forests and shrubs	VIII Subtropical semi-desert	IX Subtropical desert
More than 75 kcal/cm² per year (Tropical latitudes)	—	Xa Regions of sharp predominance of equatorial swamps	Xb Heavily over-moistened (very swampy) equatorial forest	Xc Moderately over-moistened (moderately swampy) equatorial forest		Xd Equatorial forest grading into clear and tropical forests and forested savannas	XI Dry savanna	XII Desert savanna (tropical semi-desert)	XIII Tropical desert

processes. In particular, the character and regime of the soil and subsoil moisture depends upon the amount of humidity and its relationship to the radiation balance. The soil and subsoil moisture in turn (together with the magnitude of the radiation balance) exercises an enormous influence on the character and intensity of both the biotic and many abiotic processes taking place in the outer tier of the geographic envelope.

In comparing the character and regime of the above factors of the soil and subsoil moisture in different zones and subzones of the temperate, subtropical, and tropical belts, one is struck by the fact that in each of these belts there is a zone of optimal moisture with a radiation index of dryness of 0.8-1.0, which is the zone of maximum production of the plant cover and animal world of the given belt.

To one side of the zones of optimal moisture lie the zones with an ever-increasing excess of moisture (as far as the tundras and the equatorial forests with a predominance of swamp area, where the index is less than 0.45). Toward the other side lie the zones with an ever-increasing deficiency of moisture (as far as the deserts, inclusive, where the index of dryness is more than 3). In both cases the productivity of the plant cover and animal world drops progressively. All this tells us that the systems of zones of these belts have a monotypic structure, differing chiefly in the intensity of the natural processes occurring in them and in the phenomena related therewith. Hence, if the geographic belts are arranged vertically according to the growth in the magnitude of the radiation balance of the earth's surface, and the main gradations of the radiation index of dryness are arranged horizontally, we obtain a single regular *periodic system* of geographic belts and zones of the land mass of the globe (see Table I, facing page).

Consequently, the structure of the outer tier of the geographic envelope is based on the *periodic law of geographic zonality*. This in turn evidences the fundamental internal unity of the structure and development of the outer tier of the geographic envelope throughout all the belts and zones, and at the same time evidences the unity of the structure of all the taxonomic territorial units composing the zones, however different they may be externally.

According to the latest investigations, variations in the productivity of the plant cover and, consequently, of the animal world also are based on the intensity of the photosynthesis and the rate of outflow of the resulting organic products from the foliage (the presence of these impedes photosynthesis).

In each belt they attain a maximum in the zone of optimal moisture. In the various belts, they increase with the magnitude of the radiation balance of the earth's surface in these zones.

Variations in the structure, dynamics, and development of the geographic envelope in the various zones are connected, on the one hand, with the variations of the radiation regime of the earth's surface and, on the other hand, with the different degrees of participation in the structure and dynamics of this envelope by water in liquid form, as well as by biocomponents — with the "degree of completeness" of the structure of the geographic envelope.

Also connected with the degree of participation by water in liquid form, by the soil cover, and by the animal world in the structure of the geographic envelope of the various zones are the qualitative characteristics of these components and the nature of their influence on other components, including the atmosphere and the lithosphere. This degree of participation by the hydro-component and the bio-components is inseparably connected with the qualitative characteristics of these components themselves, and with those of the structure of the geographic envelope as a whole.

The "degree of completeness" of the geographic envelope is determined by the participation of various components in its structure, which is connected both with the history of its development in the geologic past (especially with its latest stages) and with the diversity of composition of its components. Connected, in turn, with the latter is the degree of diversity of the natural

NOTE TO TABLE I, facing page:
In conformity with the methods of determining radiation indices of moisture, the values of the radiation balance used in constructing this table relate to the conditions of the moistened underlying surface. For regions with a dry climate, these values differ substantially from the magnitudes of the radiation balance relating to the actual state of the underlying surface. They are considerably less.

processes occurring in the geographic envelope. Thus, characteristic of each zone are definite common features of the chemical composition of its components and, consequently, the common features of the chemical processes occurring in these components. These features are connected primarily with the hydrothermal conditions characteristic of each zone, but likewise with the geologic history.

From the above-characterized general laws of the zonal structure and territorial differentiation of the geographic envelope follow two important conclusions: (1) with nearly alike annual quantities of radiation heat, the completeness of the structure, the multiformity of the dynamics, and the diversity of the composition of the geographic envelope increase as the ratio between the radiation heat and annual precipitation becomes more and more nearly proportional (nearer and nearer to unity), taking into account the influence of the development of the territory in the geologic past; and (2) with close relationships between the annual radiation balance and the annual precipitation (except for certain cases of extreme disproportion between them) the completeness of the structure, the multiformity of the dynamics, and the diversity of the composition of the geographic envelope (with similar conditions of underlying surface) increase with the magnitude of the annual radiation balance of the earth's surface, again taking into account the influence of the development of the territory in the geologic past.

As shown by investigations, altitudinal belting in mountains depends upon the vertical change in hydrothermal conditions, similar to those underlying horizontal zonality. The systems of altitudinal belts in mountains form regular complexes with the horizontal zones situated at the foot of mountain elevations.

The geographic complexes (landscapes) of which, in the final analysis, the integral system of natural plains and mountain territories is composed represent local manifestations of general physical geographic laws governing the structure and development of the geographic envelope within each zone, area, subzone, district, or altitudinal belt. The geographic landscapes of each zone, each altitudinal belt, with all their individual differences, have very much in common with each other, and many typical features distinguishing them from the landscapes of other zones, other altitudinal belts, in accordance with the characteristics of their structure and development. Hence, each zone (or each altitudinal belt) has its own types of landscapes, its own "species" of geographic complexes. Each of these species may form a number of subspecies associated with different intrazonal areas of a given zone (in mountains, with different districts of a given altitudinal belt). These subspecies may, in turn, form varieties [raznovidnosti] associated with the different subzones of a given zone (in mountains, with the different regions of a given altitudinal belt). All these species, subspecies, and varieties of geographic complexes have been formed in the process of the development of a given zone or altitudinal belt in the course of a more-or-less protracted period of geologic time. Their further development is proceeding at present. It is on this genetic basis that the genetic classification of the landscapes of the land masses of the globe must also be constructed.

Such are the most important physical geographic laws, the larger part of which have been established by Soviet geographers in the last twenty years. They testify to the very great progress made in the field of the theory of physical geography. The knowledge of these multiform laws is being used more and more for the purposeful alteration of natural conditions in the interest of the national economy.

BASIC LITERATURE

Berg, L. S. Geographic Zones of the Soviet Union (Geograficheskiye Zony Sovetskogo Soyuza), vol. 2, Moscow, 1952.

Blauberg, I. V. "The Problem of Integrity in Physical Geography". Voprosy filosofii," 1959, no. 4.

Budyko, M. I. "On the Laws of the Physico-geographic Surface Process," Meteorol. i gidrol., 1948, no. 4.

Budyko, M. I. "Concerning the Theory of the Intensity of the Physico-geographic Process," Voprosy geografii, sb. 15, Moscow, 1949.

Budyko, M. I. "The Climatic Factors of the External Physico-geographic Process", Tr. Glav. geofiz. observ. im. A. I. Voyeykova, no. 19 (81), Leningrad, 1950.

Budyko, M. I. "Climatic Conditions of Moisture on the Continents", Izv. AN SSSR, seriya geogr., 1955, nos. 2 and 4.

Gerasimov, I. P. "The World Soil Map and the General Laws of the Geography of Soils," Pochvovedeniye, 1945, nos. 3 and 4.

Gozhev, A. D. "On certain Laws of the Development of the Nature of the Land Surface," *Uch. zap. Leningr. gos. ped in-ta im. Gertsena,* vol. 49, 1946.

Grigor'yev, A. A. "On certain Interrelations between the Elements of the Physico-geographic Environment and their Evolution," *Probl. fiz. geogr.,* vol. 3, AN SSSR, 1936.

Grigor'yev, A. A. An Experiment in the Analytic Characterization of the Composition and Structure of the Physico-geographic Envelope of the Globe *(Opyt analiticheskoy KHarakteristiki Sostava i Stroyeniya Fiziko-geograficheskoy Obolochki Zemnogo SHara),* Geografo-ekonomicheskiy n.-i. institut, Leningrad State Univ., 1937.

Grigor'yev, A. A. "On certain Questions of Physical Geography," *Voprosy filosofii,* 1951, no. 1.

Grigor'yev, A. A. "Geographic Zonality and some of its Laws", *Izv. AN SSSR, seriya geogr.,* 1954, nos. 5 and 6.

Grigor'yev, A. A., and Budyko, M. I. "On the Periodic Law of Geographic Zonality," *Dokl. AN SSSR,* vol. 110, 1956, no. 1.

Grigor'yev, A. A. "Concerning the Present State of the Doctrine of Natural Zones," *Voprosy geografii,* Moscow-Leningrad, AN SSSR, 1956.

Grigor'yev, A. A. "On the Interrelation and Mutual Causality of the Components of the Geographic Environment and the Role of the Exchange of Matter and Energy in them", *Izv. AN SSSR, seriya geogr.,* 1956, no. 4.

Grigor'yev, A. A. "On some Basic Problems of Physical Geography," *Izv. AN SSSR, seriya geogr.,* 1957, no. 6.

Grigor'yev, A. A., and Budyko, M. I. "Classification of the Climates of the USSR," *Izv. AN SSSR, seriya geogr.,* 1959, no. 3.

Kalesnik, S. V. Fundamentals of General Geography *(Osnovy Obshchego Zemlevedeniya),* 1947-1955.

Kalesnik, S. V. "On the System of Geographic Sciences," *Nauchnyye doklady Vysshey shkoly, geol.-geogr. nauki,* 1959, no. 1.

Markov, K. K. "Basic Laws of the Development of the Geographic Environment", *Vestn. MGU* (Moscow State Univ.), 1950, no. 3.

Stanyukovich, K. V. "Main Types of Belting *(poyasnost')* in the Mountains of the USSR," *Izv. VGO,* vol. 87, 1955, no. 3.

CHAPTER 23

PROBLEM OF THE ZONALITY OF THE WORLD OCEAN

V. G. Bogorov

It is known that in nature all phenomena and processes proceed, not in isolation, but in mutual relationship and causality, representing a single interconnected whole. While in experiments we may single out separate physical, chemical, biologic, or geologic processes, in nature none of them exists in "pure" form, but all represent a part of the single nature of the ocean. The imperfectness of our methods and the limitations of the personal opportunities of the investigator make us study the various phenomena and processes separately. B. B. Polynov bitterly bewailed this fact when he said (1953, p. 30): "Our modern science concerning nature is not only broken down into departments, each of which examines only a definite group of phenomena and objects, but these too are separated from one another by the solid walls of faculties, sections, associations,…" The development of modern science is causing greater and greater specialization, which moves science swiftly forward but leads to further isolation and "disruption" in the investigation of various aspects of a single and undivided nature. Alongside this progressing specialization there is a growing need for synthesization of the heterogeneous material and for ascertainment of the causality of phenomena and their mutual relationship.

Since the world ocean occupies 71 per cent of the earth's surface and extends from the North Pole to the shores of Antarctica, its surface is the scene of phenomena resulting from the unevenness in the action of solar radiation in different parts of our planet. This gives rise to geographic zonalities: climatic, water, biologic, and others.

The great merit of V. V. Dokuchayev (1948) was that, instead of the formerly widely practiced study of the geographic distribution of the various characteristics of nature on the earth's surface, he proposed the study of geographic zonality on the basis of the genetic interrelationship of the phenomena occurring within each zone.

The ideas of V. V. Dokuchayev (1948), V. I. Vernadskiy (1926), B. B. Polynov (1958), and others among our outstanding natural scientists concerning the characterization of geographic zones by types of interrelations between the different physical, biologic, chemical, and geologic processes have been widely used by various authors in studying the continents. However, with respect to the world ocean this type of research has still been little developed. This is pointed out by B. B. Polynov (1953, p. 39): "Usually the concept of landscape in geography is connected with the surface of the dry land. Yet there are no grounds for not extending this conception to the underwater areas of the oceans and seas, inasmuch as they also differ from one another in 'climatic conditions' (i.e., temperature and salinity of the water, its content of dissolved air, etc.), the composition and state of the floor deposits, and the forms of organic life. And while the data on the study of the laws governing the distribution of these conditions at present form the property of general oceanography, there will undoubtedly come a time when the study of the subaquatic (underwater) landscapes of the oceans and seas will be set apart as a special branch."

In order to establish the geographic zones of the ocean, in which occur the types of interrelations characteristic of them, the boundaries of the zones must first of all be determined. L. S. Berg writes (1947, p. 10): "Any geographic landscape can only be characterized and distinguished when we establish the boundaries separating one landscape from another. By natural boundaries we mean boundaries whose location is determined by the properties of the objects to be delimited themselves, not those artificially imposed upon them."

For the surface layers of the ocean, the boundaries of the powerful surface currents will be the logical natural boundaries of the geographic (landscape) zones. At the same time, they will also be the boundaries of the surface water masses, which are distributed zonally. The currents in the surface layer run principally in a latitudinal direction. This connects them still more closely with the conditions of the zonal variations of climate.

Let us see what natural geographic zones we encounter in the surface layer of the central part of the Pacific Ocean. Let us use for this purpose the materials obtained on the 26th expedition of the "Vityaz'," which operated in the central part of the Pacific Ocean from November, 1957, to February, 1958, and on which integrated investigations were made along the meridians 174° west longitude and 172° east longitude (Bogorov, 1958). The region of exploration embraced the expanse from 40° north latitude to 40° south latitude (New Zealand). In this area of the ocean, the following geographic zones are well distinguished for the surface layer of the Pelagic Zone [pelagial'] 200 meters): the Northern Subtropical Zone, whose waters move eastward; the Northern Trade Wind (Equatorial) Current Zone; the Inter-Trade Wind Current (Equatorial Counter-Current) Zone; the Southern Trade Wind (Southern Equatorial) Current Zone; and the Southern Subtropical Zone, whose waters move eastward. From the biogeographic viewpoint, all these zones belong to the single Tropical Area whose live population is united in the tropical fauna and flora. The latitudinal location of the boundaries of each zone is not the same in different parts of the Pacific Ocean or in the various seasons. Along 174° west longitude the location of the boundaries during the time of investigation was as follows: the Northern Subtropical Zone from 40° north latitude to 20° north latitude; the Northern Trade Wind Zone from 20° north latitude to 8° north latitude; the Inter-Trade Wind Zone from 8° north latitude to 4° south latitude; the Southern Trade Wind Zone from 4° south latitude to 14° south latitude; and the Southern Subtropical Zone from 14° south latitude to 40° south latitude.

Let us look at the mutual relations of the various phenomena as illustrated by the zone of the Inter-Trade Wind Current (often called the Equatorial Counter-Current). In this zone the rise of the deep-seated waters to the surface takes place over an immense expanse of sea. This can easily be seen from the lower temperature and other peculiarities. Here at a depth of 300 meters the water temperature is 3-4° lower than in the neighboring trade-wind zones. The uppermost layer of water near the equator is strongly heated by the direct rays of the sun, but a good indicator of the deep-seated origin of the surface waters as well is the small quantity of oxygen in them (4.1 milliliter/liter) and the high phosphate content.

The rise of the deep-seated water enriches the zone of photosynthesis (0-200 meters) with phosphates and nitrates. This results (Fig. 8, profiles 1 and 2) in an increase in the quantity of phytoplankton — 20,000 cells per cubic meter; of zooplankton, 46 milligrams/cubic meter; of fish, 1.4 milligrams/cubic meter; and of bacteria, 150 per 50 milliliters. King (1953, 1954) has shown for the central Pacific, to the south and east of Hawaii, that an increase in the quantity of plankton and fish occurs near the equator in the region with large concentrations of phosphates in the surface layer.

The large amount of life in the Inter-Trade Wind Zone influences many phenomena: the increase in suspended particles results in a reduction in the transparence of the water by 10 meters in comparison with the trade-wind zones. The loose-lying skeletons of dead planktons dropping to the bottom in the regions of the ocean far from the shores form a considerable part of the sediment, so that the latter has a smaller volumetric weight (0.9 gram per cubic centimeter).

Thus, the physical phenomenon of the rise of waters leads to a change in the chemistry of the surface waters, and this to the peculiarities of the biology of the waters; the abundance of life affects the transparence of the water (physical phenomenon) and the sediments (geology of the ocean). Thus we obtain a graphic picture of the mutual relationship of the phenomena which determine the single nature of the ocean.

The chain of mutual relations evolves in a different manner in the trade-wind zones. Here the rise of the waters occurs near the shores of America, under the action of offshore-drive phenomena caused by the trade winds. The trade-wind currents carry the water westward, so that deep-seated waters rise in the coastal area and enrich the surface with nutrient salts. Hence, much plankton develops here (Brandhorst, 1958) and there are very rich sardine, anchovy, and other deep-sea fisheries. The farther west the waters of the trade-wind currents move, the more are salts necessary for the development of phytoplankton consumed, and in the central part of the Pacific Ocean the

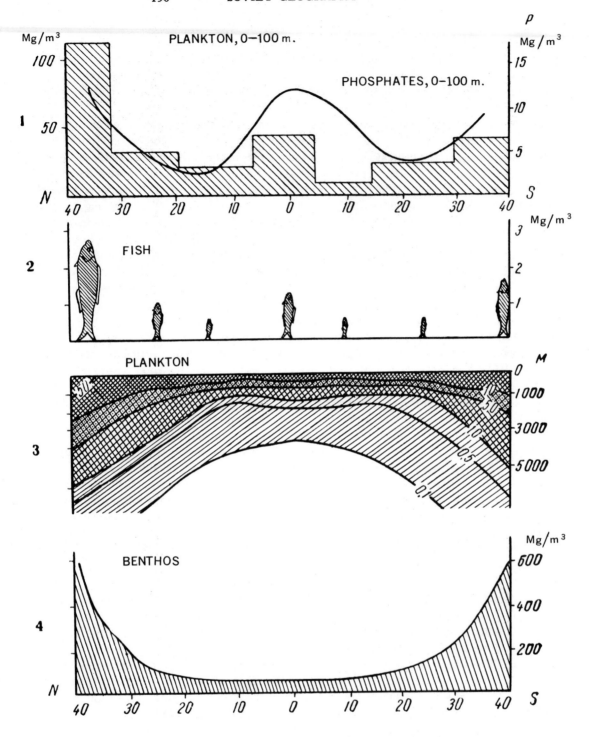

Fig. 8. BIOLOGICAL PRODUCTIVITY OF VARIOUS LATITUDINAL ZONES OF THE OCEAN

waters are very poor in phosphate (Austin, 1958). In waters poor in nutrient salts there is little plankton and few fish and birds. A similar picture is exhibited by Hentschel (1936) for the Atlantic Ocean, and it may be regarded as common to all the oceans.

As we have pointed out earlier (Bogorov, 1958, International Geophysical Year), the latitudinal location of the boundary of geographic zones shifts on different meridians (172° east longitude and 174° west longitude). For meridians situated still farther apart, the boundaries of the zones (with respect to latitude) should differ still more.

It must be borne in mind that the characteristics of each geographic zone are also confirmed by seasonal variations. Here, the farther north or south from the equator, the more substantially do the characteristics of a zone vary with the seasons (Bogorov, 1941).

The number of geographic zones differs for the surface layers of water (down to 200 meters) and for deep-seated layers. In the surface layer the zonality is naturally very minute, inasmuch as the surface of the ocean is under the direct action of the atmosphere. In the deep-seated and especially in the natural layers, the number of zones is smaller. For example, the above-mentioned three zones are well distinguished in the surface layer of the tropical area of the ocean, but in the deep-seated and bottom layers there is only one zone, the tropical. The latter fact can easily be seen from the composition and quantity of the benthos. The bio-mass of benthos in the whole tropical area from 23° north latitude to 23° south latitude is everywhere very small — about 50 milligrams per cubic meter. It increases toward the north and south, beginning with the zone of subtropical waters. Exceptions are observed only near the coasts, where the continental runoff and the shallow-water algae increase the food possibilities of life on the bottom. In remote regions of the ocean the main source of food for the inhabitants of the bottom is the organic matter produced by plankton. When the waters of the ocean are many kilometers deep, the plankton remains will be used repeatedly, and only a very little food will reach the animals on the bottom.

The geographic zones of the ocean are not isolated from one another. The boundaries are more sharply marked in the surface layers, where the zonal (latitudinal) transfer greatly exceeds the meridional. In the depths, the significance of the meridional transfer increases considerably, and the water masses move from the high latitudes toward the equator. These waters bring gases and various nutrients, which then rise in the equatorial region. The waters here rising to the surface exert different influences on the development of life in the photosynthesizing layer and in the deep-seated layers. In the surface layer there is an enrichment of the water with nutrient salts, and the feeding conditions for plankton are improved. Below the photosynthesizing layer, the constant inflow of deep-seated water which is poor in organisms and detritus does not contribute to the enrichment of life. This results in a still more considerable impoverishment, in comparison with the temperate and sub-tropical zones, in the life of the depths in the whole tropical area (Fig. 8, profile).

Large quantities of plankton are developed in the temperate areas. The descending waters carry into the depth plankton and detritus which, being caught up in the meridional transfer, moves toward the equator and enriches the deep-seated layers of water and the life on the bottom, especially in the subtropical zone (Beklemishev, 1959; Vinogradov, 1959). Enrichment of the deep-seated waters also results from the vertical migration of plankton.

In the Subtropical Zone, the winter chilling also results in a mixing of the waters, which improves the food possibilities for the development of life in the depths. As a result, in comparing the quantity of zooplankton at like depths (see Fig. 8), we find that the plankton in the 100-1,000 meter layer in the equatorial region is 16-30 times poorer than on the latitudes of the 40's; in the 1,000-2,000 meter layer, 22-55 times; in the 2,000-4,000 meter layer, 80 times; and in layers deeper than 4,000 meters, more than 100 times poorer.

The characteristics of the types of circulation of substances typical of the various geographic zones create conditions favorable in differing degrees to the development of life. Back in 1948, L. A. Zenkevich constructed a theoretical scheme of the latitudinal quantitative distribution of ocean plankton. Now, after integrated investigations on a meridional cross section in the central part of the Pacific Ocean, we have material confirming the ideas expressed by Zenkevich and permitting us to compose, along 174° west longitude from 40° north latitude to 40° south latitude, a picture (see Fig. 8) of the quantitative distribution of the phosphates of plankton, pelagic fish (small), and benthos and to note the mutual relations between them.

In the upper part of Figure 8 (profile) is given the average quantity of phosphates and plankton by zones. The maximum quantities of zooplankton, on the average for the 100-meter surface layer, are found in the northern part of the Northern Subtropical Zone, in the Inter-Trade Wind Zone, and in the southern part of the Southern Subtropical Zone. The quantity of phosphates is maximal in these same zones, which explains the abundance of zooplankton, providing it along the line: phosphates ➡ phytoplankton ➡ zooplankton. The large concentrations of phosphates (as well as other nutrient salts) in the photosynthesizing layer of these regions is to be explained by various causes. In the Inter-Trade Wind Zone, it is caused by the rise of deep-seated waters; in the Subtropical Zones, by the mixing of the waters as a result of winter chilling.

The bio-mass of pelagic fish (profile 2 in Figure 8), gauged by standard catches with a 2-square-meter anchovy net in the 0-1,000 meter layer, shows that the average weight of small fish in one cubic meter of water (conventionally represented for these zones in the form of small fishes of corresponding sizes) quite naturally duplicates in full the character of the variations in the bio-mass of plankton. In general, the bio-mass of pelagic fishes is twenty to thirty times smaller than that of the plankton.

It is usually considered that, in going from high latitudes toward the equator we encounter a large species diversity in the fauna, and that this diversity is accompanied by a diminution in the total bio-mass. Actually, this is not always so: wherever there is a rise of the waters from the depths (the "storehouse" of nutrient salts), there is also a simultaneous increase in the bio-mass and number of species. This is also easily seen in the tropical area. For example, in the central part of the Pacific Ocean in the Inter-Trade Wind Zone both the number of species of fish and their bio-mass are greater than to the north and south, i.e., in the Trade-Wind zones. Investigations made by Soviet scholars into primary production in the oceans (V. G. Bogorov and K. V. Beklemishev, Yu. I. Sorokin, O. I. Koblents-Mishe, L. A. Klyashtorin, and others) have shown that it is especially large in the coastal area of the northwestern part of the Pacific Ocean. In its northeastern part, considerable production has also been observed even in the winter period (29th voyage of the "Vityaz'" in 1958-1959). In the central part of the Pacific Ocean the production is very small, although it is greater in the Inter-Trade Wind Zone than in the Trade Wind zones. In the Atlantic Ocean, the regions of the rise of waters near the coasts of Europe and Africa are marked by considerably greater production than is the central part of the ocean.

It is usually considered that the abundance of diatoms diminishes sharply as one passes from the higher latitudes toward the equator, with the tropical area being characterized by an abundance of Peridinae. This is to be explained not only by the temperature conditions but also by the fact that diatoms require larger concentrations of biogenic elements, including phosphates. Hence, in the temperate areas, the spring maximum of phytoplankton (the "flowering") is formed as a result of the abundance of diatoms using for their development the supply of phosphates and other nutrient salts accumulated during the winter. On the other hand, the fall maximum is formed to a considerable extent by Peridinae as well (Bogorov, 1941). Looking through the material on phytoplankton while still on the expedition, G. I. Semina has shown that the percentage of diatom species is larger in the subtropical zones and diminishes sharply in the Trade-Wind zones, where there are few phosphates. But in the Inter-Trade Wind Zone, where there are many phosphates, the diatoms occupy nearly half the species composition. In the Southern Hemisphere, where there were more phosphates in the surface layer at that time of the year than in the Northern Hemisphere, the percentage of diatom species was higher.

Thus, the picture of seasonal variations in the abundance of diatoms in the temperate area has, as it were, evolved in a meridional direction. Naturally, the percentage of diatom valves also increases in the ooze on the bottom of the Inter-Trade Wind Zone.

A regular chain of phenomena influences the distribution of life at all depths of the ocean (profile 3 in Figure 8), in all layers of the water down to the bottom. The bio-mass of zooplankton (according to M. Ye. Vinogradov) in the central part of the Pacific Ocean is larger in the subtropical zones than in the Trade Wind and Inter-Trade Wind zones. Wherever little plankton develops in the surface layer, a considerable impoverishment with respect to plankton is also observed in great depths.

The only direct or indirect source of food for animals on the bottom in ocean regions remote from the continents is plankton and its remains or, more accurately, the organic matter produced in the upper photosynthesizing layer. For this reason, we have a right to expect that there must also be minimal quantities of benthos in the whole central part of the tropical area. Indeed, the determinations of the bio-mass of benthos, made on the expedition by Z. A. Filatova, G. M. Belyayev, and N. G. Vinogradova, have fully confirmed this supposition.

From a comparison of the arched isoplankts with the mirror image of the concave isobenth (profile 4 in Figure 8), the dependence of the quantity of benthos upon the sources of food—the plankton—becomes quite evident. Many attempts are now being made to establish fine differences in the surrounding hydrologic conditions at great depths in the temperate and tropical biogeographic areas, which would make it possible to explain the differences in the deep-water fauna and the quantity of benthos. It is known that at depths of over 3 to 4 kilometers the differences in temperature are very small, and the differences are insignificant under other conditions as well. Hence, for regions of the ocean distant from the coasts, it is very difficult to explain by abiotic features the differences observed in the distribution of the deep-water fauna by areas, especially their quantity. Various areas are substantially distinguished only by the abundance and quality of the food produced in the surface layer of the Pelagic Zone of the temperate and tropical areas and ultimately reaching the bottom. This difference, and hence the special food relations of the Pelagic Zone with the bottom inhabitants, affects the composition, distribution, and bio-mass of the benthos. Here it must be borne in mind that the silt serving as a medium of life and food for certain animals and deposited far from the shores is also directly or indirectly connected to a greater extent with the photosynthesizing layer—this zone of life for the whole ocean.

We shall not deal here with the differences in fauna connected with the history of its origin, since we are principally discussing the trophologic factors which play a primary ecologic role.

The chemical investigations of plankton on the 26th voyage of the "Vityaz'" (the fat, nitrogen, and carbohydrates were determined) have furnished interesting results concerning the variation in the fattiness of plankton on different latitudes. Being an energy reserve, fat varies most easily in dependence upon various conditions. The fattiness of plankton constantly diminishes as one moves from the subtropical zones toward the equator. It is least in the Inter-Trade Wind Zone. But since the plankton bio-mass is greater in this zone than in the neighboring ones, the total quantity of fat per cubic meter of water does not vary so considerably as does the total plankton bio-mass, and fluctuates about 0.4 milligrams per cubic meter for the 100-meter surface layer. Despite the relative paucity of plankton, many planktophages inhabit the surface layer of the tropical waters, such as flying fish and various fry of predatory fishes. This seeming contradiction is to be explained by the fact that the planktophages and predators feeding on them live principally in a thin surface layer which is richer in plankton than the whole underlying mass of ocean water. To explain this picture it is very important to have data on the number of generations of plankton organisms. Thus far, there are still very few materials on this question. It is known that the number of generations of *Calanus finmarchicus* in the English Channel is three times as great as in the Arctic (Bogorov, 1958). In the warm tropical waters, the development of organisms proceeds still more rapidly than in cold waters, and the number of generations increases sharply. R. A. Woodmasee has pointed out that certain plankton copepods have 12 generations a year in tropical waters. The large number of generations makes up for the lack of bio-mass produced at one time by fishes feeding on plankton. The great abundance of generations results in a reduction of the fattiness of plankton in the equatorial region. During the short life span of each generation the organisms do not have time to accumulate a large quantity of fat. In the tropical area, where there are no sharp seasonal changes in the life conditions, there is obviously no need for reserves of fat to provide for an unfavorable period.

The organic matter produced in the surface layer of the ocean in the form of skeletons and detritus or in the amorphous state is transmitted to all depths of the ocean and settles on the bottom. The bottom sediments are a unique kind of mirror reflecting the whole transformation of substances from the surface to the bottom. This can be judged with sufficient completeness by examining a map of the distribution of types of sediments in the World Ocean (Zenkevich, 1951), which, quite naturally, coincides well with the distribution of diatoms, radiolaria, and pteropods in the plankton. The chain of conversions, from the formation of carbohydrate as a result of photosynthesis to the production of plankton, then to fish and, finally, to the accumulation of organic substances in the ooze, has been demonstrated by us for the northwestern part of the Pacific Ocean (Bogorov, 1958).

The mutual relations of these phenomena are so evident that an idea of the productivity of the whole water mass of the ocean, especially of the photosynthesizing surface layer, can be formed from a map of the quantitative distribution of organic matter in the ooze. Such a map could be of practical significance for the development of fishing in the ocean. It could also have unique merits, inasmuch as the distribution of organic matter in the ooze reflects the mean quantitative regularities extending over a large number of years. The quantitative distribution of plankton or fish, however, varies greatly by seasons and years.

The characteristics of the deposition of organic matter on the bottom, as well as the skeletal remains, can be used in the paleogeographic evaluation of the bottom deposits. Thus, ooze poor in organic matter has been formed in regions with a small amount of plankton in the Surface Zone, which fact is characteristic of tropical waters. On the other hand, ooze with a high organic-matter content is common in boreal waters.

The aggregate action of the various conditions results (Vinogradov, 1949) in the formation of different biogeochemical provinces. Each geographic zone creates its own special type of mutual relationships between organic and inorganic nature.

Thus, the productivity of the geographic zones of the ocean and their parts depends upon the characteristics of the type of mutual relations between the various processes. Wherever a rise of water to the surface is observed, there is a fertilizing of the photosynthesizing layer of the ocean and then an increase in the production of plankton and fish.

BASIC LITERATURE

Beklemishev, K. V. "The Role of Deep-seated Waters of Polar and Subpolar Origin in the Enrichment of Abyssal Plankton," *Byull. Mosk. ob-va ispyt. prirody,* 1959, no. 1.

Bogorov, V. G. "The Biologic Seasons of Plankton in the Different Seas," *Dokl. AN SSSR,* vol. XXXI, 1941, no. 4.

Bogorov, V. G. "The Production of Plankton and Characterization of the Biogeographic Areas of the Ocean," *Dokl. AN SSSR,* vol. 118, no. 5, 1958.

Bogorov, V. G. "The Second Expedition on the 'Vityaz'' in Accordance with the IGY Program," *Informats. byull.* no. 5, *MGG* [=IGY], Izd-vo AN SSSR, 1958.

Vernadskiy, V. A. Biosphere I—II *(Biosfera I—II),* Nauchno-khimichesko-tekhnicheskoye izd-vo, 1926.

Vinogradov, A. P. "Biogeochemical Provinces", *Tr. yubileynoy sessii, posvyashch. stoletiyu so dnya rozhd. V. V. Dokuchayeva.*

Vinogradov, M. Ye. "The Vertical Distribution of the Deep-water Plankton of the Pacific Ocean and its Relation to the Circulation of Deep-seated Waters," *Dokl. AN SSSR,* 1959.

Dokuchayev, V. V. "On Soil Zones in General and Vertical Zones in Particular," *Ucheniye o zonakh prirody,* Geografgiz, 1948.

Zenkevich, L. A. "The Biologic Structure of the Ocean," *Zool. zhurnal,* vol. XXVII, no. 2, 1948.

Zenkevich, L. A. "The Fauna and Biologic Productivity of the Sea" *(Fauna i Biologicheskaya Produktivnost' Morya),* vol. 1, Sovetskaya nauka, 1951.

Polynov, B. B. "Study of Landscapes," *Voprosy geografii,* sb. 33, 1953.

Sorokin, Yu. I., and Koblents-Mishke, O. I. "The Primary Production of the Sea of Japan and a Part of the Pacific Ocean adjacent to Japan in the Spring of 1957," *Dokl. AN SSSR,* vol. 112, no. 6, 1958.

CHAPTER 24

SNOW COVER

G. D. Rikhter

A considerable part of the earth's surface is covered annually for a more or less protracted period with a layer of snow of varying thickness. To these regions belong the polar and the temperate zones, in which the predominant majority of the population lives, as well as the mountain lands in all the belts of the earth, down to the equator.

The snow cover represents a unique kind of rock, with sharply differing physical-mechanical properties. It consists of ice crystals, the spaces between which are filled with air containing water vapor or liquid water. Depending upon the surrounding meteorologic conditions (temperature, humidity, pressure, etc.), the relationship between the solid, liquid, and gaseous particles of water in the snow varies, and the physical-mechanical properties of the snow also change along with it. Possessing the capacity for strong reflection (high albedo) of radiant energy and low heat conductivity, the snow cover interferes sharply with the heat exchange between the soil and the atmosphere, exerting an enormous influence upon their heat regime.

The layer of snow protects the soil from deep freezing and sharp fluctuations of temperature and creates favorable conditions for plants and animals hibernating under the snow to endure the difficult cold period. Investigations have shown that the habitat areas of many wild plants and animals are determined to a considerable degree by the character of the distribution and the properties of the snow cover.

Both soil processes and geomorphologic processes take a different course under the protection of the snow cover than on sections devoid of it. In the opinion of the well-known Russian soil scientist, Professor S. S. Neustruyev, the variety of the soil cover of the steppe zone, its humus content, and the degree of salinity depend to a considerable extent upon the character of the snow distribution.

The winter precipitation accumulated in the snow cover is the main source of water supply to streams and lakes. On the plains rivers of the European part of the USSR, with melt waters forming tempestuous floods, from 50 to 75 per cent of the entire annual runoff occurs in spring, while the rivers of the extreme southeast are fed exclusively by snow melt waters; current is observed in them only in springtime. The supply of soil and ground water also depends to a considerable degree upon the distribution of the snow masses and the character of their location and thawing. Finally, glaciers are formed from the snows in the mountains and descend along the slopes to feed the mountain streams. Almost all the farming in the desert regions of Middle Asia is based on artificial irrigation with glacier water.

Along with its enormous effect on all the natural processes, snow also exerts an influence on all branches of the national economy, especially farming. The well-known Russian agrotechnician, Academician V. P. Mosolov, wrote in one of his works (1926): "Success or failure in surviving the winter (on the part of winter crops—G. R.) depends upon the snow cover. With little snow, the winter crops are destroyed by frost; with too much, they are ruined by dampness or by sweating. If the snow falls on thawed ground, they are again sweated to death; etc." Thus, the role of the snow cover in hibernation may be regarded as exceptional. Of no less significance is snow for spring crops, because it provides the soil with moisture in addition to protecting it from frosts.

The utilization of the hydro-energy resources of our rivers and the operation of lake and river water transportation are directly dependent upon the water regime of the rivers, which, as pointed out, are fed chiefly by snow melt waters. The drifting of snow on ways of communication causes traffic stoppages and brings enormous loss to transportation; an enormous quantity of labor and materials is expended yearly in protecting roads and tracks from snow or in clearing it away. At the same, the snow cover makes it possible, by means of *sled transportation,* to travel, for example, to those swampy regions to which no kind of surface transportation can penetrate in summer. Snow is used as a building material for the construction of snow-and-ice roads, for temporary shelters and dwellings in the Extreme North (the "igloo" of the Eskimos), as well as for building snow-and-ice cold storages for preserving perishable products.

Not a few difficulties are caused by the annual clearing of snow from streets and courts in our towns and cities and industrial enterprises. The mechanization of this labor-consuming work encounters difficulties owing to the exceptional diversity of the physical-mechanical properties of snow of different densities. In mountain regions, powerful snow avalanches destroy roads and structures and often take a toll of human victims.

Despite this immense role of the snow cover in nature and in the national economy, until recently no adequate attention had been paid to its study. With the powerful development of socialist agriculture, industry, and transportation, with the winning of distant regions, especially the northern ones, the need for an all-around study of the snow cover has become evident, and many scholars have begun to interest themselves in snow.

Until recently, meteorologists have studied snow as one of the forms of precipitation; the hydrologists have studied the distribution of snow in connection with the water reserves contained in it; and transportation workers and some agricultural workers have studied the physical properties of snow. Only later did geophysicists and geographers take up the study of the snow cover. The elaboration of the whole complex of questions connected with the study of the snow cover requires the unification and co-ordination of the efforts of various specialists.

The fact that snow was studied by specialists with different ranges of qualifications, who approached its study from their own points of view, is to be explained by the lack of uniformity in the degree of study coverage of the manifold questions connected with the physical properties and dynamics of the snow cover and its distribution.

The young branch of science known as "snow science" [*snegovedeniye*], which has lately been undergoing rapid development in the USSR, has the task of thoroughly studying snow and snow cover for the purposes of rational utlization of its properties in the development of the national economy. The study of snow is being done from the viewpoint of its composition (the mineralogy and petrography of snow), its physico-mechanical and chemical properties (the physics and chemistry of snow), its distribution and influence on the natural processes (the geography of snow).

Because snow is exceptionally variable in its properties, which depend upon the meteorologic conditions, the study of the regime of the snow layer in different geographic areas acquires special significance.

The foundations of snow science were laid by the great Russian climatologist and geographer, Professor A. I. Voyeykov, about eighty years ago. In a brief note on "The Influence of the Snow Surface on Climate" (1871), he was the first in world literature to call attention to the enormous influence of snow on climate and the water regime, and to point out the need for studying it. Later (in 1885 and 1889), Voyeykov published detailed investigations in this question and outlined a program for the all-around study of snow. At this scholar's initiative, regular observations of snow were begun at the meteorologic stations and these have continued down to the present time. However, Voyeykov's appeal for an all-around study of snow found no adequate response, and the snow cover was studied from one occasion to another, in conjunction with practical requirements, at the initiative of individual persons.

Systematic observations of snow are being made at the hydrometeorologic stations, but are confined to the dates of fall, establishment, decay, and disappearance of snow, determinations of the mean thickness and density of snow, i.e., the gathering of materials for the solution of only one task—the recording of the water reserves in snow, data which is necessary for hydrologic forecasts and calculations. To perform this same task, profound investigations into the processes of snow melt and the runoff of melt waters have been made in the last few years in the system of scientific-research institutions of the Hydrometeorologic Service: the Main Geophysical Observatory, the State Hydrologic Institute, and the Central Forecasting Institute (P. P. Kuz'min, V. D. Komarov, and others). A reliable method has now been worked out for calculating snow melt and runoff by means of the heat-balance equation.

Before the October Revolution, snow investigations underwent their greatest development in conjunction with the organization of protection of railroad tracks from snowdrifts. The first experiments in thaw control were made in 1863 by Engineer Titov. Later, investigations were instituted into the transfer and deposition of blizzard snow at especially organized stations, where, in addition to observations of snow transfer, tests were also made of different types of protection of tracks from snow. Major physicists and aerodynamicists were engaged to study the phenomenon of snow transfer, including Professor Zhukovskiy, the greatest aerodynamicist and "father of Russian aviation." The railroad scientific research organizations made a substantial contribution to the development of snow science.

At almost the same time, experiments were begun in the utilization of snow in farming. The peasants of the arid regions had from time immemorial perceived the importance of snow for crop yield: "Snow in the fields, grain in the bins," says an old Russian proverb. In the works of many foremost Russian scholars (A. I. Voyeykov, V. V. Dokuchayev, P. A. Kostychev, A. A. Izmail'skiy, N. P. Adamov, N. G. Vysotskiy, and others) there are numerous recommendations of methods for utilizing snow to raise the crop yield. However, the development of work on snow retention before the Revolution was impeded by the minuteness of the plots of land.

A great qualitative jump in the development of snow science occurred after the Revolution, especially after the termination of the restoration period, owing to the immense amount of construction, embracing all regions of the country, including the Extreme North and the high-mountain regions, where the role of the snow cover is especially great.

Of especial significance for the development of snow science has been water-power construction. In connection with this construction, studies were instituted on the laws governing the distribution of the water reserves in snow, the processes of melting and runoff of melt waters and the forecasting of floods. The solution of these questions engaged the attention of such major scientific institutions as the State Hydrologic Institute, the Central Forecasting Institute, the Main Geophysical Observatory, the Hydro-energy Designing Office [*Gidroenergoproyekt*], and many others. The development of the network of railroads and motor highways made it necessary to investigate the transfer and physico-mechanical properties of snow for the purposes of working out rational methods of protecting the tracks from drifting snow, as well as designing snow-removing machines. Interesting and very detailed work on the study of the physico-mechanical properties of the snow cover has been performed in connection with the construction and operation of temporary snow-and-ice roads and winter airfields. Investigation of snow in the mountains has also been considerably developed in connection with road and industrial construction in mountain regions and the necessity for protecting them from avalanches. Besides the scientific-research institutes for railroad and motor transportation (the Central Scientific Research Institute for Railroad Transportation and the All-Union Road Scientific Research Institute), work is also being done by certain production and scientific institutions, such as the "Apatite" Trust, Lomonosov Moscow State University, and the Institute of Geography of the Academy of Sciences of the USSR.

Of decisive significance in the development of work on the utilization of the snow cover for increasing agricultural crop yields has been the socialization of the land, which has permitted snow retention over extensive areas and mechanization of this labor-consuming process. The broad network of experimental agricultural stations has made it possible to obtain comparative material and to proceed to work out snow-control procedures for different natural zones.

The extensive material accumulated has made it possible to proceed to generalize it. The first summary, since the works of A. I. Voyeykov, was the book by Professor P. N. Chirvinskiy, "Snow and Snow Retention," in which snow was characterized as a mineral and rock, and the forms of the snow surface, the methods of combating snow drifts, and the utilization of snow in cultivation were examined. Considerable space is devoted to snow in the detailed summary by E. T. Loske on "Agricultural Meteorology."

Special compendia by B. P. Veynberg (1940), G. D. Rikhter (1945), P. P. Kuz'min (1957), and P. A. Shumskiy (1955) are devoted to the physico-mechanical properties of snow. An extensive literature is devoted to the study of the processes of snow thaw and runoff. The formation of avalanches is examined in a book by G. K. Tushinskiy (1949). A summary by G. D. Rikhter (1948) is devoted to the role of the snow cover in the physical geographic process, and summaries by A. N. Formozov (1946) and A. A. Nasimovich (1955) are specially concerned with the influence of the snow cover on the life of mammals. In the last few years, the Institute of Geography of the Academy of Sciences of the USSR has begun systematic publication of collections of works on the study and utilization of snow.

The above-enumerated summary works form a solid foundation for the evolving new scientific discipline of snow science, which is of great practical significance. The compilation of a large collective work summarizing all the experience gained in these investigations has now been undertaken.

The complex interactions of the snow cover with all the elements of nature and man's economic activity determine the various scientific directions in snow science and the various methods of research.

The study of snow must begin with the moment of its *formation in the atmosphere* (snowflakes, granular snow, hail, etc.) and on terrestrial objects (hoarfrost, rime, ice coating, etc.). The processes of ice-crystal formation under different natural and laboratory conditions are studied with the aid of crystallo-optic and physical methods. The conditions of formation of crystals of different forms in the natural setting and under laboratory conditions have been studied comparatively well. The labors of many scholars have ascertained the main dependences of the form of ice crystals upon the surrounding conditions.

The study of the form and size of ice crystals is of great significance, since a number of *physical mechanical properties of the snow cover* (volumetric weight, heat conductivity, mobility, etc.) depend upon them to a considerable extent. A detailed monograph by A. D. Zamorskiy (1955) is devoted to questions of the formation and fall of snowflakes, their morphology, and the processes of their transformation.

The *snow* accumulating on the earth's surface in the form of snow cover has substantially different properties than separate ice crystals and may be regarded *as a rock*. Of the greatest significance in the formation of the snow cover are the processes of transformation of the ice crystals in the cover (metamorphosis of snow). The study of the very complex processes of the metamorphosis of ice in the snow cover is being carried out by a number of investigators. Many questions of metamorphosis still remain to be discovered, however, and an enormous amount of research work is still to be done in this direction. Digests of the scientific results of the study of metamorphosis processes have been published by B. P. Veynberg (1940), G. K. Tushinskiy (1948, 1953), P. A. Shumskiy (1955), and by other authors.

The *physical properties of the snow cover* have begun to be intensively studied in the last few years. B. P. Veynberg, the well-known Russian geophysicist, who has engaged a great deal in the study of snow cover, wrote in 1936: "If you were told that physicists and chemists know of a mineral easily obtainable in pure form and available on the earth's surface in a quantity somewhat larger than 2-3 milligrams, and that not a single physical property of it except its melting point—neither its specific gravity, nor its indices of refraction, nor its light diffusion, nor its heat capacity, nor its heat of fusion, to say nothing of vapor tension, dielectric constant, electroconductivity, magnetic permeability, double refraction, etc.—is known, you would probably smile at the speaker and, perhaps out of curiosity or pity for him, would deign to ask him: 'What kind of a material is that?' That material is snow, which is to be found on the surface of the globe in millions of millions of tons."

A great deal of work on the study of the physical properties of snow has been done in various countries, yet very many properties of snow are still completely unknown. The slight extent of the study of the physics of snow is due to the exceptional variability of these properties in dependence upon the surrounding meteorologic conditions, the composition of the snow, and the structure of the snow layer.

During the whole time that it lies on the surface of the earth, snow undergoes continuous changes both in time and in space. The statistical indices of physical properties obtained under one set of conditions by precise experimental methods can characterize only to a small degree of approximation the properties of this same snow but at another time, or of snow in other localities.

Best known among the physical properties of snow are density (volumetric weight), radiation properties, and certain thermal properties. Considerably less studied are its porosity, water and air permeability, as well as its electric, radioactive, and acoustic properties. Also still poorly studied are many mechanical properties of snow in the cover (expansion, contraction, density, hardness, friction coefficient, viscosity, etc.). The study of the physico-mechanical properties of snow is hampered by the lack of evolved standard apparatus and techniques, which fact sometimes makes it difficult to compare the results of different investigations.

The long-range observations by the network of meteorologic stations make it possible to get an idea of the *distribution of snow on the territory of the USSR,* but in view of the considerable fluctuations, from year to year, both of the dates of appearance and disappearance of snow and of its greatest thickness, as well as the great dependence of the beds of snow upon local conditions (relief, vegetation, etc.), information about the beds of snow is not marked by great accuracy. Until not long ago, observations of snow accumulation were made from a fixed rod, set in a sheltered or an open place. The influence of the surrounding objects on the readings of the rod was so great that the value of the snow accumulation obtained could not characterize the true distribution over an extensive area. Now, in addition to the observations from the fixed rod, the network of stations has begun to make periodic traverse or area snow surveys which better characterize the mean snow accumulation. The techniques of working up these materials have still not been adequately worked out.

Especially complex is the distribution of the snow cover in mountain regions, where it is influenced both by the absolute altitude of the place and also by the exposure, the steepness of the slope, and the vegetation. Investigations made in the last few years in the Tyan'-Shan' (M. I. Iveronova, V. L. Shul'ts), in the Caucasus, and in other mountain regions show that with all the seeming disorderliness of the beds of the snow, there are still definite regularities depending upon the relief and the exposure of the slope. Definite regularities are also discovered in the distribution of snow reserves depending on relief under the conditions of the Russian Plain (V. N. Parshin, I. S. Grishin). The discovery of the laws of distribution of snow in the USSR, as well as the regime of its depth, is the task of further investigations by snow geographers.

A great deal of work is also still to be done in the field of the *study of the influence of the snow cover on the natural processes.* The role of the snow cover in the hydrologic regime and in the distribution and ecology of animals has proved to have been studied best of all. Less well studied is the question of the role of snow in the formation of relief and the plant cover. There have been almost no investigations into the question of the action of snow on the processes of soil formation and the shaping of local weather.

A profound and all-around study of the physico-mechanical properties of the snow cover, its regime, and their dependence upon the surrounding conditions is necessary for the elaboration of *practical measures for the utilization of the snow cover* in agriculture [snow control *(snezhnyye melioratsii)*], in the construction and operation of winter ways of communication and airfields, in the mechanization of the labor-consuming processes of snow removal, and in combating snowdrifts and avalanches.

The proper choice and application of the procedures of snow control, strictly adapted to the local peculiarities of nature, to the properties and regime of snow, as well as to the uses to which they are to be put, should considerably increase their efficiency and cheapen their execution. Retention of snow on fields adjacent to the ways of communication and prevention or substantial reduction of its transfer by blizzard winds will eliminate the menace of snowdrifts to transportation and will permit the land of the "condemned strips" [*polosy otchuzhdeniya:* lit. "strips of alienation (i.e., legally appropriated)] adjacent to the ways of communication to be included in agricultural exploitation.

The procedure now used for protecting tracks and roads from drifting snow—setting various mechanical obstacles such as fences, shields, shelter belts of trees and shrubs in the way of the snow-and-wind current — although reliably protecting the tracks and roads from snow drifts, requires enormous annual expenditures of labor and money. It is necessary to seek other and more economical methods of combating drifts, based on fundamentally different methods of tying the snow down on the spot where it falls (chemical, electric, and other agents).

A profound, all-around study of the interaction of the snow cover with the surrounding natural environment will make it possible not only to understand the natural processes better but also to find new methods of acting upon nature with the aid of the snow cover.

Snow science as a branch of geography is developing in close connection with all the other sciences of the geographic series. This science, which originated in Russia, has great prospects in the Soviet Union, where the development of the productive forces is being built on the fullest utilization of all natural resources.

BASIC LITERATURE

Anisimov, M. I. Snow and Snow Slides *(Sneg i Snezhnyye Obvaly)*, Izd-vo AN SSSR, Moscow, 1958.

Antonov, F. I., Pryad'ko, V. S., and Mel'nik, D. M. The Combating of Snow Drifts in Railroad Transportation *(Bor'ba so Snezhnymi Zanosami na ZHeleznodorozhnom Transporte)*, Moscow, 1951.

Byalobzheskiy, G. V. Snowdrifts and their Control *(Snezhnyye Zanosy i Bor'ba s nimi)*, Moscow, 1952.

Veynberg, B. P. Ice. The Properties, Rise, and Disappearance of Ice *(Lëd. Svoystva, Vozniknoveniye i Ischeznoveniye L'da)*, Moscow-Leningrad, 1940.

Voyeykov, A. I. "The Influence of the Snow Surface on Climate", *Izv. RGO*, vol. 7, 1871, No. 1; *also Izbr. soch.*, vol. 2, Izd-vo AN SSSR, 1949.

Voyeykov, A. I. "The Snow Cover, its Influence on Climate and Weather and Methods of Investigation", *"Zap. RGO po obshch. geogr."*, vol. 15, 1885, No. 2; *also Izbr. soch.*, vol. 2, Izd-vo AN SSSR, Moscow-Leningrad, 1949.

Voprosy Izucheniya Snega i Ispol'zovaniya YEgo v Narodnom KHozyaystve (Questions of the Study of Snow and its Utilization in the National Economy) (collection of articles), Izd-vo AN SSSR, Moscow, 1955.

Voprosy Ispol'zovaniya Snega i Bor'ba so Snezhnymi Zanosami i Lavinami (Questions of the Utilization of Snow and the Combating of Snowdrifts and Avalanches) (collection of articles), Izd-vo AN SSSR, Moscow, 1956.

Voprosy Teorii i Praktiki Zashchity ZHeleznykh Dorog ot Snezhnykh Zanosov (Questions of the Theory and Practice of Protecting Railroads from Snowdrifts) (collection of articles), *Tr. Transp.-energ. in-ta Zap.-Sib. fil. AN SSSR*, no. IV, Novosibirsk, 1954.

Zamorskiy, A. D. Atmospheric Ice *(Atmosfernyy Led)*, Izd-vo AN SSSR, Moscow-Leningrad, 1955.

Komarov, V. D. The Hydrologic Analysis and Forecasting of Spring High-water in the Plains Rivers *(Gidrologicheskiy Analiz i Prognoz Vesennego Polovod'ya Ravninnykh Rek)*, Leningrad, 1955.

Kuz'min, P. P. The Physical Properties of the Snow Cover *(Fizicheskiye Svoystva Snezhnogo Pokrova)*, Leningrad, 1957.

Kungurtsev, A. A., and Sarsatskikh, P. I. Winter Maintenance of Motor Roads *(Zimneye Soderzhaniye Avtomobil'nykh Dorog)*, Moscow, 1950.

Mel'nik, D. M. The Prevention of Snowdrifts at Railroad Stations *(Preduprezhdeniye Snezhnykh Zanosov na ZHeleznodorozhnykh Stantsiyakh)*, Moscow, 1955.

Nasimovich, A. A. The Role of the Regime of the Snow Cover in the Life of Ungulates on the territory of the USSR *(Rol' Rezhima Snezhnogo Pokrova v ZHizni Kopytnykh ZHivotnykh na Territorii SSSR)*, Izd-vo AN SSSR, Moscow, 1955.

Rikhter, G. D. "The Role of the Snow Cover in the Physico-geographic Process", *"Tr. In-ta geogr. AN SSSR,"* no. 40, Moscow-Leningrad, 1948.

Rikhter, G. D. The Snow Cover, its Formation and Properties *(Snezhnyy Pokrov, yego Formirovaniye i Svoystva)*, Izd-vo AN SSSR, Moscow, 1945.

Rol' Snezhnogo Pokrova v Zemledelii (The Role of the Snow Cover in Agriculture) (collection of articles), Izd-vo AN SSSR, Moscow, 1953.

Sneg i Talyye Vody, ikh Izucheniye i Ispol'zovaniye (Snow and Melt Waters, their Study and Utilization) (collection of articles), Izd-vo AN SSSR, Moscow, 1956.

Tushinskiy, G. K. Avalanches. Their Rise and Protection from Them *(Laviny: Vozniknoveniye i Zashchita ot Nikh)*, Moscow, 1949.

Tushinskiy, G. K. Avalanches and Protection from Them in Geologic Prospecting *(Laviny i Zashchita ot Nikh na Geologorazvedochnykh Rabotakh)*, Moscow, 1957.

Formozov, A. N. The Snow Cover as a Factor of the Environment, its Significance in the Life of Mammals and Birds of the USSR *(Snezhnyy Pokrov kak Faktor Sredy, yego Znacheniye v ZHizni Mlekopitayushchikh i Ptits SSSR)*, Moscow, 1946.

Chirvinskiy, P. N. Snow and Snow Retention *(Sneg i Snegozaderzhaniye)*, Rostov-na-Donu, 1931.

Shul'gin, A. M. Soil Climate and Snow Retention *(Pochvennyy Klimat i Snegozaderzhaniye)*, Moscow, 1954.

Shumskiy, P. A. Fundamentals of Structural Ice Science *(Osnovy Strukturnogo Ledovedeniya)*, Izd-vo AN SSSR, Moscow, 1955.

CHAPTER 25

LANDSCAPE SCIENCE

S. V. Kalesnik

The rise of landscape science [*landshaftovedeniye*] as a special branch of physical geography was predetermined by the development of all geographic science and world geographic thought. In our country the sources of the most general conceptions of landscape science (though without use of this term) date back to the materialist geographers of the Dokuchayev school. V. V. Dokuchayev called for the study, not of individual bodies and natural phenomena, but of certain integral territorial aggregates of them. This embodied the idea of natural complexes, later given the name of geographic landscapes. Dokuchayev expounded this idea in the form of the doctrine of natural zones and the differences within each zone from place to place.

The earth's surface has, in the course of evolution, been broken up into sections differing from one another in a number of features. Insofar as such sections (landscapes) exist objectively, they must be investigated with respect to their material composition, external appearance, internal structure, location, geographic distribution, taxonomic co-subordination (i.e., classification), and laws of development. There is also a worldly sense in this research, since landscapes are the direct theater of man's economic activity.

An exceptionally favorable setting for the cultivation of the study of landscapes has arisen in the years of Soviet rule. It has been promoted by the rapid flowering of expeditionary exploration in the country, which furnishes the immense amount of fresh factual material needed for systematization and thereby impels scientific thought toward new theoretical generalizations, as well as by the extensive utilization of Marxist methodology in science.

We owe the first experiment embodying the fundamentals of landscape science to L. S. Berg ("Landscape-Geographic Zones of the USSR," 1931). In the three decades since that time the theory and practice of the young branch of physical geography has made notable progress.

It is known that the creation of exhaustive and precise formal definitions belongs to the complex problems in any science. Landscape scientists thus far have not succeeded in finding an irreproachable and universally satisfactory definition of landscape [*landshaft*], but there are no serious disagreements as to the essence of this concept and term. As we have noted, it concerns a complex of peculiarities possessed by a certain territory which distinguish and delimit it from other territories on the surface of our planet. The combination of objects, phenomena, and processes characteristic of a given territory is the regular result of its existence and development as an integral natural system, in which the component parts are internally interrelated and interact continuously.

At one time the term "landscape" was given a very broad sense, being treated as a general concept analogous to "soil," "climate," etc. The possibility of such an understanding is not denied even now. But the chief dispute is now between the representatives of only two viewpoints: (1) the word "landscape" should be used to designate a typologic concept, (2) "landscape" is a region [*rayon*], a geographic individual [*individuum*]. Still, both the regional and the typologic trends in landscape science exist as two inseparable aspects of a single problem. The regional trend seeks in landscapes unduplicable features; the typologic trend seeks similar and common features. The typology of landscapes should become the basis of their systematization, but typologic categories are also used in the physical geographic regionalization of large and small territories.

New progress in the theory of the landscape was registered when its internal morphologic characteristics were studied. L. G. Ramenskiy has pointed out that the landscape consists of heterogeneous territorial complexes — "epifacies" [*epifatsii*] and tracts* [*urochishce*]. These notions of the morphology of the landscape, later worked out in detail by N. A. Solntsev, have deepened the understanding of the landscape and its structure and have also made it possible to define the object of field investigations of landscape scientists and the contents of landscape maps.

Field work experience has shown that the division of the landscape into tracts and tracts into facies (the latter term has ousted "epifacies") has vindicated itself in principle, although in many concrete cases the division has also proved inadequate, because nature is naturally always richer than any scheme whereby its representation is sought. "Groups of facies" (they are sometimes called "formations") have, in practice, to be isolated as an intermediate link between the facies and the tract, and the tracts have to be united into a "complex of tracts" (otherwise called "localities" [*mestnosti*]). "Series of facies" are also distinguished—a system in which the facies located higher up a slope exert an influence on the lower lying facies (K. G. Raman). In all cases the facies is regarded as the "cell" of the landscape, i.e., the ultimately indivisible geographic unit.

The morphologic units are regularly repeated within the landscape, and each landscape has its own definite "spectrum" of tracts and facies. Hence, when one speaks of the structure of a landscape one has in mind not only the character of the interrelations between the components of the landscape (relief, climate, water objects, soil, biocoenoses, etc.), but also the character of the combination and distribution of the morphologic units. The concept of the structure of the landscape has lately been supplemented by a characterization of its seasonal rhythm, expressed by the alternation of aspects.

The landscape and its morphologic parts serve as direct objects of field physical geographic investigations. The main content of the landscape scientist's field work consists in ascertaining the morphologic units existing in the landscape, their characterization, and recording on the map in as much detail as the scale of the landscape survey being made will possibly permit. It is also evident that the chief content of a large-scale landscape map consists in representing facies, tracts, or other morphologic units of the landscape.

Landscape maps were compiled by various authors as long ago as the 1920's (B. B. Polynov, I. V. Larin, A. D. Gozhev), but the production of such maps, and on a new theoretical basis, underwent an especially broad evolution after the Second World War. The groundwork for physical geographic field investigations was laid by the geographers of Moscow University, headed by N. A. Solntsev. Their example was soon followed by the geographers of other universities—Leningrad, Voronezh, L'vov, Latvian, Tbilisi. The names of the pioneers of landscape surveying (N. A. Solntsev, A. G. Isachenko, O. N. Kazakova, F. N. Mil'kov, K. I. Gerenchuk, P. N. Tsys', K. G. Raman, K. V. Kavrishvili, and others) are now well known to all USSR geographers.

In order to summarize the results of field landscape investigations and discuss the most important questions of landscape science, the Geographic Society of the USSR has since 1955 regularly convoked all-Union conferences on landscape science. By 1960 four such conferences had been held— in Leningrad, L'vov, Tbilisi, and Riga. These conferences discuss only those concepts which can be argued with materials from the personal field investigations of the author of a paper. Speculative schemes drawn up purely at a desk are not included in the program. The conferences are accompanied by excursions, making it possible to carry on discussions directly "in nature." These conferences testify to the swift accumulation from year to year of materials relating to landscape surveying, and to the intensive elaboration, principally by university geographers, of various local landscape-typologic schemes (Carpathian, Karelian, Caucasian, Middle Russian, Baltic, etc.), which are to serve further as a basis for the creation of a single classification of territorial complexes. At each conference, dozens of new landscape typologic maps and maps of physico-geographic regions in a broad range of scales are exhibited.

Methods of field landscape investigation are, of course, still in the elaboration stage, but the general scheme of organization of such investigations has already been outlined. Without speaking of the pre-field and office periods, let us note only that field work proper in landscape surveying is usually divided into three stages: traverse reconnoitering work, having the object of getting generally acquainted with the region and making a preliminary singling out of the landscapes; traverse work (planned on the basis of the traverse reconnoitering work) for mapping the tracts and fixing

---

*The Russian term in general usage designates a plot distinguished from surrounding localities by natural features; for example, a glade in the midst of a forest. The term is now employed by some geographers as one of the units of a hierarchical classification of landscape regions. See the English use of "tract" by J. F. Unstead in 1933 (*Geography*, vol. 18, pp. 175-187) and by David Linton in *London Essays in Geography*, 1951, pp. 199-218.—Ed.

more precisely the boundaries of the landscape; and finally, investigations in "key" sections, i.e., the most typical morphologic units of the landscape (the data on the "keys" are then extended to all the intralandscape territorial complexes having the same type as the "key."

The program for the study and characterization of the geographic landscape has also been delineated in its general features and has been well formulated by A. G. Isachenko. It covers:

1. The position of the landscape in the system of physical geographic regionalization
2. The analysis of the boundaries of the landscape and its external relations
3. The history of the development of the landscape
4. The present zonal and azonal landscape-forming factors
5. The basic intralandscape laws, the structure of the landscape, and the characteristics of the individual components and their mutual relations
6. The morphology of the landscape, the dynamics of the heat, moisture, mineral particles, and organic substances, and their redistribution in the landscape by tracts and facies
7. The seasonal dynamics of the landscape
8. The general tendency of the development of the landscape; its progressive traits and features
9. The influence of man's economic activity on the landscape
10. The evaluation of the natural resources and general economic recommendations.

A large role in landscape science has thus far been played by qualitative, descriptive characterizations, the constancy of macro-processes and macro-phenomena. This is to be explained by the fact that the usefulness of the methods long employed by geographers has by no means been exhausted, to say nothing of the fact that, without "description," i.e., without factual material, no science can exist at all. However, the dispassionate observer will easily note that geographers are not at all averse to new methods of investigation stemming from the achievements of mathematics, physics, chemistry, technology, etc. The slowness or restricted character of the introduction of these methods into geography is to be explained by the complexity of the objects to be studied. Mathematical constructions based on abstraction and simplifications cannot be applied to the analysis of such a complex system as the landscape, for abstraction and simplification are inadmissible in geographical analysis. Much closer are the ties of landscape science with physics: in studying the landscape the geographer perhaps turns his attention first of all to the physical essence of the phenomena occurring in the landscape (the circulation of the atmosphere, the water circulation, the heat regime, the water regime of the soil, physical weathering, etc.). Not long ago, the application of new physical methods of calculating the heat and moisture balance on the earth's surface made it possible to discover the periodic law of geographic zonality (works by A. A. Grigor'yev and M. I. Budyko).

Mastery by physical geographers of the ideas of geochemistry is proceeding fairly rapidly, so that a new and fruitful trend has arisen — the geochemistry of landscapes, for which B. B. Polynov has laid the groundwork. It is now being successfully developed by the labors of A. I. Perel'man, M. A. Glazovskaya, M. M. Yermolayev, and others.

The endeavor to obtain materials on the dynamics and seasonal rhythm of landscapes, as well as quantitative indices for the characterization of the intensity and rate of certain processes, has led physical geographers to the idea of organizing stationary geographic observations as well as field landscape investigations. There are geographic stations in the Tyan'-Shan', on the Karelian Isthmus, in the vicinity of Moscow, and at other places, but the network of stations does not as yet correspond to the size of our country, or to the great benefit that science can derive from stationary geographic observations, which unquestionably contribute to a more profound understanding of landscapes.

The study of geographic landscapes is complicated by the fact that many natural landscapes have been altered in one degree or another by man's activity. This should, of course, find its expression in the classification of landscapes, and one has to speak of at least two types of them: pristine [pervobytnyye] and cultural. The natural landscape is converted into a cultural landscape when its structure has been altered by man through the destruction of the existing proportions between the various components or through the introduction into the landscape of objects, bodies, and formations alien to it: the introduction of plants, the erection of dams, the digging of canals or ponds, the building of roads, and so forth.

Landscape science is one of the most important components of physical geography, having found application in the national economy earlier than others. The resolutions of the Communist Party and

Soviet Government point out the necessity of taking into account both the zonal and the local natural differences in developing the economy (especially agriculture). Even a cursory glance at a landscape map which objectively reflects the diversity of tracts and landscapes will convince a practical man of the necessity of providing various schemes and procedures for dealing with different territories. Consideration of the local natural characteristics in planning the economy is greatly facilitated by preliminary landscape investigations. The universities of Moscow, Leningrad, Voronezh, L'vov, Saratov, and other cities outfit special landscape expeditions to study sovkhoz and kolkhoz lands. The landscape investigations of Leningrad University in the northern Lake Lagoda region, on the Karelian Isthmus, and in Vologda oblast, similar investigations by Moscow University in the Zaraysk rayon of Moscow oblast, the Sapozhok rayon of Ryazan' oblast, and other places, as well as the landscape surveys being made by the geographers of other institutions of higher learning, are being completed with lists of practical recommendations in the tradition which is now becoming established.

The usefulness of landscape science, also, in working out measures for the transformation of nature is obvious. To change this or that component in the landscape, it is necessary to foresee in what direction the landscape will change in general, and this requires a knowledge of the structure of the landscape.

Certain Soviet geographers take a reserved attitude toward the study of landscapes; others, even a very critical one. Each critic has his own motives for this: landscape science is a "past stage" of geography, the study of landscapes is metaphysical, landscape science is fruitless for practice, and so forth. Landscape science, like any other branch of knowledge, of course, needs criticism. But criticism aimed at Soviet landscape science without having a constructive character gives little aid to the common cause. In any case, it gives no grounds for rejecting the principles and methods of landscape science. This is evidenced by the development of field landscape investigations and the growing success of the all-Union landscape-science conferences.

BASIC LITERATURE

Gerenchuk, K. I. "Questions of the Medium-scale Mapping of Landscapes," *Nauchn. zap. L'vovsk. un-ta*, vol. 40, 1957.

Isachenko, A. G. "Tasks and Methods of Landscape Investigation," *Izv. VGO*, 1955, no. 5.

Isachenko, A. G. "The Development of Landscape Science in the USSR during 40 years," *Izv. VGO*, 1957, no. 5.

Kalesnik, S. V. "A General View of the Development of certain Branches of Geography in the USSR during the Years of Soviet Rule," *Izv. VGO*, 1957, no. 5.

Solntsev, N. A. "The Present State and Tasks of Soviet Landscape Science," *Nauchn. zap. L'vovsk. un-ta*, vol. 40, 1957.

CHAPTER 26

NATURAL REGIONALIZATION

G. D. Rikhter

Natural regionalization, i.e., the division of a territory into more or less large parts relatively homogeneous with respect to their nature but differing from one another, must be resorted to in all stages of the geographic study of a locality. Before proceeding to a detailed study of the nature of any territory it is necessary to divide the territory preliminarily, according to the available information, into more or less naturally homogeneous parts. As a result of the study of the territory and the revelation of the regularities in the formation of its nature, the whole of it will be found to be suitable for division into genetic homogeneous sections which possess unity of structure of the geographic environment and dynamics (the character of the processes occurring in it). Thus, every geographic investigation of a territory begins and ends with regionalization.

Regionalization may pursue different practical aims and represent either a particular (branch) regionalization by separate components of the natural environment (climatic, geomorphologic, soil, geobotanical, etc.), or a general (landscape) regionalization by the complex of natural conditions. In any form, however, regionalization will reflect the objectively existing natural territorial differences.

Integrated landscape regionalization is often called physical geographic, or natural. The latter designation better reflects its essence, since, in addition to physical phenomena, the great complex of biologic, chemical, and other natural phenomena are taken into consideration in regionalization.

In the present article we shall confine ourselves only to a discussion of the questions of general natural regionalization.

The theoretical significance of regionalization work lies in the uncovering of new geographic laws governing the interaction of the components of nature and the territorial distribution of natural characteristics. Its practical significance lies in the fact that the division of a territory into genetically homogeneous parts permits a more profound and accurate evaluation of the natural resources and conditions for their fullest and most efficient utilization. In evaluating the nature of each region thus distinguished, not only must its natural resources be ascertained, but also the natural conditions which favorably or negatively influence their economic utilization. From the results of such an evaluation are derived practical recommendations of methods for the most efficient exploitation of the favorable conditions, and for eliminating or weakening of the effect of unfavorable ones. The genetic unity of nature in the regions distinguished will make it possible to recommend for application to each one of them a single complex of economic and reclamational measures to insure the fullest development of the natural resources. It is natural that in a planned socialist economy questions of regionalization should become a problem of statewide significance.

Owing to the immense theoretical and practical significance of natural regionalization, it has occupied a conspicuous place in all stages of development of science and is deemed a most important task of modern physical geography. The first experiments in natural regionalization in our native geography go back to the 18th century, when M. V. Lomonosov, I. I. Lepekhin, P. S. Pallas, and later P. I. Rychkov, V. N. Tatishchev, Kh. A. Chebotarev, and others not only singled out the main natural zones and gave a characterization of them, explaining their differences by the unequal intake of solar heat, but also gave samples of integrated natural regionalization of the territories studied (P. S. Pallas for the Crimea, I. I. Lepekhin for the Solovetskiye Islands, P. I. Rychkov for the Orenburg steppes, and so forth).

In the 19th century there appeared more detailed and better grounded regionalizations of the territory of European Russia (Arsen'yev, 1818; Trautfetter, 1851; Keppen, 1885; Tanfil'yev, 1896; and others). Of immense significance for the development of the theory of regionalization was the work of V. V. Dokuchayev (1899), who outlined a system of soil and natural zones on the territory of European Russia and laid the foundation for the progressive landscape trend in physical geography. Dukuchayev's ideas were developed in the works of A. N. Krasnov, P. I. Brounov, A. A. Kruber, G. I. Tanfil'yev, L. S. Berg, A. A. Grigor'yev, S. V. Kalesnik, S. P. Suslov, and many others, who defined more precisely the boundaries and characteristics of the natural zones.

A. A. Grigor'yev gave an analysis of the natural conditions in the main natural belts of the whole globe (1938-1942). Though this author's works carried out no regionalization, the immense amount of material gathered and generalized, and the methods of characterization proposed, played a big role in the development of the theory of regionalization.

The history of the development of regionalization work in Russia and the USSR has been treated in special works by I. S. Lupinovich ("Natural-historical Regionalization," 1947), B. A. Val'skaya (1950), A. G. Isachenko (1953), F. N. Mil'kov (1956), V. I. Prokayev (1955), N. I. Mikhaylov (1955), and others. A large number of articles have been devoted to the methodological questions of natural regionalization in various geographic journals; among them should be especially noted the works by D. L. Armand (1952), N. I. Mikhaylov (1955, 1956), V. I. Prokayev (1955, 1959), A. G. Isachenko (1953), F. N. Mil'kov (1956), and V. B. Sochava (1956).

Owing to the rapid growth of the Soviet planned national economy, much attention has been paid in recent years to regionalization work. The Council for the Study of the Productive Forces of the Country *(SOPS)*, under the Presidium of the Academy of Sciences of the USSR, has undertaken a big project for the natural-historical regionalization of the USSR (1947), based on particular (branch) regionalizations of the country made by the workers of many institutes of the Academy of Sciences of the USSR. The map of the regions of the USSR created in the SOPS, with a text characterizing them, was an important stage in the development of regionalization work. At many institutions of higher learning (universities and teachers colleges), special courses have been given in natural regionalization (Mikhaylov, 1955; Mikhaylov and Fedina, 1959). In recent years, the geographic faculties of the universities have been engaged in natural regionalization work and have done a great deal of work on regionalizing their districts.

To exchange experience and to work out methods, special conferences of the participants in this great collective work are convoked at Moscow State University. Parallel to this, regionalization work is being continued at the SOPS of the Academy of Sciences of the USSR (Letunov, 1956), in the Institute of Geography of the Academy of Sciences of the USSR, and by geographers of the academies of sciences of the Union republics.

★ ★ ★

The natural conditions of a locality are determined by its geographic location, morphostructure, amount of solar-energy intake, and the ratio between the amounts of heat and moisture, which determine the climatic, geomorphologic, soil, and biologic processes. All the factors determining the natural conditions operate simultaneously and in mutual relationship, but each of them possesses definite spatial regularities reflected in the distinctiveness of the natural environment.

In regionalizing the earth's surface, it is necessary first of all to examine separately the land mass and the water areas, on which the natural processes take place in quite a different manner. The separation of continents and oceans is due to the complex manifestations of the morphotectonic processes, whose spatial laws have as yet been only inadequately ascertained.

The preponderant majority of works on regionalization pertain to the land, whereas regionalization of the seas and oceans has as yet not been sufficiently worked out. Below, we shall discuss only questions of land-mass regionalization.

The basic spatial law which most geographers use as the basis of regionalization, and to which they have long directed their attention, is latitudinal zonality, i.e., the regular variation of natural conditions with geographic latitude. This variation is due to the unequal intake of solar energy, the main energy base for all processes occurring on the earth's surface. A study of the natural conditions has shown, however, that latitudinal zonality manifests itself fully and distinctly only on plains territories and at some distance from seashores. In coastal regions and in localities with mountain relief the zonal features are masked by the superimposition of other factors.

The deviation from latitudinal zonality is due to the fact that, in addition to radiant energy, which, on the yearly average, increases from the poles toward the equator, great significance for the natural processes also attaches to the advective thermal energy brought in by air and sea currents and subject to the laws of the circulation of the atmosphere and sea waters. The distribution of advective heat depends chiefly upon the position of the locality in the system of air circulation, the degree of distance from the seashores, the surrounding relief, and to a considerably lesser degree upon the geographic latitude. Moreover, under the same heat conditions, the natural processes take a different course depending upon the quantity of moisture circulating at a given place. The distribution of moisture is likewise not subject to latitudinal zonality and has its own distribution laws.

The investigations of A. A. Grigor'yev and M. I. Budyko (1956) have ascertained the regular relations of the natural zones to the ratio between the amount of heat and moisture and have established the "periodic law of natural zonality," reflecting the objectively existing natural regularities.

The relief and geologic structure of a locality exert substantial influence on the natural processes. As is known, a profound and vividly manifested relationship exists between the present forms of the earth's surface, the history of the geologic development, and the structure of the earth's crust. This relationship permits one to distinguish various morpho-structural units of different structure, age, and surface forms: plains, plateaus, mountain ridges, massifs, etc. (Gerasimov, 1946, 1958-1959). The morpho-structures, not subject to latitudinal zonality, are nonetheless distributed regularly, although the laws of their distribution have not yet been sufficiently ascertained. The morpho-structural characteristics of a territory, which result from a long historical development, impose a substantial imprint upon the distribution of heat and moisture and their ratios, which is reflected in the development of the natural processes. Under mountain conditions, for example, latitudinal zonality is blurred by vertical belting and in some cases the latitudinal extension of the natural zones disappears owing to orographic conditions; for example, in North America.

Relief exerts its chief influence on the natural processes through alteration of the conditions of heat and moisture transfer, but alteration of the radiant-energy intake is also of no small significance. The complex combination of slopes with different inclinations and exposures results in great diversity in the absorption of the solar radiation received, and the sharp fluctuations of altitude and the associated changes in the climatic regime result in the appearance of a vertical succession of natural factors (vertical belting).

Various investigators take the one or the other of the ascertained basic natural territorial laws as the foundation of regionalization of complex and integral nature. In the first stages of the development of geography, chief attention was paid to the unequal intake of radiant energy in the different latitudinal belts and the main heat belts were at first distinguished by this feature. Radiation conditions manifest themselves clearly not only in climate, but also in the character of the vegetation, which also reflects the moisture conditions. For this reason, zones later came to be distinguished by vegetation conditions with the use of vegetation as a climate indicator. The employment of vegetation as a basic index in regionalization made it possible not only to broaden, but also to deepen and considerably particularize the division of the earth's surface into natural zones approximating landscape zones. Zonal principles were made the foundation of regionalization by I. I. Lepekhin, A. N. Beketov, P. P. Semenov-Tyan-Shanskiy, V. V. Dokuchayev, L. S. Berg, G. I. Tanfil'yev, and by others.

The second basic natural territorial law—the dependence of the entire natural complex upon the morpho-structure—has also been taken as the foundation of regionalization by many investigators: V. P. Semenov-Tyan-Shanskiy, B. F. Dobrynin, I. P. Gerasimov, N. A. Solntsev, and others.

The laws of the distribution of natural conditions depending upon the location on the continent, the conditions of relief and geologic structure, etc., not being subject to latitudinal zonality, are usually called "azonal" or "provincial." Different opinions exist as to which of the characteristics—zonal or provincial—should be used as the foundation for regionalization and what their relationship is. Depending on these points of view, several schemes of taxonomic subdivisions, based both on zonal and on provincial characteristics, have been proposed. A number of investigators (Isachenko, 1953, and others) consider it possible to distinguish two independent series of regionalization units: by zonal and azonal characteristics, the units of these two series not being co-subordinated.

If territorial differences are viewed from the standpoint of the ratio between the quantities of heat and moisture, a ratio which depends, as has been pointed out, upon zonal and provincial factors, the controversial question as to which of the characteristics—zonal or azonal—should be recognized as the leading ones in regionalization loses its acuteness. In regionalizing, it would be a mistake to rely upon any one of the laws established and to neglect the others. Any natural regionalization should reflect the actually existing diversity of nature, in which the territorial laws—both zonal and provincial—manifest themselves in complex interaction. One must agree with F. N. Mil'kov (1959) that "provinciality represents a concrete expression of the phenomenon of zonality."

Thus, the peculiarities of nature are determined by two basic and mutually independent laws:

1. Zonal, latitudinal laws, connected with the unequal intake, from one latitude to another, of the solar energy which constitutes the main energy base for all exogenic (external) processes.

2. Structural-tectonic laws, connected with the differentiation of the magma and the history of the development of the earth's crust and determining the areas, arrangement, and configuration of the land and the structure and character of its relief.

With these two mutually independent laws are connected the following derivative ones:

3. The laws connected with the position of a territory in the system of the radiation zones and advection (sea and air currents), the ratios between the amounts of heat and moisture, determining the bioclimatic processes.

4. The law of the vertical variation of climatic conditions with altitude.

All the natural conditions have become constituted as a result of the long geologic development and history of formation of nature, as reflected in the present natural conditions.

With the growth of technology, continually increasing significance is accruing to the action of the economic activity of human society upon nature. In regionalization, these conditions have to be given careful consideration.

Among Soviet geographers, there is still no generally accepted *system of taxonomic units of regionalization,* just as there is no adequately based and generally accepted terminology. Such a system, however, is gradually being worked out in regionalization practice.

The largest unit of the regionalization of continents is called by most investigators a *land* [*strana*]. Because of its common geologic development, the *land* possesses a genetic unity with respect to geology and geomorphology (morpho-structure). Occupying a definite position on a continent, the *land* possesses a definite degree of continentality and specific traits of atmospheric circulation. The common major traits of relief, climate, and biologic complex determine the unity of a territory in the degree of complexity of the structure and diversity of its nature. This diversity is expressed in the number, degree of pronouncedness, and character of the latitudinal zones on a plain and in the type of vertical belting in the mountains.

The *segment of a zone* [*otrezok zony*], possessing common bioclimatic characteristics of nature, is taken as the second degree of natural regionalization within a *land.* The degree of pronouncedness of the zonal peculiarities of nature differs according to the character of the relief and location. In mountain regions, the traits of zonality manifest themselves in the character of the vertical belts, while in maritime regions the zonal features are not infrequently masked by the advection of different quantities of heat and moisture.

The intrazonal differences in relief, in the degree of continentality, and in the history of the development of nature cause one to distinguish smaller units, or *provinces,* within the segment of a zone. The provinces are divided, according to the practical trend, scale, and tasks of natural regionalization, into smaller units: *areas* [*oblasti*], *districts* [*okruga*], and *rayons* [*rayony*], which are the lowest units of integrated landscape regionalization. The rayon represents a regular combination of those *types of locality* which may be regarded as elements of the region. Unlike the region and other regional units possessing territorial community and continuity, the types of locality are distinguished and classified by the principle of like type and analogy. Within different regions, one and the same type of locality may be encountered in different combination (Mil'kov, 1959).

The methods of regionalization depend upon the aims and scale of work, as well as upon the extent to which the territory has been studied. Regionalization is done both in the office and by the field exploration method in combination with the working up of the materials of air-photo surveys and large-scale maps. The office method is employed more often in the small-scale regionalization of well-studied major territories; in large-scale regionalization, especially of little-studied territories, the field-exploration method is more often used.

Owing to the steady enhancement of the role of planning in the utilization of natural resources and to the development of work on the economic conquest of the territory of the USSR, the significance of the problem of natural regionalization is constantly increasing.

BASIC LITERATURE

Armand, D. L. "The Principles of Physico-geographic Regionalization," *Izv. AN SSSR, Seriya geogr.*, 1952, no. 1.

Berg, L. S. Geographic Zones of the Soviet Union *(Geograficheskiye Zony Sovetskogo Soyuza)*, vol. 1, 1947; vol. 2, 1952.

Val'skaya, B. A. "A Survey of the Experiments in the Regionalization of Russia from the End of the 17th Century down to 1861," *Voprosy geografii*, sb. 17, 1950.

Gerasimov, I. P. "An Experiment in the Geomorphologic Interpretation of the General Scheme of Geologic Structure of the USSR," *Probl. fiz. geogr.*, no. 12, 1946.

Gerasimov, I. P. "The Major Features of the Relief of the Earth's Surface on the Territory of the USSR and their Origin" *(Krupnyye CHerty Rel'yefa Zemnoy Poverkhnosti na Territorii SSSR i ikh Proiskhozhdeniye)*, 1959.

Grigor'yev, A. A. "An Experiment in the Characterization of the main Types of Physico-geographic Environment," *Probl. fiz. geogr.*, nos. 5 and 6, 1938; 7, 1939; 11, 1942.

Grigor'yev, A. A. "Geographic Zonality and some of its Laws," *Izv. AN SSSR, Seriya geogr.*, 1954, nos. 5 and 6.

Grigor'yev, A. A., and Budyko, M. I. "On the Periodic Law of Geographic Zonality," *Dokl. AN SSSR*, vol. 110, 1956, no. 1.

Dokuchayev, V. V. Concerning the Study of the Zones of Nature. Horizontal and Vertical zones *(K Ucheniyu o Zonakh Prirody. Gorizontal'nyye i Vertikal'nyye zony)*, 1899; "The Natural-historical Regionalization of the USSR," *Tr. Komissii po yestestv-geogr. rayonirovaniyu SOPS AN SSSR*, vol. 1, 1947.

Isachenko, A. G. Basic Questions of Physical Geography *(Osnovnyye Voprosy Fizicheskoy Geografii)*, 1953.

Letunov, P. A. "The Principles of Integrated Natural Regionalization for Purposes of the Development of Agriculture," *Pochvovedeniye*, 1956, no. 3.

Materialy Soveshchaniya po YEstestvenno-istoricheskomu i Ekonomiko-geograficheskomu Rayonirovaniyu SSSR dlya TSeley Sel'skogo KHozyaystva 1-5 Fevralya 1958 g. (Materials from the Conference on the Natural-historical and Economico-geographic Regionalization of the USSR for Agricultural Purposes, 1-5 February, 1958). Izd. geogr. fakul'teta MGU (Moscow State University) 1959 (multigraphed).

Mil'kov, F. N. The Physico-geographic Region and its Content *(Fiziko-geograficheskiy Rayon i yego Soderzhaniye)*, 1956.

Mil'kov, F. N. Basic Problems of Physical Geography (selected lectures) (Osnovnyye Problemy Fizicheskoy Geografii (izbrannyye lektsii). Izd. Voronezhsk. universiteta, 1959.

Mikhaylov, N. I. "Selected Lectures on Physico-geographic Regionalization *(Izbrannyye Lektsii po Fiziko-geograficheskomu Rayonirovaniyu)*, izd. MGU (Moscow State Univ.), 1955.

Prokayev, V. I. "On Certain Questions of the Method of Physico-geographic Regionalization," *Izv. AN SSSR, Seriya geogr.*, 1955, no. 5.

Prokayev, V. I. Physico-geographic Regionalization of the USSR *(Fiziko-geograficheskoye Rayonirovaniye SSSR)*, 1959.

Sochava, V. B. "Principles of Physico-geographic Regionalization," Sb. *Voprosy geografii*, 1956.

CHAPTER 27

INTEGRATED MAPPING

K. A. Salishchev

The solution of many national-economic tasks arising in the process of communist construction in the USSR is founded on a profound study of the natural conditions, resources, and productive forces. Such a study is most fruitful with a geographic approach, i.e., with a many-sided investigation of nature and economy, taking into account the mutual relations and the development of phenomena. For practical work, the geographic approach is especially important when the results of the study are presented in the form of geographic maps, i.e., in a form convenient for survey, analysis, and treatment, and permitting one to characterize many phenomena by measure and number. Of course, maps are also of great scientific value, because they furnish the geographer with a source of new conclusions and knowledge, and an active means for scientific generalization and forecasting. All this determines the significance of integrated [*kompleksnyy*] mapping as a method of many-sided and integral representation of the reality by cartographic means.

In integrated mapping there are three paths:

1. The organizationally independent but programmatically co-ordinated creation of series of various special-purpose maps, which insures their comparability, mutual supplementability and, consequently, the possibility and convenience of joint utilization.

2. The preparation of a complex [*kompleks*] of maps differing in content but furnishing altogether a full characterization of the integral group of phenomena, their relationships and mutual causation. To this group of cartographic products belong the integrated [*kompleksnyy*] geographic atlases.

3. The independent preparation of integrated maps.

Integrated mapping may differ in the breadth of the complex: from a comparatively limited range of phenomena (for example, those taken into account in making a qualitative appraisal of agricultural lands), to a complete cartographic digest of scientific knowledge on physical, economic, and political geography, which is territorial in scope, and from maps of key sections a few square kilometers in size to a survey of the planet as a whole.

Let us first examine the special-purpose "branch" maps and their role in integrated mapping. Special-purpose surveys and mapping for the solution of concrete or scientific tasks are carried out in the USSR by many government departments and scientific institutions. Some work is done on a countrywide scale and has nationwide significance. Such, for example, are the geologic, soil, botanical, peat-reserve, and other surveys. Certain ones among them, within the limits of their interests, acquire an integrated character; for example, geographic surveys have the object of obtaining interrelated maps: geologic, geomorphologic, and mineral, often supplemented by lithologic, hydrogeologic, and other maps. But it is especially important that the surveys serve as sources for the creation of nationwide maps—geologic (1:200,000 and 1:1,000,000), soil (1:1,000,000), geobotanical (1:1,000,000) and others, issued with the same grid as the nationwide general geographic maps to the corresponding scales.

Each map has its own purpose. For example the State Soil Map of the USSR to a scale of 1:1,000,000, compiled for the whole country according to a unified method in a unified system of subdivision and nomenclature of soils, permits one to establish and compare the character of the soil conditions and the qualitative make-up of the lands of any region of the USSR, which is necessary for the general planning of agricultural production and the distribution of crops. But the conclusions that can be obtained by using this map can be considerably broadened by comparing it with other maps to the same scale—general geographic, geologic, and geobotanical. A joint analysis of them opens the way to geographic generalizations based on the relations between the distribution of soils, the character of the relief, the composition of the soil-forming rocks, the types of vegetation, and so forth.

Also very valuable in this sense are the series of special-purpose maps of the USSR to a scale of 1:2,500,000 and the series of maps of nature in the USSR for institutions of higher learning to a scale of 1:4,000,000.

Special-purpose topical maps on a uniform scale may rightly be regarded as components of integrated mapping. Hence, it is important to insure their concordance with respect to topographic bases, the amount of detail in legends and classifications, the character and depth of generalization. With this object in view, the Third Congress of the Geographical Society of the USSR (1960) recommended principles for the programmatic and methodical co-ordination of the general and special-purpose state mapping of the USSR, as well as the organization of a state inventory of special-purpose surveys and maps.

Integrated mapping has attained especially great success in the USSR in the elaboration and production of geographic atlases. Their methodologic foundations were pointed out by V. I. Lenin in his letters of 1920-1921 on the occasion of the preparation of the first Soviet geographic atlases. (See Chapter 7, "Cartography.")

The realization of Lenin's ideas required considerable time and great effort. The first major integrated atlases—economic-geographic in content—were published in the years of the socialist industrialization of the country, the execution of the first five-year plans for the development of the national economy. The earliest of them, the great "Atlas of the Industry of the USSR" (1929-1931), included a characterization of the natural conditions, but its main economic maps were of a narrow topical character, with statistical methods of representation predominating.

The "Atlas of the Industry of the USSR at the Beginning of the Second Five-year Plan" (1934) reflected the progress of the country's industrialization resulting from the execution of the first five-year plan. The precise location of industrial enterprises, the indication of their sizes, time of foundation, and reconstruction are merits of this atlas, which still retained a topical structure. The idea of an integrated atlas was more fully embodied in the "oblast" atlases—the "Atlas of Moscow Oblast" (1933) and the "Atlas of Leningrad Oblast and the Karelian ASSR" (1934), which are marked by a very full, many-sided and, at the same time, integral, representation of the natural conditions, economics, and cultural construction.

The work on these atlases was of service in the preparation of the "Great Soviet Atlas of the World" [Bol'shoy Sovetskiy Atlas Mira], (vol. I, 1937; vol. II, 1940), in which were realized Lenin's suggestions about the fullness and many-sidedness of the representation of the world, the unity and modernity of the maps, the showing of phenomena in their relationships, development, and contradictions. This atlas, at once world-wide and national, was widely discussed in the geographic literature and hence there is no need to review it. We shall only note that all the maps of the BSAM were worked out anew, many of them having had no predecessors or analogues (for example, the maps of the financial dependence of the capitalist countries, and the maps of commodity markets and raw-material markets).

New work on the publication of integrated geographic atlases has evolved in the USSR since the end of the Second World War. The scope of this work is very wide—from atlases of individual oblasts to atlases of the world; from integrated atlases on individual branches of geography to all-embracing atlases on physical, economic, and political geography; from atlases intended for a wide circle of readers* to major scientific works. The creation of integrated atlases belongs to the most important sections of the seven-year plan of Soviet cartography.

Especially valuable are the great world-wide atlases. Of outstanding interest among them is the three-volume "Marine Atlas" [Morskoy Atlas], the fundamental cartographic handbook on the geography of the oceans and seas. The first volume—"Navigational-Geographic" (1950)—contains general geographic maps of the oceans and seas, distinguished by an abundance of data, by uniform detail in the portrayal of sea and land, and by hypsometric representation of the relief. The second volume is devoted to the physical geography of the World Ocean and is noteworthy for its methodological foundation. The earth is viewed in it as a single physical whole, characterized by

---

*Among these may be classed the "Geographic Atlas for Teachers of the Middle School," 1954; the second edition of this atlas came out in 1959.

complex interrelationships and mutual connections between the lithosphere, the hydrosphere, the atmosphere, and the biosphere. Since the natural conditions of the ocean cannot be fully clarified outside of their relations to the natural conditions of the land, the representation of the natural phenomena, when necessary, is not confined to the limits of the World Ocean, but is extended to the whole planet.

A number of processes are shown together with the factors engendering these processes. For example, the maps of currents are combined with supplementary maps of the prevailing direction of the wind. The relations and interactions of phenomena are portrayed most clearly in the complex of hydrologic and climatic maps. Thus, the maps of the heat balance enable one to understand the causes and characteristics of the atmospheric circulation, which in turn causes the sea currents, the transfer of heat by them and, consequently, the action upon the heat balance. A substantial merit of the maps lies in the distinction of the chief relations upon which the course of the mutually conditioned phenomena depends in the highest degree. In the wake of the "Great Soviet Atlas of the World," the "Marine Atlas" has raised integrated map-making to the next higher level of development. The third volume of the "Marine Atlas" (part 1, 1958), devoted to the history and development of naval art, belongs in the field of the historical sciences and is mentioned here because it was created on the same methodologic base, with integrated treatment of the basic subjects. Thus, for example, the third volume includes military-economic maps enabling one to see the dependence of the modes of warfare upon the development of the productive forces, and political maps showing the political setting, the disposition of forces, the consequences of war, and so forth.

A "Physical-Geographic Atlas of the World," now being prepared as a continuation of the reference-work "Atlas of the World" of 1954 (see chapter 7, "Cartography"), is to be still more diversified, in the characterization of the natural conditions of the planet. It is designed to summarize the present state of knowledge about the natural conditions of the globe, to show the laws of the distribution and mutual relations of the most important natural phenomena on a planet-wide scale and to characterize these phenomena qualitatively and quantitatively. This is virtually a second part of the "Atlas of the World" and is planned in three sections: the world, the continents, and the USSR. Each section will cover the following subjects: orography, historical geology, tectonics, minerals, Quaternary deposits, paleogeography, geomorphology, climate, hydrology, soils, distribution of farming, natural and cultivated vegetation, animal world, and physical geographic regionalization.

The Atlas will not only concentrate and generalize an enormous amount of factual material, but will also present it in a unified system of classification, in legends and symbols common to all the sections. The solution of this task will facilitate the subsequent elaboration of comparable legends on the maps of the individual lands and regions and will be of service in the preparation for the establishment of legends on international maps of natural conditions, about which life itself propounds the questions. The section of USSR maps forms, in the atlas, just as was the case in the "Great Soviet Atlas of the World," a sort of physical-geographic part of the national atlas of the USSR.

Another group of atlases under preparation are large atlases of the USSR: an integrated one (including maps of the natural conditions and economic maps as well as general geographic maps), a climatic one, and an agricultural one. In particular, the latter atlas will contain integrated and topical maps of agriculture for the USSR as a whole, and by republics and regions. These maps will show the present state of socialist agriculture, its territorial shifts and dynamics, and the prospects for development. Inclusion of maps of the natural conditions as an introductory section will enhance the practical significance of the atlas in working out measures for improving land utilization, increasing crop yields, introducing systems of farming that take into account the zonal conditions of the country, improving the productivity of animal husbandry, and so forth.

Especially numerous, however, will be the integrated atlases of the individual republics and oblasts. The intensification of the work on them is due to two main causes: (a) the raising of the culture and the growth, among a broad strata of the population, of deep interest in the nature, economy, and prospects of development of their republic or oblast, (b) the new forms of economic administration on the territorial principle and of the planning of agricultural production, which open up the possibility for, and demand many-sided consideration of, the geographic conditions, the full and rational utilization of the natural wealth for the purpose of the rapid development of all the branches of the national economy and cultural construction.

The first-born in the post-War group of these atlases was the integrated "Atlas of the Belorussian SSR" (1958). Giving a diversified notion of nature, the population, economy, culture, history, and political-administrative division of the republic, it successfully combines the value of a scientific publication, a practical orientation, and interest and accessibility of the maps for the mass reader. Integrated maps are being prepared for the Ukrainian and Moldavian SSRs, the republics of Transcaucasia and Middle Asia, a number of republics and oblasts of the RSFSR: the Komi ASSR, Vologda, Irkutsk, and other oblasts, certain areas of the Kazakh SSR such as Kustanay Oblast, the Karaganda Economic Region, and for others.

Even when the integrated atlases are intended for a wide circle of readers, they have both an instructive and practical significance, and a serious scientific value. Their creation is the result of the joint labors of the scientific institutions, institutions of higher learning, and cartographic enterprises, and the collaboration of scientific and production workers. As a rule, the undertaking is not limited to the concentration and generalization of the results of earlier investigations; many maps are compiled from materials gathered by specially organized, integrated geographic expeditions.

The 18th International Geographic Congress classed the creation of national atlases, i.e., integrated atlases of individual countries, among the central tasks of modern geography and founded the Commission of National Atlases to aid this cause. At the plenary meeting of the Commission, held on 11-20 August, 1958, in Moscow, Soviet scholars pledged themselves to make a systematic survey and analysis of national atlases, to generalize the available experience, and to work out recommendations concerning the structure and content of national atlases. This work, presented to the 19th International Geographic Congress in Stockholm, may prove useful for integrated atlases in general and will serve as basic material for the subsequent elaboration of proposals for the improvement of regional atlases, particularly for the purpose of insuring their concordance and comparability along with the representation of the characteristics of the local conditions.

The creation of integrated atlases is, scientifically and practically, the most characteristic and important part of integrated map-making. Such integrated atlases are very important for planning and instituting topical and integrated investigations on a larger scale. In certain cases, an atlas can eliminate the need for preliminary field reconnaissance.

But the scales of the atlases are inadequate for the detailed study of the phenomena of nature and society, their mutual relations and interactions. When the need arises for a detailed study of the phenomena of the natural environment and social life, and geographic investigations are instituted for this purpose, the phenomena essentially acquire an integrated character. Later, in studying individual objects, the latter are viewed as parts of intricate natural or economic complexes. In such investigations, special-purpose maps on a large scale are often prepared, interrelated and supplementing each other and hence convenient for joint analysis. It is precisely these maps that insure the "single-scale" study of the individual components of a complex, and enable the geographer to express the results of his work by measure and number. A group of maps—unique "regional" atlases—are quite often compiled as a result of geographic expeditions undertaken in connection with concrete practical measures.

Such map complexes satisfy many practical demands and therefore play a big role in strengthening the ties of geography with life. However, depending upon their purpose, different investigations furnish nonhomogeneous cartographic material, usually integral within itself, but difficult to compare by individual regions. To compile complexes of maps of the territory of the whole country it is necessary to institute co-ordination of the work on special-purpose State map making.

The third path of integrated map making—the independent preparation of integrated maps—mentioned at the beginning of this article, is widely followed only in the topographic study of a locality. The general geographic maps belong to the integrated type. Integrated physical geographic and economic geographic maps which show jointly the main components of the geographic environment (waters, relief, soils, vegetation, and climate) or a wide range of economic phenomena are, in view of their complexity, in most cases compiled on the basis of "topical" maps covering a narrower list of subjects as well, and are used in conjunction [kompleks] with them.

BASIC LITERATURE

See the list of literature for Chapter 7, "Cartography," and also the following atlases:
Atlas Promyshlennosti SSSR (Atlas of industry of the USSR), 5 parts, publ. by VSNKh (Supreme Council of National Economy), Moscow, 1929-1931.

Atlas Promyshlennosti SSSR na Nachalo Vtoroy Pyatiletki (Atlas of industry of the USSR at the beginning of the second five-year plan), publ. by Vsesoyuzn. kartogr. tresta GGU NKTP, Moscow, 1934.

Atlas Moskovskoy Oblasti (Atlas of Moscow oblast). Moscow Oblast Planning Commission, Scientific-Research Institute of Economics, Moscow, 1933.

    Appendix: Atlas Moskovskoy oblasti (text), Moscow, 1934.

Atlas Leningradskoy Oblasti i Karel'skoy ASSR (Atlas of Leningrad oblast and the Karelian ASSR). Geographico-economic Scientific-Research Institute of Leningrad State University, Leningrad, 1934.

Bol'shoy Sovetskiy Atlas Mira (Great Soviet Atlas of the World), vol. I, Moscow, 1937; vol. II, Moscow, 1940.

Geograficheskiy Atlas Dlya Uchiteley Sredney SHkoly (Geographic atlas for teachers of the middle-school), Moscow, 1954, 1959.

Morskoy Atlas (Marine Atlas), vol. I, navigational-geographic, Moscow-Leningrad, 1950; vol. II, physical-geographic, M.-L., 1953; vol. III, military-historical, part. 1, M.-L., 1958.

Atlas Mira (Atlas of the World), Moscow, 1954.

Atlas Belorusskoy SSR (Atlas of the Belorussian SSR), Minsk-Moscow, 1958.

CHAPTER 28

ECONOMIC REGIONALIZATION

P. M. Alampiev

CHARACTERIZATION OF THE PROBLEM

Economic regionalization is not only one of the most urgent questions, but also one of the pivotal problems of economic geography. The economic geographic study of any country is unthinkable without an analysis of its economic regions, their characteristics, and the internal and interregional economic ties.

The essence of economic regionalization consists in a scientific determination of the system of national-economic territorial units which become constituted in a given country in the process of the territorial division of labor. Every economic region is an organic part of a country's national economy, a territorial link in it, fulfilling one or another productional function.

One of the most important region-forming factors is the *productional specialization* of a region. It determines the region's place in the general system of the country's national economy, its economic ties with other regions, with which it exchanges industrial and agricultural products. At the same time, each region has firm *intraregional economic* ties, with the development of which it becomes consolidated and thus strengthens its unity and economic integrity.

Under the conditions of capitalism, where the territorial division of labor has wide distribution, economic regions are formed spontaneously, in the process of the anarchic development of the economy. Under the conditions of a socialist society, the economy is conducted according to plan. For the first time in history this has created the possibility of placing the formative and developmental processes of regions under the control of society and of regulating these processes deliberately by a definite policy in the distribution of capital investments, the construction of production enterprises, the specialization of regions, their integrated development, and so forth.

The regulation of the processes of region formation does not mean arbitrariness or voluntarism. A planned economy is subordinated to the objective economic laws of a socialist society, and any whimsy, not reposing on these laws, is doomed to sterility. No system of regions can be created arbitrarily. Economic regionalization in a socialist society is built on a profound study of the existing economic reality and the actual distribution of production, evaluating it critically from the viewpoint of the solution of the country's next tasks. Such study determines the real possibilities and ways of further developing the economy of the various parts of the country. Regionalization is connected with the working out of scientific hypotheses of the development of each region's economy for a foreseeable future period. Not infrequently, in the course of the fulfillment of a plan, the plan proposals and intentions undergo changes under the influence of technical progress, the discovery of new natural resources, and so forth. But this does not change the significance of economic regionalization as a powerful tool for the territorial planning of the national economy.

Economic regionalization in socialist countries is based on the study of existing economic territorial units and on hypotheses or general schemes of further development. The region [*rayon*] is consequently "discovered" by science and is "constructed" by it, inasmuch as economic regionalization, under the conditions of a planned economy, is prospective in character.

The complex intertwining of territorial economic ties renders difficult the task of precisely determining the composition and boundaries of the existing economic regions, the more so because there are transitional zones whose assignment to definite regions is not easy. "Constructing" regions can be done within the framework of various general schemes of national-economic development, and it can be done according to different variants. This may give rise to controversial questions in economic regionalization, and to different variants of economic regionalization. Thus, both the first and the second foundations of economic regionalization reveal possibilities for different competing variants of regionalization.

In socialist countries, economic regionalization acquires great political and economic significance. Planned management of the national economy in the territorial cross section is very closely bound up here with the territorial structure of the organs of the state itself. Hence the necessity of *unity between economic regionalization and administrative-territorial division*. This is entirely uncharacteristic of capitalist countries, where administrative division is usually not related to economic regionalization and where it has not changed substantially in the course of many decades, or even in one or two centuries, despite radical and repeated changes in the system of economic regions during the same time. Administrative-territorial division in socialist countries and in those effecting the transition to socialism is much more mobile, which is due to the great dynamism of the economic regions owing to the great changes in the development and distribution of production, proceeding at a heretofore unparalleled rate.

Hence, too, the new relationship between science and practice in this field. By confronting economic geographic science with complex tasks fascinating in their scope and economic significance, the practice of socialist construction fructifies science and arms it with new, revolutionary ideas. In its linkage with life, economic geography receives new, enlivening sap for its development.

Territorial-productional units, on the basis of which networks of economic regions are created, differ in scale. Actually existing, for example, are such territorial economic units as the European part of the USSR and, within it, the regions of the Center or the West. Within the latter exist smaller units, subdivided in turn into still smaller component parts. A kind of "taxonomic ladder" is created, embracing economic regions of different orders. The rungs of this ladder are not always clearly delimited because there are transitional phenomena in it. In the Soviet Union there now exist the following most important and typical kinds of economic regions:

1. The smallest — *the lower rank (local) administrative-managerial regions* [*nizovyye administrativno-khozyaystvennyye rayony*]. The number of these in the USSR is over 4,000.

2. The *economic administrative regions* [*ekonomicheskiye administrativnyye rayony*], represented by the individual republics, krays, oblasts, and sometimes by small groups of oblasts. There are 103 such regions in the USSR (Fig. 9, page 218).

3. The major economic-geographic regions [*krupnyye ekonomiko-geograficheskiye rayony*], typified by Transcaucasia, Middle Asia, the Urals, the Far East, and so forth. The Soviet Union is divided into 16 major regions (Fig. 10, page 220).

Of a quite different character is the work on the economic regionalization of the capitalist countries. While under the conditions of a planned socialist economy the economic regions, as has been noted, are not only "discovered" by science, but are also "constructed" by it, economic regions which are formed spontaneously in capitalist countries can only be "discovered." This "discovery" is made by unlike methods, on the basis of different methodologies. Soviet economic geographers, as a rule, are not satisfied by the regionalization done by foreign bourgeois scholars. Hence, Soviet economic geographers studying capitalist countries make their own regionalization of these countries, proceeding from the Marxist-Leninist methodology customary in Soviet science for the economic regionalization of the countries of the capitalist world.

THE RISE AND FORMATION OF SOVIET ECONOMIC REGIONALIZATION

The need for economic regionalization of a new type, responding to the requirements of a planned economy, arose with the first steps taken by the Soviet State.

In pre-Revolutionary Russia, in the 19th and the beginning of the 20th century, many scholars (K. I. Arsen'yev, P. P. Semenov-Tyan-Shanskiy, D. I. Mendeleyev, V. P. Semenov-Tyan-Shanskiy, D. I. Rikhter, A. I. Skvortsov, and others) made experiments in natural-managerial and economic regionalization, both general and particular. They started from different methodologic standpoints, and employed diverse methods. The sphere of application of the results of this work was extremely limited; indeed, it could not be otherwise under the historical conditions of Tsarist Russia.

Of very great methodologic importance were the works of V. I. Lenin ("The Development of Capitalism in Russia," and others), which were the first to give a Marxist analysis of the formation of regions under the conditions of capitalism. From the first days of the existence of Soviet Russia a search began for new ways of solving the problem of economic regionalization in conformity with the tasks of socialist construction. This search was conducted in the center and in the provinces, in the Administrative Commission of the All-Russian Central Executive Committee, in the Supreme Council of the National Economy, in the Commission for the Electrification of Russia, in the local economic, planning, and administrative organs. In the process of this search the component elements and characteristic features of Soviet economic regionalization became outlined and its main fundamental propositions were formulated.

Since 1921, work on economic regionalization has been evolved in Gosplan [State Planning Commission], in a specially organized subcommission, headed by the well-known Soviet scholar I. G. Aleksandrov. As a result of this work, the main methodologic propositions of Soviet economic regionalization were formulated and the Gosplan project for a network of economic regions was worked out. These propositions and network of regions were examined in 1921-1922 by a special commission of the All-Union Central Executive Committee under the chairmanship of M. I. Kalinin, which formulated certain theses on economic regionalization and adopted the Gosplan project for a network of regions, introducing some corrections of its own.

The basic methodologic standpoints of the Gosplan economic regionalization of this period were the following. It distinguishes as a region [*rayon*] a distinctive, insofar as possible economically complete, but not closed part of the country, which is a link in its national economy. Regionalization is prospective in character, being organically linked with the plan for the development of the region's economy for a foreseeable period. Regionalization is built on the energy principle, meaning the best utilization of all the possibilities of the region with the smallest expenditure of forces and means. The regions are developed as major economic territorial systems tied together by a suitable division of labor. The idea of the self-sufficiency, the autarky, of the economic regions, is categorically rejected.

Gosplan regionalization proceeded from the unity of the economic regionalization and administrative-territorial division under the conditions of a country with a planned economy. Regionalization is tied to the national-political structure of the country; the rights of the national [-minority] republics and oblasts are not infringed upon and their boundaries are not disturbed. The project proposed by Gosplan provided for the complete reorganization of the administrative-territorial division of the country in application to the new economic regionalization.

The elaboration of the theoretical and practical questions of economic regionalization by the GOELRO commission and in Gosplan greatly interested V. I. Lenin, who followed this work daily and more than once made suggestions of his own. The Gosplan's work in the field of regionalization was given a positive evaluation by Lenin as being done on a genuinely scientific basis.

After repeated discussion of the Gosplan regionalization project in the center and in the provinces, it began to be carried out. In the period 1923-1929 the new regionalization was put into effect over the whole vast territory of the USSR. The territorial cross section of the first and second five-year plans was worked out on this basis.

The questions of economic regionalization again acquired great timeliness at the end of the 1930's, in connection with the working out of the third five-year plan. By that time, for a number of reasons, there had been a sharp increase in the number of oblasts and krays, and their sizes had been reduced. The territorial planning of the national economy on a countrywide scale required the division of the USSR into a small number of major, "principal" economic regions, in which it would be possible to insure the integrated development of the national economy. Such regions were singled out. In its final shape, this regionalization was cast in the form of a network of 13 groups of economic regions which, until recently, was used by the central planning organs.

In 1957, a reorganization of the administration of industry and construction was carried out in the Soviet Union on the territorial principle. Until that time, the administration of major industry and construction having nationwide significance had been effected in a centralized manner, through ministries and other government agencies. One result of the immense growth of the economy of the

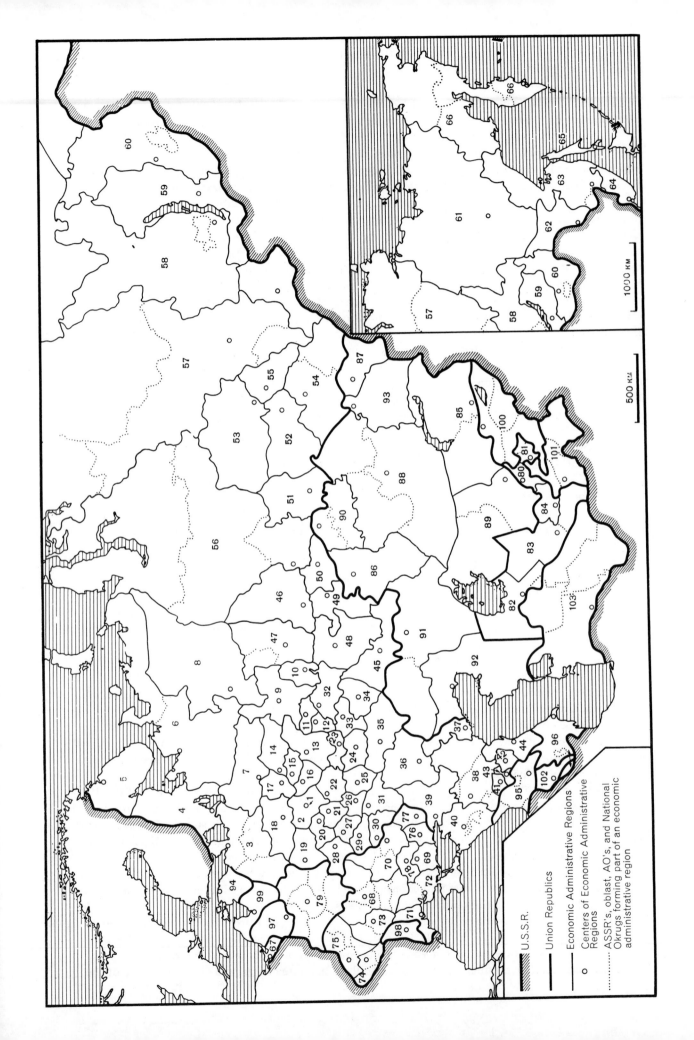

U.S.S.R.

Union Republics

Economic Administrative Regions

○ Centers of Economic Administrative Regions

.... ASSR's, oblast, AO's, and National Okrugs forming part of an economic administrative region

1000 КМ

500 КМ

Fig. 9. THE ECONOMIC ADMINISTRATIVE REGIONS [*RAYONY*] OF THE USSR
(as of 1 November, 1959)

RSRSR:
1. Moscow city 2. Moscow oblast 3. Leningrad 4. Karelia 5. Murmansk 6. Arkhangel'sk 7. Vologda 8. Komi 9. Kirov 10. Udmurt 11. Mari 12. Chuvash 13. Gor'kiy 14. Kostroma 15. Ivanovo 16. Vladimir 17. Yaroslavl' 18. Kalinin 19. Smolensk 20. Kaluga 21. Tula 22. Ryazan' 23. Mordva (Mordovskiy) 24. Penza 25. Tambov 26. Lipetsk 27. Orel (Orlovskiy) 28. Bryansk 29. Kursk 30. Belgorod 31. Voronezh 32. Tatar 33. Ul'yanov 34. Kuybyshev 35. Saratov 36. Stalingrad 37. Astrakhan' 38. Stavropol' 39. Rostov 40. Krasnodar 41. Kabardino-Balkar 42. Checheno-Ingush 43. North-Ossetian 44. Dagestan 45. Orenburg 46. Sverdlovsk 47. Perm' 48. Bashkir 49. Chelyabinsk 50. Kurgan 51. Omsk 52. Novosibirsk 53. Tomsk 54. Altay 55. Kemerovo 56. Tyumen' 57. Krasnoyarsk 58. Irkutsk 59. Buryat 60. Chita 61. Yakut 62. Amur 63. Khabarovsk 64. Maritime (Primorskiy) 65. Sakhalin (Island) 66. Magadan 67. Kaliningrad

Ukrainian SSR:
68. Kiyev 69. Zaporozh'ye 70. Khar'kov 71. Odessa 72. Kherson 73. Vinnitsa 74. Stanislav 75. L'vov 76. Stalino (Stalinskiy) 77. Lugansk 78. Dnepropetrovsk

Belorussian SSR:
79. Belorussian

Uzbek SSR:
80. Tashkent 81. Fergana 82. Kara-Kalpak 83. Bukhara 84. Samarkand

Kazakh SSR:
85. Alma-Ata 86. Kustanay 87. Eastern Kazakhstan 88. Karaganda 89. Southern Kazakhstan 90. Northern Kazakhstan 91. Aktyubinsk 92. Gur'yev 93. Semipalatinsk

Estonian SSR: 94. Estonian
Georgian SSR: 95. Georgian
Azerbaydzhan SSR: 96. Azerbaydzhan
Lithuanian SSR: 97. Lithuanian
Moldavian SSR: 98. Moldavian
Latvian SSR: 99. Latvian
Kirgiz SSR: 100. Kirgiz
Tadzhik SSR: 101. Tadzhik
Armenian SSR: 102. Armenian
Turkmen SSR: 103. Turkmen

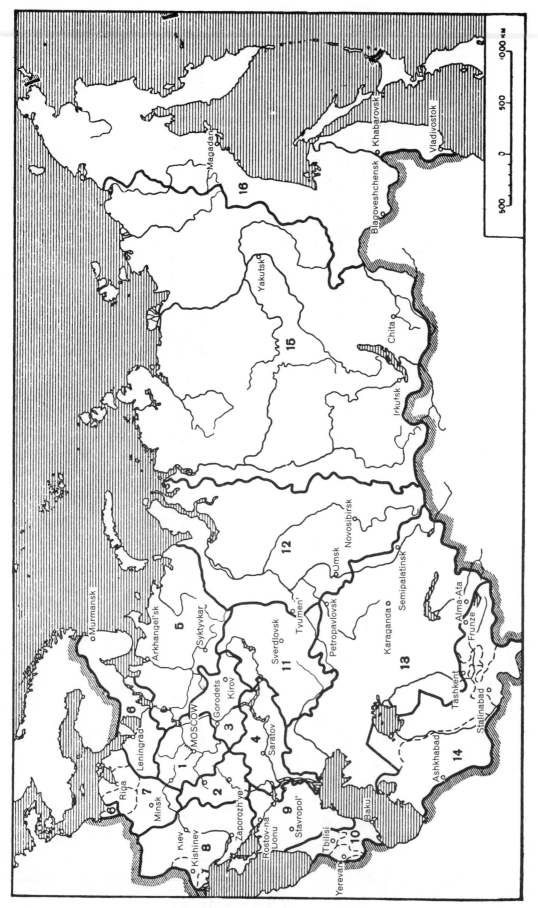

Fig. 10. MAJOR ECONOMIC GEOGRAPHIC REGIONS [*RAYONY*] OF THE USSR

1. Central 2. Central Chernozem (Black-Earth) 3. Volga-Vyatka 4. Volga (Povolzhskiy) 5. Northern 6. Northwestern 7. Western 8. Southern 9. North Caucasian
10. Transcaucasian 11. Urals 12. West Siberian 13. Kazakhstan 14. Middle Asiatic 15. East Siberian 16. Far Eastern.

USSR in the postwar period was that such an organization of administration had ceased to respond to the requirements of life. In the territorial cross section, non-correlations began to appear in the development of individual branches, and there were disproportions between them; the local resources and potentials in the economic regions were not being sufficiently exploited. Under the new conditions, the centralized administration by branches was not sufficiently flexible and operative, and did not promote the full manifestation of local initiative, the participation of the broad masses in the management and planning of the economy.

The reform carried out in 1957 in the administration of industry and the construction and the creation of the National-Economy Councils [*Sovety Narodnogo Khozyaystva*] in application to the economic administrative regions again attracted the attention of the public in the USSR to questions of economic regionalization. In this connection, work in the regionalization field was stimulated both in the planning organs and in the scientific-research bodies. The elaboration of the seven-year plan of national-economic development for 1959-1965 and the preparation for drawing up the plan for the period reaching to 1975 stimulated work on the general economic regionalization of the country, i.e., its division into major (main) economic regions. These applied to the new conditions of the period of evolved construction of communism.

The history of economic regionalization in the Soviet Union shows that the theory and practice of regionalization are developing in dependence upon the economic and political conditions of the country. Each new stage in the development of the USSR has brought forth new forms of economic regionalization. Economic geography has, each time, been confronted with new tasks, requiring further development of the methodology of economic regionalization and participation in the elaboration of practical measures for the improvement of the economic regionalization and the administrative-territorial division of the USSR.

MAIN SCIENTIFIC TRENDS, METHODS OF INVESTIGATION, AND CHARACTERIZATION OF THE RESULTS

Scientific elaboration of the questions of economic regionalization of the Soviet Union has, from the very beginning, been very closely connected with national-economic planning and the territorial organization of the state apparatus. These close ties with life have promoted the consolidation of economic geographers and the unity of their ideas in regionalization questions. All Soviet economic geographers proceed in their work from the unanimous recognition of the basic principles of economic regionalization worked out by Gosplan and the commission of the All-Union Central Executive Committee under the chairmanship of M. I. Kalinin and the subsequent resolutions of the Communist Party on economic-regionalization questions.

In applying these main fundamental propositions to concrete questions of regionalization of the USSR various opinions and controversial questions arise, about which discussions are held among the individual scientific workers. Not one of the disagreements, however, has reached such proportions as would involve the formation of any clearly pronounced scientific trends having definite platforms of principles diverging from one another.

Among the questions about which discussions are going on among Soviet economic geographers may be mentioned, for example, the following: the significance and interrelationship of the specialization of regions and their integrated development in working out a network of major economic regions; the scales of the major (main) economic regions; the interrelationship of the general and branch (particularly agricultural) regionalization, the specific boundaries of individual regions, particularly the regions of the Center, the Volgaland, the Urals, and others. The principal question is that of the sizes of the major (main) economic regions.

There have been proposals to increase the number of major regions to 28 or 29, proceeding from the proposition that the rapid growth of the economy of the USSR causes the formation of new regions on the newly won territories and a differentiation of the regions in the old, long since won parts of the country. The adherents of the other solution have proposed that the number of regions be reduced to 9 or 10, motivated by the fact that, in the course of the economic development of the USSR, the region-forming role of the major bases of heavy industry is growing, particularly that of the metallurgic and oil industries. Around these bases, more extensive and powerful regions are becoming consolidated than was the case fifteen to twenty years ago. Hence the proposals to regard as main economic regions such economic units as all Siberia, Kazakhstan together with Middle Asia, the Urals together with the Volgaland, and the European North together with the Northwest. Both these proposals are grounded in the objective processes taking place in the national economy of the USSR. Unquestionably, there exist both the tendency toward the formation of new, smaller regions and the opposite tendency toward the merging of regions into larger ones.

One of the ways of taking these tendencies most correctly into account is the proposal to distinguish, in addition to the major (principal) [krupnyye (osnovnyye)] regions, also very large [krupneyshiye] "zones" representing the most complete (but not closed) territorial-economic units capable of developing within their limits an almost full complex of machine manufactures and of having their own powerful metallurgic, energy, chemical, and production bases. Three such "zones" are distinguished: Western, Middle, and Eastern. It should be noted that the formation of such "zones" is not in the same stage of development in the different parts of the USSR; the Eastern "zone," for example, is distinguished as a "prospective" one.

Work on economic regionalization in the USSR is being carried on in the USSR Gosplan's Council for the Study and Distribution of Productive Forces, in the USSR Gosplan's Economic Scientific-Research Institute, in which there is an economic-regionalization sector, and in many other scientific-research institutes and institutions of higher learning in Moscow (the Institute of Geography of the Academy of Sciences of the USSR, the Institute of Economics of the Academy of Sciences of the USSR, the Moscow State University, the Central Economic Scientific-Research Institute under the RSFSR Gosplan, and others). Many scientific workers in the provinces are working on the theoretical and practical problems of economic regionalization: in Leningrad, Alma-Ata, Tashkent, Orenburg, Riga, Odessa, and other places. The nationwide discussion of the theses of N. S. Khrushchev's report on the remodeling of the administration of industry and construction has involved hundreds and thousands of Soviet citizens in a discussion of economic-regionalization questions.

The methods of the work being done on economic regionalization are determined by the peculiarities of the tasks confronting the regionalization of the Soviet Union. The main kinds of economic regionalization of the USSR have now become established and have been vindicated in practice: the lower-rank administrative-managerial, the economic administrative, and the general. It is now not a matter of complete replacement of the whole system of economic regions and administrative-territorial division, but of improving this system, of introducing into it the changes deriving from the new requirements. Hence there is no need to build everything anew, proceeding from a definite statistical basis and other materials.

The scientific-research work in the field of economic regionalization of the USSR is directed above all toward a critical evaluation of the existing network of economic regions and administrative-territorial units, toward the determination of the weak spots in this system, and a search for ways of improving it, proceeding from the new conditions of the country's economic development at present and for the foreseeable prospective period. This has required an investigation of the real economic ties within and between the regions on the basis of transportation statistics and other sources, the analysis of the structure of industrial and agricultural production on the basis of the current statistics, and the study of existing hypotheses concerning the development of individual branches, industrial nodes, major construction projects, and other materials necessary for the most general idea of the ways to develop the regions and economic ties for the prospective period. The statistical materials are being selected and worked up and cartographic work is being done with a view to the solution of definite tasks, trips are being made to the provinces, discussions are being held in the circle of specialists, and so forth. A most important component of this work is the study of the practical experience in regionalization and the thorough elaboration of individual methodological problems.

As a result of the work on regionalization of the USSR, practical proposals are being advanced for the improvement of the system of economic regions. These materials are being submitted to Gosplan and published in newspapers, journals, and books. They play a substantial role in the solution by the state organs of questions relating to economic regionalization.

Inseparably connected with economic regionalization are the integrated investigations of the major economic regions and the elaboration of hypotheses for the further development of their economy for the long prospect. Of the greatest scientific and practical significance among work of this sort are the investigations of a number of the eastern regions of the USSR, made by the Institute of Economics of the Academy of Sciences of the USSR. Interesting work of this sort has been done by the Academy of Sciences of the Uzbek SSR and other scientific institutions of Middle Asia in the study of the Fergana Valley region.

In the economic regionalization of the capitalist countries, Soviet economic geographers are guided by the methodology employed by V. I. Lenin in his works "The Development of Capitalism in Russia," "New Data on the Laws of the Development of Capitalism in Farming," and others. This means that economic regions are distinguished on the basis of territorial differences in the level, character, and characteristics of the development of capitalism. Differences in production specialization, so important for the "discovery" of a region, are viewed in close relationship with the character of the social relations. Relying on this methodology, Soviet economic geographers have drawn up schemes of economic regionalization for many capitalist countries. These schemes have no small educational and scientific significance.

PROSPECTS

At present, elaboration of the methodologic questions of economic regionalization and assistance to the Soviet State in improving the network of economic administrative regions, districts [*kraya*] and areas [*oblasti*] stands out as one of the chief tasks requiring considerable efforts on the part of economic geographers. The substantial defects in this matter have already been pointed out in the Soviet press, and life itself is placing this problem on the order of the day.

In the last few years, economic geographers have furnished a number of works on questions of intra-oblast economic regionalization, which is of great significance for differentiated planning within individual parts of the oblasts, krays, and republics in accordance with their internal economic and natural differences. In the prospective future, this work must be completed by the creation of the methodologic foundations of intra-oblast regionalization and the elaboration of its methods.

For a long time, economic geographers have paid little attention to the lower-rank administrative-managerial regionalization of the USSR; almost no works on this question have appeared. Yet the scientific elaboration of the methodologic and methodical questions of lower-rank administrative-managerial regionalization and practical proposals for the improvement of the network of lower-rank regions is a very important matter for the state. This question is also of great significance for economic geography as a science, since it cannot dispense with a profound study of the basic cells of which the economic regions of higher order are composed.

Questions concerning the economic regionalization of the USSR can be worked out only in direct relation to the assignments of Soviet planning and administrative organs. The great work contemplated by the geographic scientific-research bodies in the field of the creation of the "Great Geography of the USSR" is unthinkable without a thorough elaboration of the questions of economic regionalization at all levels.

BASIC LITERATURE

See also the literature to Chapter 5, "Economic Geography" and Chapter 29 "Investigations into the Integrated Development of the Productive Forces of the Economic Regions of the USSR."

Khrushchev, N. S. "On the Further Improvement of the Organization of the Administration of Industry and Construction." Report to the 7th session of the Supreme Soviet of the USSR, Moscow, 1957.

Alampiyev, P. M. Economic Regionalization of the USSR *(Ekonomicheskoye Rayonirovaniye SSSR)*, Gosplanizdat, Moscow, 1959.

Alampiyev, P. M. "Questions of the Economic Regionalization of the USSR in the Present Stage." In collection of articles (Sbornik) *Voprosy Planirovaniya i Razmeshcheniya Promyshlennosti*, Gosplanizdat, Moscow, 1959.

Alampiyev, P. M. "On the Tendencies in the Development of Major Economic-Geographic Regions," *Izv. AN SSSR, seriya geogr.*, 1959, No. 3.

Aleksandrov, I. G. Fundamentals of Economic Regionalization of the USSR *(Osnovy Khozyaystvennogo Rayonirovaniya SSSR)*, Moscow, 1924.

Belousov, I. I. "On the Project of Economic Regionalization of the USSR drafted by N. N. Kolosovskiy," *Voprosy geografii*, no. 41, Moscow, 1957.

Val'skaya, B. A. "A Review of the Regionalization of Russia from the End of the 18th Century down to 1861," *Voprosy geografii*, no. 17, Moscow, 1950.

Voprosy Ekonomicheskogo Rayonirovaniya SSSR (Questions of economic regionalization of the USSR), Collection of materials and articles (1917-1929) under the general editorship of G. M. Krzhizhanovskiy, Moscow, 1957.

Kolosovskiy, N. N. Fundamentals of Economic Regionalization *(Osnovy Ekonomicheskogo Rayonirovaniya)*, Gospolitizdat, Moscow, 1958.

Komar, I. V. "On the Major Economic Geographic Regions of the USSR," *Izv. AN SSSR, seriya geogr.*, 1959, No. 3.

Konstantinov, O. A. "Soviet Regionalization on the Fortieth Anniversary of the Great October Socialist Revolution," *Izv. VGO*, 1957, no. 5.

Konstantinov, O. A. "Economic Geographic Investigations into Economic Regionalization in the USSR," *Izv. VGO*, 1959, no. 6.

Rayonirovaniye SSSR (Regionalization of the USSR), Collection of articles (Sbornik) under the editorship of K. D. Yegorov, Moscow-Leningrad, 1926.

Saushkin, Yu. G. "Problems of Economic Geographic Regionalization of the USSR," *Vestn. MGU* (Moscow State Univ.), *seriya biologii, pochvovedeniya, geologii, geografii*, 1958, no. 3.

CHAPTER 29

INVESTIGATIONS INTO THE INTEGRATED DEVELOPMENT OF THE PRODUCTIVE FORCES OF THE ECONOMIC REGIONS OF THE USSR

Yu. G. Saushkin

The problems of the integrated development of the productive forces of the country's economic regions are inseparable from the prospective planning of the entire national economy. The prospective planning of a country's national economy was first begun in the USSR, where a plan for the development of the entire economy of Soviet Russia on the basis of electrification, known by the name of GOELRO plan (Plan Gosudarstvennoy Komissii po Elektrifikatsii Rossii, the plan of the State Commission on the Electrification of Russia), was drawn up back in 1920. In connection with the drafting of this plan and its execution, questions were posed for the first time concerning the prospective economic regionalization of the country for the planning and management of the economy, and the integrated development of the productive forces of the economic regions. Thus, the problems of this integrated development were first posed and solved in the Soviet Union, and only later also in other countries, principally the socialist ones.

The integrated development of the productive forces of the economic regions of the USSR sets as its task the best, fullest and most economical utilization of the natural resources and natural conditions, the labor resources (taking into account the labor skills and traditions of the population), and the material-technical values created at an earlier date. Integrated development of the productive forces of all the country's regions results in the highest general productivity of national labor. In the integrated development of each region's productive forces, one distinguishes the chief kinds of economic activity providing its nationwide specialization. The integrated development of a region's economy does not make the region closed and self-sufficient; on the contrary, it contributes to the intensification of the region's specialization, its development as a link in the country's national economy, and as one of the participants in the nationwide territorial division of labor, as expressed in the interregional economic ties. Integrated development of a region's productive forces does not mean that all the productive forces, all the branches of the economy, develop equally. Integrated development of a region is expressed in the fact that the *chief* productive forces, for the development of which all the others having local significance are united, are moved into the foreground.

After the October Revolution, when big industry, and particularly the capitalistic trusts, was nationalized, the complex problem of the organization of Russia's nationalized industry had to be solved. In the first years after the revolution, the system of trusts built on the branch principle was preserved. Furthermore, the young Soviet state supplemented the nationalized trusts with individual enterprises of the same branch of industry and united in the manner of these trusts those enterprises of branches of industry which had not been made into trusts before the Revolution. This converted Soviet industry into a number of big vertical associations not connected with one another in the individual localities. By the beginning of 1920 the unsatisfactoriness of a single vertical association of industrial enterprises, isolated in the individual localities and unable to make joint use of the common resources of raw materials, fuel, power, transportation, etc., had become quite clear. It was decided to combine the vertical centralism of the trusts with horizontal co-subordination of the enterprises in economic regions, where the various branches of industry were to be fed from the same sources of local raw materials, fuel, and power and served by the same means of transportation, to rely on the labor of the population of the same points, and so forth. From the idea of a regional organization of the productive forces—an entirely new form of production organization—was born plans for the integrated development of the productive forces of a region.

At the very end of 1920, the celebrated GOELRO plan was ratified—a plan for placing the developing national economy of the Soviet land on a new, technically and economically most complete material base by means of systems of regional electric stations, with subsequent electrification of all the most important branches of the national economy. This intensified still more the practical need for a prospective economic regionalization of the country and integrated development of the economic regions which were forming around the major electric-power systems.

The GOELRO plan stated with sufficient definiteness that the significance of individual branches of the economy varies according to the *territorial combination* in which they are included, and that it is therefore necessary to study and compare territorial *systems of the economy,* not individual branches. For this reason, the GOELRO plan effected a change-over to a division of the country into a number of economic regions and to the drafting of regional plans for the development of the economy as links in a nationwide plan.

The early 1920's saw the beginning of broadly thought-out work on the scientific basis of the prospective economic regionalization of the USSR. In accordance with the Gosplan (State Planning Commission) project, twenty-one rather large economic regions were distinguished. In the formulation given by the Gosplan, an economic region is a combined production aggregate with a definite specialization on a countrywide scale, in which the individual elements have been brought into mutual relationship both by the unity of the locality and by the mutual causality of the production processes themselves, on the basis of the latest scientific and technical achievements. Thus, the very definition of economic region states the principle that the integrated development of a region's productive forces must be on the basis of applying positively the latest science and technology.

Work on the country's economic regionalization in the 1920's was carried on not only in the center, but also in the provinces. Regionalization "from below," which was combined with the Gosplan regionalization conducted "from above," led to the creation, in the provinces, of a considerable number of projects in which the problems of integrated development of the productive forces of individual economic regions were posed and resolved.

In connection with the drafting and execution of the five-year plans for the development of the national economy of the Soviet Union, the Academy of Sciences of the USSR (the Committee on the Study of the Natural Productive Forces, later converted into the Council on the Study of Productive Forces) organized a number of large integrated expeditions to the eastern regions of the country. The task of these expeditions was the investigation of the natural resources, population, and economy for the integrated development of the region. An immense amount of material was collected by the Yakut, Buryat, Kazakhstan, and other expeditions. The achievements of these expeditions were very considerable, but they also had a substantial shortcoming. In a number of cases the expeditions amounted only to interesting investigations of a particular character, and did not reveal the relationship between phenomena, a knowledge of which is so important for planning prospective economic complexes. No proper attention was paid to this relationship, and it remained outside the field of vision of individual narrow specialists. This shortcoming was more or less successfully overcome at the big conferences on the development of the productive forces of the republics and major economic regions, which were repeatedly organized during the first and second five-year plans. Such were the conferences on the development of the productive forces of Kazakhstan, the republics of Middle Asia, the Urals, Siberia, etc. The collective discussion of the problems of the integrated utilization of resources and the development of the economy by specialists in the individual elements of the natural environment and in the various branches of technology and economics has yielded good results, even in the absence, from this group, of people of broad vision who could themselves erect the intricate structure of the territorial-productional complex of an economic region or (in some cases) even groups of them. But when scholars who think in a broad geographic way have joined the group of narrow specialists, the result has, as a rule, proved magnificent.

As examples of broad scientific geographic projects for the integrated development of the productive forces of economic regions executed in prewar years one may cite the works by N. N. Kolosovskiy on the Ural-Kuznetsk Kombinat, and Academician A. Ye. Fersman on the Kola Peninsula. N. N. Kolosovskiy (1932) conceived and carried out an investigation of the prospects for the development of a group of economic regions in the Urals, Siberia, and Kazakhstan known as the

"Ural-Kuznetsk Kombinat." In this work, Kolosovskiy revealed the significance of the new form of organization of the productive forces of the Soviet Union—the form of immense regional (and interregional) production kombinats: "Thus, the spatial, regional form of our kombinats is the characteristic which is of decisive significance for us in the prospective future. By overcoming the spatial isolation of the natural resources by means of regional organization of power with its forms of electric transmission and sometimes pipelines, by creating the most favorable combinations of natural and productive forces in the shape of economic regions, and by creating within the regions the most advantageous specialized (industrial—Yu. S.) enterprises, partly situated in the immediate vicinity of each other, partly scattered among the agrarian socialist enterprises (sovkhozes and kolkhozes—Yu. S.), and united into a common regional kombinat by means of correctly organized regional transportation and power, we can achieve really unparalleled economies in production by reducing losses in power, transportation, raw materials, labor power, and equipment and by shortening the time required for production" (Kolosovskiy, 1932, pp. 7-8).

The scientific prognostication of the integrated development of the productive forces of the Ural-Kuznetsk Kombinat made by N. N. Kolosovskiy on the basis of the theoretical principles of the economic regionalization of the country proved very correct. In practice, some links of the kombinat were created earlier, others later, while some were replaced by others; but the general contour of the UKK was boldly and rationally thought out. Kolosovskiy's work is a brilliant example of the union of economic geographic and technical thought in the planning of regional kombinats (complexes) of productive forces.

A. Ye. Fersman (1941) followed a similar path in his analysis and prognostication of the integrated development of the productive forces of the Kola Peninsula, a territory considerably smaller than the Ural-Kuznetsk Kombinat, but exceptionally peculiar in its combination of many unique natural resources and its geographic position beyond the Arctic Circle. It should be especially noted that Fersman, as a result of his analysis of the mineral raw materials, discovered on the Kola Peninsula a number of potential industrial (mining-chemical) nodes. Since the mining and working of minerals were to become the leading branch of the economy of the Kola Peninsula, Fersman examines in detail the prospects for the development of the separate branches of industry, down to the technological schemes, paying chief attention to the full and integrated exploitation of the mineral raw materials. In the depth of its penetration into the natural (geochemical) territorial complexes and in the diversity of their economic and technical evaluation, Fersman's work may be regarded as exemplary. It blazes new trails in the science of the integrated development of the productive forces of economic regions.

In the postwar years, interest has again been aroused concerning the problems of integrated development of economic regions, the solution of which was, of course, greatly interfered with by the Second World War. The theoretically and practically important book by Professor N. N. Kolosovskiy (Moscow University), on "The Productional-territorial Combination (Complex) in Soviet Economic Geography" was published in 1947. This work summarizes the results of a large number of investigations and outlines means for the further development of the complexes of productive forces of economic regions. It sets forth systems of regular combinations of production processes arising around a basic process. Kolosovskiy called such systems "energo-productional cycles," having in mind that each of them has its own type of energy used in the chief production process.

Regional territorial-productional complexes represent combinations of different energo-productional cycles. Kolosovskiy distinguished 30 major regional complexes of productive forces in the USSR, showing for each of them the chief types of energy and the typical combinations of energo-productional cycles. The employment of this method of cycles enables one to see the real structure of the productional relations of the country's economic regions, the chief links of production, the main trend of economic development, related to the supplying of its missing links.

The changeover in 1957 to the management of big industry and construction in territorial cross section, by economic administrative regions, has again stimulated interest in problems of the integrated development of the productive forces of the country's regions. A number of works devoted to these problems have been appearing (Vasyutin, 1957; Bedrintsev, 1957; Shkol'nikov, 1957). Somewhat before this time and since 1957, a number of integrated expeditions have been made, including those of the geographic faculty of Moscow University: the Caspian Expedition (*Trudy* of the Caspian Expedition, 1957-1958), the East-Siberian (Kolosovskiy, 1953), the Central-Chernozem (*Voprosy geografii,* no. 32, 1953), and the East-Kazakhstan, Kustanay, Volgaland, and other expeditions. These integrated expeditions have resulted, for example, in the compilation of atlases of Kustanay and Irkutsk oblasts, characterizing nature, population, and economy in their mutual relations.

The problems of integrated development of the productive forces have begun to be examined at large conferences, not only within the framework of the economic administrative regions, but also in groups of them. Such, for example, was the conference on the development of the productive forces of Eastern Siberia in 1958, at which problems relating to the East-Siberian group of economic administrative regions were solved. It is interesting to note that even when conferences have been convoked on problems of any one economic administrative region, e.g., the Kustanay conference in 1957, and the Karaganda conference in 1958, the posing and solution of economic and technical problems at these conferences quickly went beyond the bounds of that region, because the problems of integrated development of productive forces are most suitably posed and solved within the boundaries of the major (main) economic regions of the country. The problems of integrated development of the productive forces of the main economic regions of the Soviet Union have acquired especially great significance through the enactment of the seven-year plan of USSR economic development (1959-1965). In the course of this plan, 2,000 billion rubles will be invested in the country's economy— as much as has been invested during the forty years of Soviet rule. The immense capital investments, more than 40 per cent of which will be directed toward the eastern regions of the country, demand especially great attention to the rational geographic distribution of productive forces. And its rationality is determined by the achievement of the highest productivity of nationwide labor. The integrated development of the productive forces of the major (principal) economic regions is one of the most important ways of raising the productivity of labor.

The control figures for the development of the USSR national economy for 1959-1965 provide for "the further integrated development of the economic regions on the basis of the most efficient utilization of natural resources, taking into account the need for specialization of enterprises and the improvement of cooperation and for the liquidation of irrational hauls." Integrated development of the economic regions, i.e., achievement of the highest productivity of labor in the full utilization of the resources of a region and the best mutual relationship between its enterprises, does not mean economic autarky of the region, i.e., a closed economy. On the contrary, integrated development of the regions must be accompanied by an intensification of their Unionwide specialization, the greatest development of branches of nationwide significance, the raising of the proportion of commodity production, and the strengthening of the territorial division of labor between the regions.

When we speak of the integrated development of the productive forces of the country's regions we have in mind, above all, the main economic (major economic geographic) regions—the chief units in the system of the territorial division of the labor of the Soviet Union (Saushkin and Kalashnikova, 1959). But alongside the problems of the integrated development of the productive forces of these regions there also arise other problems, interregional and intraregional. As examples of interregional integrated problems we mention the irrigation and integrated use of the drained lands of Poles'ye (the scholars of Belorussia and the Ukraine are engaged in solving this problem), the development of the economy on the reclaimed virgin lands (western Siberia and northern Kazakhstan), the the reconstruction of the Volga (the regions of the Volgaland), the maintenance of the level of the Caspian Sea (the regions of the Volgaland, Kazakhstan, Middle Asia, the North Caucasus, Transcaucasia), and so forth. Among the important inter-republic problems should be mentioned that of the integrated development of the productive forces of the Fergana Valley (Uzbekistan, Kirgizia, Tadzhikistan).

The intraregional territorial problems of the integrated development of productive forces are inseparable from those of the development of the major region as a whole; they can be posed and solved only in conjunction with them. For example, in the Central-Industrial region local problems have arisen concerning the integrated development of the region around Moscow, the winning of the Meshchera Lowland, the development of the Transvolga lumber industry, etc. The correct posing and solution of these local problems is only possible in the light of the problems of the Central-Industrial Region as a whole.

The great and diversified territory of the Soviet Union and the immense scope of construction being accomplished according to a scientifically elaborated prospective plan open up broad opportunities for the advancement and solution of a multitude of territorial problems concerned with the integrated development of the productive forces in regions of different scales. The task of Soviet science is to pose and solve a multitude of such problems, which will be not only of practical significance for the planning of the national economy, but also of great theoretical interest.

BASIC LITERATURE

Bedrintsev, K. N. Questions of the Investigation of Regional Economic Problems *(Voprosy Issledovaniya Rayonnykh Ekonomicheskikh Problem)*, Tashkent, 1957.

Vasyutin, V. F. "On the Integrated Development of Economic Regions," *Voprosy ekonomiki,* 1957, No. 4.

Kolosovskiy, N. N. The Future of the Ural-Kuznetsk Kombinat *(Budushcheye Uralo-Kuznetskogo Kombinata).* Gos. sots.-ekonom. izd-vo, Moscow-Leningrad, 1932.

Kolosovskiy, N. N. "The Productional-territorial Combination (complex) in Soviet Economic Geography," *Voprosy geografii,* no. 6, 1947. This article has been reprinted in Kolosovskiy's book: Fundamentals of Economic Regionalization *(Osnovy ekonomicheskogo rayonirovaniya),* Gospolitizdat, Moscow, 1958.

Kolosovskiy, N. N. "The East-Siberian expedition," *Vestn. MGU,* 1953, No. 12.

Kolosovskiy, N. N. "Scientific Problems of Geography," "Vestnik MGU," 1955, No. 2; *Voprosy geografii,* no. 37, 1955.

Saushkin, Yu. G., and Kalashnikova, T. M. "The Main Economic Regions of the USSR," *Voprosy geografii,* no. 47, 1959.

Trudy Prikaspiyskoy Ekspeditsii (Work of the Caspian Expedition), publ. by the Geographic Faculty of Moscow State University, 1957-1958.

Fersman, A. Ye. Minerals of the Kola Peninsula. Present state. Analysis. Prognostication. *(Poleznyye Iskopayemyye Kol'skogo Poluostrova. Sovremennoye Sostoyaniye. Analiz. Prognoz),* Izd-vo AN SSSR, Moscow-Leningrad, 1941.

Shkol'nikov, M. "Some Problems of the Development of the Angara-Yenisey Energo-industrial Complex," *Planovoye khozyaystvo,* 1957, No. 1.

CHAPTER 30

ECONOMIC GEOGRAPHIC RESEARCH ON AGRICULTURE

A. N. Rakitnikov

In pre-Revolution Russia, the most widespread type of economic geographic work dealing with questions of agricultural geography was investigation of a mainly statistical character. Such, in particular, was the material published by the *zemstva* [provincial councils], as well as by the resettlement administration. Alongside this, questions of agricultural geography were the object of attention from many naturalists and agronomists. The scientific-methodologic elaboration of questions of agricultural regionalization has evolved on the basis of statistical economic and natural-scientific research.

A socialist society imposes new and ever-increasing demands upon the scientific investigation of the distribution of agriculture. The socialization of agricultural production and its development according to the national-economic plan has made it possible and necessary to exercise deliberate control over the evolving regional characteristics of agricultural production. Not only a treatment of the existing distribution of agriculture, but also a critical evaluation of the degree of its rationality and a basis for the most suitable regional differentiation of production are demanded of the investigator. In order to solve these questions, the investigator must, in particular, proceed from a definite economic appraisal of lands. Agricultural exploitation of the natural environment is accomplished through a system of agrotechnical and reclamational actions upon this environment. Consequently, *in order to clarify the conditions of the formation of the local characteristics of agriculture, it is necessary to utilize special data on the technical and organizational forms of the existing agriculture.* But as a basis for the proposals for a more rational regional differentiation of production it is necessary to solve the questions concerning the improvement of the system of cultivation, the methods of keeping livestock, and so forth. Consideration for the characteristics of the natural environment in agricultural production is also expressed in the definite mode of formation of the territory of an agricultural enterprise. It is necessary to investigate the forms of organization of a territory, the transportation-geographic location, the characteristics of the local road network, the manifold ties of agricultural production with industry (both within and without a given region), the labor resources, and the conditions of their utilization.

Thus, only on the basis of a many-sided investigation does it become possible to make a critical evaluation of the existing distribution of agriculture (the first stage of the work) and to provide grounds for a more rational distribution of it (the second stage).

The mere possession of a method of statistical study and a knowledge of the general questions of the economics and organization of agriculture (on which investigators usually relied formerly) have clearly become insufficient for work involving the solution of the above-mentioned tasks. The procedures worked out in preceding periods for studying the natural environment likewise failed to correspond adequately to the new practical purposes. The questions of the distribution of agriculture have for the time being been relatively more fully worked out within limited sections of the territory of the country (individual administrative oblasts, krays, or still smaller territories) than on a countrywide scale.

The published maps with division of the USSR into agricultural regions are schematic. They repose on limited material or on generalized data on the regionalization of separate parts of the country, carried out at different times, and by unlike methods (Fig. 11).

The most recent period in the elaboration of questions concerning the rational distribution of agriculture is characterized by work on a nationwide scale, on a scientific basis, of the systems of

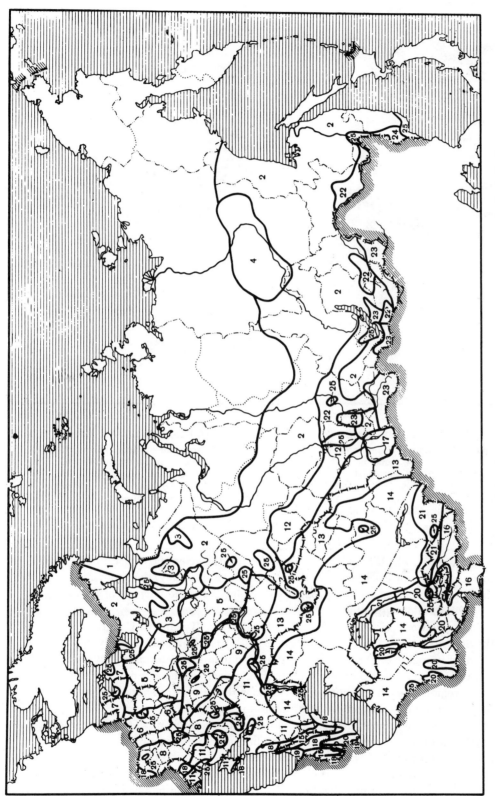

Fig. 11. REGIONS OF AGRICULTURAL SPECIALIZATION IN THE USSR (According to A. N. Rakitnikov)

1. Hunting and reindeer raising   2. Hunting and agriculture   3. Dairying and livestock raising of the North   4. Animal husbandry and farming of Yakutia   5. Flax and potato growing with strongly developed dairy cattle raising   6. Potato and grain growing, dairy cattle, and hog raising   7. Dairy cattle and hog raising with principally fodder farming   8. Sugar-beet and grain growing with strongly developed dairy and beef cattle and hog raising   9. Grain, potato, and hemp growing with developed dairy and beef cattle and hog raising   10. Grain farming and dairy and beef cattle raising   11. Grain farming with cultivation of sunflowers and other industrial plants, with developed dairy and beef cattle raising, and hog, sheep and poultry husbandry   12. Grain and dairy region of West Siberia   13. Grain region with beef and dairy cattle, and sheep raising   14. Animal grazing in the deserts and semideserts, primarily sheep raising (in the semideserts, also, beef cattle raising)   15. Mountain animal husbandry regions of the Caucasus, with dairy and beef cattle, and sheep raising   16. Mountain animal-husbandry region of the Tyan'-Shan' and Pamir-Alay, primarily sheep and beef and dairy cattle raising   17. Mountain animal-husbandry region of the Altay, with beef and dairy cattle and sheep raising   18. Fruit and nut, grape and tobacco raising   19. Subtropical perennial crops   20. Cotton growing   21. Southern intensive crops and grain farming with developed beef and dairy cattle and sheep raising   22 and 23. Grain and animal-husbandry regions and animal-husbandry and grain regions of Eastern Siberia and the Far East   24. Grain, rice-and-soy, and animal husbandry region of the Far East   25. Suburban vegetable and potato farming and dairying

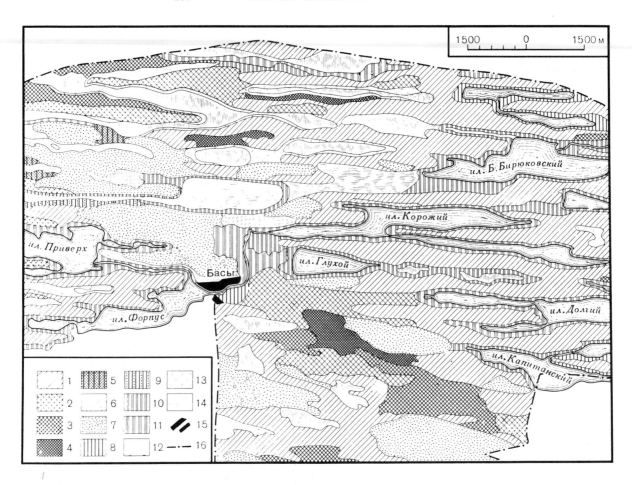

Fig. 12. PORTION OF A SOIL MAP OF THE LANDS OF THE V. I. LENIN KOLKHOZ IN LIMANSKIY RAYON

Soils: 1. Brown clayey sand 2. Brown clayey sand in combination with half leached-out salt marshes [*solontsy*], up to 25 per cent 3. Same, up to 50 per cent 4. Same, up to 75 per cent 5. Brown clayey sand in combination with meadow-gray slough [*il'men'*] soils, slightly salt-marshy 6. Brown clayey sand, poorly developed 7. Sands tied down by vegetation 8. Meadow-gray *il'men'* soils 9. Meadow dark-gray *il'men'* soils 10. Meadow *il'men'* soils 11. Meadow *il'men'* salt-marshy [*solonchakevyye*] soils 12. Swampy *il'men'* soils 13. Meadow-gray salt-marshy soils 14. Salt marshes [*Solonchaki*] 15. Populated points 16. Boundary of land use by the kolkhoz

[Translator's remark: The abbreviation " *ил.* " before the names of the numerous sloughs in Figs. 12 and 13 stands for *il'men'*, abandoned or only occasionally flooded inlets on the lower Volga.]

management in the different zones, which is being carried out by all the scientific agricultural institutions of the country. Here, fuller use is made of data on production outlay, the production cost of agricultural products in different regions, and the productivity of labor for the purpose of providing grounds for a suitable distribution of agriculture.

The tasks of the distribution of agriculture were formulated at the Twentieth Congress of the Communist Party of the Soviet Union in the following manner: "To insure an economically appropriate distribution of the individual branches of agriculture and the specialization of farming and animal husbandry by regions of the country with consideration for the natural and economic conditions of each region and, within the region, of each kolkhoz and sovkhoz, with a view to a sharp increase in yield per 100 hectares of land with a minimum expenditure of labor and funds."*

In the light of the above, it is extremely important to work out methods of scientific research which best answer the present practical requirements and to find suitable forms of co-operation and division of labor between the representatives of the various sciences.

Geographers began comparatively late to participate actively in the study of the distribution of agriculture. The overwhelming majority of investigations into the distribution of agriculture have been carried out in the agricultural scientific institutions; a substantial part, in the economic; and a small part, in the geographic institutions. While the number of monographic works of a geographic character

*Directives of the Twentieth Congress of the CPSU on the Sixth Five-year Plan for the Development of the USSR National Economy for 1956-1960. Gospolitizdat, Moscow, 1956, pp. 34-35.

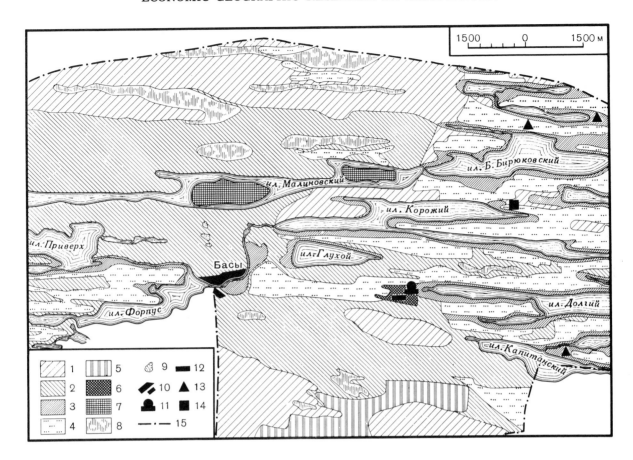

Fig. 13. PORTION OF A MAP OF ECONOMIC LAND USE IN THE V. I. LENIN KOLKHOZ
IN LIMANSKIY RAYON IN 1953

1. Desert-steppe pasture lands used in the fall-and-winter period 2. Same, used in all seasons, principally in the warm half of the year 3. Floodplain hay fields, partly used for summer grazing of livestock 4. Idle lands [*zalezhi*], used as livestock ranges 5. Desert-steppe hay fields (acres actually mown in 1953) 6. Sowings on lands with mechanical irrigation 7. Sowings on desiccated sloughs [*il'meni'*], periodically flooded 8. salt marshes [*solonchaki*] 9. Shifting sands 10. Settlements 11. Pumping stations 12. Field camps 13. Wintering places of individual flocks of sheep 14. Wintering places of individual herds 15. Boundaries of land use by the kolkhoz

is small, it should be noted that the books, which are agronomic, natural-scientific, or economic in their basic trend, have often contained a very detailed analysis of the regional characteristics of agriculture.

The final stages of the study of the distribution of agriculture—the provision of the basis for suitable systems of management in conformity with the different parts of the country, with different combinations of local conditions—should repose essentially on the work of specialists of the various sciences—natural, agronomic, technical, geographic, and economic. Landscape-geographic investigations and the economic geographic analysis of the existing agriculture should be represented as important components of this integrated [*kompleksnyy*] work.

It is characteristic that economic geographic research in agriculture in the USSR is being conducted in organizational and methodological relationship with natural-scientific (physical geographic) research.

Natural-scientific and economic studies represent two elements which are equally necessary for the solution of one common task: provision of a basis for the suitable distribution of agriculture. But the volume of economic geographic work is still inadequate even by comparison with physical geographic work and natural-scientific work in general, and only a small number of economic geographers specialize in agricultural questions.

The study of the natural environment from the agro-ecologic angle is evolving in the form of special departments of the individual physical geographic (particularly climatology) as well as agricultural, sciences. The present chapter sets forth briefly the series of questions constituting the main content of the present economic geographic investigations of agriculture in the USSR and the most important methodological procedures employed therein.

TYPES OF LAND USE

A most important procedure of economic geographic analysis is the comparison of data on the natural properties of a territory with data on the leading type of agriculture on it. The greater the differentiation with which we can show both agricultural land use and the natural types of land (soil differences, types of plant cover) with which it is associated, the greater are the results afforded by this comparison. Hence, great significance attaches to the scale-coordinated study and mapping of the natural conditions and the agriculture. At the beginning of the investigation, it is desirable to determine the localization of the individual types of land use, the association of these types with the individual natural types of land (with the outlines of soil, geobotanical, and other maps).

The actual diversity of land use can be ascertained most fully on the spot, when it is possible to employ the methods of field study. Such complete special exploration of large expanses is difficult to accomplish; hence, it has thus far most often been confined to the inspection of small typical sections of territory—the "keys." The surveys made by the land-organization organs throughout the country furnish uniform cartographic materials showing the main agricultural lands. The unified land classification adopted by the agricultural organs is naturally more schematic than that which can be applied to the individual region on the basis of a special study of it.

Tying together the data characterizing agricultural production with the outlines of the soil, geobotanical, and other maps enables one to determine with what natural types of lands the individual kinds of agricultural use are associated, and to what degree. In some cases, several substantially different natural types of lands serve for a single economic purpose; in other cases, in contrast, one and the same natural type of land is used for several entirely different purposes. By the geographic-comparison method it can be ascertained what economic conditions determine the different use of lands which are analogous in their natural properties.

A sufficiently detailed cartographic comparison of the data on land use and on the natural properties of the lands is a most important step in the critical evaluation of the existing use of the land and the ascertainment of the land reserves for one purpose or another, and for planning the most suitable use of the territory. On the other hand, such a comparison also serves as a necessary base for analyzing questions relating to the alteration of the natural landscape under the action of agricultural production, for the very classification of land types and for the performance of natural regionalization (Figs. 12 and 13).

SYSTEMS OF FARMING

It is important to establish not only the economic use to which the different natural land types are put but also the diverse modes of acting upon these lands which are actually applied in the existing economy. The system of farming is a generalized expression of all these individual actions. Ascertainment of the actual geographic diversity in the ways of tilling the land, rotating crops, fertilizing, reclaiming, etc., is of primary significance. Unfortunately, a systematic and careful description of such data is not met with very often.

Types of Organization of a Territory. The production forms of agriculture are closely related to the natural landscape. It is not only that different types of land use and different systems of farming are associated with different natural types of land. The specific internal structure of the territory within which the producing is done is adapted to the natural landscape. Several different but conjugate types of economic land utilization are usually employed on a given area. For example, the task of restoring the fertility of the soil and other motives determine the necessity of combining crop production and animal husbandry. For example, to obtain the fodders necessary for animal husbandry, one type of land (A) is especially favorable, while types B or C are favorable for the leading branches of crop production. Consequently, the territory which will prove best for the functioning of a given production type of agriculture is one consisting not only of lands of type A, but also including lands of type B or C. In reality, more complex combinations are usually encountered. Thus, the size and outline of a kolkhoz or sovkhoz tract of land, as well as the relationship between the areas occupied by the individual branches of crop production, by different fodder crops, their mutual location, and their position with respect to the farmstead of the kolkhoz or sovkhoz affect the organization of production in a most substantial manner (Figs. 14 and 15).

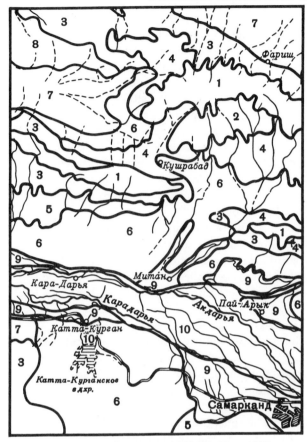

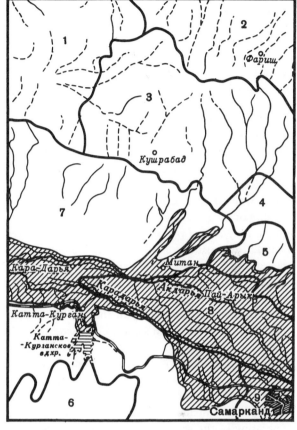

Fig. 14. [*above, left*] PORTION OF A MAP
OF THE NATURAL LANDSCAPES OF
SAMARKAND OBLAST

1. Crests and dissected slopes of mountains
2. Gentle slopes of mountains with cover of loess-like clays and loams; turf and brown-earth (cinnamon-colored) soils
3. Foothills with more or less dissected relief; soils chiefly dark gray-earths, skeletal, on rubbly eluvium
4. Foothills with loess cover, dark gray-earths, dry-farming crops
5. Piedmont plains with pebble-and-rubble, gravelly and fine-earth alluvium; typical gray-earths with gravel or with pebbles and loam
6. Piedmont loess plains, typical gray-earths; dry-farming crops on large areas
7. Desert plains, light-colored gray-earths
8. Hill and low-mountain desert expanses, light-colored gray-earths
9. Irrigated lands on well drained piedmont plains, alluvial fans and upper river terraces; typical gray-

earths, more or less altered by irrigation cultivation; in western part of territory, light-colored gray-earths
10. Irrigation lands of the Zeravshan River valley with hydromorphic soils

Fig. 15. [*above, right*] PORTION OF A MAP OF
THE EXISTING SPECIALIZATION OF
AGRICULTURE IN SAMARKAND OBLAST
(Irrigated lands are hatched)

1. Sheep (karakul) grazing with accessory farming
2. Sheep (karakul) grazing and silk growing, with accessory farming
3. Sheep (karakul) grazing and beef and dairy cattle raising, grain farming, grape and silk growing
4. Grain farming, beef and dairy cattle and sheep raising
5. Cotton growing with mixed animal husbandry and silk growing, with accessory farming
6. Sheep (karakul) grazing and grain farming
7. Cotton growing, sheep (karakul) grazing and silk growing, with accessory grain farming
8. Cotton and silk growing
9. Fruit and nut growing and sheep raising

The farms in which one and the same combination of the chief types of land use is repeated and each kind of use is tied to one and the same natural types of land can be assigned to one type of territorial organization. Here, naturally, there is also observed a similar mutual arrangement of lands and farm centers. Ascertainment of the types of territorial organization enables one to show in a generalized way the forms of land use on small-scale maps (direct recording of the individual types of land use on the maps is possible only to scales from 1:10,000 to 1:50,000).

Study of the Economic Conditions of Agriculture. The laws of the distribution of agriculture are inseparable from those of the distribution of the productive forces in general. The geographic forms of the ties between agriculture and industry are highly varied. In studying the geography of agriculture it is necessary to take into account the non-agricultural occupations of the rural population, the transport-geographic location and the characteristics of the local transportation network, the export routes, and the possibilities of processing all the most important agricultural products, as well as supplying agriculture with the means of production. To each production type of agriculture there corresponds a definite type of network of collection points and supply bases, a network of industrial enterprises processing the agricultural produce and serving agriculture, and consequently definite conditions for the formation and type of local economic centers among the agricultural territories. Hence, the study of agricultural geography is usually accompanied by a study of the network of industrial, collecting, and supplying enterprises, very closely connected with agriculture.

The supply of labor force to agriculture, the mutual relations between the size of the rural population, and the character of the agriculture which has actually become established in a given locality (as well as the character of the economy most suitable under the given natural and economic conditions) are important questions of the economic geographic study of agriculture. Consideration of them contributes, in particular, to the planned establishment of a definite agreement between the distribution of the labor resources and a distribution of agricultural production capable of insuring the highest productivity of labor. However, the redistribution of labor resources among the various regions, because of the historically changing conditions of the distribution of production, is usually not effected as quickly as these conditions change. Hence, the actually constituted geography of the rural population is always taken as one of the conditions that must be considered in solving the questions of the proper distribution of agriculture, especially in the period immediately ahead.

Study of the Geography of the Individual Branches of Agriculture. A crop or a branch of animal husbandry, taken separately, is studied in isolation by representatives of agronomic, statistical, or economic science. But geographers usually analyze the whole complex of productionally interrelated branches of agriculture and investigate the distribution of the individual branches in conjunction with this complex. Some branches create the conditions for the development of other branches; hence, ascertainment of the causes of the localization of one branch is possible only if the other branches are examined simultaneously. At the same time, the examination of the geography of the separate branches is a necessary analytical stage in the study of the history of the productional types of agriculture.

Interaction Between Agricultural Production and the Natural Environment. By this is meant the tendencies toward alteration of the natural landscape under the action of agricultural production and the successive adaptation of agriculture to the various stages of this alteration of the landscape (in part deliberately transformed, but also partly evolving in an unforeseen manner). The study of this series of phenomena requires the employment of methods of research in economic geography as well as in the natural sciences. In the Soviet literature in economic geography of the last few years this question has been the object of considerable attention. It is in principle an obligatory element in any study of the laws of agricultural distribution.

Agricultural Regions. The elementary analytical procedures of investigation corresponding to a large-scale degree of study are of very great importance in themselves and also serve as a necessary foundation for the successive discovery of the most general and principal laws of the distribution of agriculture. Work of the agricultural regionalization of the individual parts of the territory of the USSR, accomplished by geographers on the basis of field exploration and the elaboration of the statistics by the smallest territorial units — separate kolkhozes and sovkhozes — began to be published in the 1930's. There are also authors who have confined themselves principally to small-scale study on the basis of an elaboration of statistics by administrative regions.

The most essential differences in the natural and economic conditions under which agricultural production is carried on are reflected in the various functions performed by the agriculture of the various regions with respect to the whole national economy. The division of labor among the individual parts of the country whose agricultural products are necessary for the national economy is expressed both in the specialization of agriculture in the production of various products, in the unequal degree of land use for agricultural production, in different levels of intensity of agriculture.

The general, synthesizing features which are most often used in modern Soviet literature in ascertaining regional differences in agriculture are the statistical indices of specialization (the

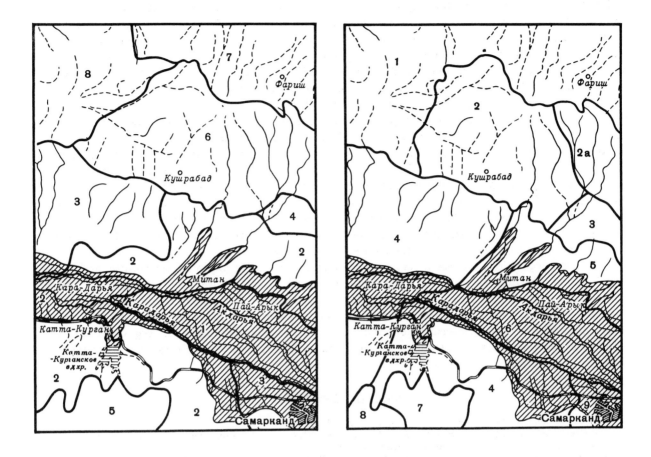

Fig. 16. [*above, left*] PORTION OF A MAP OF THE TYPES OF ORGANIZATION OF THE TERRITORY OF SAMARKAND OBLAST (Irrigated lands are hatched)

1. Farms on irrigated lands without substantial use of lands outside of oases
2. Farms using irrigated lands of the Zeravshan Oasis, and, in addition, also the dry-farmed plow lands and pasturages of the foothills and mountain slopes
3. Farms using the lands of the Zeravshan Oasis and the dry-farmed plow lands, as well as lands in the small foothills oases fed by mountain brooks and springs (to which viticulture, in particular, is confined), and pasture lands of the foothills and mountain slopes
4. Farms using dry-farmed plow lands, the irrigated lands of small oases and the adjacent foothill pasture lands
5. Farms on dry-farmed plow lands and adjacent pasture lands of undulating plains and foothills
6. Farms on pasture lands of foothills and mountain slopes, used in combination with dry-farmed plow lands and with irrigated lands of small oases (with viticulture, mulberry plantations and, in part, fodder crops)
7. Farms on a combination of pasture lands, dry-farmed plow lands and irrigated lands (in small oases), but with use of desert plains pasture lands (clayey sand, sand, and salt marsh) as well
8. Principally or almost exclusively pasturage use of foothills and mountain slopes, in combination with pasture lands of the desert zone, to which livestock is driven from great distances

Fig. 17. [*above, right*] PORTION OF A MAP OF PROSPECTIVE AGRICULTURAL REGIONS IN SAMARKAND OBLAST (Irrigated lands are hatched)

1. Sheep (karakul) grazing with accessory fodder growing   2. Beef cattle and sheep raising and grain growing
2a. Subregion with focal points of commercial grape growing   3. Grain farming and beef and dairy cattle raising
4. Cotton and silk growing and karakul raising with focal points of commercial grape growing
5. Cotton and silk growing with dairy cattle raising and focal points of commercial grape, fruit and nut growing
6. Cotton and silk growing   7. Grain farming, karakul and beef cattle raising
8. Karakul raising with accessory fodder growing   9. Fruit and nut growing and sheep raising

composition of commodity production and total production) of agriculture, as well as the level of its intensity (cost of the means of production and amount of live labor expended per unit of agricultural area or, in addition, the volume of total production per unit of area).

In classifying agricultural regions, the modern literature proceeds principally from the basic categories of commodity products, and the regions are designated by corresponding names (Figs. 16

and 17). Within territories performing similar functions with respect to the national economy, however, there may be differences in natural and economic conditions which cause essentially different solutions of production problems, and therefore are of great significance for agricultural practice. Hence, within territories with a similar agricultural structure (specialization) it is often advisable to distinguish smaller parts — subregions with essentially different local conditions and therefore different solutions for the problems of production organization, though with homogeneous specialization.

For the purposes of planning agriculture in the USSR, the territory of the country is divided into natural (or physical geographic) regions as well as into agricultural regions. Physical geographic regionalization is one of the foundations of agricultural regionalization. The ascertainment and classification of agricultural regions are, of course, impossible without studying the most important conditions upon which the regional differences in agriculture depend. On the other hand, the data of agricultural geography are needed in physical geographic research and physical geographic regionalization. The differences in agricultural land use, in the level of crop yields, and so forth, enable one to see the economic significance of specific differences in the natural environment. At the same time, the systems of classification of the territorial units of physical geographic and agricultural regionalization cannot coincide, since their criteria are different.

Economic conditions exercise a very strong influence on the geography of agriculture, and therefore one may observe great variations in the character of agriculture under analogous or very similar natural conditions. These two kinds of regionalization are not identical; they cannot replace one another. Each of them has its own sphere of practical application. For example, in choosing agro-technical and reclamational measures, one naturally turns to physical geographic regionalization, while in working out questions of production organization one turns to agricultural regionalization (Figs. 13, 15, and 16).

BASIC LITERATURE

Voyeykov, A. I. Selected Works (Izbrannyye Sochineniya), vol. IV, Moscow, 1957.

Voprosy Razmeshcheniya i Spetsializatsii Sel'skogo Khozyaystva (Questions of the distribution and specialization of agriculture), sbornik (collection of articles), Moscow, 1957.

Zamkov, O. K. "The Floodplain as an Element of Agricultural Territory," Nauchnyye doklady vysshey shkoly. Seriya geologo-geograficheskikh nauk, 1958, no. 2.

Karnaukhova, Ye. S. The Distribution of Agriculture in Russia in the Period of Capitalism (1860-1914), Razmeshcheniye Sel'skogo Khozyaystva Rossii v Period Kapitalizma (1860-1914 gg.), Moscow, 1951.

Kazanskiy, N. N. "The Agricultural Conquest of the Middle Angara Region in connection with the Building of the Bratsk Hydroelectric Station," Izvestiya AN SSSR, seriya geograf., 1957, No. 3.

Krylov, N. V. "Concerning the Theory and Practice of Integrated Geographic Investigations for Agriculture," Izvestiya Vsesoyuznogo geograficheskogo obsch., vol. 87, 1955, No. 1, pp. 3-10.

Kryuchkov, V. G. "Questions of the Agricultural Use of Lands in the Volga Delta in connection with Hydro-construction," Vestnik Mosk. Gos. Univ., 1957, No. 2.

Mukomel', I. F. "Agricultural Zones of the Ukrainian SSR. Part 1. Laws of the Development and Methods of Economic-Geographic Investigation of Agricultural Zones" (Sel'skokhozyaystvennyye zony USSR. Chast' 1), Kiyev, 1954.

Obukhov, V. M. Crop Yield and Meteorologic Factors (Urozhaynost' i Meteorologicheskiye Faktory), Moscow, 1949.

O Sisteme Vedeniya Sel'skogo Khozyaystva v Novosibirskoy Oblasti (On the system of agricultural management in Novosibirsk oblast), Novosibirsk, 1958.

Osobennosti Sel'skogo Khozyaystva Adayevskogo Uyezda (Characteristics of the Agriculture of Adayevskiy Uyezd). Otchet o rabotakh pochvenno-botanicheskogo otryada Kazakhstanskoy ekspeditsii Akademii nauk SSSR, issue VI, Leningrad, 1928.

Prirodnyye Usloviya Severo-zapadnogo Kavkaza i Puti Ratsional'nogo Ispol'zovaniya ikh v Sel'skokhozyaystvennom Proizvodstve (The natural conditions of the Northwestern Caucasus and ways of making rational use of them in agricultural production), part I, Moscow-Leningrad, 1950.

Rakitnikov, A. N., and Solovtsova, T. A. "The Yergeni and the Caspian Lowland," Uchenyye zapiski Moskov. Gos. Univ., no. 160, 1952.

Rakitnikov, A. N. "Questions of the Regionalization of Agriculture in the USSR," Voprosy geografii, no. 49, Moscow, 1959.

Saushkin, Yu. G. Geographic Essays on Nature and Agricultural Activity of the Population in the various Regions of the Soviet Union (Geograficheskiye Ocherki Prirody i Sel'skokhozyaystvennoy Deyatel'nosti Naseleniya v razlichnykh Rayonakh Sovetskogo Soyuza), Moscow, 1947.

Strumilin, S. G. "Results of the Natural-historical Regionalization of the USSR." In the book Yestestvenno-istoricheskoye rayonirovaniye SSSR, Moscow, 1947.

Trudy Prikaspiyskoy Ekspeditsii. Ekonomicheskaya Geografiya Zapadnoy Chasti Prikaspiyskoy Nizmennosti (Work of the Caspian Expedition. Economic geography of the western part of the Caspian Lowland), issues 1 and 2, Moscow, 1957.

Ural'skiy Okrug i yego Rayony (The Ural District and its regions), issues I-VIII, Ural'sk, 1929.

CHAPTER 31

PROBLEMS OF TRANSPORTATION GEOGRAPHY

I. I. Belousov

The important role of transportation in the development of the Soviet land is due to the enormous size of its territory, the economic conquest of which requires mass hauling of goods and passengers over great distances. This task is solved through improved transportation, insuring cheaper hauling and bringing remote regions economically closer to one another. V. I. Lenin emphasized that railroads "are one of the manifestations of the most salient ties between town and country, between industry and farming, on which socialism is wholly founded."*

The Communist Party and the Soviet Government have constantly devoted especial attention to the rationalization of economic ties and the transportation of commodities and materials. The geography of transportation has evolved in this country under the influence of the practice of socialist construction, and has helped to solve important national-economic tasks. Being one of the departments of economic geography, it studies in the territorial aspect of transportation, analyzing interregional and intraregional ties and the freight and passenger flows relating thereto, as well as investigating the transportation network, consisting of lines for different kinds of transportation, transportation nodes, technical means of transportation, and storage facilities.

In works relating to the initial period of the formation of Soviet transportation geography, main attention was devoted to the study of the network of ways of communication and the flows of freight and passengers passing over them (Bernshteyn-Kogan, 1930). But, because of the change-over from the principle of centralized departmental planning and administration of industry and construction to the principle of territorial management by economic administrative regions, the investigation of inter-regional and intraregional ties are acquiring special significance.

Transportation geography is closely connected with topical economics, technology, and statistics, from which it receives many data, but makes its generalizations and draws its conclusions by methods peculiar to geographic science, making wide use of mapping in recording the phenomena studied.

ECONOMIC REGIONALIZATION AND TRANSPORTATION

There are two aspects to this problem: first, ascertainment of the role of transportation in the formation of economic regions and, second, the regionalization of transportation itself.

Transportation substantially affects the formation and development of economic regions, not directly, but through the geographic division of labor. The latter evolves only under the condition that the economy of labor from its division exceeds the expenditure for additional hauls.

The specialization of regions presupposes an exchange of the necessary quantities of specific products between them. The distribution and exchange of commodity and material values govern the geography of interregional and intraregional ties, which are effected through the means of transportation.

Between the development of economic regions and transportation there exists a two-sided dependence, which may be represented in the form of the successive mutual relationship: transportation of freight ➤ distribution and exchange of commodity and material values ➤ specialization of regions and geographic division of labor ➤ formation and development of economic regions.

---

*V. I. Lenin, *Works,* vol. 27, p. 277.

Different notions exist with respect to the regionalization of transportation itself. Some think that the specific characteristics of transportation furnish grounds for distinguishing special transportational-economic regions differing from the general economic regions (Nikol'skiy, 1958). Others, in analyzing transportation, use the general economic regions and do not distinguish special transportational-economic regions (Khachaturov, 1939; Khanukov, 1955).

REGIONALIZATION OF TRANSPORTATION AND INTERREGIONAL TIES

The interregional ties which become established in the process of the economic life of a country represent a complex intertwining of relations between economic regions with respect to different kinds of raw materials, fuels, semimanufactures, and finished products. In order to use the results of an analysis of the ties and hauls for the distribution of the productive forces, for the planning of the distribution and hauling of commodity and material values, and for the development of an integrated [kompleksnyy] transportation network, it is important to exclude the non-essential, incidental ties and distinguish the basic, permanent ones. To do this it is necessary, in addition to the economic regions established by productional features, to define sales zones or zones of distribution of commodity and material values. The elements of the sales zone are: the base, that is, the region or center of production from which the supplies come, and the areas of demand. The interregional wheat sales zones are given as an example (Fig. 18, page 242).

The geography of the raw-material, fuel, and other bases of different products does not coincide, nor do the areas of demand, i.e., the boundaries of the zones of sales or distribution of different products. They often differ with respect to different types of one and the same product, and often vary for different years.

Unlike economic regions, whose boundaries are stable for a long time, distribution zones are established by individual products, their types, grades, and sizes for short periods, determined by market conditions; hence their boundaries are distinguished by great mobility. The sales zones are at the same time zones of transfer of individual products. The economic regions are basic, while the distribution zones or transfer zones are derived from them. But they in turn substantially affect the composition of the territories, the boundaries, and the structure of the economy of the economic regions. However, the multiplicity and mobility of the transfer zones do not enable one to construct a network of economic regions by regionalizing distribution and transfer, using the transport gravitation of the various territories as the point of departure. On the contrary, rational transfer (or sales) zones can be established only on the basis of a network of economic regions by compiling regional balances of production and consumption by individual products, their types and grades for each region. Regions with a deficit of a given product — the areas of demand — are attached in rational flows to the regions with a surplus — the bases —, thus defining rational interregional ties and boundaries of zones for each kind of freight.

In establishing rational sales zones, i.e., rational interregional and intraregional ties, it is necessary that the supplies come from the nearest raw-material, fuel, and other bases, and only in case of a lack of resources in them is it permissible to attach regions of consumption to the next nearest base. Likewise, it is advisable to export surpluses of products to more distant regions only after providing for the needs of the nearest regions. In cases of necessity, the efficiency of transferring a given product in "competing" directions should be compared in forming a rational sales zone, since this may change the interregional ties, i.e., the boundaries of the sales zone. Finally, it is necessary to take into account the capacity of the individual lines of transportation. This factor may prove decisive in analyzing the actual interregional ties and sales zones and for planning them for the period immediately ahead.

In establishing regional zones, use is made of the method of finding the point of equal cost, i.e., determining the dividing-line point to which it is advisable to haul the same kind of freight from different bases. This equal cost should be composed of the cost of production at different bases, as well as the cost of delivery from each base to the dividing-line point. The equal-cost method is used to fix the boundaries of the sales zone, beginning with estimates per ton of product. The total requirements of such a zone, however, may not coincide with the volume of production of a given product at the attached base. Furthermore, the cost is not the only index of national-economic efficiency. Hence, the equal-cost method serves only as an auxiliary procedure in planning zones of distribution and transfer.

The balances of production and consumption by regions, needed for regionalization of sales and transportation, may be replaced by transportation-economy balances of imports and exports; these two balances coincide. The volume of imports and exports analyzed in the transportation balance is taken from the statistical reports on transfers as the sum of all kinds of transportation.

ANALYSIS OF INTERREGIONAL TIES

The study of interregional ties is necessary for a characterization of the geographic division of labor — the specialization of the regions — and for determining the place of each region in the country's economy and its interaction with the other economic regions.

The plans for the development of the national economy of the USSR, beginning with the first five-year plan, have devoted much attention to the rationalization of interregional relations. Many scientific-research and designing institutes, especially those planning the volumes and directions of hauls, concern themselves with these same questions.

In analyzing interregional ties by the methods of regionalizing sales and transportation, a comparison is made of the report data on hauls between the regions with the established rational schemes and sales zones. In so doing, one discovers cases where the actual hauls of a given kind of freight deviate from the rational scheme, ascertains the causes of the deviations, and finally determines the irrational hauls. For this work, wide use is made of the cartographic method: special cartograms of interregional ties are compiled for different products; a comparison of these cartograms brings out graphically the opposite, excessively long, duplicated, and other irrational hauls. The irrational hauls are usually due to deficiencies in the geographic distribution of production, to the improper technical structure of the enterprises, and to defects in the planning of distribution, exchange, and hauls.

The opposite hauls discovered in the transportation of raw materials and the products derived from them indicate deficiencies in the distribution of production and processing. In some regions, the producing capacities are small (or non-existent) with relation to the raw-material base and the consumption of a given product. In other regions, there are capacity surpluses, so that raw materials have to be imported and manufactured products exported, often in opposite flows.

Opposite hauls of different kinds, grades, and sizes of products made of one and the same raw material reveal deficiencies in the technical structure of the enterprises and the economy of whole regions: improper specialization of production, backward technology, non-integrated use of raw materials, and overly high capacities of individual enterprises. Finally, opposite hauls of homogeneous and interchangeable products indicate deficiencies in the planning of the distribution, exchange, and transportation of commodities and material goods.

Regionalization of sales and transportation enables one to establish an objective criterion for determining the rationality of hauls. Non-rational are hauls which violate established sales zones; in particular, hauls beyond the rational zone will be excessively long.

Analysis of the interregional ties by the methods of sales and transportation regionalization enables one to establish not only the causes, but also the volume, of the irrational hauls and to plan ways of eliminating the deficiencies in the distribution of production, the technical structure of the enterprises, and the planning of distribution and transportation. This method is also applicable to the analysis of projects for the further development of production. It is necessary, however, to take into account the fact that the material-technical base of production is constantly evolving. In each individual period, in each branch and region, some sections are put into operation earlier, others later. Temporary disproportions are sometimes overcome through additional transportation work, and such incidental phenomena are inevitable under the conditions of the growth of a socialist national economy.

The investigation of interregional ties has shown that the geographic distribution of production, the technical structure of enterprises, and the distribution and transfer of commodities and material goods interact with one another. Thus, overly high capacities and improper specialization of an enterprise (i.e., defects in the technical structure) make the local raw-material base inadequate to satisfy the increased requirements of the enterprise, and the region of consumption cannot use the excess

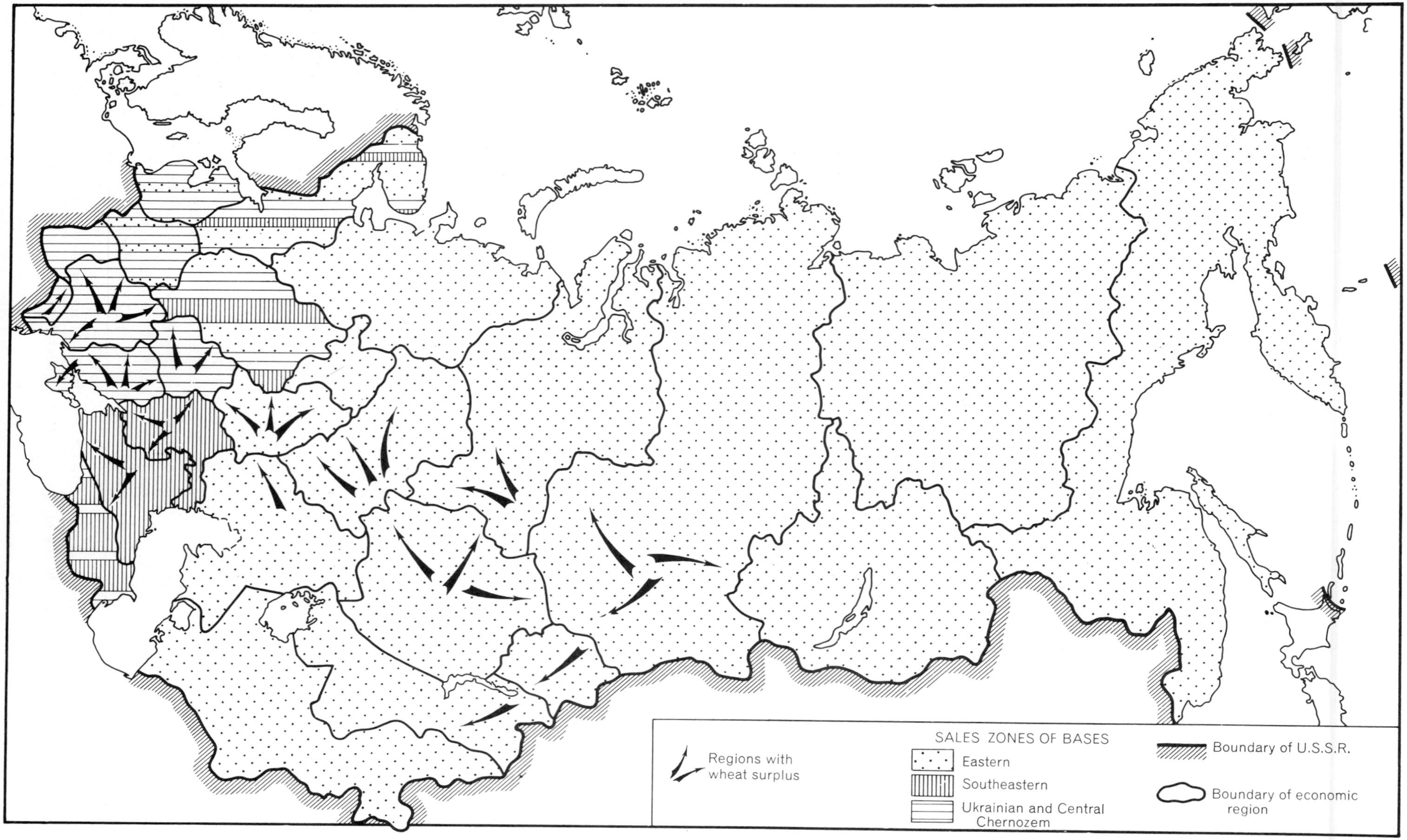

SALES ZONES OF BASES

Eastern

Southeastern

Ukrainian and Central
Chernozem

Boundary of U.S.S.R.

Boundary of economic
region

Regions with
wheat surplus

Fig. 18. ZONES OF WHEAT SALES

production. Thus, the enterprise is found to be irrationally located. The uniform disposition, over the whole country, of the production of raw materials and the products obtained therefrom (favorable geographic distribution) becomes a negative factor and complicates distribution, exchange, and transfer if the processing capacities are concentrated in a small number of excessively big enterprises. The application of a backward technology, admitting the use of only high-quality raw materials, reduces the raw-material base of an enterprise and thus impairs its location and renders distribution and transfer difficult. Deficiencies in the organization of a branch of the economy, particularly the incomplete reflection of the transportation outlays in the calculation of production costs, erroneously orient the planning and managing organs in the direction of an increase in excessive capacities and in narrow specialization of enterprises. This impairs the distribution of production and gives rise to superfluous hauls in delivering raw materials and in shipping products.

Thus, the scientific analysis of the geography of productive forces should cover not only their distribution, but also the investigation of the technical structure of the enterprises and the organization of distribution, exchange, and transfer. Such an integrated approach is very important in planning the production, transportation, and distribution of commodities and material goods. In accordance herewith, it seems advisable to strengthen the basic principle of the distribution of socialist production by including in it not only a qualitative characterization—an approximation of the sources of raw materials and fuel to the regions of consumption—but also a quantitative characterization, imposing a combination of the enterprise's productivity with the capacity of the raw-material and fuel base and with the volume of consumption in the region of demand.

FREIGHT FLOWS

An economic geographic investigation of freight and passenger flows cannot be limited to an examination of the hauls on individual trunk lines. It is necessary to characterize the geography of traffic over the entire transportation network as a whole, wherein the degree of generalization may differ with the tasks of the concrete analysis.

The employment of a single network of integrated economic regions and the regionalization of sales and transportation enable one to divide all traffic into two main groups: intraregional (short distance) and interregional (long distance).

In planning intraregional traffic, consideration is given to the tasks of the integrated development of the economy of a region, the maximum possible suitable satisfaction of the requirements by local production, and the distribution of the individual factories of the regional complex, in an effort to reduce internal hauls and make their directions conform with the interregional freight flows.

In working out a rational system of interregional hauls, one orients oneself toward the boundaries of the zones of distribution of the individual products, being guided by the prospects of a suitable interregional division of labor and the satisfaction of nationwide requirements.

The volume and directions of interregional hauls are determined by the aggregate of interregional ties, but the latter are not the same for different products, their types, grades, and sizes. Their intricate interlacement does not lend itself to generalization by a simple superimposition of one upon the other. One has to group them by community of direction from region to region, so that the main directions of the interregional freight flows and their volumes are established.

The essence of the methods of changing over from a multitude of diversely directed interregional ties to concentrated freight flows consists in determining, for each region, other regions which exchange goods in the main directions either with it or through it with each other. Then, using checkerboard tables of interregional hauls, one estimates for each direction and for each cargo the volume shipped out of the region of origin, how much has entered the next region, and how much has remained or has been added anew in it, i.e., how much altogether has passed from the second region into the third, and so forth from region to region.

Thus one obtains the freight-flow density, just as is done in determining the railroad lines from station to station. A group of scientific workers of the Institute of Integrated Transportation Problems of the Academy of Sciences of the USSR, composed of N. N. Kazanskiy, Yu. V. Lasis, T. V. Larionova, and others, has worked out a method of performing this work by rapid mechanical calculation with the aid of auxiliary tables.

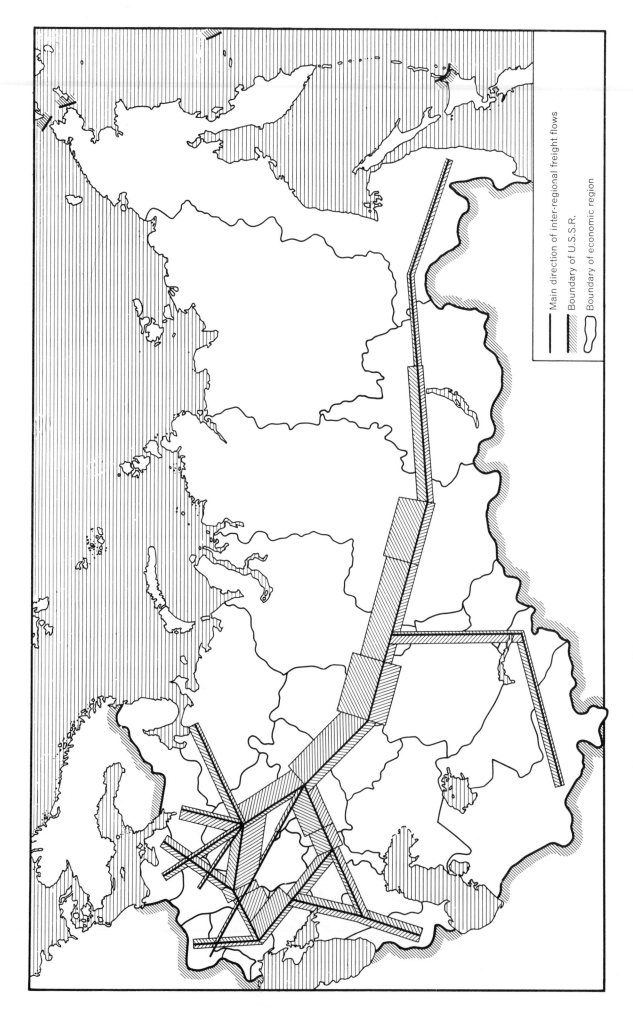

Main direction of inter-regional freight flows

Boundary of U.S.S.R.

Boundary of economic region

Fig. 19. MAIN DIRECTIONS OF INTERREGIONAL FLOWS OF MASS TYPES OF FREIGHT

Calculations made by the above methods for the main cargoes (coal, petroleum, ferrous metal, ore, lumber, and grain) furnish a summary characterization of the network hauls. The system of them is united, in the most general form, into four groups of main interregional directions of freight flows (Fig. 19). This map shows:

1. Freight flows from south to north on the railroads and partly on the Dnepr, mainly from the Ukraine, and back — from north to south;

2. Freight flows from south to north and northwest on the Volga and the railroads, mainly from the Caucasus and from the Volga-Don region, and back — from north and northwest to south;

3. Freight flows from east to west on the railroads with the use of the Kama and Volga Rivers, mainly from Siberia, Kazakhstan and the Urals, and back — from west to east;

4. Freight flows from Siberia and Kazakhstan to Middle Asia and back.

Other freight flows are inferior to these main interregional ones in volume and distance of movement.

In case of necessity (for example, for the successive distribution of the traffic of each main direction among the individual lines of the various kinds of transportation), the above-named four groups of freight flows may be differentiated and supplemented by other directions. To illustrate, two flows from Middle Siberia are distinguished in the east-west direction: via the Northern Urals and via the Southern; the freight flows from Siberia to Middle Asia are subdivided into two branches; additional freight flows from Middle Asia to the European regions are calculated; and so forth.

The proposed method insures any degree of differentiation of freight flows by directions. In order not to make an arbitrary division, however, a preliminary calculation of the interregional ties and freight flows is necessary. Only then does one pass on to the balances of production and consumption by subregions, to the intraregional ties and freight flows. Finally, adhering to the same logic of analysis, one determines the ties and freight flows between the production nodes.

TRANSPORTATION NETWORK

In the unified transportation network of the Soviet Union, the various kinds of transportation are combined in accordance with a plan and are operated in an integrated manner. Their proportional development and smooth operation are insured by the socialist ownership of the means of production and the planned management of the national economy.

Since the time of the GOELRO plan and the concentration of the traffic of the Ural-Kuznetsk Kombinat on the Siberian trunk line, the single transportation network has been divided into a main skeleton of trunk lines, lines of local significance, and the internal network of transportation nodes.

The main directions of freight flows determine the geographical characteristics as well as the technical and operational characteristics of the transportation skeleton. It is made up of a small number of powerful trunk lines, including railroads, waterways, pipelines, and high-voltage transmission lines. These trunk lines insure the rapid and cheap transfer of immense masses of freight by the big routes to great distances from one region to another.

Transportation lines of the second order, i.e., the local ones, are made up of railroads, waterways, motor roads, and pipelines of intraregional significance. Besides serving communications within the regions, they perform the role of feeder lines to the interregional trunk lines.

The distribution and characteristics of the intranode transportation network are determined by the local and transit freight flows of the transportation nodes.

Thus, the single transportation network of the USSR is built on the principles of specialization and co-operation of the individual lines, so that the passing and carrying capacity of the network is considerably increased and its operation cheapened.

The rational geography and prospects for development of the transportation network are established by making a comparative analysis of the freight flows by the main directions with the capacities of the trunk lines serving them. Such an analysis has the object of distributing the traffic in an economically well-grounded manner among the different kinds of transportation and the lines of one and the same kind of transportation in a given direction. This possibility is offered only under the conditions of a socialist economy.

In distributing freight flows consideration is given to the existing passing and carrying capacity of the transportation trunk lines, to the expenditures for their reconstruction and new construction, to operational outlays, to times of delivery, to the seasonal nature of water transportation, and to certain other indices. The alternatives of distribution are compared with respect to total expenditures for all kinds of transportation in a given direction.

Economic geographic analysis of the transportation network includes investigation, by regions and directions, of the technical equipment of the network, its methods of operation, and the influence of natural conditions on transportation operations. The limits of this investigation are determined by the task of insuring the requirements of the national economy for hauls in the main directions of the network at minimum expenditures of labor, materials, and money.

The transportation nodes, which form an organic part of populated points, are important elements in the unified transportation network. The populated points determine to a rather large extent the distribution of the transportation nodes in the network of ways of communication and their technical structure.

In analyzing the geographic location of the transportation network, one distinguishes a region of closest gravitation with its population, industry, power, and other branches, and more distant regions of gravitation, participating in its own freight flows and the transit freight flows of the transportation node. It should be noted that final decisions about the development of concrete lines of the transportation network are adopted after a detailed study of the transportation nodes in the direction under examination.

The comparative coverage of the individual regions and lands by the transportation network is determined on the basis of the above-mentioned analysis of the carrying and passing capacity of the network and its sections, in comparison with the necessary volumes and directions of freight flows.

Statistical indices of the ratio of the length of the transportation network to the area of the territory or to the number of inhabitants are inaccurate because they do not take into account the degree of utilization of the network's capacity. Owing to the planned management of the economy, the mean freight intensity on the railroad network of the USSR is 4.5 times greater than in the USA and many times greater than in European countries. The better utilization of transportation capacities makes it possible to serve the planned freight turnover in the Soviet Union with a considerably smaller length of track and routes than would be required in capitalist countries.

TRANSPORTATION AND THE STORAGE NETWORK

To eliminate defects in distribution and traffic, it is necessary to supplement the data on planning by branches of the economy with integrated planning by economic regions and, in so doing, to combine the interests of production with the requirements of consumers and with the rational utilization of transportation. Consideration must also be given to the continuous growth of the volumes of production and consumption, to changes in their geography, as well as to the demands for assortment by individual regions and points as the requirements grow and become differentiated.

The problem of the rationalization of the planning of distribution and traffic is not only a matter of establishing once for all, but also of constantly maintaining the proportions between the enterprises, branches of the economy, and regions. For this purpose, cargoes are sometimes re-addressed or additional ones are shipped. However, maintenance of proportions in the national economy, even if only partially, at the price of irrational hauls, is not a satisfactory solution of the problem of planning distribution.

In the line of regulation of distribution, and consequently also hauls, the following conflicts arise:

1. It is necessary to be guided strictly by the plan established for the year or a longer period; at the same time, the plan has to be deviated from in concrete cases, in consideration of current changes;

2. Planning is done at the center only as to enlarged assortment, whereas it is carried out with respect to individual types, grades, and sizes;

3. It is necessary to provide for the firm assignment of points of production and points of consumption, yet under the conditions of inevitable current changes the rigid attachment of consumer enterprises to producer enterprises often has to be violated.

These conflicts with respect to a number of mass products can be eliminated by means of specialized distribution bases. The limits of the activity of such distribution-base warehouses are fixed with consideration for the rational sales zones of the respective products. All the suppliers and consumers in the planned sales zone are attached to each other through the distribution bases. In so doing, the direct tie between producers and consumers is preserved, but under the control of the distribution base, which regulates current deviations from the long-range plans by means of its own resources. Provision is made for the combination of the centralized management of the distribution of commodities and material goods with local initiative in the solution of operative questions of current material and technical supply.

At points having a favorable geographic situation several distribution bases may be located, specializing in different products. In these cases, their work must be co-ordinated.

Rationally located distribution bases will have a substantial effect on the geographic location of a number of industrial enterprises which process the raw materials and semimanufactures concentrated by the bases. Such distribution bases represent so many sources of raw materials, to which the respective enterprises gravitate. Rationalization of the ties between suppliers and consumers by means of distribution bases insures a stable geography of freight flows and frees transportation from a number of duplicated, opposite, excessively long and circuitous hauls, resulting from defects in planning.

The distribution bases aid in solving the task of transportation by trunk lines. They insure regular and rapid mass movement over the specialized interregional trunk lines, and make it possible to enlarge and stabilize the freight flows, to shorten their standing time, and to arrange the through-routing of cargoes. The distribution bases play a big role at transshipment points in the development of concentrated freight flows in mixed communications.

The distribution bases are located in the path of mass flows of the respective types of freight, at points suitable for serving the established sales zone, and coinciding with the points of considerable consumption or transshipment and, for certain products, with the points of production.

The integrated utilization of different kinds of transportation and of the network of warehouses to rationalize the geography of traffic, and the existence of a unified transportation network are great advantages of the socialist system which are not available to the capitalist economy. They require subordination of the various branches to a single planned management and presuppose a rational regionalization of sales and traffic, obligatory for every supplier and consumer.

PROSPECTIVE QUESTIONS OF TRANSPORTATION GEOGRAPHY

Let us dwell briefly on the four main questions of economic geographic investigation in the field of transportation which await solution.

1. *Investigation of transportation as a part of the productional-territorial complexes, including the analysis of interregional ties.* This work is done by economic-regionalization methods and aids in establishing proportionality between transportation and other branches of the national economy, as well as between the various kinds of transportation. It is necessary to study the following interdependence: distribution of lines of production by regions + interregional ties + main directions of freight flows + main transportation trunk lines. If rational interregional ties have been established, the freight flows and transportation network calculated on their basis will also be rational.

To regulate the interregional ties for concrete products, a change is often required in the distribution and technical structure of enterprises producing these products. But before making a change it is necessary to determine which is more advantageous for the national economy: to bring a given product from a distance or to produce it on the spot, i.e., it is necessary to estimate the total expenditure by the national economy on production and transfer. Thus, the problem of regionalization of interregional ties and traffic is combined with the general problem of the formation of productional-territorial complexes and the distribution of the productive forces, and its solution is of great significance for the refinement of the network of economic regions of the USSR.

2. *The problem of a unified transportation network* is connected with the regionalization of inter-regional ties and receives therefrom a rational scheme of main freight flows. A decisive influence is exerted on the geography of the transportation network by interregional hauls of the main types of

cargo (coal, petroleum, metal, ore, lumber, and grain), but to determine the capacity of specific trunk lines it is necessary to analyze the transportation of all other types of freight and passengers, not only interregional, but also intraregional.

The distribution of freight flows by types of transportation should insure the satisfaction of the demands of the national economy for carriage with the minimum total expenditure.

In order to construct a rational transportation network it is necessary to make a complex technical economic analysis, taking into account the natural factors that may considerably increase the expense of construction and operation of the ways of communication. One has to examine the various alternatives of freight flows corresponding to the different alternatives of the distribution of productive forces and interregional ties, and of the development of transportation nodes, and to take into account the progress of means of transportation and the elaboration of foremost methods of operation.

3. *Geographic methods are still insufficiently utilized in special transportation investigations.* Of especial significance is the application of methods of planning regional complexes, of which transportation is a part. Soviet geographers mean by economic regions, not an arbitrary grouping of territories, but actually existing productional-territorial complexes. This permits a scientific basis for a single network of economic regions. Its use, instead of a multitude of networks for different kinds of transportation and products, insures a higher level of national-economic planning, including that of transportation.

Geographic investigations of the mobility of the population furnish a foundation for working out more modern methods of planning passenger flows.

In analyzing transportation problems and projecting transportation lines, it is necessary to make greater use of cartographic methods, especially when it is required to give an integrated notion of the geography of transportation lines in mutual relation to the economics of the regions and the natural environment.

4. The time has come to create a series of *transportation maps and a transportation atlas* both for the Soviet Union and for foreign countries. These maps should show the trunk lines of all kinds of transportation with the necessary characterization of the technical conditions and work to be performed. The basic features of the maps should be the distribution of production and consumption of the articles which form mass cargoes in transportation, the distribution of the population and those elements of the natural environment which substantially influence the geography of the ways of communication, and the conditions of their construction, and operation. Such maps are necessary for the study of the present distribution of transportation and the provision of a basis for its prospective development in the countries of socialism.

BASIC LITERATURE

Aleksandrov, I. G. "On the Question of the Trunk Lining (*magistralizatsiya*) of Railroads," in the book: *Elektrifikatsiya Sovetskoy Rossii*, 1921.

Aleksandrov, I. G. "The Drafting of a Plan of Railroad Development," *Materialy Transportnoy Komissii AN SSSR*, Moscow, 1934.

Bernshteyn-Kogan, S. V. Essays on Transportation Geography (*Ocherki Geografii Transporta*), Moscow-Leningrad, 1930.

Belousov, I. I. "On the Role of Transportation in Economic Regionalization," *Trudy MTIPP*, Moscow, 1957.

Belousov, I. I. Interregional Ties and Grain Shipments (*Mezhrayonnyye Svyazi i Perevozki Khlebnykh Gruzov*), Moscow, 1958.

Bogoslovskiy, M. A. Internal Waterways (*Vnutrenniye Vodnyye Puti*), Moscow, 1948.

Voprosy Ratsionalizatsii Perevozok Vazhneyshikh Gruzov (Questions of the rationalization of the most important types of shipments), collection of articles (*sbornik*), Moscow, 1957.

Gibshman, A. Ye., and Danilov, S. K. The Economics of Transportation (*Ekonomika Transporta*), Moscow, 1955.

Gladtsinov, B. N. Questions of the Development of Pipeline Transportation (*Voprosy Razvitiya Truboprovodnogo Transporta*), Moscow, 1958.

Gorinov, A. V. Questions of the Projecting of Trunk Lines of Interregional Railroad Communication (*Voprosy Proyektirovaniya Magistraley Mezhrayonnykh Zheleznodorozhnykh Soobshcheniy*), Moscow, 1936.

Zvonkov, V. V. The Interrelationship of the Individual Kinds of Transportation and the Principles of the Organization of Mixed Shipments (*Vzaimosvyaz' Otdel'nykh Vidov Transporta i Osnovy Organizatsii Smeshannykh Perevozok*), Moscow, 1953.

Koldomasov, Yu. I. The Rationalization of Hauls in Railroad Transportation (*Ratsionalizatsiya Perevozok na Zheleznodorozhnom Transporte*), Moscow, 1954.

Kolosovskiy, N. N. The Great Siberian Super-Trunk Line (*Velikaya Sibirskaya Sverkhmagistral'*), Moscow, 1930.

Kolosovskiy, N. N. "The Principles of Economic Regionalization" *(Osnovy Ekonomicheskogo Rayonirovaniya),*
    Moscow, 1958. [A typed English translation by Lawrence Ecker of this volume is available for consultation
    at the American Geographical Society.]

Krzhizhanovskiy, G. M. "Concerning the Problem of the Siberian Super-Trunk Line," *Na Planovom Fronte,* 1930, no. 5.

Lavrova, I. V. "The Transportational-economic Ties of Kazakhstan," *Trudy Instituta ekonomiki AN Kaz. SSR,* 1959, 3.

Mitaishvili, A. A. The Internal Water Transportation of the USSR and Ways of Increasing its Cheapness
    (Vnutrenniy Vodnyy Transport SSSR i Puti Povysheniya Yego Ekonomichnosti), Moscow, 1957.

Mikhal'tsev, Ye. V. Outlays for Railroad Hauls *(Izderzhki Zheleznodorozhnykh Perevozok),* 1932.

Nikol'skiy, I. V. Economic Geography of the USSR *(Ekonomicheskaya Geografiya SSSR),* issue VI,
    Moscow State Univ., Moscow, 1958.

Nikol'skiy, I. V. "Some Questions of Transportation Geography in the USSR," *Nauchn. Dokl. Vysshey Shkoly,*
    1958, no. 4.

Sarantsev, P. L. Geography of the Ways of Communication *(Geografiya Putey Soobshcheniya),* Moscow, 1957.

Khanukov, Ye. D. Transportation and the Distribution of Production *(Transport i Razmeshcheniye Proizvodstva),*
    Moscow, 1955.

Khachaturov, T. S. The Distribution of Transportation *(Razmeshcheniye Transporta),* Moscow, 1939.

Chernomordik, D. I. Railroad Freight Rates *(Zheleznodorozhnyye Gruzovyye Tarify SSSR),* Moscow, 1958.

Chuprov, A. Railroading *(Zheleznodorozhnoye Khozyaystvo),* Moscow, 1875.

CHAPTER 32

MEDICAL GEOGRAPHY

V. P. Byakov, Ye. I. Ignat'yev, A. P. Markovin, and A. A. Shoshin

Among other tasks, Soviet geography studies the manifold relations of the natural and socioeconomic conditions of concrete territories to the state of health of the population and to the distribution of man's diseases over the globe. The treatment of this problem is due to the practical requirements of the development of the national economy and the public health of the USSR. The enormous amount of factual material accumulated by geography and medicine convincingly confirms the existence of these relationships and requires theoretical generalization.

Medical geography, on the borderline between geography and medicine, became established as an independent branch of science in Russia as far back as the middle of the 19th century. In its present stage of development, Soviet medical geography (a) studies the positive and negative influence of the natural and socioeconomic conditions of different territories on the state of health of the population, (b) ascertains the causes of the rise and geographic spread of man's diseases over the globe, and (c) works out scientifically based measures aimed at exploiting the positive influence of natural and socioeconomic factors, or at neutralizing their negative influence, in the interests of the preservation of public health.

Investigations in the field of medical geography substantially supplement the work on physical and economic geography with materials relating to the influence of natural and socioeconomic conditions upon the development of society. This contributes to a fuller and more thorough evaluation and utilization of the country's natural resources, the execution of integrated measures for the conservation of nature, and the scientific anticipation of the results of the transformation of nature in the interests of the national economy, and of the health of the population.

No less important for the theory and practice of public-health preservation is research in medical geography. It contributes to the execution of special measures aimed at improving sanitation and preventing the rise and spread of the various diseases of man, as well as to the most rational organization of medical service to the population.

Soviet medical geography differs substantially in content and tasks from foreign medicine. Abroad, the object of medical geography is the diseases of man viewed from the spatial aspect, as well as the causes of the spread of human diseases over the globe (Jacques M. May, Ernst Rodenwaldt, Calzada, and others). Soviet medical geography studies the natural conditions and socioeconomic characteristics of a territory which either aid in strengthening the health of the population, prolong its labor capacity, and increase the life span of man, or which cause disturbances in man's health, a reduction in working capacity, or the rise of diseases.

The investigation of the natural conditions and socioeconomic characteristics with the object of ascertaining their influence on the state of health of the population, the rise and geography of diseases on the globe permits the working out of medico-geographic forecasts for sparsely inhabited and economically undeveloped territories. Such a study also makes it possible to foresee the possible influence of new complexes of natural and socioeconomic conditions, arising as a result of the wide transformation of nature. Any limitation of the content of medical geography to the study of the geography of diseases considerably diminishes the practical significance of medico-geographic research.

Soviet medical geography is based on the materialistic doctrine of the unity of the external environment and the human organism, which has been successfully elaborated through the labors of our fellow-countrymen (I. M. Sechenov, I. P. Pavlov, I. V. Michurin, and others). It is also based on the dialectic understanding of the role of natural and socioeconomic conditions in the rise and spread of human diseases over the globe. Finally, its development reposes upon the many years of experience in medico-geographic research in Russia.

Medico-geographic information may be found in the earliest descriptions by Russian travelers. At the beginning of the 18th century, the Russian geographers I. K. Kirilov, V. N. Tatishchev, and later M. V. Lomonosov, in sending out special questionnaires to the provinces to collect geographic information, included medico-geographic questions. In his major work, "Description of the Land of Kamchatka" (1755), S. P. Krasheninnikov gives a special section "On diseases and medicaments in Kamchatka." The programs of the "academic expeditions" of 1768-1784 provided, in particular, for making "precise investigations" about local diseases and about the means of curing and preventing them, which found considerable reflection in the works of the leaders of the detachments of these expeditions, who, as a rule, were naturalist-physicians (I. I. Lepekhin, P. S. Pallas, S. G. Gmelin, and others). At the same time appeared the first program of independent medico-geographic study of a locality (P. Z. Kondoidi) and the first such investigations (V. Ya. Gevitt, S. A. Andriyevskiy, I. G. Geogi, Ye. F. Rappe and others). It should be noted that special medico-geographic works did not appear abroad until the very end of the 18th century (Fink, 1792).

The most intensive development of medical geography in Russia and its establishment as an independent branch of science took place in the second half of the 19th century. During this period about 1,500 different medico-geographic investigations were carried out, among them a large number of doctoral dissertations (E. Ikavitts, M. Shmelev, P. Gryaznov, I. Yavorskiy, and others). In 1870-1871, a special two-volume "Medico-geographic Collection [*sbornik*]" was published under the editorship of S. Lovtšev and G. A. Arkhangel'skiy. It is noteworthy that many physicians took a constantly active part in the work of the Russian Geographic Society, often being at the same time prominent travelers (A. A. Rafalovich, P. Ya. Pyasetskiy, A. V. Yeliseyev, A. A. Bunge, I. L. Yavorskiy, and others). Many of them have major medico-geographic investigations to their credit, and medico-geographic information is widely represented in their descriptions of travels.

Attention to integrated geographic investigations of concrete territories flagged at the end of the 19th and the beginning of the 20th century, owing to the intensive differentiation of geography into a number of branches. This fact, in turn, led to the dropping of medico-geographic questions from the geographers' field of vision. Moreover, the further development of hygiene, the rise of bacteriology, epidemiology, and other branches of medicine led to a discontinuation of the study of the integrated influence of natural and socioeconomic conditions on the state of health of the population, and on the rise and spread of diseases.

Since the Great October Socialist Revolution the productive forces of the individual regions of the Soviet Union have been studied from all sides, in the interest of the wide development of the country's national economy. This task is being successfully solved by Soviet science, particularly geography, through integrated research. In a number of regions, especially the remote ones, integrated medical expeditions are also operating. For example, the integrated zoologo-parasitologic expeditions under the direction of Academician Ye. N. Pavlovskiy have carried on their activity in Middle Asia, the Far East, and other regions of the Soviet Union.

As a result of these investigations there has been an intensive accumulation of new factual materials about the influence of natural and socioeconomic conditions on the state of health of the population, and the rise and spread of human diseases. In the course of the theoretical generalization of these facts, studies concerning the natural focality of human diseases and landscape epidemiology, by Ye. N. Pavlovskiy, have received wide recognition.

Thus, the progress in the development of geography and medicine has created conditions for the revival and further development of medical geography. The establishment of medical geography has been greatly promoted by the labors of D. K. Zabolotnyy, Ye. N. Pavlovskiy, and others.

Among the main scientific trends of Soviet medical geography at present are:

1. The study of the influence of the individual components of the natural and socioeconomic conditions on public health and the rise and geography of diseases on the globe

2. The investigation of the influence of natural complexes on public health in application to the largest units of natural regionalization (natural zones, lands, provinces, and so forth)

3. The investigation of the influence of all the natural conditions and socioeconomic characteristics on public health and the geography of human diseases within specific units of economic regionalization (national-economic complexes and administrative-territorial units)

4. The elaboration of medico-geographic forecasts for sparsely inhabited regions, intended for economic development in the future, as well as for territories in which the most intensive transformation of nature is taking place as a result of man's economic activity (the winning of the virgin and idle lands, the supplying of water to the deserts, the construction of artificial reservoirs, etc.)

5. The study of the noso-complexes and noso-areas of human diseases, and the creation of maps of their distribution on the territory of the Soviet Union and adjacent countries

6. The production of special medico-geographic maps showing the influence of natural and socioeconomic conditions on public health, with ascertainment of the leading factors of positive and negative influence.

In accordance with the main trends and experience in medico-geographic research, a general (theoretical) part and specialized departments have become outlined in Soviet medical geography as an independent branch of science. The general part works out the subject and tasks of medical geography, the history of its development in the Soviet Union and abroad, and the theoretical principles and methods of medico-geographic research. It studies, with respect to medical geography, the individual elements of the natural and socioeconomic conditions. To the specialized departments of medical geography belong: medical landscape science (medico-geographic study of natural complexes), medical regional geography, nosogeography, and medical cartography.

The following main methods of investigation have become defined in Soviet medical geography: (1) medico-geographic descriptions, (2) medico-geographic analysis of statistics, and (3) cartographic analysis. Furthermore, the methods of the allied branches of geography and medicine are used in certain cases such as key sections and populated points and ecologic and hygienic investigations.

In the last few years definite results have been achieved in working out the main trends of Soviet medical geography. An especially large amount of attention has been paid to working out theoretical principles and methods of medico-geographic research, particularly the more precise determination of the subject and tasks of medical geography, in accordance with the present level of the development of geography and medicine. These questions were reflected in the work of the Second Congress of the Geographic Society of the USSR in 1955. The theoretical principles and methods of Soviet medical geography have been widely discussed at the scientific meetings of the Commission on Medical Geography of the Geographic Society of the USSR. Much work has been done in gathering and systematizing the materials dealing with the history of the development of medical geography in Russia and abroad. Finally, the Commission on Medical Geography has gathered a large amount of bibliographic material on native and foreign works. About 6,000 titles have now been found in libraries and archives.

Great progress has been achieved in the field of the study of the geography of a number of human diseases (plague, tularemia, spring-and-summer tick encephalitis, helminthiasis, endemic goiter, Kashin-Beck's disease, and others). The principles and methods of studying the geography of diseases are being worked out, particularly the method of compiling noso-maps (maps of the distribution of individual human diseases and animal diseases dangerous to man). Especially great progress has been achieved in the study of the geography of natural-focus and parasitic diseases, and maps of the geographic distribution of certain natural-focus and transmissible diseases in the USSR are being prepared for publication.

In the last few years much attention has been paid to medical regional geography. A number of scientific works have been written on the medico-geographic characterization of many regions of the Soviet Union, as well as certain foreign countries. Medico-geographic investigations are being made in the Arctic, the Antarctic, and certain other landscape zones.

In the Soviet Union, under the conditions of a socialist national economy with planned scientific research, broad prospects are opened for the further development of medical geography. The requirements of the evolving national economy and the further increase in the productivity of labor, the tasks of preserving public health, and the demands of Soviet sanitation dictate the necessity of organizing a consistent and systematic medico-geographic study of the territory of the Soviet

Union and of composing medico-geographic descriptions on this basis. Such descriptions of concrete territories of the country are destined to contribute to the timely and scientifically based elaboration of measures aimed at sanitizing the natural conditions of these territories, at the rational distribution of the population and the construction of populated points, and at the most efficient organization of medical services.

Exceptionally important and promising is the study of the geography of diseases which have the greatest impact on the pathology of the population (cardiovascular diseases, malignant tumors, natural-focus and parasitic diseases, etc.), and the compilation of the respective medico-geographic maps. It is intended to prepare and publish a medico-geographic atlas of the Soviet Union and adjacent states. The execution of the contemplated program of medico-geographic research in the Soviet Union is being effected by the geographic scientific-research institutions, particularly the medical-geography departments in the leading institutes of geography of the Academy of Sciences of the USSR. An important place in the study of the geography of individual diseases belongs to the medical scientific-research institutions (institutes of district medicine; institutes of hygiene, epidemiology, and microbiology; the branch clinical institutes of the Academy of Medical Sciences, and others).

BASIC LITERATURE

Vusovich, Yur. Medico-geographic Description of Kaluga (*Mediko-geograficheskoye Opisaniye g. Kalugi*), Kaluga, 1929.

Gnezdilov, V. G. "Materials on the Geographic Distribution, Epidemiology and Prophylaxis of Amebiosis," *Medits. parazitologiya i parazitarnyye bolezni*, 1947, No. 5.

Zabolotnyy, D. K. "Medical geography," *Bol'shaya Medits. Entstiklopediya*, vol. 6, Moscow, 1929.

Ignat'yev, Ye. I. "The Main Tasks and Trends of the Medico-geographic Study of Siberia and the Far East," *Materialy I Soveshch. geografov Sibiri i Dal'nego Vostoka*, Irkutsk, 1959.

Kaminskiy, L. I. The Geography and Statistics of Typhoid Fever (*Geografiya i Statistika Bryushnogo Tifa*), Dissertation, Moscow, 1937.

Kuzyakin, A. P. "The Geography of Foci and the Mass Prophylaxis of Tularemia," *Zhurnal mikr., immun. i epidemiologii*, 1946, No. 11.

Maksimov, A. A. "The Main Types of Tularemia Foci, their Characteristics and Geographic Distribution in the RSFSR," *Dokl. AN SSSR*, vol. 7, 1947, No. 5.

Markovin, A. P. "The Views of Foreign Authors about the Subject and Task of Medical Geography." *Sb. rabot I LMI im. I. P. Pavlova*, Leningrad, 1958, no. III; "Concerning the History of the Development of Medical Geography in the USSR and Abroad," in the book: *Pervaya Vsesoyuznaya Nauchn. Istoriko-meditsinskaya Konferentsiya*, Medgiz, 1959.

Markovin, A. P., and Noshchinskiy, V. R. "Some Data on the State of Medical Geography Abroad," in the book, *Sborn. rabot fakul'teta pri I Leningr. meditsin. in-te akad. I. P. Pavlova*, Leningrad, 1958, no. III.

Pavlovskiy, Ye. N. "Natural Focality and the Concept of the Landscape Epidemiology of Transmissible Human Diseases," *Medits. parazitologiya i parazitar. bolezni*, 1944, No. 6. By the same author: "On the Principles of the Study of the Geography of Natural-focus and Transmissible Diseases," in the book, *Materialy ko II s"yezdu Geogr. obl. SSSR*, izd-vo AN SSSR, 1954. By the same author: "Methods and Tasks of Medical Geography," in the book, *Voprosy geografii, Sbornik stat. k XVIII Mezhdunar. geogr. kongr.*, Moscow-Leningrad, 1956.

Petrov, B. D. "Medico-topographic Descriptions in Russia (down to 1861)," *Sovetskoye zdravookhraneniye*, 1960, No. 1.

Sigal, B. S. "The First Medico-geographic Descriptions in Russia," *Tr. Leningr. san.-gigiyenich. med. in-ta*, vol. I, issue 1, Leningrad, 1949.

Sokolov, N. P. "The Winning of New Lands and the Tasks of Medical Geography," *Sov. meditsina*, 1956, No. 1; by the same: "Tasks of Medical Geography," *Sov. zdravookhraneniye*, 1957, No. 9; by the same: "Main Tasks of Medico-geographic Map-making in the USSR," *Sov. zdravookhraneniye*, 1958, No. 9.

Sokolov, N. P., and Abdullayeva, A. A. "Concerning the Medico-geographic Investigations of the Oblasts of the Fergana Valley," *Sov. zdravookhraneniye*, 1960, No. 1.

Chumakov, M. P. and others. "The Geographic Distribution and Certain Characteristics of Tick Encephalitis in the European Part of the USSR, Siberia and Kazakhstan," *Nevropat. i psikhiatr.*, vol. 13, 1944, No. 2.

Shevelev, A. B. "Medical Geography as a Method of Studying the Sanitary Condition of the Population," *XII Vsesoyuzh. s"yezd gigiyen., epidemiolog., mikrobiolog. i infektsion.*, Moscow, 1949.

Shoshin, A. A. The Content and Methods of the Medico-geographic Study of a Locality (*Soderzhaniye i Metody Mediko-geograficheskogo Izucheniya Mestnosti*), Leningrad, 1951, p. 109.

CHAPTER 33

ORIGIN OF GEOGRAPHIC NAMES

E. M. Murzayev

The study of the geographic names of the USSR and their origin represents a very complicated and labor-consuming task. This is to be explained first of all by the vastness of the country, which is not comparable with any other state in the world, as well as by the multinational composition of its population, speaking various languages, sometimes very remote from one another in their genealogic or morphologic linguistic classification. Toponymic research is further complicated by the inadequate extent of the historical study of such large areas of our country as Siberia and the Far East, the materials on the archeology and ancient history of which have only become the property of science in the last few decades.

Toponymics is a scientific discipline that is at once linguistic, historical, and geographic, a fact which also aggravates the difficulty of toponymic research. Scholars of different specialties engage in the latter; perhaps for this reason, toponymy, being the "servant of two masters," has thus far not received a definite place in the system of sciences. Specialists of different fields often use the toponymic method in their work, but it is hard to say just who regards toponymy as his main specialty, i.e., engages solely or principally in the study of geographic names.

One thing is clear: toponymic investigations can be fruitful when they employ the methods both of linguistics and of the historical or geographical sciences. Finally, the geographic name as an element of language is a linguistic category and hence is subject to linguistic laws. But this name has originated and evolved, i.e., changed its form and perhaps also its content, under definite historical conditions and therefore reflects them. Hence, it is also a historical category. But the toponym is an element of the geographic map, and not an accidental one either, since there are no accidental geographic names, but is an element which reflects the natural conditions and wealth of the district, the history of the population, the historical geography, i.e., the concrete geographic setting. Therefore it is legitimate to regard the toponym also as a geographic category. The map furnishes an abundance of comparative material for toponymic investigations, unfortunately not sufficiently utilized by linguists, who often shut themselves up within the framework of a modern territory populated by a people speaking some specific language.

Geographic names have evolved historically, and their origin is closely connected with the social life and languages of the peoples who have settled in this or that locality. In the course of millenniums, the historical conditions, languages, and peoples have changed; hence, there is not a single country in which there is a uniform geographic nomenclature. It has been created gradually and is a multi-stratified formation consisting of elements of different ages and languages, distorted by time, and altered as a result of the action of new languages and new settlers.

A correct understanding of geographic names provides the geographer with a wealth of material for comprehending the characteristics of the natural conditions and man's economic activity, and correct description permits him to ascertain the transcription closest to the original, which is very important for cartography. Yet in toponymy, as in no other science, the situation is still bad with respect to the establishment of the general and particular laws governing the formation, evolution, and distribution of geographic names. Generally accepted methodologic principles for their study still remain to be worked out, and this leads to a plethora of fantastic guesses and homespun explanations based on legends and the folk etymology customary in interpretations of the genesis of toponyms and their semantics, such as is characteristic of many works, both Russian and foreign.

Still, toponymy now possesses an extensive literature, which is being supplemented annually.

In many countries of the world there exist toponymic institutions and societies, and special publications, occasional and periodic (in the form of toponymic journals). Questions of the study of geographic names and their transcription also engage the attention of the United Nations Organization and the International Toponymic Congress, which meets once every few years in different cities of the world. Great progress in the study of geographic names abroad has been achieved in Poland, Italy, England, the Scandinavian countries, Germany, and Czechoslovakia.

In Russia many outstanding scientific figures have concerned themselves with toponymy. Already in the "geographic lexicons" of the 18th century one may find attempts to interpret and give an analytic treatment of geographic names. Here one should mention V. Tatishchev, and, in the 19th century, V. Dal', I. Filevich, and N. Barsov. And yet it may be stated that in the past there have not been many systematic investigations into toponymy, and those that have been undertaken have been of a casual character. If one does not count the small dictionary of geographic names by A. Ivanovskiy, which pursued the objective of aiding geography teachers in high schools, and a work by N. Berezin showing the relations between certain names against the background of the history of geographic discoveries, the only attempt at a systematic analysis of toponymy in Russia was made by A. Orlov, who in 1907 published the great work, "The Origin of the Names of Russian and Certain Western European Rivers, Cities, Tribes, and Localities."

In Soviet times, owing to the general development of science, interest in toponymic research has grown greatly and has attracted the attention of many outstanding scholars of the USSR. Valuable thoughts on the origin of geographic names are to be found in the works of Academician A. I. Sobolevskiy, who concerned himself specially with the toponymy of the Russian Plain. Among the great works devoted to Slavic toponymy, we shall point out the investigations of A. M. Selishchev (1939). The numerous works of Academician V. V. Bartol'd contain materials on the geographic names of Middle Asia and the Near East. Academician S. B. Veselovskiy has shown the helpfulness of the toponymic method in historic research (1945). In solving questions of ethnogenesis and establishing the ethnic boundaries of a territory, this method has been used with success by P. I. Kushner (1951). The study of geographic names has attracted the attention of such prominent geographers as V. P. Semenov-Tyan-Shanskiy and Academician L. S. Berg.

In the last few years, toponymic investigations have come to be made on a mass scale, and the number of publications is growing from year to year. It suffices to recall that, in the literature index printed by V. A. Nikonov (1958), the works on geographic names number 129 just for the five-year period 1950-1954 in the USSR, in the Russian language alone. Interesting investigations have been made by B. A. Serebrennikov on Volga-Oka toponymy (1955-1957). Deserving of attention are the works by A. I. Popov on Finno-Ugric toponymy (1948, 1957), K. K. Tseluyko on the Ukraine (Tseluyko, 1957), I. D. Voronin on Mordovia (1951) and A. P. Dul'zon on Western Siberia (1950), A. Z. Rozenfel'd on the Iranian toponymy of Middle Asia and adjacent areas (1940, 1951, 1953), A. N. Kazakov on the Kola Peninsula (1949), V. A. Kazakevich on Mongolia (1934), V. M. Sergiyevskiy on Bessarabia (1946), V. A. Il'inskiy on the Komi ASSR (1930), and E. R. Rygdylon on Buryatia. A collection of interesting toponymic materials has been published in Kiyev under the editorship of K. K. Tseluyko. One should note the merits of Academician Ya. M. Endzelin, who has engaged for many years in the study of Baltic toponymy and has published a large dictionary, "Toponymic Names of the Latvian SSR" (1956).

Within the framework of this short survey chapter it is, of course, impossible even to enumerate the main works on the toponymy of the USSR. The time has now come to compile a systematic bibliography of them. Let us dwell on certain results of toponymic research.

It is most important for geographers to have explanatory etymologic dictionaries of geographic names and local geographic (so-called nomenclatural) terms. The need for them is due to the natural interest in semantics and content; the correct understanding of them reveals many aspects of the local geographic characteristics in the field of both physical and economic geography and the history of settlement and economy for the purpose of historico-geographic research.

Finally, it is difficult to conceive of an explanatory toponymic dictionary on such a country as the Soviet Union, if oriented toward the lists of geographic names on the map to a scale of 1:1,000,000 or even 1:2,500,000. The solution of such a vast task would require a series edition of dozens of thick volumes and the work of a large group of investigators for many years. However, such work has been performed for individual oblasts and republics. Here one may name the "Geographic Dictionary of the Kola Peninsula," published in 1939 under the editorship of V. P. Voshchinin, and the above-mentioned work by Ya. M. Endzelin. Among dictionaries of nomenclatural terms actively participating in the formation of geographic names one may name the "Dictionary of Local Geographic Terms" by E. and V. Murzayev (1959), in which an attempt is made to collect and explain 2,800 popular words relating to various geographic objects, and examples are given of toponymic forms composed of local terms. Here one should mention the information-packed work by G. K. Konkash-payev, "Kazakh Popular Geographic Terms" (1951); the article by V. P. Androsova, "Local Terminology for the Seacoasts of the USSR" (1937); and the book by P. L. Mashtakov, "Materials for an Oblast Water Dictionary" (1931).

Important for the satisfaction of the scientific interests of geographers, local-lore students, and other naturalists are toponymic investigations revealing the meaning of geographic names, their areas of distribution, migrations, and local dialectic forms. Very many such works have lately been published in the form of articles; an enumeration of them would constitute a basis for a bibliography of USSR toponymy. As a rule, they are devoted to particular questions and have, moreover, been written by linguists and are sometimes specialized in character, so that they are little known to the geographic community. Among such investigations may be numbered the work by V. A. Abayev (1956), who did not have as his main object the study of geographic names, but does offer interesting toponymic material. The same may be said of the article by B. Ya. Serebrennikov, "The Problem of the Substratum" (1956), and the book by Gr. Kapantsyan, "The Historico-Linguistic Significance of the Toponymy of Ancient Armenia" (1940) and his brochure, "Suffixes and Suffixed Words in the Toponymy of Ancient Asia Minor" (1948).

The applied significance of toponymy for practical purposes of the transcription of foreign-language, and the correct rendition of Russian, geographic names has been treated in a number of instructions by the transcription section of the Head Administration of Geodesy and Cartography.

In the last few years, toponymic research has made it possible to outline interesting laws and demonstrate the community of original toponymic forms for immense territories now inhabited by peoples speaking languages of the same family, or beyond the limits of their present distribution. Thus, the influence of the Baltic elements in the formation of the toponymy of the Center of the European part of the USSR has been ascertained: Baltic-language forms are also discovered in Moscow, as well as in the regions adjoining it to the south and east. Against the background of Slavic toponymy, the significance of Finno-Ugric language influences is becoming more and more clearly outlined, even in those regions of the European part of the USSR and Western Siberia where there are at present no inhabitants speaking any one of these languages. Also interesting are the toponymic parallels between the geographic names of Finno-Ugric and Turkic origin, which are closely intertwined in a number of areas such as, for example, the Volgaland and Western Siberia. Turkic toponymic proves to be very stable in its distribution and is found over vast territories from the western borders of the USSR (from the Danube basin) to the shores of the Pacific Ocean.

It has long been known, thanks especially to the labors of A. I. Sobolevskiy, that there is a stratum of Iranian-language toponymy in the Ukraine, on the Don and, of course, in the Transcaucasian and Middle Asiatic republics. In these republics, with their variegated and multilingual population and their rich historical past, the investigation of geographic names proves very interesting and enables one to confirm the presence of old Indo-European and Semitic elements — the languages of Hellas, India, the Iranian, Arabic, and perhaps also several now dead languages of this group, as well as the presence in Middle Asia of Greek, Chinese, Tibetan, and especially Mongolian names.

Of especial interest is the study of the toponymy of Eastern Siberia, which is only just beginning. Alongside past Russian toponyms (chiefly from the European North of the RSFSR), the main stratum here is formed, of course, of Asiatic elements: Tungus-Manchurian, "Paleoasiatic," Turkic, Mongolian, complicated by the later influence of Chinese and sometimes Japanese in the Far East.

The toponymy of any region is always a many-aged and polygenetic formation which often reflects both new and also very ancient historical and linguistic ties and relationships. Hence, one can confine oneself to the above considerations only for the expression of the most general laws. Further comparative study of geographic names enables one to note certain extremely interesting laws governing the structure of the name itself and the system of suffixal endings. It has long since been noticed that in individual limited territories names end in the same suffix. Characteristic of the modern toponymy of Russian towns and cities is the ending *sk*: Smolensk, Ryazhsk, Bryansk, Minsk, Kamensk, Sverdlovsk, Kirovsk, and so forth. The establishment of suffixal laws governing the stream toponymy of Siberia was undertaken more than thirty years ago by V. G. Shostakovich (1926). Later one may find attempts by many authors to systematize suffixes for the correct understanding of historical and ethnogenetic processes peculiar to this or that territory. Thus, a special investigation by Gr. Kapantsyan (see the above-mentioned work, 1948) is devoted to toponymic suffixes. A. P. Dul'zon (1950) has also used the analysis of suffixes to prove the ancient population distribution in Tomsk oblast; likewise B. A. Serebrennikov (1956) and many others. V. A. Nikonov, generalizing the method of the comparative study of suffixes, has written a great work on "The Geography of Russian Suffixes" (now being printed). Incidentally, it must be stated that the suffix method, like other one-sided methods, cannot furnish a universal answer to many semantic and genetic affinity questions concerning the origin of geographic names, but substantially aids in their explanation.

Comparative research brings out the toponymic laws and interrelations over extensive territories with regard to the bases (roots) of names as well. In this sense, toponymic parallels reveal certain unclear aspects of the distribution of toponyms having the same base at great distances from one another. Comparative linguistics has long made use of this method in seeking affinities in the Slavic countries or in Turkic, Iranian, and other language areas. The research done by certain Soviet scholars shows the affinity and vitality of one and the same toponyms (perhaps in several similar forms) far beyond the limits of territories occupied by people belonging to a specific language family. Here one may refer to the above-mentioned works by V. A. Abayev and A. I. Popov, as well as to certain articles by E. M. Murzayev (1946, 1948). A very large amount of such comparative materials has already been accumulated, so that it is impossible to ignore them without coming into conflict with the facts.

It is interesting to note that some of our long-established toponymic concepts are being shattered as a result of new data. We may cite as examples the Turkic *karakum, karasu, akum, aksu,* which have got even into the school geography textbooks in the sense of: (1) black, evil, bad sands, (2) spring waters, streams arising from sources, (3) white shifting sands, and (4) mountain rivers white with foam. As a result of the interesting work by A. K. Kononov (1954), it turns out that in this case the polysemantic significance of the words *kara* and *ak* permits one to interpret these toponyms in other ways. *Kara* in the ancient Turkic languages is also "earth" and *karasu* means "earth water," "water from the earth," i.e., "spring water"; *karakum* is "earth sand," "immobile, tied-down sand"; *ak,* in its verbal meaning is "to run, flow, pour," so that *aksu* is "running water," "water passing through, flowing down from the mountains," and *akkum* is "wind-blown, drifting, mobile sands."

An interesting attempt to discover the laws governing the distribution of geographic names has been made by V. A. Nikonov (1958), who was able to demonstrate the existence of toponymic groups consisting of names of the same type (for example, Berezovyy Gay (Birch Grove), Vyazovyy Gay (Elm Grove), Lipovyy Gay (Linden Grove), forming one series in one region. The establishment of toponymic series makes it possible to check the attempts to study the semantics of a name, taken separately, which fits into the system of one or the other series. Thus, the base *bud* forms numerous names of populated points over an enormous expanse from the Rhine to the Volga and is now present in certain Slavic languages in the sense of "building," "hut," "tar-maker's shed." The active participation of this term in the formation of geographic names thus becomes understandable. According to this author, toponyms originating from tribal names indicate the limits of distribution of this or that people, just as the geographic names containing the word *gora* ("mountain") are peculiar to plains (in mountain land they would be devoid of sense and would have ceased to perform their proper functions).

In the present survey it has not been possible to tell about the great amount of work by Soviet scholars in the study of geographic names. Let us point out that toponymy is being successfully introduced into school geography courses and into transcription work, and is attracting the attention of students of local lore. Thus far, toponymists in the Soviet Union have been very isolated, and not a single scientific institution is concerning itself with toponymy as a planned subject. In the 1920's there was a toponymy section operating under the Commission for the Study of the Tribal Composition of Russia (the KIPS) of the Academy of Sciences of the USSR. This commission has long since ceased to exist. After a long interruption, a toponymic commission was organized in 1959 under the Moscow branch [*filial*] of the Geographic Society of the USSR, which has already begun to function regularly and has prepared a collection of interesting publications on the toponymy of Russia. Among the linguistic institutions one should point out the A. A. Potebni Institute of Linguistics of the Academy of Sciences of the Ukrainian SSR, which is doing systematic research in this field.

BASIC LITERATURE

Abayev, V. A. "Etymologic Remarks," *Tr. In-ta yazykozn. AN SSSR*, Moscow, 1956, no. 6.

Androsova, V. P. "The Local Terminology for the Seashores of the USSR," *Uch. zap. MGU*, vol. 16, 1937.

Veselovskiy, S. V. "Toponymy in the Service of History," *Istoricheskiye zapiski*, no. 17, Moscow, 1945.

Voronin, I. D. "Concerning the Question of Mordva Toponymy," *Zapiski Nauchno-issled. in-ta pri Sovete Ministrov Mordovskoy ASSR*, no. 13, Saransk, 1951.

Geograficheskiy Slovar' Kol'skogo Poluostrova (Geographic dictionary of the Kola Peninsula), vol. I, under the editorship of V. P. Voshchinin, Leningrad, 1939.

Dul'zon, A. P. "Ancient Successions of Peoples on the Territory of Tomsk Oblast according to Toponymic Data," *Uch. zap. Tomskogo ped. in-ta*, vol. 6, Tomsk, 1950.

Il'inskiy, V. A. "Problems of the Toponymy of Komi Oblast," *Zapiski Obshchestva izucheniya Komi Kraya*, no. 5, Syktyvkar, 1930.

Kazakevich, V. A. "Modern Mongolian Toponymy," *Tr. Mong. Kom. AN SSSR*, no. 13, Leningrad, 1934.

Kapantsyan, G. R. "The Historico-linguistic Significance of the Toponymy of Ancient Armenia," *Nauchn. tr. Yerevansk. un-ta*, vol. 14, Yerevan, 1940.

Kapantsyan, G. R. Suffixes and Suffixed Words in the Toponymy of Ancient Asia Minor (*Suffiksy i Suffigirovannyye Slova v Toponimike Drevney Maloy Azii*), AN Arm. SSR, Yerevan, 1948.

Konkashpayev, G. K. "Kazakh Popular Geographic Terms," *Izv. AN Kaz. SSR, seriya geogr.*, No. 99, issue 3, Alma-Ata (1951).

Kononov, A. N. "On the Semantics of the Words '*kara*' and '*ak*' in Turkic Geographic Terminology," *Izv. otd. obshch. nauk AN Tadzh. SSR*, 1954, issue 5.

Kushner (Knyshev), P. I. Ethnic Territories and Ethnic Boundaries (*Etnicheskiye Territorii i Etnicheskiye Granitsy*), Moscow, 1951.

Mashtanov, P. L. Materials for an Oblast Water Dictionary (*Materialy dlya Oblastnogo Vodnogo Slovarya*), Gidrometeorol. komitet pri SNK SSSR, Gidrolog. in-t, 1931.

Mel'kheyev, M. N. "Local Geographic Terms of Eastern Siberia," *Tr. Irkutsk. gos. un-ta im. A. A. Zhdanova*, vol. 24, *seriya geogr.*, issue 1, 1958.

Murzayev, E. M. "Toponymic Parallels," *Izv. VGO*, vol. 78, 1946, issues 5-6.

Murzayev, E. M. "An Experiment in the Explanation of the Name '*Krym*' (Crimea)," *Izv. VGO*, vol. 80, 1948, no. 3.

Murzayev, E. M. "Studies on the Toponymy of Middle and Central Asia." *Voprosy geografii*, no. 8, Moscow, 1948.

Murzayev, E. M. "The Study of Geographic Names." *Spravochnik Puteshestvennika i Krayeveda*, vol. II, 1950.

Murzayev, E. and V. Dictionary of Local Geographic Terms (*Slovar' Mestnykh Geograficheskikh Terminov*), Moscow, 1959.

Nikonov, V. A. "Toponymy in the Five-year Period 1950-1954." Index of literature, *Izv. VGO*, 1958, no. 3.

Nikonov, V. A. "The Law of the Series in Geographic Names," journal *Onomastica*, vol. IV, 1958, Warsaw, issue 1 (printed in Russian).

Popov, A. I. "The Toponymy of the Beloye Ozero District," *Uch. zap. Leningr. gos. un-ta, seriya vostokovedch. nauk*, no. 2. Sovetskoye finnougrovedeniye, Leningrad, 1948.

Popov, A. I. "The Toponymic Study of Eastern Europe," *Uch. zap. Leningrad. gos. un-ta, seriya vostokovedch. nauk*, no. 2. Sovetskoye finnougrovedeniye, Leningrad, 1948.

Popov, A. I. "Materials on the Toponymy of Karelia," *Sovetskoye ugrovedeniye*, no. 5, Petrozavodsk, 1948.

Popov, A. I. "Toponymy as a Historical Science," *Uch. zap. in-ta yazykoved. AN USSR, Movoznavstvo*, vol. 14, Kiyev, 1957.

Popov, A. I. From the History of the Lexicography of the Languages of Eastern Europe (*Iz Istorii Leksiki Yazykov Vostochnoy Yevropy*), Leningrad, 1957.

Rozenfel'd, A. Z. "The Name '*Langar*' in the Toponymy of Tadzhikistan," *Izv. VGO*, vol. 72, 1940, no. 6.

Rozenfel'd, A. Z. "*Qala*—a Type of Fortified Iranian Settlement," *Sovetskaya etnografiya*, 1951, No. 1.

Rozenfel'd, A. Z. "Materials on the Ethnography and Toponymy of Vanch," *Izv. VGO*, vol. 85, 1953, no. 4.

Rygdylon, E. G. "Toponymic studies," *Zapiski Buryat-Mongol. in-ta kul'tury*, Ulan-Ude, 1955, no. 20.

Selishchev, A. M. "From Old and New Toponymy," *Sbornik statey po yazykovedeniyu*, vol. 5. Mosk. gos. in-t istorii, filosofiii i literatury, Moscow, 1939.

Sergiyevskiy, M. V. "The Toponymy of Bessarabia and its Testimony to the Settlement of the Territory," *Izv. AN SSSR, Otd. literatury i yazyka*, vol. V, 1946, no. 4.

Serebrennikov, B. A. "Volga-Oka Toponymy on the Territory of the European Part of the USSR," *Voprosy yazykoznaniya*, 1955, no. 6.

Serebrennikov, B. A. "The Problem of the Substratum," *Doklady i soobshcheniya In-ta yazykoznaniya AN SSSR*, no. 9, 1956.

Serebrennikov, B. A. "The Origin of *Chuvash* according to the Data furnished by the Language," Sb. *O proiskhozhdenii chuvashskogo naroda*, Cheboksary, 1957.

Tseluyko, K. K. "The Toponymy of the Pokrovskiy Rayon of Dnepropetrovsk Oblast'" [in Ukrainian], *Movoznavstvo Naukovi zapiski*, vol. 14, Kiyev, 1957.

Shostakovich, V. G. "The Historico-ethnographic Significance of the Names of the Rivers of Siberia," Sbornik *Ocherki po Zemlevedeniyu i Ekonomike Vostochnoy Sibiri*," no. 11, Irkutsk, 1926.

Endzelins, J. "Toponymic Names of the Latvian SSR" (*Latvijas RSR vietvardi* [in Latvian]), I, No. 1, Riga, 1956; foreword in Russian.

Part IV

THE ROLE OF
GEOGRAPHERS IN
THE TRANSFORMATION
OF NATURE

V. Yu. Vize (1886-1953)

A. S. Barkov (1873-1954)

F. P. Litke (1797-1882)

N. I. Vavilov (1887-1943)

CHAPTER 34

THE STUDY, RATIONAL UTILIZATION, AND PRESERVATION, OF NATURAL RESOURCES

I. P. Gerasimov

The geographic sciences in the USSR have great achievements to their credit in the discovery and characterization of the manifold natural resources in our vast country. They have been obtained as a result of the broad scope of scientific and practical scientific work. Thus, for example, the systematic study of the *climatic and water* resources has for a very long time been conducted in the USSR on an ever-growing scale by the meteorologic and hydrologic stations, observatories, and the scientific institutions of the Hydrometeorologic Service. The numerous hydroclimatic reference books, maps, and surveys compiled for the entire country as a whole, by union and autonomous republics, as well as for the individual administrative oblasts, represent the main result of this great and prolonged effort.

The study of the *available lands* in our country has always been carried on, and is now being conducted by the land-organization agencies of the Ministry of Agriculture of the USSR and of the union republics. As a result, we have the so-called agricultural land statistics, i.e., an inventory of the areas of plowlands, pasturelands, hayfields, forests, and other types of lands used in agriculture, made on various scales which embrace the whole country, a republic, an administrative oblast, a rayon, or an individual enterprise. A very important supplement to such an inventory of agricultural lands is the study and mapping of soils, executed by the soil detachments of the land-organization agencies, as well as by various scientific institutions (for example, the soil institutes of the Academy of Sciences of the USSR and the union republics) and by the higher educational institutions. Lately, the geographic scientific research institutions and higher educational institutions have also begun to take a great part in the study of the country's land resources.

The *vegetation resources*—forest, fodder, and technical—are being studied by a very large number of practical and scientific institutions. Among them should be mentioned first of all the forest-organization parties and agencies, as well as the already mentioned land-organization agencies, which are making an inventory of the natural fodder lands. A great amount of work on the investigation of vegetation resources is being accomplished by various botanical institutes of the Academy of Sciences of the USSR and the union republics, by the institutes for the study of forests, fodders, etc.

Among the practical and scientific institutions studying the *game animal resources* are many zoological scientific-research institutes, fishery institutes, hunting and fur industry institutes, game inspectorates, nature preserves, and other organizations.

Still, the present state of the study of the natural resources in the USSR cannot be acknowledged to satisfy the many-sided demands which are being made and will continue to be made upon them by the rapidly developing planned socialist economy.

Firstly, the study and characterization of the main types of natural resources in the USSR are conducted by various official agencies and numerous institutions. The co-ordination of the work is sometimes inadequate and not arranged in an organized manner. It sometimes happens that the institutions, in studying one and the same resources, act parallel to one another, using different working methods. Yet certain objects remain little studied. A positive exception in this respect is the study and rational utilization of the mineral resources, which are united in the system of the Ministry of Geology and Conservation of Mineral Wealth, as well as the study of the peat resources, concentrated in the system of the special Peat-Reserve Administration.

Secondly, a considerable part of the work on the study of the natural resources of the Soviet Union is of a purely practical and specialized character. This work is often not carried to the point of a systematic generalization of the primary data obtained and is usually not conducted in a sufficiently integrated manner. All this greatly complicates the use of the available data on the natural resources by the planning and designing organizations, particularly in drafting prospective plans for the development of the Soviet national economy and of its individual parts.

Such gaps in the scientific generalization of the data on the natural resources of the USSR are due in considerable degree to the insufficient participation of geographers in this work. After all, the most rational methods of generalizing the data under consideration are special geographic reference publications of the cadastral type for the whole country or for individual parts of it; geographic survey maps and atlases; integrated geographic descriptions of concrete territories and characterizations of individual large and small regions and of the country as a whole. The reference publications on the climatic conditions of the individual territories, systematically issued by the Hydrometeorologic Service, are examples of this type of publications. As is known, a similar publication for the water resources were the so-called reference handbooks on the water cadaster of the USSR, the systematic compilation and publication of which, however, has been interrupted. It is extremely necessary not only to resume this important publication, but also to organize similar ones — cadasters of the land, forest, fodder, and other natural resources of the Soviet Union. Organization of the work of obtaining the necessary data for such cadasters, as well as the elaboration of co-ordinated methods of working them up, the scientific digesting of the materials obtained, and the compilation of systematic issues of cadastral handbooks, should be not only the object of persistent concern on the part of geographers, but also, to a considerable extent, the direct object of their activity (especially that of hydrologists, soil scientists, geobotanists, etc.).

Soviet cartography has very large scientific and practical achievements to its credit. To them belong not only the full coverage of the whole USSR with precise, up-to-date general geographic maps to various scales, but also progress in the field of special-purpose scientific cartography and mapping of an integrated character. For example, the whole territory of the USSR has been covered by the State Geologic Map to a scale of 1:1,000,000, which has served as the scientific point of departure for the discovery and characterization of the mineral raw-material resources. A similar State Soil Map has been compiled and published, and is being used for the land inventory and for the distribution of agro-reclamational measures; sheets of this map already cover all the main farming regions of our country. A start has also been made on the compilation of similar maps of the vegetation (particularly forests). It is now necessary to display persistent initiative in evolving work on the State Geomorphologic Map, as well as on the Hydrologic Map, and to speed up the rate of compilation of soil and geobotanical maps. Not only must this responsible cartographic work be introduced into the nationwide plan of scientific work throughout the Soviet Union, but care must also be taken to have it performed in accordance with mutually coordinated plans and methodical programs, with wide utilization of aerial photogrammetry and other modern methods of map making.

As is known, the basic method for the integrated characterization of natural resources of this or that territory is the compilation of an all-around geographic description, as well as the creation of an integrated geographic atlas. Soviet geography has highly valuable methodological experience in doing work of this type. Among its assets are many models of modern regional-geographic description of the individual union republics, the major economic geographic regions, etc., written by groups of workers of the local and central scientific institutions, and excellent integrated geographic atlases. Among the latter may be mentioned the editions of the "Great Soviet Atlas of the World," the "Marine Atlas," or the integrated atlases for the USSR, the atlases of Belorussia, the Ukraine, and other republics, and oblasts. It is necessary to expand such work by Soviet geographers in every possible way and to insure for it a scope and significance commensurate with the demands of the national economy. At the same time, the methods both of regional-geographic characterization and of cartographic production must, of course, be improved.

In the broad problem of the study of natural resources by geographers, the questions of rational resource utilization and conservation are now acquiring more and more significance. For a long time it was thought that the chief scientific task—and, above all, the task of the geographic sciences—was the discovery and characterization of this or that type of natural resource, the determination of its geographic distribution and its size and reserves. Elaboration of procedures for the practical exploitation of the discovered and studied natural resource, and still more its direct utilization usually dropped out of the geographer's field of vision and was only the object of the attention of technologists and economists. Now, however, the situation in this field of practical activity is changing radically.

Modern geography, unlike that of the past period, has as its chief object of study not so much the little investigated and remote territories with unstudied natural resources as those long since discovered and rather well explored lands and countries with a large population, developed economy, and profoundly altered nature. The degree of alteration of nature, due above all to the exploitation of natural resources, differs greatly in different countries and in the various regions of one and the same country. In many countries, especially the economically developed ones, the alterations of nature under the influence of the economic activity of human society are very great, and the modern geographer studying natural resources actually has to deal with a very complex object of investigation, profoundly different from the original, purely natural formation.

It is known that the systematic utilization of natural resources, when done with sufficient intensity by unwise methods and without the proper consideration for the conditions of its preservation or restoration, may and often does lead to very undesirable and grave consequences. The plundering destruction of forests and the shallowing of rivers, the total plowing-up of lands on steep slopes and the development of soil erosion, the complete extermination of many valuable representatives of the fauna, the pollution of the surface waters by sewage and of the atmosphere by the noxious wastes of industrial production are the most massive examples of such phenomena. The prevention or complete elimination of haphazardly destructive natural processes engendered by the irrational utilization of natural resources is becoming one of the most important tasks of modern science and, above all, of the geographic sciences. Under such conditions, the geographic sciences must concern themselves not so much with discovering and characterizing new sources of natural resources as with serving in a comprehensive scientific manner the branches of the national economy engaged in the direct utilization of the natural resources, and with seeking and providing the groundwork for new ways of exploiting them rationally. Thus, it now falls precisely to the lot of the geographic sciences, which once engaged chiefly in discovering new sources of natural wealth by studying formerly unknown lands, to have one of the most important scientific tasks of the present day—the elaboration of the most rational methods and means of utilizing the already discovered natural resources in order to insure their efficient restoration and protection from haphazard destruction. This task is an especially urgent one for Soviet geographers.

Under the conditions of a planned socialist economy conducted on scientific principles, the practical exploitation of natural resources must be linked in an especially close manner with the preservation of the natural wealth from irrational utilization entailing excessive exhaustion or complete destruction of it. *The utilization of the natural resources in our country can and must be founded on the principle of the continuous restoration of their reserves or even the progressive augmentation of the volume of exploitable resources.* Such a state of affairs can be insured in two main ways:

1. *Continuous scientific work of an exploratory character* aimed at increasing the known reserves of a natural resource through new discoveries.

2. *Application of those methods of exploitation which will increase the size of the natural resource in the process of its utilization.* Such, for example, is the rational system of land use with preservation or even progressive enhancement of the effective fertility of the soil, a correct system of forest management with artificial measures for accelerated forest renewal, the winning of steppes and deserts on the basis of radical reclamation measures, and so forth.

Finally, a third way is also possible: *the use of special protective measures* in all cases where the intensive exploitation of a natural resource causes side phenomena of a destructive or harmful character which must be prevented, stopped, or liquidated. Examples of such phenomena are the intensive gully erosion and the washing away of plowed-up soils, the pollution of the air, soil, and water by harmful industrial wastes, and the reckless diminution of the number of rare and valuable representatives of the flora and fauna.

The execution of the above-enumerated measures is based, first, upon thorough care for the preservation of the health of the Soviet people from the harmful consequences of the pollution of nature and upon the endeavor to prevent occurrences of recklessly destructive processes; second, upon the immense national-economic effect from a planned and integrated rational utilization of natural resources; and, third, upon the endeavor to preserve the many valuable elements of nature from progressive diminution and disappearance.

An important role in the nationwide enterprise of preserving and rationally utilizing natural resources belongs to the activity of the community of local students [*krayevedy*]. The Geographic Society of the USSR is also destined to play a definite organizing and propagandistic role in the movement under discussion.

Soviet geographers are already taking part in the systematic study, rational utilization, and conservation of their country's natural resources. But this participation is at times still clearly insufficient, and the collective teams of many scientific institutions of a geographic character must intensify their systematic work on the discovery of this or that kind of natural resources, its conservation, and rational utilization. In this field it is necessary:

1. To continue to work out and improve the scientific methods of inventory and economic characterization of natural resources.

2. To improve the new rational methods of exploiting the various kinds of natural resources, based on the principle of the continuous restoration of their reserves and size, the prevention or liquidation of recklessly destructive phenomena causing damage to the natural resources.

3. To make a systematic generalization of the most important materials for the inventory and evaluation of natural resources so that, on the basis of an objective analysis of them, the necessary conclusions may be drawn and the necessary proposals made concerning the further development of scientific-research work and the practical exploitation of the various natural resources.

The successful solution of all these vast and responsible tasks will be an important contribution by geographers to the construction of communism which has been effected in our country.

CHAPTER 35

THE EXPLORATION AND DEVELOPMENT OF POLAR LANDS

Ya. Ya. Gakkel'

In the development of Soviet geography, exploration of the Arctic and, in recent years, also of the Antarctic, occupies a conspicuous place. The progress achieved here is due above all to the fact that scientific geographic investigations in these almost inaccessible regions have, in Soviet times, been conducted as enterprises of a national character. They have come to be planned and purposeful and have assumed an unprecedented scope. The polar explorers have all possible means of modern technology at their disposal.

The purpose of exploration in the Arctic has been the search for, and subsequent utilization of, the very rich natural resources of the remote northern margins of the country, as well as the raising of the material welfare and culture of the poorly developed small nationalities of the North. But the first task was the solution of the transportation problem of Arctic navigation.

As is known, many daring navigators and scholars have made repeated attempts to carry out the idea of mastering the Northeast Passage, which was first advanced in the 16th century by D. Gerasimov. One of the early attempts of this sort is attested by the remarkable archeologic find made by Soviet hydrographers in 1940 on the Thaddeus Islands [*Ostrova Faddeya*] and in Sims Gulf [*Zaliv Simsa*] (Laptev Sea). As established by A. P. Okladnikov (1945) and by other scholars, the objects of equipment, instruments, utensils, and coins found here unquestionably belonged to unknown seafarers who penetrated into the Laptev Sea back in the first quarter of the 17th century.

The long history of the exploration of the Arctic seas and their shores abounds in many glorious names. Among them are, in particular, the participants in the Second Kamchatkan Expedition of 1733-1743: S. Chelyuskin, V. Pronchishchev, D. Sterlegov, F. Minin, S. Malygin, A. Chirikov, the brothers D. and Kh. Laptev, and their bold companions. The idea of gaining a sea route passing through the Arctic seas was developed and reinforced by the scientific data in the works of the great Lomonosov and, at the beginning of the 20th century, in the utterances and projects of D. I. Mendeleyev and other outstanding Russian scholars. This idea captivated A. M. Sibiryakov and M. K. Sidorov, the well-known industrialists and social figures who sacrificed large sums of money for the development of the sea route to Siberia. In the years preceding the October Revolution, much was done by G. Ya. Sedov, V. A. Rusanov, and other daring explorers to discover a Northeast sea passage. They set out with extremely scanty means, undaunted by the menacing elements.

The progress achieved by such remarkable lone-wolf, daredevil pioneers in the mastery of the Northern Sea Route, having at their disposal only feeble technical means quite insufficient for the solution of such a difficult task, instilled in Soviet scholars and seamen the confidence that, with the employment of modern technology and the wide support of the State, the Northeast Passage could be converted into a sea route wholly suited for freight transportation between the ports of the Atlantic and Pacific Oceans. On 2 July, 1918, they received the first order: the government decree over V. I. Lenin's signature to outfit a large hydrographic expedition (of 22 vessels) with the principal task of establishing regular sea communication, primarily on the route to the mouths of the West Siberian rivers. All the further undertakings, the planning and the realization of the broad program of work for the mastery of the Northern Sea Route and the raising of the productive forces in the regions facing toward it, were directed by the Communist Party and the Soviet Government.

In the 1920's began the systematic study and mastery of individual sections of the Northern Sea Route — by the Kara Sea Expeditions in the west (to the mouths of the Ob' and Yenisey), and in the east by voyages from Vladivostok to the mouth of the Kolyma, and then to the mouth of the

Lena. The year 1932 was marked by the historic voyage of the icebreaker "A. Sibiryakov," which traveled the whole Northern Sea Route in one navigation season. Since then this through route has developed rapidly, and with it the whole economy of the Far North of the country. This has also been promoted to no small degree by the arrangement for regular navigation on the northern sections of the great Siberian rivers: the Ob', Yenisey, and Lena, as well as the Pyasina, Khatanga, Anabar, Olenëk, Yana, Indigirka, and Kolyma, which had formerly not been used at all for transportation. Because of their connecting role, all these rivers, traversing Siberia in meridional directions, together with the Northern Sea Route (mainly latitudinal in direction), constitute a single, highly ramified transportation network suited for penetrating into the heart of the northern regions of Siberia, where hitherto there had been no ways of communication aside from trails little suited for the industrial conquest of these vast territories. The glorious and heroic history of the exploration and mastery of the Northern Sea Route has been the subject of detailed works by Soviet scholars V. Yu. Vize (1946), M. I. Belov (1952, 1956, 1959) and D. M. Pinkhenson (1960).

In all stages of development in the Soviet Arctic of the sea, river and, later, air transportation and the economic conquest of the North, scientific research work of broad geographic scope has always played a considerable role, and, in the first stages, a leading one. On the continent and the islands of the Arctic seas a geologic survey and mining-geologic, topo-geodetic, and hunting-and-fishing biologic work are being carried on; and in the waters of the Arctic Ocean and on the northern parts of the Siberian rivers, oceanographic, hydrometeorologic, and hydrographic investigations are being made.

In characterizing the present extent of the geographic study of the Soviet Arctic one must speak first of all about its *cartographic portrayal*. Its entire land mass, including the islands, now solidly covered by an aerial photogrammetric survey, is in no way inferior in topographic coverage to the rest of the Soviet Union. The new 1:1,000,000 State Map of the USSR produced as a result of this survey, and very valuable in itself, has also served as a basis for the compilation of various general geographic maps of the whole country to scales of 1:2,500,000 and 1:5,000,000, embracing the Arctic expanses. Noteworthy special-purpose maps generalizing our geographic knowledge and portraying the extent of the study of the Soviet Arctic in its various aspects are being compiled and published on the same wholly reliable base.

In accord with the interests of the development of the national economy and above all for the utilization of minerals, the geologic structure of the Soviet Arctic has been studied in the most detail. The geologic survey to a scale of 1:1,000,000, and in some regions still larger, now covers its entire territory. Geologists have made wide use of aerial photography and geophysical methods of investigation and have conducted a very effective search for minerals. The results of these investigations, made chiefly by the most experienced geologists of the Scientific-Research Institute of Arctic Geology, have been generalized in a collective work in the form of regional essays ("Geology of the Soviet Arctic," 1957) with an appended geologic map of the Soviet Arctic to a scale of 1:2,500,000. Also very valuable is the map of Quaternary deposits (to the same scale), as well as the earlier works by V. N. Saks on the Quaternary geology of the Arctic (1953).

As a result of the geologic survey and the geologic-geophysical explorations in the Soviet Arctic, innumerable mineral deposits have been discovered. For example, deposits of nickel and platinum in the Noril'sk region; cassiterite on Chukotka [peninsula], in the Yana River basin, and in other regions; gold on the Kolyma River; and diamonds in the center of the Siberian Platform. Also discovered have been very valuable deposits of apatite in the Khibiny [mountains] and very large coal deposits: the Pechora River Basin; the Tunguska Coal Basin; the Zyryanka deposit on the Kolyma River; seams in the region of Ugol'naya Bay (Bering Sea); and many others. All these minerals are a part of the inestimable riches hidden in the depths of the Soviet Arctic. Mining enterprises have been created on some of these deposits: pits, mines, whole kombinats of the mining and metallurgic industry. Thanks to this, industrialization is being successfully developed, and along with it the entire economy of the Soviet Arctic. A no less important precondition for this has been the mastery of the Northern Sea Route, and the bringing in of heavy industrial equipment over it. On the other hand, the mastery of the Northern Sea Route could likewise not have attained its proper development if the geologists had not discovered coal deposits in the regions of the Arctic itself, the exploitation of which makes it possible to supply local coal to the icebreakers and transport vessels navigating this route.

With the development of industry, new workers' settlements have arisen around the mines and other enterprises and have now become large towns; for example, Kirovsk, Vorkuta, Noril'sk, and the seaports of Amderma, Dudinka, Pevek, and Egvekinot.

In designing major industrial and public-utility enterprises, ports, railroads and highways, bridges, and dwellings under Arctic conditions characterized by "perpetual" frost, an important role has been played by extensive *investigations of the distribution, thickness, and temperature regime of the perenially frozen subsoil.* As a result of this study, methods suited to these conditions for building roads and industrial and civilian structures have been worked out and are now being widely applied.* Of great scientific importance are the investigations of fossil ice, particularly those made by P. A. Shumskiy (1952).

The most considerable field investigations in the study of the *soil and plant cover* of the Arctic territories have been made by Professor B. N. Gorodkov (1939, 1947, 1949). During many years of field activity, he has made rich collections of plants and has produced important generalizing works on the vegetation of the Arctic (1935, 1946). Interesting works on Arctic geobotany have also been written by B. A. Tikhomirov, who also has to his credit, in particular, an investigation into the reconstruction of the vegetation cover of the Arctic in the Quaternary period (1944).

Considerable attention is now being paid, also, to the generalization of all the available floral data, among which is much new material gathered in the last few years concerning the tundras: East European, Polar Urals, and especially Siberian. On the tundras of the Kola Peninsula, such generalization has been done in the five-volume publication "Flora of the Murmansk Oblast," which is now being completed. The Botanical Institute is now compiling a multi-volume work on "The Arctic Flora of the USSR."

The Arctic tundras form a considerable part (15 per cent) of the territory of the Soviet Union and, together with the sparse forests of the forest-tundra, more than one-third (35 per cent). Investigations of the plant cover here are important from the viewpoint of the rational utilization of the fodder resources for reindeer raising—one of the main branches of the local economy, as well as in the interest of conserving the stock of wild reindeer. The study of these and other questions is engaging the attention of the Botanical Institute of the Academy of Sciences of the USSR and its branches, as well as the specialized Scientific-Research Institute of Agriculture of the Extreme North (at Noril'sk), which has a network of experimental stations. Farming was formerly limited by the Arctic Circle, but has now been extended in the European part of the country to 69° north latitude, and in Siberia even to 72°. Separate focal points of farming with early vegetable raising in covered and partly in open ground, as well as focal points of meat-and-dairy animal husbandry, are penetrating still farther northward (to Dikson Island). Discovery has been made of the immense role of many tundra plants used in the diet of the Chukchi, the Eskimos, and other nationalities of the North.

A considerable part of Siberia, and not only its Arctic territory proper, gravitates toward the Northern Sea Route with respect to transportation and economy; since the 1920's, extensive use has been made of the immense timber resources of Siberia, especially Western. The shipment of lumber from here, particularly for export, to satisfy the ever-growing demand for it on Western European markets has in turn contributed considerably to the development of the sea route. It was for this reason that the town of Igarka, accessible for seagoing vessels, was founded in 1929 on the Yenisey, far from its mouth. It has now become a large industrial center, in which many wood-working enterprises are concentrated.

Zoogeographic and hydrobiologic investigations on the land and in the seas of the Soviet Arctic are being conducted chiefly in the interest of the industrial utilization of fur-bearing animals, the ichthyofauna, the sea mammals in the coastal regions, etc. The study of these hunting-and-fishing resources engages the attention of the Zoologic Institute and the northern branches of the Academy of Sciences of the USSR, as well as the Institute of Agriculture of the Extreme North.

The generalization of works dealing with the individual aspects of nature, in summary works on the physical geography of the whole Soviet Arctic, is still a matter for the future. In a very schematized form, such generalizations, made earlier, are contained in the collective work of V. Yu. Vize and his co-authors (1946). For the adjacent geographic zone, the Subarctic, this has been done in the very

---

*For more details on this see Chapter 11, "Permafrost Science (Geocryology)."

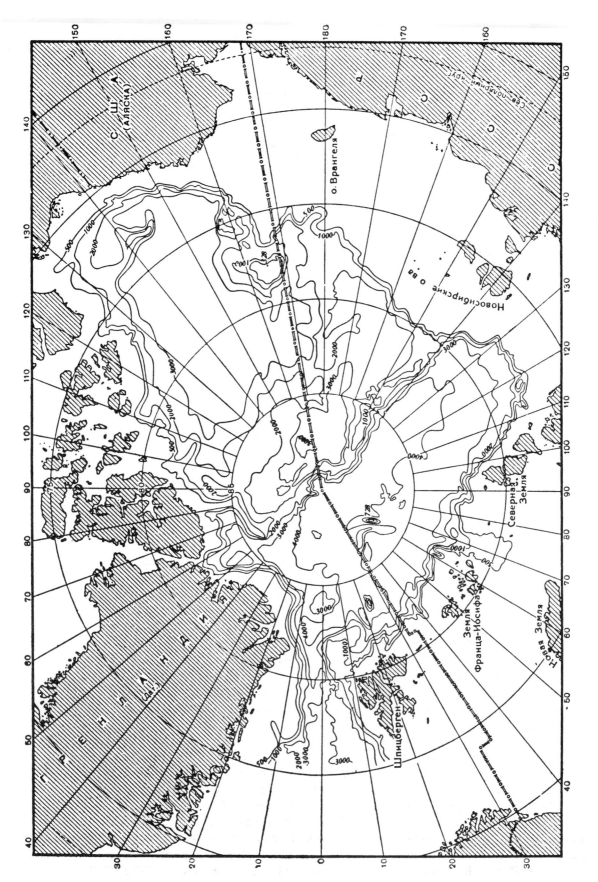

Fig. 20. RELIEF OF THE BOTTOM OF THE ARCTIC BASIN (as of 1 March, 1959)

interesting investigation by Academician A. A. Grigor'yev (1956). As for the regional physical geography of the Soviet Arctic, the Arctic and Antarctic Institutes have prepared for publication monographs on Northern Yakutia and other regions of the Arctic lands.

Regular *aerometeorologic, hydrologic, and ice observations* occupy a prominent place in the study of the Arctic, its vast territories, and expanses of water. The materials from these observations are used above all by the synoptic service, as well as in investigations into problems of physical geography, particularly the circulation of the atmosphere, the waters, and drifting ice. Such observations are made by an extensive network of permanent polar stations; on the shores and islands of the Arctic seas alone there are about a hundred Soviet hydrometeorologic and aerometeorologic stations. In accordance with a broader program embracing many geophysical phenomena (terrestrial magnetism, earth currents, cosmic radiation, aurora borealis), observations are conducted in the Arctic observatories (Dikson, Pevek, Tiksi, Franz Josef Land; in the latter two, seismic observations are also made).

A very important role in the *investigation of the layers of water and the floor and of the meteorologic and ice regimes of the Arctic Basin* and the marginal seas of the Arctic Ocean is played by systematic aerial ice reconnaissance and observations by oceanographic expeditions, particularly on vessels regularly patrolling the ice edge in the Arctic seas and, in the high latitudes, on the "Severnyy Polyus" ("North Pole") drifting scientific-research stations. Two stations have operated annually since 1954. Some stations have operated without interruption, but with a yearly change of observation personnel, for more than three years (for example the SP-6). The drifting stations have traveled a total distance of more than 27,000 kilometers. The stations' workers have written interesting works, for example P. A. Gordiyenko (1958) on the questions of ice drift and B. A. Savel'yev (1958) on the physical properties of sea ice in the melt period.

Alongside stations of this sort, dozens of automatic radio-meteorologic units operating by themselves (without servicing personnel) are now placed annually on the ice floes of the Arctic Ocean. These stations play an important role in the synoptic service and in the systematic study of ice drift over vast expanses.

Large high-latitude air expeditions are made annually to arrange and supply the ordinary drifting stations. These expeditions themselves also make oceanographic observations at many points (about 600 since 1948) of the Arctic basin, with observations being made daily, or every other day at some points, and here and there in fifteen-day series. In conjunction with the drifting stations, whose long series of observations form cross sections across the whole Arctic basin in different directions, the aerial expeditions have carried out a fairly detailed oceanographic survey. These investigations have been marked by major scientific discoveries, as a result of which the geographic and paleogeographic notions of the nature of the Arctic basin have been radically changed and this vast, almost inaccessible basin of the Arctic Ocean may now be placed in one of the first positions among the other basins of the World Ocean with respect to the extent to which it has been studied (see Fig. 20). These achievements are expressed most graphically in the bathymetry of the Arctic Basin, characterized by spot depths of almost 7,000 meters, measured by all the Soviet expeditions and drifting stations, as well as by the American stations T-3 and "Alpha" (Fig. 20).

Among the largest morphologic features characterizing the floor of the Arctic Basin, three main mountain structures stand out: the Lomonosov Ridge [*Khrebet Lomonosova*]; the Mendeleyev Ridge [*Khrebet Mendeleyeva*], equally great in extent but somewhat less high, the stretch from Wrangel Island to Ellesmere Island and other features which in the most general manner had first been tentatively fixed in 1948, as well as those of the Lomonosov Ridge parallel to it, and had later been gradually determined more precisely (Gakkel', 1957); and the mountain system of the youngest Cenozoic formation, also extending parallel to Lomonosov Ridge (but in the opposite direction) and to the Eurasian continental slope (northward from Spitzbergen, Franz Josef Land, and Severnaya Zemlya, as well as eastward from the latter).

One of the submarine summits (86° 54′ N. and 61° 40′ E.) of this mountain system, according to measurements made on drifting station SP-6 on 15 February, 1959, is only 728 meters below the surface, whereas the depth only five miles from there reaches 4,320 meters. In this region the mountains form a solid system of virgations, so that individual depressions here have the greatest depths (5,449 meters) (among those measured) in the "Litke" sink (1955, at 82° 24′ N. and 19° 32′ E.) and over 5,220 meters in the "G. Sedov" sink.

The chief features of the *tectonic* structure of the Arctic Basin now present themselves in the following form: the oldest formation is the Hyperborean (according to Academician N. S. Shatskiy), an oceanic platform occupying the expanse of the Beaufort Basin. On the north and west this platform is bordered by the pre-Paleozoic Mendeleyev Ridge, on the other side of which lies the Makarov Basin (Kotlovina Makarova). As in the continental platforms too, the formation next in age that frames in these structures is the Lomonosov Ridge, assigned by geologists to the Mesozoic formations (as are also the like-aged northern part of Ellesmere Island and the Novosibirskiye Ostrova [Islands]). Still farther along the periphery, in the Nansen Basin, these structures are hemmed by the above-outlined, thus far unnamed, Cenozoic structure, which is a direct continuation of the Middle Atlantic Ridge. In keeping with this general scheme, the depths of the Arctic Basin increase from the Beaufort Basin (less than 4,000 meters) to the Makarov Basin (more than 4,000 meters at places) and to the Nansen Basin, in which the half adjacent to the Lomonosov Ridge is everywhere deeper than 4,000 and at places reaches depths of 5,000 meters. The relative altitudes of the submarine ridges and their seismic activity increase in the same direction. In all these respects, an intermediate position is held by the Mesozoic Lomonosov Ridge, which still retains traits of seismic (D. G. Panov) and volcanic (Gakkel', 1957) activity, absent in the Mendeleyev Ridge. The third, unnamed ridge, on the contrary, is characterized by the least activity; precisely along this ridge lies the seismic belt which extends to here, and on to the mouth of the Lena River, from the Atlantic. With respect to structure, the unnamed ridge may be regarded as the immediate continuation of the Middle Atlantic Ridge, which extends to here, into the Arctic Basin, through Iceland and the Greenland Sea. Incidentally, as to the Greenland Sea, the main morphologic features of its bottom, greatly broken up into structures having a double trend, also correspond to such a treatment, in accordance with seismology. This trend is from southwest to northeast and perpendicular to the former, with the two directions being the same as along the fracture lines recorded in Iceland and on Jan Mayen, as well as on Spitzbergen.

Deep-seated fractures of enormous extent, having the form of radial or radially concentric formations, such as may also be seen on maps of the Antarctic, have likewise been noted in the Arctic Basin. The existence of radial systems of "fissures" in the ocean floor, diverging from the centers of domed uplifts, was first indicated two centuries ago, in the form of a supposition that has now been brilliantly confirmed, by M. V. Lomonosov in his work "The First Foundations of Metallurgy and Ore Bodies." These formations, also reflected in the configuration of the seashores, river valleys, and lake basins, were noted by G. D. Rikhter (1955). Such systems of fractures, as well as folded and other formations in the shape of ring-formed mountains, mountain and island arcs, are not peculiar to the earth alone. They are found on the moon and on certain planets accessible to telescopic observation.

One of the most considerable radially concentric systems is the Siberian Platform with its central ancient core and successive peripheral mountain formations (including the Aleut-Kamchatka arc), as well as volcanic and geochemical belts (according to Fersman). It is noteworthy that the Siberian and Canadian centers of evolvement of tectonic, geochemical, baric, and other formations are simultaneously centers of world magnetic anomalies (the Asiatic and Canadian maxima of geomagnetic-field intensity). All these natural characteristics have made it possible to characterize these areas as distinctive energy centers in which the tectonic, geomagnetic, and other forces have extreme intensity (Gakkel', 1957). With this approach to the phenomena under discussion it becomes evident that the sources of magnetic anomalies of this sort are to be sought in the deep-seated layers of the earth's crust or even in the substratum under the crust. It is interesting to note that the deep-seated origin of the sources of the East-Siberian magnetic anomaly follows from an analysis of the magnetometric data obtained from the third Soviet artificial satellite of the earth ("The Universe Reveals Its Secrets" ["Vselennaya raskryvayet svoi tayny", *Pravda* July 15, 1959]).

Let us turn to the results of the latest investigations of the *floor deposits in the Arctic Ocean.* An analysis of the collections of cores (3.5 meters long) gathered in the Arctic Basin reveals various conditions of deposition of the sediments, expressed in the sharp difference between the cores from the basins and those from the mountain ridges. This analysis also throws light on the paleogeographic conditions, which have changed considerably during the last 180-190 thousand years. The warm periods, corresponding to the cinnamon-brown interlayers of the deposits containing many foraminifera, were succeeded by cold periods (gray layers) when the entrance of warm Atlantic waters into the Arctic Basin ceased almost entirely or even totally (Belov and others, 1955). It is interesting that the periods when the gray ooze was deposited, as noted by V. N. Saks, correspond to the same periods of chilling of the climate as are characterized by the glacial Quaternary deposits on the present dry land.

These data confirm, in particular, the views of those scholars who believe that the Atlantic waters pouring into the Arctic Basin with the deep-seated current, warm it and exert a definite influence on the ice conditions. In this respect, a certain significance attaches to the study of the *water masses,* especially the Atlantic ones, which pour in here chiefly through the strait between Greenland and Spitzbergen. This is why Soviet oceanographic expeditions in the last few years have engaged in systematic investigations of this region, in different seasons. A study is also being made of the warming and freshening influence of the entrance of river waters into the Arctic seas and thence into the Arctic Basin, and their effect upon the formation of the sea currents in this basin (Zubov, 1945; Antonov, 1958). Of importance in the study of all these questions are the observations made at the permanent hydrologic stations located near the mouths of rivers.

No less important is consideration of the *atmospheric influence on the ice conditions* of the Arctic Basin and the marginal seas of the Arctic Ocean. Thermically, this influence changes with the conditions of advection of heat brought with the air masses and registered in the form of positive or negative temperature anomalies. These anomalies manifest themselves in an intensified or, on the contrary, in a retarded freezing-over of the seas and melting of the ice. Dynamically, the transfer of air masses governs the influence of the winds on the development of the surface currents and the ice drift, promoting or else impeding the carrying out of the ice. Hence, investigation of the complex questions of atmospheric circulation is of prime significance not only over the Arctic Ocean proper, but also in the whole Northern Hemisphere. A great contribution to the study of these questions has been made by the investigations of G. Ya. Vangengeym, who discovered three main types of atmospheric circulation — western, eastern, and meridional —, and also those of A. A. Girs (1955); long-range weather forecasts are being compiled on the basis of their work and under their direction. Still earlier, B. L. Dzerdzeyevskiy had elucidated in a new manner the conditions of atmospheric circulation in the high Arctic latitudes, and given his classification of atmospheric circulation.

Ever increasing prognostic significance now also attaches to *heliogeophysical research* which, beginning with the works of V. Yu. Vize, have brought out more and more clearly the influence of the changes in solar activity upon the circulation of the atmosphere and the hydrosphere and upon the fluctuations of the icing of the Polar seas. A great generalizing work on this problem has been written by M. S. Eygenson (1957) on the basis of heliogeophysical premises. He was the first to give, in 1959, a super-long-range forecast, to the effect that solar activity, growing slowly from 1900 to 1950, would drop in the impending period 1960-1980.

As regards the ordinary *long-range ice forecasts* (on sea ice), the state of the ice and the navigation conditions (in the eastern part of the Kara Sea) were first predicted back in 1915 by B. P. Mul'tanovskiy, and that very successfully. Especially great efforts in this field have been made by V. Yu. Vize, who, without counting his earlier predictions on the Barents Sea, began in 1932 to forecast the ice conditions for navigation over the whole Northern Sea Route. The principles of investigation into questions of ice forecasting were generalized in his work of 1944.

Finally, in ice forecasts, without which no operation on the Northern Sea Route is now conceivable, one cannot dispense with consideration of the atmospheric-circulation conditions expected for the same time and, consequently, the justifiability of the ice conditions predicted depends to a considerable extent upon the reliability of the weather forecasts. In particular, this depends upon the calculation of the isobaric drift, i.e., the drift of the ice by isobars — in accordance with the rules of N. N. Zubov, who proposed this method (1945) and, in general, has made a great contribution to oceanology and ice science by his many works.

Of no less importance in ice forecasts is a profound knowledge of the *hydrologic regime* of the seas, the laws of its formation and variability in dependence upon such and such conditions. The progressive method here employed for the integrated typing of the hydrologic regime, worked out by V. N. Stepanov (1957) — unlike the usual statistical method, which brings out only certain average characteristics of the individual elements of the regime — makes it possible to clarify the role of the main factors, the laws governing the interaction between them, their changes by seasons in dependence upon the synoptic conditions, etc.

In synthetic geographic terms, the substantial results of ascertaining the regime and other aspects of the nature of the Arctic Ocean have been reflected in the fact that Ya. Ya. Gakkel' (1957) has assigned the continental slope delimiting the Arctic Basin from the shelf seas to a separate oceanographic landscape zone. This zone, according to all indices, is characterized by entirely distinctive hydrologic, hydrochemical, aero-meteorologic, and zoohydrobiologic, particularly endemic, conditions.

In Antarctic waters, Soviet scientists have been conducting major systematic explorations since 1947, during the operations [*promysly*] of the Soviet "Slava" ["Glory"] whaling flotilla, and since 1955, and later during the International Geophysical Year and the International Geophysical Congress, also by the integrated Antarctic expedition aboard the diesel-electric vessels "Ob'" and "Lena."

Interesting work in the field of the geography of the Southern Hemisphere has been done by V. Kh. Buynitskiy, who on the basis of many features quite justifiably proposed that the zone of the Antarctic convergence of the oceanic waters be regarded as the natural physical-geographic boundary of the southern polar area (1956). This proposal was quickly accepted by the International Conference of the Special Committee on Antarctic Expeditions (SKAAR) held in The Hague in February, 1958.

For the whole Southern Hemisphere, K. A. Brodskiy, K. K. Markov, and V. I. Shil'nikov have proposed a division into natural zones — an Antarctic (including a Subantarctic) Zone, a Southern Temperate Zone, and a Subtropical Zone — as natural boundaries between which it is most correct to regard, in the main, the Antarctic convergence and divergence, and likewise the subtropical (Subantarctic) convergence (1959). The latitudinal zonality (four zones) in the character of the floor deposits in the oceans washing Antarctica have been noted by A. V. Zhivago and A. P. Lisitsyn. It is interesting that the analysis of long cores of bottom make it possible to reconstruct the paleogeographic conditions not only of the Quaternary, but also that the upper stage of the Tertiary deposits has shown a displacement of the boundaries between these zones. This southward displacement, the authors believe, reflects a general warming of the climate in Quaternary times (1958).

No less considerable are the results of Soviet explorations on the Antarctic continent, especially in the almost unstudied regions most difficult of access. Besides the main "Mirnyy" observatory, the "Oazis" station, now handed over to Poland, as well as the "Lazarev" station (since 1959), the inland continental stations "Pionerskaya," "Komsomol'skaya," "Vostok," and "Sovetskaya" were established to operate during the IGY period, with a lengthy cycle of observations under the IGY program, and later with a short-term collection of materials at the Pole of Relative Inaccessibility.

The observations at the "Vostok" station are interesting in that the lowest absolute minimum air temperature on the earth's surface has been recorded here (the Cold Pole): −87.4° C., with a mean monthly temperature of −71.8° for August (at "Sovetskaya" station the corresponding figures are −86.8° and −71.6°, respectively). The unusually severe intracontinental climatic conditions of Antarctica are further aggravated by the greater altitude (up to 4,000 meters) above sea level and, consequently, by the low atmospheric pressure and lack of oxygen.

Among the work done during the long sled-and-tractor treks into the heart of the southern polar continent, the seismic sounding of the depths at which the bedrock surface of the continent lies beneath its armor of ice has perhaps proved the most substantial in its results. Thanks to this sounding, the thicknesses of the glacial cover have been determined (as much as 4,000 meters) and a profile of the bedrock of the continent has been obtained over the whole immense distance from "Mirnyy"; that is, from the coast of Antarctica to the South Pole with a branch (more than 550 kilometers) from "Komsomol'skaya" station to the Pole of Inaccessibility.

As was discovered at a distance of 100 kilometers from the coast of Antarctica, its bedrock surface in many sections lies below sea level or at this level, which evidences the fjord-like or even insular character of the given zone, which in this case may be assigned to the shelf. Of the same character is the profile of the bedrock surface of eastern Antarctica, recorded by the seismic sounding done by the Norwegian-Anglo-Swedish expedition of 1949-1952 in the region of Queen Maud Land over a 600-kilometer stretch, and also the profile established by the French expedition on the route from Dumont d'Urville to Charcot, about 500 kilometers long. With such an understanding of the structure of the peripheral part of Antarctica, which apparently does not have a very broad shelf, we see that, contrary to existing opinion, its antipode, the Arctic Basin is not surrounded by an exceptionally broad shelf but by one of about the same size as in Antarctica, a shelf which in this geologic epoch is occupied by the marginal seas of the Arctic Ocean.

In the central area of eastern Antarctica, in the section of the profile from "Sovetskaya" station to the Pole of Inaccessibility, the bedrock rises to 3,000 meters or more; here it is covered with a comparatively small thickness of ice: 800-900 meters. Here too, however, a considerable depression with a relative depth of not less than 1,000 meters and a width of more than 100 kilometers has been noted in this bedrock. P. S. Voronov (1959) connects this depression with the zone of meridional block structures (400-500 kilometers broad) which may be traced for an immense distance southward from Olaf Pruds Bay, and also northward from it, on the shelf, where the Soviet expedition (1956) found a meridional trough. This immense graben-like depression buried under the ice, and corresponding to the regional meridional fractures, is supposed by P. S. Voronov to be bordered on both sides by belts of block mountains. Their summits, in the form of nunataks and under-ice elevations, clearly distinguished already as far as 80° S. latitude, have been uplifted 1,500-2,000 meters above the depressions in the bedrock. This zone of block structures, including the Prince Charles Mountains, the American Highland (Amerikanskoye Nagor'ye), and also, apparently, King Edward VII Plateau and the Queen Maud Mountains, joins in the region of the latter with the analogous structures of the Great Antarctic Horst (bounding the Ross Shelf Glacier [=Barrier] and the Ross Sea on the west) and with those which border all of eastern Antarctica. The meridional block mountain systems outlined according to P. S. Voronov's concepts (1959) break up eastern Antarctica into two main compensatory structural depressions.

With respect to gravitation, the central area of eastern Antarctica has been found to represent a great regional negative anomaly. This agrees well with the earlier conclusion by I. D. Zhongolovich (1952) to the effect that the earth's center of gravity, which does not coincide with its geometric center, has been displaced into the Northern Hemisphere. One of the interesting results of this eccentricity of the force of gravity is that, according to press reports, the American artificial satellite revolving around the earth in a meridional plane is at a greater distance from the earth in the periods of perigee over the South Pole than over the North Pole.

As may be seen from our brief survey, Soviet physical geography of the polar lands has achieved notable progress. Great geographic discoveries have been made, and they naturally have been especially noteworthy in the least-studied polar regions, so difficult of access. In the Arctic, these achievements have been very closely connected with the practical mastery of the Northern Sea Route and with the utilization of very valuable minerals and other natural resources in the national economy. Predetermining in many ways the success of practical activity, these achievements are themselves of definite scientific value.

By reason of its regional specificity, the ties of polar physical geography with geophysics, which in recent years has achieved immense progress, have been considerably broadened and strengthened. This is especially characteristic of the IGY and IGC period, marked in the USSR by the launching of the first artificial earth satellites and cosmic rockets — the grandest of the achievements of Soviet science and technology.

BASIC LITERATURE

Antonov, V. S. "The Role of Continental Runoff in the Regime of the Currents of the Arctic Ocean," Sb. *Probl. Severa,* no. 1, 1958.

Belov, M. I. "Russian Seafarers in the Arctic and Pacific Oceans," Sb. *Dokumentov XVII v.,* 1952.

Belov, M. I. "Arctic Navigation from the most Ancient Times down to the Middle of the 19th Century," *Istoriya otkrytiya i osvoyeniya Severnogo morskogo puti,* vol. I, 1956.

Belov, M. I. "Soviet Arctic Navigation in 1917-1932." *Istoriya Otkrytiya i Osvoyeniya Svernogo Morskogo Puti,* vol. III, 1959.

Belov, N. A., Lapina, N. N., and Saks, V. N. "Modern Notions of the Geology of the Central Arctic," *Priroda,* 1955, No. 7.

Brodskiy, K. M., Markov, K. K., and Shil'nikov, V. I. "The Zonality of the Temperate and High Latitudes of the Southern Hemisphere," *Priroda*, 1959, No. 7.

Buynitskiy, V. Kh. "The Antarctic Convergence as the Physico-geographic Boundary of the Antarctic." *Vestnik LGU*, No. 24, 1956, issue 4.

Vangengeym, G. Ya. "Fundamentals of the Macro-circulation Method of Long-range Meteorologic Forecasts for the Arctic," *Tr. Arktich, n.-i. in-ta*, vol. 34, 1952.

Vize, V. Yu. "Fundamentals of Long-range Ice Forecasting for the Arctic Seas," *Tr. Arktich, n.-i. in-ta*, vol. 190, 1944.

Vize, V. Yu. Seas of the Soviet Arctic (*Morya Sovetskoy Arktiki*), 3rd ed., 1948.

Vize, V. Yu., Gorbatskiy, G. V., Gorbunov, G. P., Gorodkov, B. N., Saks, V. N. *Sovetskaya Arktika*, 1946.

Voronov, P. S. "On the Supposed Zone of Buried Block Structures of Eastern Antarctica between the South Pole and Olaf Pruds Gulf," *Inform. byull. sov. antarktich. eksp.*, 1959, No. 4.

Voronov, P. S. "The Geologic Significance of the Discovery of New Mountains to the South of the Prince Charles Mountain Chain in Eastern Antarctica." *Inform. byull. sov. antarktich. eksp.*, 1959, No. 5.

"The Universe reveals its secrets. Exploration of cosmic space with the aid of rockets and satellites," *Pravda*, No. 196, 15 July, 1959.

Gakkel', Ya. Ya. "The Continental Slope as a Geographic Zone of the Arctic Ocean," *Izv. VGO*, 1957, No. 6.

Gakkel', Ya. Ya. Science and the Development of the Arctic (*Nauka i Osvoyeniye Arktiki*), 1957.

"The Geology of the Soviet Arctic," *Tr. n.-i. in-ta geologii Arktiki*, vol. 81, 1957.

Girs, A. A. "Concerning the Question of the Study of the General Circulation of the Atmosphere," *Izv. AN SSSR, seriya geogr.*, 1955, No. 4.

Gordiyenko, P. A. "The Drift of Ice in the Central Part of the Arctic Ocean," Sb. *Problm. Severa*, issue 1, 1958.

Gorodkov, B. N. The Vegetation of the Tundra Zone of the USSR (*Rastitel'nost' Tundrovoy Zony SSSR*), 1935.

Gorodkov, B. N. "On the Characteristics of the Soil Cover of the Arctic," *Izv. VGO*, vol. 71, 1939, no. 10.

Gorodkov, B. N. "Botanico-geographic Essay on the Extreme North and the Arctic," *Uch. zap. Leningr. ped. in-ta im. Gertsena*, vol. 49, 1946.

Gorodkov, B. N. "The Polar Deserts and Arctic Tundras," *Botanich, zhurn*, vol. 32, 1947, No. 1.

Gorodkov, B. N. "On the Soil and Plant Complexes of the Tundra and Polar-desert Landscapes," *Tr. II Vses. geogr. s"yezda*, vol. III, 1949.

Grigor'yev, A. A. The Subarctic. An Experiment in the Characterization of the Main Types of Geographic Environment (*Subarktika. Opyt Kharakteristiki Osnovnykh Tipov Geograficheskoy Sredy*) 2nd ed., 1956.

Zhivago, A. V., and Lisitsyn, A. P. "The Relief of the Floor and the Sediments of the Southern Ocean," *Inform. byull. antarktich. eksped.*, 1958, No. 3.

Zhongolovich, I. D. The External Gravitational Field of the Earth and the Fundamental Constants Related to It (*Vneshneye Gravitatsionnoye Pole Zemli i Fundamental'nyye Postoyannyye, Svyazannyye s Nim*), 1952.

Zubov, N. N. The Ice of the Arctic (*L'dy Arktiki*), 1945.

A historic Monument of Russian Arctic Navigation in the 17th Century (*Istoricheskiy Pamyatnik Russkogo Arkticheskogo Moreplavaniya XVII Veka*), Sbornik statey (collection of articles), 1951.

Okladnikov, A. P. "Archeologic Finds on the Northern Faddey (Thaddeus) Island," *Probl. Arktiki*, Nos. 5-6, Leningrad, 1945; the same: Russian Polar Seafarers of the 17th Century along the Coasts of the Taymyr (Peninsula) (*Russkiye Polyarnyye Morekhody XVII v. u Beregov Taymyra*), Moscow-Leningrad, 1948.

Panov, D. G. "The Problem of the Origin of the Continents and Oceans in the Light of New Investigations," *Priroda*, 1950, No. 3.

Pinkhenson, D. M. "The Study of the Arctic and the Struggle for the Mastery of the Northern Sea Route in the Epoch of Capitalism," *Istoriya Otkrytiya i Osvoyeniya Severnogo Morskogo Puti*, vol. II, 1960.

Rikhter, G. D. "The Main Features of the Orography of the Northern Polar Areas," *Izv. AN SSSR, seriya geogr.*, 1955, No. 4.

Savel'yev, B. A. "The Study of the Ice in the Region of the Drift of Station SP-4 in the Period of its Melting and Destruction in 1955," Sb. *Probl. Severa*, no. 2, 1958.

Saks, V. N. "The Quaternary Period in the Soviet Arctic," *Tr. n.-i. in-ta geologii Arktiki*, vol. 77, 1953.

Stepanov, V. N. "Integrated Typing of the Hydrologic Regime of the Sea," *Probl. Arktiki*, no. 2, 1957.

Tauberg, G. M. *Antarktika*, part I, Leningrad, 1956.

Tikhomirov, B. A. "Main Features of the Quaternary History of the Vegetation Cover of the Soviet Arctic," *Bot. zhurn.*, vol. 29, 1944, Nos. 2-3.

Shumskiy, P. A. "The Present Glaciation of the Soviet Arctic," *Tr. Arktich. n-i. in-ta*, vol. II, 1949.

Shumskiy, P. A. "Investigation of the Fossil Ice of Central Yakutia," *Issled. vechn. merzl. v Yakutsk. resp.*, no. 3, 1952.

Eygenson, M. S. Essays on the Physico-geographic Manifestations of Solar Activity (*Ocherki Fisiko-geograficheskikh Proyavleniy Solnechnoy Aktivnosti*), L'vov, 1957.

Eygenson, M. S. "The Ice of the Antarctic, Fluctuations of Climate and Solar Activity," *Byull. sov. antarktich. eksp.*, 1959, No. 8.

CHAPTER 36

GEOGRAPHIC STUDY OF THE TAYGA AND
THE TRANSFORMATION OF ITS NATURE

V. B. Sochava

The northern part of the Temperate Zone, with its high radiation-balance indices, cold winters, and uniform humidity, where the original vegetation consists of coniferous forests of the boreal type on podzol and other kinds of tayga soils, is called the tayga.

Originally, the term tayga was used in Russian literature principally in a biogeographic sense. Later, a broader geographic concept of the tayga gradually became established, as a special type of geographic environment, all of whose components are distinguished by special qualities peculiar to them alone. This furnished L. S. Berg with grounds for recognizing a tayga subzone (we now prefer to say zone) on the landscape map of Russia. The tayga zone is represented by a large number of landscapes on the plains and plateaus and in the mountains. They consist not only of forest lands, but also of upland and lowland swamps, meadow-and-shrub expanses of the stream valleys, and other kinds of natural landscapes genetically related to the tayga zone. The tayga landscapes include also the cultivated lands, the proportion of which is fairly high in the southern tayga of the Russian Plain, as well as in the Urals.

PRINCIPAL STAGES OF THE STUDY OF THE NATURE OF THE TAYGA

Throughout the history of the development of industry and agriculture and the building of transportation routes in the tayga, considerable difficulties due to the rigors of nature have had to be overcome. As early as the beginning of the 18th century, the government of Russia displayed interest in scientific geographic information about the tayga regions, which at that time formed about half the entire area of the Russian state. The geographic investigations of I. Gmelin, S. Krasheninnikov, and later S. Pallas and V. Zuyev, I. Lapekhin, and others, laid the groundwork for the study of the nature of the tayga and also contributed to the rise of the scientific regional concept in world literature.

Down to the beginning of the second half of the 19th century, the nature of the tayga had been studied on the general geographic plane by individual naturalists having broad interests. Especially outstanding among the works of that period is that of A. F. Middendorf, in which we find the rudiments of certain ideas that have not lost their significance down to our times.

Since the second half of the 19th century there has been a development of specialized topical explorations of the tayga regions. The work of the geologists, particularly in the gold-bearing regions, as well as along the contemplated route of the Transsiberian rail trunk line, has enriched our notions of the geomorphology of the tayga. Information is continually being accumulated on the permanently frozen subsoils and *naledi,* which must be taken into account in construction work. A network of meteorologic observations is being developed, the results of which enabled A. I. Voyeykov already in 1884 to make a number of important generalizations about the climatology of the tayga zone. The increase in the population (including resettlements) of Siberia necessitated soil and geobotanical investigations for the purpose of finding plowlands and fodder areas. The demands from hunting and fishing enterprises, as well as from agriculture, have stimulated zoogeographic and ecologic-zoologic investigations.

By the time of the First World War, definite progress had materialized in the study of the individual components of the nature of the tayga. Even then, considerable expanses of the southern tayga on the Russian Plain were being used for agriculture, and many forest land had been put under exploitation. In Siberia, the tayga remained only very slightly exploited; logging was done selectively, industry, except mining, was almost entirely lacking, and the mineral wealth was utilized very incompletely and was insufficiently explored. The overwhelming part of the agricultural territory in western Siberia and the Amur basin was concentrated to the south of the tayga zone.

At the end of the past century and the beginning of the present century, specialized topical work dominated the exploration of nature in the tayga. Hardly any integrated regional work was done and it was recognized by many as untimely. A radical change came about after the Great October Socialist Revolution. The tempestuously evolving economy imposed more complicated demands upon science. The planned economy was interested in an integrated evaluation of the natural resources. Synthetic concepts of the natural conditions were needed for a full utilization of the productive forces, the more so because the conquest of the tayga had assumed other forms (organization of industrial complexes and focal points on the basis of local power resources, with parallel development of agriculture). In the new political setting, more attention was directed toward raising the material welfare of the small nationalities which had inhabited the tayga regions from time immemorial. Special explorations of the tayga regions, including the most remote ones, were needed for working out measures to rationalize their economy (hunting and fishing, reindeer raising, etc.).

Characteristic of the present stage of exploration of the tayga is the endeavor to combine the thorough topical studies of its nature with the solution of integrated geographic problems. Of great significance are the integrated expeditions which have been outfitted during the last forty years to go into various regions of the tayga. In 1920, work was begun on the Kola Peninsula and soon resulted in the discovery of apatite ores. In the 1930's this work was continued; its results have been widely utilized in developing industry, in advancing farming into the northern tayga, and for other purposes connected with the radical alteration of the economy of this region. The Yakut expedition, which began to operate in 1924, has had the participation of geographers of various specialties, who have studied nature in connection with the demands of agriculture and forestry and the evolving mining industry. Integrated exploration of the Yakut tayga continued in the 1950's, in conjunction with the discovery of large diamond deposits in the remote regions of western Siberia. In the 1930's, exploration began of the nature of the tayga expanses of the northeast Russian Plain, to insure the further development of agriculture and forestry, as well as to ascertain the conditions for construction in regions of permanently frozen subsoil. The groundwork was also laid in the 1930's for integrated exploration in Transbaykalia (the Buryat Expedition of the Academy of Sciences of the USSR) and in the Amur basin (the Amgun'-Selemdzha Expedition of the Academy of Sciences of the USSR). Work in Transbaykalia and the Far East assumed a new scope in the 1940's and 1950's, when geographers were confronted with the task of furnishing the necessary basis for the plans of economic development of the eastern regions of the country with the wide utilization of local hydro-power resources. Similar tasks were also solved in the tayga of middle Siberia (the Krasnoyarsk kray). The integrated study of the nature of Kamchatka determined the prospects for the utilization of its agricultural and forest lands, as well as the thermal springs.

Knowledge of nature in the tayga was promoted by investigations at fixed stations of the Academy of Sciences of the USSR (the Suputinskiy, the Gornotayezhnyy [Mountain Tayga], the Yakutskiy, etc.), as well as in the nature preserves, of which there were about twenty in the tayga zone by the beginning of the 1950's.

Alongside the integrated expeditions, the list of which has by no means been exhausted by us, specialized investigations of nature (geologic, geomorphologic, soil, geobotanical, etc.) were conducted in the same years in various regions of the tayga, and their results have been not only of specialized, but also broad geographic significance. From among the very long list of scientists who have taken part in the exploration of the nature of the tayga in the last decade, special mention should be made of A. A. Grigor'yev, V. N. Sukachev, M. I. Sumgin, G. D. Rikhter, S. P. Suslov, Yu. D. Tsinzerling, G. G. Grigor, N. V. Dumitrashko, V. G. Zol'nikov, A. A. Korchagin, I. I. Krasnov, B. P. Kolesnikov, A. I. Kurentsov, Yu. A. Liverovskiy, V. F. Tumel', L. N. Tyulina, N. A. Florensov, and L. V. Shumilova.

The common efforts of Soviet naturalists have yielded a large amount of data on the natural conditions and resources of the tayga expanses, which has aided considerably in working out plans for their exploitation. Our generation is beholding a radical transformation of the economic map of the eastern tayga regions of the USSR.

MAPS OF NATURE IN THE TAYGA

Mapping natural conditions and resources is one of the most essential forms of geographic research. The compilation of special-purpose soil and geobotanical maps of the tayga regions, to various scales, began even before the First World War. Especially considerable cartographic progress has been achieved in the last few decades. Medium-scale geomorphologic, soil, geobotanical, and hydrogeologic maps have been compiled for many regions. Large-scale surveys have often been made on key sections in order to provide a basis for the sheets of these maps.

The compilation of various natural maps for one and the same region furnishes an idea of the complex of physical geographic conditions peculiar to it. The geographic synthesis of the cartographic data is promoted by the considerable progress in the perfecting of topographic maps, by the aerial photo surveys, and by the series of geologic maps to different scales. A generalization of this great amount of work by numerous investigators of nature in the tayga is given on the summary maps of nature in the USSR to a scale of 1:4,000,000 — zoogeographic, soil, vegetation, and geomorphologic, from a comparison of which one can get an idea of the landscapes of the tayga zone of Eurasia over a total area of about 8,000,000 square kilometers. Of equal significance for individual provinces of the tayga zone are the oblast physical geographic atlases, for example the Atlas of the Irkutsk Oblast, occupying an area of 782,000 square kilometers and diversified in its landscapes.

In exploration of the tayga regions in recent years, recourse has been had to the compilation of integrated physical geographic maps, the idea for which was advanced by G. N. Vysotskiy (1904, 1909) and later developed by I. P. Gerasimov and A. S. Kes' (1948). Maps of this kind, to a large scale, are being compiled for the tayga regions of the northwest of the European part of the USSR by the geographers of Leningrad University. Having in view the tasks of the development of agriculture, V. S. Preobrazhenskiy (1957) has compiled a map of the types of locality in Buryatia, distinguishing on it several categories of Transbaykal mountain tayga, with consideration of the heat and moisture regime, the relief, the soils, and the plant cover.

Ascertainment and mapping of the natural complexes with consideration for all the features peculiar to them present considerable difficulties, and the methods have not been completely worked out. The whole has to be perceived from parts of it. An essential part of the natural complex is its biologic component — the plants and animals which are connected with definite differences of soil. Hence, the idea has arisen of compiling maps of biologic complexes — types of biocoenoses, groups of types of biocoenoses, biomes [biomy]. In comparison with the separately compiled maps of soils, vegetation, and animal life, they represent a step forward in the creation of integrated maps of broader profile. Maps of biologic complexes to a large scale (1:5,000 to 1:10,000) have been compiled on key sections in the Amur tayga. They are designed for an ecologic evaluation of the lands and provide the necessary biologic forecasts in connection with the impending conquest of the tayga regions.

On the basis of the summary soil and geobotanic maps, cartometric calculations have been made which give an idea of the areas of the various types of tayga lands established according to the soils and vegetation peculiar to them.

STRUCTURE OF THE TAYGA LANDSCAPES AND RECOGNITION OF THE TYPES OF LANDS

In the zone of broadleaf forests and in the forest-steppe, agricultural exploitation of major tracts of land is possible, and not infrequently the entire territory of the landscape. In the tayga, these possibilities are limited, and the farther north, the more limited they become. As a rule, the tayga landscape, especially in the eastern regions of the USSR, can be put under cultivation only selectively. This necessitates the study of detailed subdivisions of the tayga landscape to ascertain the possibility of making economic use of them. Of great significance in this respect are large-scale geomorphologic investigations, revealing the quantitative indices of the erosional, solifluctional, and other processes of the formation of relief characteristic of the various types of natural landscapes. Such work has been done in the last few years in certain tayga regions.

An idea of the structure of the tayga landscapes is furnished by numerous soil and geobotanical investigations in which plant associations and the accompanying soil differences are distinguished. The prime example of this sort of investigation was the work by V. N. Sukachev on the Transbaykal tayga. Of especial significance in the eastern regions which have a sharply pronounced anticyclonic climate is a microclimatic survey such as has been made in many regions of the tayga zone since the explorations by P. I. Koloskov (1914) in the Amur tayga. Considerable climatic inversions have been noted in the Urals, Siberia, and the Far East, manifesting themselves in all seasons, even when the relief is not very broken. As a result of these inversions, the local climatic regime of the individual tracts varies substantially even within a limited region.

Detailed investigations of individual components of the landscape are supplemented by an integrated physical geographic study of the natural units of which it is composed. An example of such works, thus far few in number, is the investigation of the esker facies in the Karelian tayga (Lopatin, 1953). In the last few years, a study of the facies of which the landscape is composed has been made for the purpose of finding minerals. In the tayga on the Middle Siberian Plateau, facies formed on kimberlite pipes have been recognized from landscape features (Kobets and Komarov, 1958; Lukicheva, 1959). The work is considerably facilitated by aerial photography.

In studying the structure of a landscape, it is important to take into account the rhythms of the seasonal development of the individual facies. The groundwork for their perception was laid by the biophenologists, first in application to large expanses (Strogiy, Galakhov, 1943; Batmanov, 1934; and others). Of especial significance is the study of the phenology of the plant associations characterizing the individual facies (Shennikov, 1927; Kurentsova, 1936; Kuminova, 1948; and others). There now arises the question of the phenology of the landscapes and the facies constituting it, including the whole series of the seasonal phenomena of nature on the territory studied. Experiments in such work have been made, for example, in the tayga on the Karelian Isthmus by the Chair of Physical Geography of Leningrad University. The question of phenologic observations from airplanes is being raised. The study of the phenology of the tayga landscapes may furnish valuable results for the ecologic evaluation of lands.

SOME GEOGRAPHIC ASPECTS OF TOPICAL INVESTIGATIONS OF THE TAYGA

Lately, in scientific works devoted to the nature of the tayga, the geographic trend has become considerably intensified. This is due to the natural course of development of the respective branches of knowledge, to the definite progress in the field of the theory of physical geography, and also to the increased demands of practice.

L. S. Berg's geographic *classification of climates* (1925) specially distinguishes a "climate of the tayga"; devoted to a characterization of it by individual provinces are works by V. Yu. Vize (1927), P. I. Koloskov (1932), K. N. Mirotvortsev (1935), A. V. Molochkov (1936), I. K. Tikhomirov (1939), and others. The climate-forming influence of the circulation processes in the atmosphere has been ascertained for certain provinces of the tayga by I. V. Stremousov (1935), A. I. Bachurina and others (1936), V. A. Orlova (1939), as well as in a summary work by B. P. Alisov (1956). The expansion of the network of meteorologic stations in the tayga zone permits the raising of the question concerning a more detailed regional characterization of the climatic resources, which is, indeed, now being carried out for a number of the tayga regions marked for priority industrial construction and agricultural development.

The progress in the field of *permafrost science*, discussed in Chapter 11 of the present book, is of significance not only in building and organizing a water supply, but also in taking account of the whole complex of natural conditions of the tayga regions of new development. In the last two decades the geophysical foundations for the study of permanently frozen subsoils and their mechanics have been considerably developed. This makes it possible to proceed to new generalizations of a geographic order, particularly to the ascertainment of the characteristics of the geographic phenomena proper to the individual tayga landscapes.

In the field of *geomorphology*, special significance attaches to the study of those exogenic factors of relief formation which are specific for the tayga (solifluction, frost weathering, frost bulging of the ground, thermo-karst, the peculiar manifestation of erosion and suffosion, and so forth). Here the interests of the geomorphologists are in close contact with the questions of climatology, permafrost science, soil science, and geobotany, and respond to many practical demands. Among the works of this type produced in the last few years, we shall mention the investigations by S. L. Kushev, S. P. Kachurin, A. I. Popov, and A. I. Mordvinov, which have appeared in various geographic publications.

The geographic-genetic treatment of the processes of soil formation and the increased volume of information about the soils of the tayga have permitted a start to be made toward improving the *classification of the soils* of the tayga zone (Ivanova, 1956; Rozov, 1956). The distinction of a separate class of boreal-frozen tayga soils, embracing a number of types (iron-bearing tayga soils, field tayga soils, tayga solods, brings us to a more correct understanding of the landscapes of the northern and middle tayga. The establishment of a special type of brown forest soils in the southern tayga of the Amur basin, developing under conditions of a monsoon climate and a peculiar vegetation cover, underscores the specificity of this territory and makes possible a more precise evaluation of its agricultural prospects. The understanding of the physical geographic laws operating at the southern limit of the tayga is promoted by the concept of the subtayga soil subzone established by K. P. Gorshenin (1955).

In *geobotanical works* devoted to the tayga, especially since the 1940's, much attention is paid to the geographic connections of the plant cover. Several schemes of botanico-geographic and forest-vegetation regionalization, of the tayga zone as a whole and of individual provinces of it, have been worked out (Sochava, 1948, 1953, 1958; Shumilova, 1948; Kolesnikov, 1955; Tolmachev, 1955; Karavayev, 1958; and others). The data on the geography of swamps have been generalized, their geographic types have been ascertained, and the limits of their distribution have been established (Kats, 1946). In classifying the tayga vegetation, including the typing of forests, the geographic principle is being applied considerably more widely than in the past, which is already being vindicated in the use of these classifications in forestry practice.

In the *zoogeography of the tayga,* especially in the works by A. P. Kurentsov (1941, 1956 and others), there has been a prospective trend toward the study of the fauna in continuous relationship to the tayga biotypes. This permits a wider use of zoogeographic data in natural regionalization, a more correct evaluation of the animal-life resources, and the elaboration of more efficient measures for combating harmful animals.

NATURAL REGIONALIZATION OF THE TAYGA AND REGIONAL PHYSICO-GEOGRAPHIC SURVEYS

The need has long been felt for a natural regionalization of the tayga for the purpose of a rational distribution of agriculture. In the first half of the 19th century, three bands [*polosy*] were distinguished within the tayga on the Russian Plain: (1) forest and livestock-raising, (2) grain-growing and livestock-raising, and (3) rye and flax (Kankrin, 1834). This was the first zonal division of a major region of the tayga.

The problem of the regionalization of the tayga zone as a whole had to be solved first of all by establishing the main regions of the tayga. In 1933, I. P. Gerasimov, on a broad geographic basis, proposed the division of the plains of the USSR and adjacent countries into soil-climatic facies. In so doing, four facies were recognized, within which the tayga landscapes characteristic of them were distinguished by their peculiarity. Very essential is Gerasimov's generalization that within each facies the zonal phenomena have their own peculiar characteristics. Considering not only the plains, but also the mountains, 11 major regions are recognized in the tayga zone (Sochava, 1953), and these are further divided into subzones and provinces.

On the plains and plateaus, three bands are distinguished throughout the whole tayga zone: the northern, middle, and southern tayga. In each region, the bands are specific with regard to the possibility of agricultural exploitation as well as in other respects. Nevertheless, by comparison with the middle and northern tayga of the same region, the southern tayga everywhere presents the greatest possibilities for the development of agriculture. On this basis, some schemes of natural regionalization (Rozov, 1954; Letunov, 1956) divide the tayga first of all on the zonal principle, and then into provinces.

Yu. P. Parmuzin (1958) has proposed the most detailed division of the tayga zone of Siberia and the Far East into physical geographic provinces ("oblasts" in his terminology). In recent years, experiments have been made in distinguishing landscapes in the individual provinces of the tayga zone as main subdivisions of the physical geographic environment (Isachenko, 1955, and others).

The problem of regionalization is inseparable from regional physical geographic surveys. For the tayga regions of the USSR they have been compiled in different forms and various sizes. A monographic essay by G. D. Rikhter (1946) is devoted to the nature of the north of the European part of the USSR, one by S. P. Suslov (1947) to western Siberia, and one by Yu. A. Liverovskiy and B. P. Kolesnikov (1945) to the southern regions of the Far Eastern tayga.

An idea of the complex of natural conditions of the individual tayga regions is given by collections such as "*Yakutiya*" (1927) or the more recently published "Materials on the Natural Conditions and Agriculture of Central Yakutia" (1954). A number of collections of articles are devoted to the nature of individual administrative oblasts located in the tayga zone (Sverdlovsk oblast, Vologda oblast, and others). The nature of the tayga in connection with the distribution of agriculture has been characterized by V. P. Shotskiy (1956). Finally, some regional economic-geographic monographs also contain information about the natural conditions of the territory.

Very little has as yet been done in the generalization of the physical geographic data on individual regions of the tayga. Yet the means to the economic development of the various regions in the immense expanses of the tayga have their own peculiar characteristics. There is everywhere the necessity for maximum utilization of all the advantages embodied in the diverse natural conditions of the tayga and in overcoming those natural factors which limit the utilization of the resources of the tayga zone.

The new forms of the management of industry and construction, as well as the planning of agriculture, have created very favorable preconditions for this. The problems of regional geography are acquiring special importance. It is urgently necessary to generalize the facts from the various fields of natural science in application to the individual economic administrative regions, and to ascertain the whole complex of natural conditions without which one cannot count upon maximally efficient exploitation of the tayga. The geographer-explorers of the tayga regions are able not only to promote the solution of the current economic tasks, but also to determine this colossal potential of natural resources which mankind has at its disposal. With the modern, continually improving technical opportunities, exploitation of the natural wealth guarantees that the growth of the well-being of the toilers will accord with the increasing population.

BASIC LITERATURE

Batmanov, V. A. Bioclimatic Map of the Urals, The Spring Development of the Vegetation (*Bioklimaticheskaya karta Urala, Vesenneye razvitiye rastitel'nosti* (short explanatory text). Compiled by V. A. Batmanov, Sverdlovsk, 1934.

Bachurina, A. I. and others. "Classification and Characterization of the Air Masses in Summer in the North of the European Territory of the Union," *Geofizika*, vol. 6, 1936, issues 2-3.

Berg, L. S. "The Climatic Belts of the Earth," *Izv. Geogr. in-ta*, 1925, no. 5. Bibliog. in the text.

Vize, V. Yu. "The Climate of Yakutia." In the book: *Yakutiya*, II, 1927, pp. 241-274 with table.

Galakhov, N. N. "On the Characterization of the Landscape Zones with the aid of Bioclimatic Indices," *Izv. VGO*, vol. 75, 1943, no. 5.

Ivanova, Ye. N. "An Experiment in the General Classification of Soils." *Doklady VI Mezhdunarodnomu kongressu pochvovedov, 5-ya komissiya: klassifikatsiya pochv*, 1956.

Karavayev, N. P. "Geobotanical Regionalization of the Eastern Part of the Central Yakutian Plain." In the collection: *Voprosy fizicheskoy geografii*, 1958.

Kuminova, A. V. On Nature in the Kuzbass. Landscapes of Kemerovo Oblast (*O Prirode Kuzbassa. Landshafty Kemerovskoy Oblasti*). Lipovyy ostrov, Novosibirsk, 1948.

Letunov, P. A. "The Principles of Integrated Natural Regionalization for the Purposes of Developing Agriculture," *Pochvovedeniye*, 1956, No. 3.

Liverovskiy, Yu. A., and Kolesnikov, B. P. Nature in the Southern Half of the Soviet Far East (*Priroda Yuzhnoy Poloviny Sovetskogo Dal'nego Vostoka*). A physical geographic characterization. 1949.

Materials on the Natural Conditions and Agriculture of Central Yakutia (*Materialy o prirodnykh usloviyakh i sel'skom khozyaystve Tsentral'noy Yakutii*), no. 1, 1954.

Mirotvortsev, K. N. The Climate of the Eastern Siberian Kray (*Klimat Vostochnosibirskogo Kraya*). Irkutsk, 1934.

Parmuzin, Yu. P. "On the Zonal Nature of the Cold Pole," *Izv. VGO*, vol. 90, 1958, no. 5.

Rikhter, G. D. The North of the European Part of the USSR (*Sever Yevropeyskoy Chasti SSSR*). A physical geographic characterization, 1946.

Rozov, N. N. "Principles of Natural Regionalization of the USSR for Purposes of Agricultural Production," *Pochvovedeniye*, 1954, No. 8.

Stremousov, N. V. "Concerning the Question of the Synoptic Processes of the Eastern Part of the Asiatic Continent and Adjacent Seas," *Geofizika*, 1935, No. 2.

Suslov, S. P. Western Siberia (*Zapadnaya Sibir'*). A physical geographic characterization. 1947.

Tikhomirov, I. K. "Some Materials on the Question of the Definition of the Term 'Climate'," *Izv. VGO*, vol. 71, 1939, no. 3.

Tolmachev, A. I. Geobotanical Regionalization of Sakhalin Island (*Geobotanicheskoye Rayonirovaniye Ostrova Sakhalina*), Moscow-Leningrad, 1955.

Shotskiy, V. P. "The Natural Conditions of Agricultural Production and the Natural-historical Regions of Irkutsk Oblast." *Materialy po sel'skokhozyaystvennomu rayonirovaniyu Irkutskoy obl.*, no. 1, Irkutsk, kn. izd-vo, 1956.

Yakutiya. Collection of articles. Leningrad, AN SSSR, 1927.

CHAPTER 37

TRANSFORMATION OF NATURE IN THE
STEPPES AND DESERTS

F. F. Davitaya

The steppe and desert regions occupy vast expanses on the south of the USSR. Their total area, together with the forest-steppe, constitutes 26.6 per cent of the entire territory of the country. Of this, deserts occupy about 2,100,000 square kilometers, or 9.4 per cent (Gerasimov, 1956). In the steppes are concentrated the principal branches of agriculture: here are grown the main cereals (wheat, corn, millet, and others), industrial crops (sunflowers and sugar beets) and fruits. Animal husbandry is widely developed. The deserts present enormous potentialities for obtaining the highest yields of agricultural crops per unit of area and for developing highly productive animal husbandry (camel, horse, cattle, and sheep raising). With enough water, they offer the best conditions for growing cotton, rice, grapes, and many kinds of fruits and melons. These conditions are insured by the abundance of light and heat, which, with the low relative humidity of the air, is very favorable to the assimilative activity of the overwhelming majority of cultivated plants. At the same time, the combination of the same factors prevents the spread of pests and diseases of vegetable and animal origin.

In the steppe and desert regions the soils, as a rule, are more fertile than in the humid zone, where the nutritive substances for plants are constantly being washed by precipitation into the deeper soil horizons and hence have little accessibility for annual agricultural crops. It is no accident, therefore, that the ancient civilizations arose precisely in the arid zones. Their further vicissitudes were determined chiefly by historical causes. But here the specific characteristics of the arid territories were also of significance. Of all the natural landscapes, the arid zones are the most responsive to the activity of man. Predatory exploitation of nature here, more than anywhere else, results in devastation and barrenness. Rational utilization of arid zones, on the other hand, creates conditions for tempestuous development and abundance.

The American scholar H. L. Schantz wrote in 1956 (p. 21): "Within the life span of many of us beautiful areas of desert grassland have been reduced to bare soil and useless weeds by overgrazing, the short grass of our high plains have been replaced by wheat and summer fallow, followed by the dust bowl, and the brushlands of the Mediterranean type have been reduced to non-palatable brush by fire followed by grazing of the young sprouts, a practice generally employed and one very detrimental to palatable plants. It is almost impossible to reverse these destructive trends under increasing population pressure, but it must be done if future generations are to find the resource in as good condition as we found it."

The justice of these words is unquestionable. But we should like more. We cannot reconcile ourselves to leaving the resources of the arid lands merely at the level we have inherited from our ancestors, or to preserving the resources in that virgin condition in which nature itself maintains them. Unlike mineral raw materials, the soil-climatic and biologic resources of the earth's surface possess a remarkable property: with the right exploitation, they can be not only restored, but continually enriched. Even a factor apparently so conservative and so little dependent upon man as the radiation balance can, with irrigation, be increased in the deserts by several dozen per cent from its original magnitude. This fact, first established by the agrometeorologist A. A. Skvortsov (1928), has been confirmed by many investigations. In irrigating humid soil covered with vegetation, the albedo is substantially diminished, resulting in an increase in the solar radiation absorbed. Moreover, the expenditure of heat in evaporation on irrigated tracts lowers the temperature of the active surface and raises the humidity in the surface layer of the air. All this leads to a lowering of the effective eradiation and an increase in the radiation balance. The favorable direction of the change in heat and moisture and their ratio in the earth's crust and the surface layer of the air, with the simultaneous increase in soil fertility, result in an increase in the biologic mass per unit of area. The effect of such changes is especially striking in the steppes and deserts. In the final analysis, planned action upon the water-and-heat regime of these territories entails a change in the whole ecologic setting—the transformation of its virgin nature.

The study of the controlled alteration of the nature of arid territories was propounded in the 1890's in the works of prominent Russian scholars: V. V. Dokuchayev (1892), P. A. Kostychev (1893), A. A. Izmail'skiy (1893), and A. I. Voyeykov (1892). In a fundamental work, "Our Steppes Before and Now" [*Nashi stepi prezhde i teper'*], Dokuchayev proposed a number of hydrotechnical, forest-culture, and agronomic measures to overcome droughts and dry winds, to weaken soil erosion, diminish the surface runoff and moisten the fields, and gave a scientific basis, brilliant for those times, for their efficiency.

The foremost scientific ideas and the results of their elaboration, inherited by us from pre-revolutionary Russia, have been widely developed in the works of a whole galaxy of Soviet scholars —geographers, climatologists, soil scientists, hydrologists, and agronomists. The most important are those by G. N. Vysotskiy and V. R. Vil'yams. The investigations have brought forth very important procedures for reclaiming arid territories, connected with the system of tilling the soil, cultivating plants, and utilizing fodder lands; the creation of forest shelter belts; the retention of snow and thaw waters; irrigation and water supply. Each of these measures in combination with a complex of other measures must be applied in a differentiated manner, taking into account the local natural conditions. Their maximum effectiveness does not by any means manifest itself in the whole arid zone.

The correct *system of soil tillage* is of immense significance for the moistening of the fields and the stability of the country's hydrologic regime. It was shown in the old, but very exactly executed experiments by A. A. Izmail'skiy (1893) that, with the same amount of precipitation in the steppe, but with different soil-tillage procedures, one field will be enriched in moisture from one year to another, while another will dry out. By creating a firm cloddy soil structure it is possible to increase the moisture-holding capacity of the soil considerably, and, by periodic loosening of the surface, to diminish substantially the evaporation of the precipitation received. According to A. M. Alpat'yev's investigations (1954), the proportion of the summer precipitation unused by plants on non-structural soils may exceed 50 per cent. According to V. R. Vil'yams' data (1951), plants on structural soils fail to use only 15 per cent of the annual precipitation.

In the system of soil tillage, the fallowing of fields is of the greatest significance for the conservation of moisture. However, the influence of fallowing on the moisture of a territory is not the same throughout the arid zone. Where there is a big gap between evaporability (the possible evaporation with full water supply) and the quantity of precipitation, the moisture-retaining role of fallow is small, and the bigger this gap, the smaller is this role. In deserts where the annual precipitation averages about 70 millimeters and the possible evaporation exceeds 1,200 millimeters the influence of fallow is practically nil. Likewise in the forest zone, especially in the swampy regions, where the meter layer of soil during most of the year is saturated with water to the limit of field-moisture capacity, the influence of fallow upon the conservation of moisture in the soil will also be small, and will become less and less as evaporation comes nearer and nearer to the evaporability limit. Figure 21 shows that clean fallow in the main regions of the steppe zone preserves from evaporation 50-100 millimeters of the water (500-1,000 cubic meters per hectare) accumulated from the fall and winter precipitation. In the dry-steppe and semidesert zones, fallow preserves less than 50 millimeters of the water (500 cubic meters per hectare) in the same thickness of soil.

The use of fallow in the eastern part of the arid zone has specific characteristics due to the unique regime of the climate and the mechanical composition of the soil. Dry winds often blow here, and clayey-sand and light clay soils occupy millions of hectares. Under these conditions, wind erosion easily develops when the land is entirely plowed up, thus giving rise to the necessity of alternating solid tracts of plowed fields with forest shelter belts, and arranging the bare fallowlands alternately with strips of relatively high stubble.

Autumn plowing, obligatory for dry-farming regions, has become an important method of altering

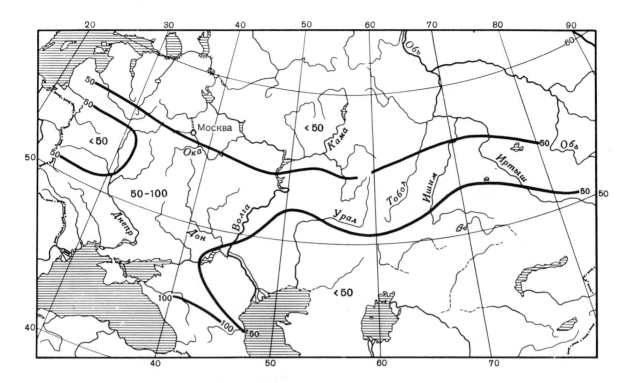

Fig. 21. DIFFERENCE IN THE SUPPLIES OF PRODUCTIVE MOISTURE (mm.) IN THE METER LAYER OF SOIL ON CLEAN FALLOW, AT THE TIME OF THE SOWING OF WINTER CROPS AND UNDER SPRING CROPS AT THE TIME OF THEIR HARVESTING (INFLUENCE OF CLEAN FALLOW).

the water regime of the steppes. Figure 22 shows that on the immense arid territory from the Volgaland to the Altay the supply of productive moisture in the meter layer of the soil at the beginning of the spring wheat sowing on land plowed in the autumn is much larger than when the sowing is done on land plowed in the spring. Essentially, the difference in moisture supply in one and the same zones, but with different soil-tilling procedures, is of the same order as the difference in the moisture supply upon passage from the steppe to the forest-steppe.

Of great significance in regulating the water balance of the steppes and deserts is the *density of the plant stand per unit of area*. As a result of many centuries of experience, farmers in the various natural zones have established their own sowing norms insuring a maximum yield under the given conditions. These norms decrease from north to south. In Leningrad, Kalinin, Vologda, and adjacent oblasts it is customary to sow about 250 kilograms of spring wheat per hectare. In Stravopol' kray this norm is less than 100 kilograms, while in Gur'yev oblast only 50-60 kilograms of wheat per hectare are sown on dry-farming land. It is quite evident that these norms reflect a regular change in the moisture of the fields from that of the forest to that of the dry-steppe zone. In Gur'yev oblast, it was not possible to harvest any crop at all with the same sowing norm as that adopted near Leningrad because the annual excessive desiccation of the soil would have converted the fields into a genuine desert. Nature furnishes astonishing examples of the natural regulation of the number of plants per unit of area. This manifests itself in an especially vivid manner in the deserts. The rarified structure of this or that phytocoenosis observed in this zone makes it possible for plants to utilize the moisture better, while nature insures the equilibrium between the soil-hydrologic and bioclimatic components constituting it. V. M. Sveshnikova and O. V. Zelenskiy (1956) point out that the "phytocoenologic" manner of regulating the water balance is represented in Middle Asia and Kazakhstan by many variants. In some cases it is manifested in the diminution of the number of plants in an association; in others, in a sharp diminution (30-50 times) of the sizes and weight of the above-ground part (including the area of the evaporating surface) by comparison with the root system delivering water from the various horizons of the soil and subsoil, and so forth.

Owing to the fact that a definite relationship between the biologic component of nature and the other elements of the landscape is peculiar to each area of the arid zone, the question arises as to the most suitable utilization of fodder lands and the rational grazing of livestock. The latter is especially

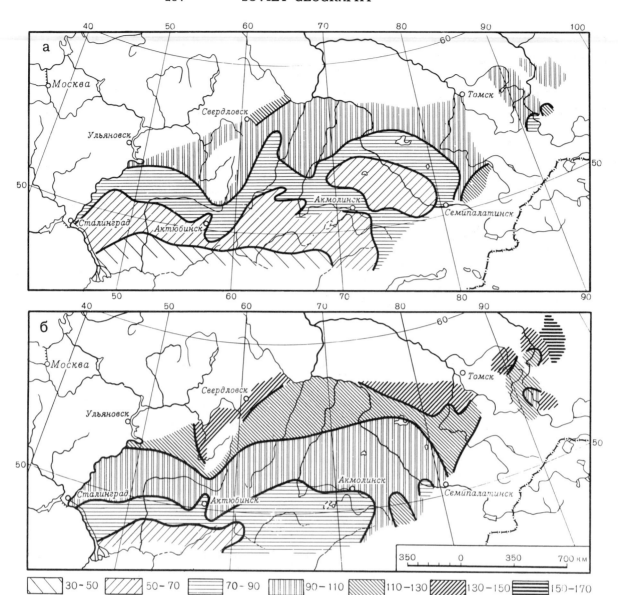

Fig. 22. SUPPLIES OF PRODUCTIVE MOISTURE (mm.) IN THE METER LAYER OF LOAMY SOILS (OUTSIDE THE INFLUENCE OF GROUND WATERS) AT THE BEGINNING OF SPRING-WHEAT SOWING: [*ABOVE*] ON LAND PLOWED IN THE SPRING, [*BELOW*] ON LAND PLOWED IN THE AUTUMN. (According to S. A. Verigo, L. A. Razumova, and S. B. Mostina)

important if one bears in mind that the vegetation typical of the steppes and deserts is preserved when there is a definite number of herbivorous animals. Without grazing, the plant cover becomes unstable, but overgrazing also results in the destruction of mutually conditioned relations and the impairment of the natural conditions. Much attention has of late been devoted to this question by the scientific institutions serving the dry-steppe and desert zones (see Fig. 22).

One of the most important means of transforming the nature of the arid zone is the planting of *forest and shrub stands*. These help to tie down the sands, regulate the water regime of fields, and improve the climate of the soil and the surface layer of the air. The planting of shelter belts has attained the widest distribution. It has been established that their windbreaking action is a principal factor in the favorable influence of forest belts on the microclimate, soil, and vegetation, determining the alteration of the whole complex of ecologic conditions in the fields between the belts. Forest belts reduce wind velocity and weaken the vertical movement of air over the fields. This reduces the transfer of water vapor by whirlwinds into the upper layers and hence contributes to the economical expenditure of water by the transpiration of plants, and thus weakens the action of droughts and dry winds. Because of the lowering of the wind velocity and the reduction of turbulent exchange, the snow is distributed more uniformly, the depth of the freezing of the soil is reduced, the supply of soil moisture is replenished through snow melt, and the blowing away of the soil and the harmful action of dust storms in summer are prevented.

While they diminish the expenditure of moisture in the drought and dry-wind period and contribute to a more uniform evaporation of the water during the growing period, the forest belts, taken separately, at the same time increase the total amount of annual evaporation in their zone of influence. The chief source of additional evaporation is the water formed from the snow accumulated on the fields. The infiltration of this water into the soil takes place even in the winter period, and in some climatic regions of the south of the steppe zone it reaches magnitudes of the order of 20 to 60 millimeters. The system of forest belts contributes to the retardation of surface runoff, the diminution of the spring high-water peak, and an increase in the mean low runoff, and prevents soil erosion. Within the forest belts, owing to the accumulation of litter and the more moderate water and heat conditions, the humus horizon is increased, the soil acquires a cloddy structure, and the thin southern chernozems of the dry steppes and the ordinary chernozems of the typical steppes are enriched in humus.

Stands of forest change the natural setting not only in the steppes, but also in the deserts. The saksaul forests (*Haloxylon aphyllum, H. persicum, H. ammodendron*) in the deserts of Middle Asia and Kazakhstan are of great economic significance and also substantially alter the ecologic conditions in their zone of growth.

Snow control [*melioratsiya*] is of great significance for the transformation of the nature in the steppes of the Temperate Zone. In the deserts this method is ineffective because of the small amount of solid precipitation and the instability of the snow cover. A 1-centimeter layer of snow melting at the beginning of spring furnishes from 20 to 35 cubic meters (metric tons) of water per hectare, depending upon the density of the layer. In the steppe zone one can accumulate 20-30 cubic meters of snow on the fields and preserve it almost entirely until spring, since comparatively little of the snowfall is expended on evaporation in the winter period, and surface runoff is practically absent in winter. Snow retention presupposes an increase in the snow cover on a given field through snow drifted from neighboring fields or into ravines and gulches. With total absence of a ravine-and-gulch network and 100-per cent plowing-up of the fields, full snow retention is obviously inadvisable, since its control significance is limited. It should, however, be borne in mind that, in most of the farming regions of the south of the European USSR, plowland forms 70 to 80 per cent of the land area. In the southeast, the proportion of plowland drops to 50 to 60 per cent. According to our calculations, 5 to 20 per cent of the snow that falls on the fields is drifted into ravines and gulches (Davitaya, 1959). This snow goes to feed the spring high water, intensifies erosion and is forever lost to the fields. Thus, even full snow retention in the steppe regions is of definite control significance. When snow is retained only on the cultivated fields, its effectiveness is considerably enhanced.

Snow control pursues yet another task. Winter crops are rather often lost in the steppe zone owing to a drop in temperature to below −15° at the depth of the branching point of the plant roots. Heavy freezing of the ground also affects the soil-forming process, and also indirectly exercises an influence on the infiltration of water and the formation of the spring surface runoff. Snow retention serves as a means of protecting winter crops from freezing and from changes in the water and heat balance of the soil and subsoil.

Of great importance in the steppes is the *retention of thaw waters*. The spring runoff from fields is from 5 millimeters (50 cubic meters per hectare) in the dry steppe of the southeast to 40 millimeters (400 cubic meters per hectare) at the southern boundary of the forest-steppe. The saturation deficit in the meter layer of soil varies in the same direction from more than 50 to 20 millimeters (Davitaya, 1959). The effectiveness of thaw-water retention in moistening fields is of the same zonal character as the influence of fallowing. The maximum effect is obtained in the typical steppes, where the saturation deficit of the soil is comparatively high (25 to 50 millimeters), and the spring runoff is rather large (15 to 30 millimeters). In the forest-steppe, the runoff is still larger (60 to 70 millimeters), but the saturation deficit is small (less than 10 millimeters), while in the dry steppe, on the contrary, the deficit is high (more than 50 millimeters) but the runoff is small (less than 10 millimeters). Retention of the surface runoff of thaw waters in the typical steppes yields the greatest effect for the additional reason that there was, as is known, no ancient glaciation in them and erosional relief forms are widely developed. The stream valleys, gulches, and ravines are often incised in loess and loess-like loams—in loose rocks easily washed away by water. Of great significance in the steppes, therefore, is the retention of the summer surface runoff, formed from the short-term but considerable shower precipitation. In the absence of a forest cover, this precipitation represents a considerable destructive force.

Soil erosion is regarded in Soviet geography as a complex process caused by the interaction of a number of natural factors (climate, soil, vegetation and relief) and anthropogenic factors (destruction of the forests, incorrect plowing, construction of roads along slopes, trampling of the plant cover by livestock, etc.). A wide complex of measures is applied in the control of soil erosion: the planting of forest shelter belts; the improvement of the water permeability of the soil by proper cultivation; the introduction of crop rotation and a system of fertilization; the retention of surface runoff waters by contour plowing, watering and terracing the fields; the suitable distribution of agricultural plants, which reduces the proportion of cultivated crops on the slopes; and so forth. Shelter belts and *kulisy* [echeloned plantings] are also widely used in controlling soil deflation.

Irrigation alters most radically the water and heat balance of arid territories. In employing irrigation in the steppes and in the deserts, however, there must be fundamentally different approaches. In the steppes, arid and humid conditions succeed one another in a rather variable manner. Over a large number of years, those favorable with respect to atmospheric moisture have a probability of about 50 per cent — the same as the droughty years. The complex mechanism of this fluctuation has now been established fairly accurately, but its exposition goes beyond the framework of the present essay. For us it is important that a sort of periodic migration of the meteorologic component inherent in the humid and the dry zones located next to each other occurs on a gigantic scale in the steppe zone. This, in particular, complicates the problem of irrigation. In years favorable with respect to atmospheric moisture the effect of additional irrigation is minimal, and the expenditures for maintenance of the inactive irrigation system and for the liquidation of the negative effects of irrigation are automatically included in the production costs. Here, the overhead expenses should be computed not only on the direct expenditures for irrigation, as is usually done, but also on the expenditures for additional cultivation of the soil, as well as for combating secondary salinification of the land — measures which require not less, but often greater efforts than the irrigation itself. This conflict is not characteristic of desert irrigation, where its high effectiveness manifests itself annually, and the total profitability of irrigation, averaged for a number of years, is more than doubled.

A diagram showing the influence of irrigation on the heat balance is given in Figure 23. Numerous observations by a number of authors have established that, in irrigating in the hottest months, the mean relative air humidity is increased by 8 to 10 per cent and the temperature is permanently reduced by 2 to 3 degrees. But on certain days the air humidity near the ground rises 30 to 40 per cent, while the temperature drops 15 to 20 degrees. The sum of the temperatures, calculated for all days with a temperature above 10 degrees, is diminished by 300 to 500 degrees.

Irrigation insures an ideal water supply to cultivated plants, taking into account their critical periods of development (the water is supplied when needed), and helps to obtain the highest yields. As a rule, the transpiration coefficients of the plants are lowered. When established watering norms are violated, irrigation also produces negative consequences and causes a secondary salinification of the soil. This phenomenon is combated by observance of a correct irrigation regime, the periodic flushing of the salinified soil, the lowering of the groundwater level (drainage), the introduction of grassland crop rotation, the planting of trees along the irrigation canals to capture the filtration water, and so forth.

Concerning the questions of the influence of *water storage* on the climate of fields and on other physical geographic conditions, there is not yet sufficient clarity in the scientific literature. Many authorities, for example, believe that the digging of canals, the building of ponds and small reservoirs and, still more, the creation of great reservoirs of the type of the Stalingrad, Tsimlyanskoye, and Kuybyshev dams will help to increase precipitation and substantially raise the humidity of the territory. This opinion, however, cannot be corroborated by scientific proofs. Water storage has an enormous significance for field irrigation, the development of animal husbandry and fishing, the propagation of waterfowl, and the supply of household and industrial water. The building of a multitude of ponds and small reservoirs using local runoff or the creation of major reservoirs may totally transform the economy, but at the same time also transform the face of nature in a given

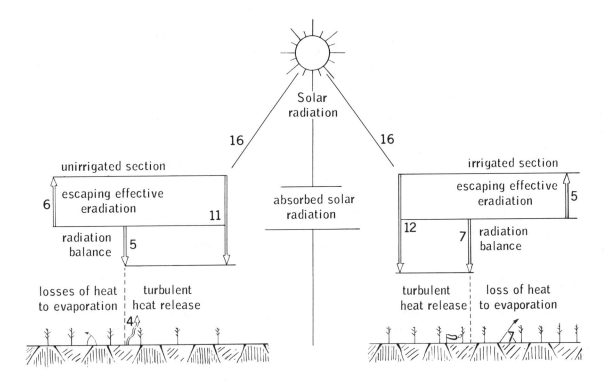

Fig. 23. CHANGES IN THE HEAT BALANCE DURING THE SUMMER MONTHS WITH IRRIGATION
(According to M. I. Budyko)

region. This effect, however, is indirect rather than direct. Investigations show that the influence of reservoirs extends only to the climate of closely adjacent territories, which, even in the case of the major reservoirs, form a comparatively narrow strip of the order of a few kilometers.

In accordance with the theory worked out in science and proven in practice, the arid zone in the USSR is being exploited in a planned manner by means of measures to transform its nature. Correct crop rotations are being introduced, a differentiated agrotechnology is being applied, forest shelter belts are being planted on a wide scale, snow retention and thaw-water detention are being practiced on tens of millions of hectares. Tens of thousands of ponds and reservoirs are being built, and medium-sized and large reservoirs are being created. These reservoirs designed specially for field irrigation, e.g., the Kolkhozbent Reservoir on the Murgab River, the Tedzhen Reservoir, and others; or used simultaneously for other branches of the national economy: water power, navigation, water supply to populated and industrial centers, and so forth, e.g., the Kuybyshev, Stalingrad, Tsimlyanskoye, Dnepr, Kakhovka, Mingechaur, Farkhad and other reservoirs. Among the biggest hydrotechnical structures should be classed the 950-kilometer-long Karakum Canal, now under construction, which will supply water to an immense territory of southern Turkmen SSR. Along it have been created a number of reservoirs for irrigating cotton plantations, orchards, and vineyards. The watering of the Karakum Canal will permit the creation of conditions for an important development of animal husbandry. The Great Fergana Canal and the Southern Fergana Canal have been built during the years of Soviet rule, the Terek-Kuma Canal is being built to irrigate and supply water to the Nogay Steppes, and a great deal of work is being done to irrigate and supply water to a number of other regions of the arid zone.

Since 1954, over 36 million hectares of virgin and idle lands have been plowed up in the Don and Volga steppes, in northern Kazakhstan, western Siberia, and the Altay, and are being exploited in a planned manner for farming. The unprecedented scale of development of this immense territory in a very short span of time is also an outstanding event from the viewpoint of the scientific solution of the problem of drought and its consequences in the steppe regions. At the same time, droughts have been extremely rare throughout the drought zone; for example, in the Ukraine and northern

Kazakhstan. Drought in Kazakhstan is usually linked with a rise in humidity in the Ukraine and vice versa (Davitaya, 1959). The mutual compensation of the natural conditions makes it possible to insure the stability of the ever-increasing nationwide harvests. Big new sovkhozes and kolkhozes have been created on the steppe expanses of the regions of reclamation of the virgin and idle lands, large, well-built settlements have arisen, and the nature of these regions has become completely different. All this testifies to the great scope of the work being accomplished in the USSR in the transformation of the nature of the steppes and deserts.

Soviet geographers are taking an extensive part in the scientific design of suitable ways of carrying out these measures. It suffices to state that in the decade 1949-1958 hundreds of scientific investigations devoted to this problem have appeared in print. A distinctive feature of them is the broad geographic approach to the transformation of nature. The basic scientific idea of this approach consists, firstly, in seeing to it that the improvement of one component of nature does not cause the impairment of another; secondly, that the maximum exploitation of the arid zones, for the sake of which the reclamation work is being carried out, shall not exhaust, but, on the contrary, shall augment their natural resources.

The history of the winning of the arid territories is full of examples where the total plowing up of the fields and frequent surface loosening of the soil to conserve moisture in it have promoted the development of erosion and deflation. Intensified cultivation of the same agricultural crop without fertilizers or proper crop rotation has resulted in exhaustion of the land and has given rise to the false theory of the diminishing fertility of the soil. Many other analogous examples are known. Reclamation work which takes into account the all-around interrelationship between natural phenomena excludes the possibility of impairing one set of conditions as a result of improving others. Nor can an intensive but rational management result in the disturbance of the established equilibrium and the exhaustion of the natural resources.

The great quantity of heat, moisture, and nutrients in the transformed steppes and deserts insures high yields from plants, but the latter in turn favorably influence the climate and soil of the fields. By weakening turbulent intermingling and diminishing the albedo, they increase the heat and moisture; their root remains improve the structure and physical properties of the soil and increase its fertility; and the plants help to increase the productive evaporation, hold back the surface runoff and reduce the wind velocity, diminishing erosion and deflation of the soil. Good harvests make it possible to develop a highly productive animal husbandry, which is extremely important also for insuring the fertilizing of the fields; increasing their fertility results in the formation of a thick stand of grass, and in improvement of the climate and the soils. The higher the level of this circulation, the more effective it is in transforming nature and raising the productivity of labor.

Effective utilization of the arid territories occupies an enormous place in plans for the development of the national economy of the USSR. Hence, an important task of Soviet geographers is to provide a scientific basis for major hydrotechnical construction, shelter-belt, and industrial forest plantings, for the tying down of sands, for irrigation, water storage and supply, and for agricultural conquest of the droughty territories. This will require a detailed study of the relief, climate, soils, water resources, animal life, production structure, and the mutual relations between the various branches of the national economy, as well as quantitative estimates of the now-existing natural conditions in order to forecast the alteration of their condition after the execution of the contemplated measures. These estimates must be made the basis of the projects for the transformation of the droughty regions of the country.

BASIC LITERATURE

Alpat'yev, A. M. The Moisture Circulation of Cultivated Plants (Vlagooborot Kul'turnykh Rasteniy), 1954.

Budyko, M. I. The Heat Balance of the Earth's Surface (Teplovoy Balans Zemnoy Poverkhnosti), 1956.

Verigo, S. A., Mastinskaya, S. B., and Razumova, L. A. "The Moisture Supply to Spring Wheat. The Agroclimatic and Water Resources of the Regions of Reclamation of Virgin and Idle Lands" (Vlagoobespechennost' Yarovoy Pshenitsy). Agroklimaticheskiye i Vodnyye Resursy Rayonov Osvoyeniya Tselinnykh i Zalezhnykh Zemel'. Under the editorship of F. F. Davitaya, 1955.

Vil'yams, V. R. Fundamentals of Farming (Osnovy Zemeledeliya), Selected Works, vol. 11, 1950.

Voyeykov, A. I. "The Modes of Man's Action on Nature" (Sposoby Vozdeystviya Cheloveka na Prirodu), 1892; republished in Selected Works, 1957.

Gerasimov, I. P. "The Arid and Semiarid Areas of the USSR and their Geographic Analogues," Voprosy geografii, Izd-vo AN SSSR, 1956.

Davitaya, F. F. "The Scientific Principles of the Combating of Drought in the Natural Zones of the USSR," *Izv. AN SSSR, seriya geogr.,* 1959, No. 1.

Dokuchayev, V. V. "Our Steppes Before and Now" *(Nashi Stepi Prezhde i Teper'),* 1892; republished in *Collected Works,* vol. VI, 1951.

Izmail'skiy, A. A. How our Steppe Dried Out *(Kak Vysokhla Nasha Step'),* 1893; republished in 1937.

Kostychev, P. A. On the Combating of Droughts in the Chernozem Area by means of Cultivation of the Fields and Accumulation of Snow on Them *(O Bor'be s Zasukhami v Chernozemnoy Oblasti Posredstvom Obrabotki Poley i Nakopleniya na Nikh Snega),* 1893; republished in *Selected Works,* 1951.

Svershnikova, V. M., and Zelenskiy, O. V. "The Water Regime of the Plants of the Arid Territories of Middle Asia and Kazakhstan," *Voprosy geografii,* Izd-vo AN SSSR, 1956.

Shantz, H. L. "History and Problems of Arid Lands Development," pp. 3-25 in the book *The Future of Arid Lands.* Papers and Recommendations from the International Arid Lands Meeting. Edited by Gilbert F. White. Publication No. 43 of the American Association for the Advancement of Science. Washington, 1956.

CHAPTER 38

GEOGRAPHIC RESEARCH IN THE IMPROVEMENT OF
THE UTILIZATION OF AGRICULTURAL LANDS

D. L. Armand

As is known, all the land in the Soviet Union is the property of the State. The State uses a part of the lands directly through the economic organizations created by it: sovkhozes [*sovetskiye khozyaystva*, State farms], factories, railroads, etc., another part it hands over for use by kolkhozes [*kollektivnyye khozyaystva*, collective farms] and social organizations, and small amounts are used by individual citizens (farmstead vegetable plots and plots for builders of their own homes). Finally, a part of the land is held in reserve and constitutes a state forest fund and a state land fund.

The kolkhoz is the most widespread form of social land use. On 1 November, 1958, there were 69,100 kolkhozes in the USSR. They had been assigned 763 million hectares of land (including forest), in the main for use without payment and without fixed term, but partly for long-term use. The lands at the disposal of the kolkhozes form 34 per cent of the entire area of the USSR. The mean area of the collective farms (not counting the fishing and handicraft guilds) is 11,000 hectares. But there are regions where the kolkhozes are still larger; thus, in the Far East the average area of a kolkhoz approaches 100,000 hectares. In such regions, however, the larger part of the area of the kolkhozes is occupied by forests and pasturelands.

The sovkhozes hold second place with respect to the area of agricultural lands. Their number reaches 6,000, and this land fund is about 178 million hectares. Thus, the average area of a sovkhoz is around 30,000 hectares. The largest sovkhoz, a reindeer farm in the extreme North, has 668,000 hectares of land.*

Each kolkhoz and sovkhoz, as a rule, comprises plots of land with very different natural conditions: lands in plains and lands with dissected relief; lands covered with meadow, forest, or shrubs; lands long since plowed up, fertile or barren. They are naturally fitted for different uses and have diverse values. The latter is not determined by the natural conditions alone: it also depends upon such economic factors as the nearness of the transportation routes and enterprises processing agricultural raw materials, the possession by the farms of a technology enabling them to do this or that kind of reclamation work, etc. On the big farms, great significance attaches to the distance of the lands from the populated points, the watering places for livestock, etc.

Diversified types of land making up a farm which is developing only one branch, for example, only crop cultivation or only sheep raising, cannot be well utilized. Hence, almost all the kolkhozes and sovkhozes represent complex diversified farms, although some one branch of production usually stands out as the leading one. The rational distribution of lands by different types of use therefore forms a complex task requiring consideration of many natural, economic, and technical factors. Its solution is a necessary prerequisite for the successful productional activity of a big kolkhoz or sovkhoz, the organization of which is not inferior in complexity to the administration of a large industrial enterprise.

Unlike capitalist countries, where the state engages only in fixing the boundaries between properties, leaving it to the land users to manage to the best of their ability, the state in a socialist country lends aid to the kolkhozes and sovkhozes in the matter of the internal farm organization of the land, i.e., the rational organization of their territory. This is natural because each farm is not in a

---

*The data on the number and area of kolkhozes and sovkhozes are taken partly from the statistical yearbook "The National Economy of the USSR in 1958" [*Narodnoye khozyaystvo SSSR v 1958 g.*], published in 1959, and partly from the book "Land-organization Designing" [*Zemleustroitel'noye proyektirovaniye*], 3rd ed., Moscow, 1958

position to maintain qualified land-organization specialists on its payroll. At the same time, the Soviet state is interested in the prosperity of every kolkhoz and sovkhoz, and in the correct use of the lands by them.

The land organizers, working in the system of republic ministries of agriculture, draw up projects for the organization of the territory of all the kolkhozes and sovkhozes. In the kolkhozes, the projects are then examined and confirmed by a general meeting; in the sovkhozes, by the directing board. The project comprises the fixing of the external boundaries of land use, the drawing of boundaries between agricultural lands of different types, the breakdown of plowland for crop rotation and the latter into fields and brigade plots, the location of animal-raising barns, the planning of roads, systems of irrigation, and so forth.

Jointly with the agronomist, the land organizer also works out a system of crop rotation. The internal farm land-organization project consists of a map drawn to a scale of 1:10,000 to 1:25,000 (depending upon the area of the lands) and an explanatory note called an "agro-basis" [agroobosnovaniye].

The internal farm land-organization projects serve as a basis for the land inventory. When the project has been drafted and the land-type areas estimated, an explication is composed; that is, a list of the lands at the disposal of the farm. The explications by administrative regions and oblasts are brought together in a State Land Inventory and Land-Use Register. The latter consists of tables in which each line corresponds to one farm, and each column to a specific type of land. The following land-types are distinguished: plowland, idle land [zalezh'], hay land, pasture, forest, orchard, brush, swamp, body of water, roads, plots with structures, unsuitable lands, and farmhouse plots. Further, within the plowland, the areas damaged by erosion or having other defects are especially distinguished. The hay lands are divided into dry-valley, flood-meadow, and swampy. In the "forest" column are shown separately the forest stands of reclamational significance, the forest belts, and also the cut-over and burnt-over areas. Thus, the land inventory book contains certain elements of their qualitative evaluation. However, the potential-productivity rating [bonitirovka] of the lands by classes is not provided.

From the foregoing it may be seen that, for work on the organization of a territory and the taking of a land inventory, the land organizer must analyze an intricate complex of natural conditions including almost all the components of the landscape. For this purpose, he endeavors to use all the available materials compiled by the various organizations for the territory to be organized. Such materials are usually topographic maps, aerial photographs, soil maps, maps and reports relating to special geomorphologic, geobotanical, and hydrogeologic investigations and expeditions, etc. The most widespread of these materials are the large-scale soil maps which are being systematically compiled for whole oblasts by the soil scientists of the agricultural organs to the same scale as that adopted for the land-organization plans of a given oblast (Malyshkin, 1959). Such maps have now been compiled for most of the old farming areas and for many new regions of virgin land reclamation, totaling more than 200 million hectares.

Regardless of what sources he has at his disposal, the land organizer, before drafting a project, is obliged to make a so-called agro-economic inspection, that is, a detailed examination of all the lands and an evaluation of their quality according to external features and the data on harvests. An agronomist, a reclamationist [meliorator], and farm managers are engaged for this inspection.

In recent years, the initiative of the local organs in questions of agricultural planning has been considerably broadened. The kolkhozes are limited only by the framework of state deliveries, the assortment of which is determined in accordance with nationwide interests, although here, too, numerous substitutions of one product for another are permitted. This in turn insures considerable freedom in the modes of land use and consequently in the organization of the territory.

Many functions which until recently came within the jurisdiction of the USSR Ministry of Agriculture have been transferred, in accordance with a decision by the 20th Congress of the Communist Party of the Soviet Union, to the [15 constituent] union republics. The guiding organs of some republics, taking into consideration the level of development of agriculture, have deemed it timely to introduce further improvements into the above-described unionwide system of the study and inventory of lands. Thus, in the Ukrainian SSR a system operates whereby the following are compiled for each kolkhoz or sovkhoz: (1) a large-scale soil map with a detailed distinction of soil differences (as many as 30-40 per kolkhoz), (2) a map of agroproductional groupings in which the soil differences are reduced to 4-5 groups representing different values and requiring various methods of utilization, and (3) a map diagram of the rational utilization of lands. The soil map is compiled by technical soil parties, while the agroproductional and the land utilization maps are compiled by integrated detachments of soil scientists, agronomists, meadow scientists, and so forth. Each map serves as the material basis for the next, and the map diagram of rational utilization of lands is used for the land-organization project drawn up by the land organizer.

Other experiments have also been made in improving and supplementing the soil maps with various special-purpose integrated or synthetic maps. In its course, the work has brought out the real demands of socialist agriculture for cartographic, statistical, and descriptive materials which should underlie its planning and organization of the territory. The further research conducted by the scientific research organizations, as well as by the faculties of geography, biology and soil, and land organization in the higher educational institutions pursue the object of satisfying these demands. Let us note their principal trends.

1. At present, the *topographic maps* that can now be used by the land organizer have, as a rule, a considerably smaller scale than the maps of land-organization projects. Hence, they cannot serve as the topographic basis of the project. As a result, the projects are outlined on "flat" bases, on which the relief is not shown. Yet, as experimental work has shown, the bases showing contours considerably broaden the possibility of making use of them: *With projects showing the relief one can determine immediately the steepness and exposure of the slopes, the degree of balance between the types of land, and so forth,* and this in turn permits a rational breakdown of the fields, a choice of agricultural machinery, the estimation of labor norms and the expenditure of fuel, and the dates of agricultural work.

2. The provision of the various territories with special-inspection materials is not uniform: some regions have been studied in detail from all sides, while in others there are only soil maps, and these also very unequal in value.

A uniform degree and great detail in the study of the territory can be achieved by *compiling a Cadaster of Land Types containing for each specific plot a complex of information important for agricultural planning.* In experimental work, this information is generalized in the form of maps reflecting the natural and economic properties of the land types, as well as annexed descriptions or tables. *The cadaster may serve as a scientific basis for the organization of the territory and the drafting of a plan for the further productional activity of the kolkhoz or sovkhoz.* The cadaster is based on the classification of types of land, which should be compiled in advance, while making a preliminary inspection of the locality.

3. A natural supplement to the Cadaster of Land Types should be a *qualitative evaluation of the lands, accompanied by a quantitative inventory of the lands of different quality.* It includes two stages: (a) elaboration of the potential-productivity rating of the lands, with assignment of each natural type of them to a definite class, as has been done already for the forests, and (b) an inventory of the economic value of the lands in dependence upon the location and organizational and economic conditions. The inventory of the economic factors can be effected, for example, by making up a sliding scale of corrective coefficients to the natural ratings. Other methods are also possible.

In the inventorying of lands and the improvement of their use, an unlimited field of action is being opened to geographers. They can be of great help here, because they possess the skills for the integrated study of nature. Among geographers there are specialists in all the separate disciplines which are important for agriculture, those pertaining to natural science and those pertaining to economics, forming a part of the system of the geographic sciences. The specialist geographers have the skills for expeditionary and stationary field work and, what is very important, they always act as enemies of the stereotype and work from the standpoint of the differentiated utilization of the natural wealth for the purposes of the national economy.

Investigations in the field of land use have long formed a tradition of Russian science, and have been cultivated by specialists in a number of branches belonging to the series of geographic sciences in the broad meaning of this term. Their founder was V. V. Dokuchayev. Subsequently, they have been developed by soil scientists (K. D. Glinka, S. S. Neustruyev, B. B. Polynov), forest scientists (G. F. Morozov, G. N. Vysotskiy) and meadow scientists (L. G. Ramenskiy, I. V. Larin).

The interest of geographers in research in the field of agriculture has increased sharply in the postwar years, when many of them have been engaged in the surveying of sites for State forest belts and in the elaboration of methods of combating erosion and deflation of soil.

The questions of *erosion and deflation* were no new ones for geographers. Thus, the Institute of Geography of the Academy of Sciences of the USSR, even before the Great Patriotic War, had taken an active part in integrated expeditions for the study of erosion processes on the Middle Russian Uplands and Volga Heights, and in the Transvolga. However, erosion was here viewed principally as a geologic process; its dependence upon the applied agrotechnology and organization of the territory was not sufficiently studied. Research was rarely carried to the point of making practical recommendations.

Participation in the work of transforming nature caused geographers to go more deeply into agricultural questions. This produced the conviction that all attempts to combat erosion without a radical remodeling of the system of agriculture in the erosion regions, primarily without revising the existing land organization, were doomed to failure. *The only effective method of combating erosion is the elaboration of zonal and regional systems of specialized economy, such that all the links in it would be designed with a view to the suppression of erosion and the restoration of the eroded soils, with a simultaneous maximally productive utilization of the lands.*

Standard projects for the anti-erosion organization of the territory of kolkhozes both before and since the Patriotic War have been drawn up by the workers of the All-Union Scientific-Research Institute of Agro-Reclamation [*agromelioratsiya*]. They have been based on the principles worked out by A. S. Kozmenko, the founder of the Russian and Soviet school of erosion control. Since 1952, the institutes of the Academy of Sciences of the USSR have joined in this work. The Institute of Geography and the Forest Institute have created an integrated Erosion Detachment, which has deepened our earlier notions of the origin and mechanism of accelerated man-made erosion, has brought out the specificity of the erosion processes under the conditions of a major mechanized farm, has expanded the arsenal of erosion-study methods, especially the quantitative ones, and has drawn up a number of standard projects for the organization of the territory. These projects have attached great significance to the correct arrangement of the forest shelter plantings. The results of the work of the Erosion Detachment and its fundamental conclusions have been published in the collections of articles: "The Significance of V. V. Dokuchayev's Ideas..." [*Znacheniye nauchnykh idey V. V. Dokuchayeva...*] (1955); "Agricultural Erosion and Its Control" [*Sel'skokhozyaystvennaya eroziya i bor'ba s ney*] (1956); "Agricultural Erosion and New Methods of Studying It" [*Sel'skokhozyaystvennaya eroziya i novyye metody yeye izucheniya*] (1958).

Much work on the study of erosion has been accomplished by the Soil-Erosion Laboratory of the V. V. Dokuchayev Soil Institute of the Academy of Sciences of the USSR. Unlike the Institute of Geography, whose expeditions have chiefly studied the development of erosional forms of relief, this laboratory has concerned itself principally with the erosion of soils (Sobolev, 1948; "Materials on the Study of Soil-erosion Processes..." [*Materialy po izucheniyu protsessov pochvennoy erozii...*] (1953).

Simultaneously with their study of erosion in the forest-steppe and steppe zones, geographers have turned their attention to combating elemental processes which menace agriculture in the more northerly regions, i.e., such phenomena as swamp development, brush growth, the covering of fields with boulders, and so forth. With the active participation of the geographers of the Academy of Sciences a collection of articles has been published "On the Improvement of the Agricultural Use of Lands in the Non-Chernozem Belt of the European Part of the USSR" [*Ob uluchshenii sel'skokhozyaystvennogo ispol'zovaniya zemel' Nechernozemnoy polosy Yevropeyskoy chasti SSSR*] (1952).

The traditional interest of geographers in questions of the conservation of nature has also taken a new direction. Formerly, it was chiefly a matter of creating nature preserves and organizing scientific work in them, but now the problem of the rational utilization and expanded reproduction of the replenishable natural resources has become central. A big role in the development of this trend has been played by the Geographic Society of the Soviet Union, which has organized a number of broad conferences devoted to this problem. The transactions of these conferences have been published in the Society's organs (*Voprosy geografii*, nos. 13, 19, 23, 28, and 48; *Geograficheskiy sbornik*, vols. 2 and 5).

The work on erosion control has led the workers of the geographic series of sciences to the more general tasks of territorial organization, and the latter have in turn stimulated them to take up the still broader subject of the qualitative evaluation of lands and the cadaster of land types. The treatment of this subject makes it possible to lay a scientific foundation not only for land organization, but also for reclamation, the planning of agricultural production and a differentiated system of taxation and state deliveries.

The beginning of investigations in this direction dates back to 1954, when a paper by I. P. Gerasimov, Ye. N. Ivanova, and V. A. Nosin (1954) was read at the congress of soil scientists, setting forth the contents of a completed guide on large-scale soil mapping. Provision was made for both the improvement of the quality and enrichment of the contents of soil maps by an all-around inventory of the most important components of the landscape viewed as factors of soil formation. It was proposed that large-scale soil maps be compiled on bases with contours and accompanied by a set of supplementary maps showing for each kolkhoz: the existing use of lands, the desirable transformations of land types, and types of crop rotation, the necessary reclamation works, etc. For certain categories of lands, it was even proposed that the soil scientists be required to draft territory-organization projects. Although the term "cadaster" was not mentioned in the project, the soil investigations contemplated in the guide actually came close to the compilation of a cadaster of land types.

In 1955, the Academy of Sciences of the USSR established under the Soil Institute a Commission for the Elaboration of a *System of Qualitative Land Evaluation*. Soil scientists, geographers, and economists took part in the Commission's work. It compiled a project for the division of the agricultural lands of each major natural area into five groups (classes), according to their relative fertility. Regarded as factors determining fertility were the genetic characteristics of the soils, their degree of homogeneity, the mechanical composition, salinity, state of erosion, etc., as well as such landscape components as relief, parent material, and biologic conditions. The Commission proposed new forms of inventorying lands, based on the elaborated qualitative evaluation. The classification it worked out was used in the experimental cadastral work performed by a number of geographic faculties in accordance with contracts with the agricultural organs of the union republics and oblasts.

The work of the Commission of the Soil Institute has been continued by the Moscow branch of the Geographic Society, which has systematically discussed the questions of qualitative evaluation and land inventory and has published a collection of articles devoted to them (*Voprosy geografii*, no. 43). Here the physical geographers have also paid main attention to soils. Unlike the above-described project of the soil scientists, however, these works view relief, parent material, microclimate, water regime, and vegetation not only as factors of soil formation, but also as conditions which, in a number of cases, directly determine the successful development of plants, the choice of agrotechniques, the principles of territory organization, and so forth. Hence it has been assumed not only that they can be established by an analysis of the soil characteristics, but also that they can be reflected directly on maps and in descriptions. In the collection of articles, a project is proposed and forms of the land-type cadaster worked out (Armand, 1958). The term "land type" [*zemel'noye ugod'ye*] itself has been defined more precisely. Natural land-types [*prirodnyye ugod'ya*]—sections with homogeneous natural conditions—should be mapped and described in the cadaster, independently of their present use, which in a number of cases may prove to be irrational. On the land-organization plane, on the other hand, the existing agricultural land types (plowlands, hayfields, forests, etc.) find representation; that is, the modes of actual land use. By superimposing any one of these maps on the other, one can form an idea of the degree of suitability of this use and prepare a project for the transformation of agricultural land types.

Since 1955, the Geographic Society of the USSR has implanted the helpful tradition of convoking annual conferences on landscape science. Each year the conference is convoked in a different city. The bulk of the work is done during excursions, the questions for discussion being dealt with in connection with concrete natural objects.

At the First Landscape Conference, in Leningrad, devoted mainly to questions of integrated physical geographic regionalization and mapping, papers by F. N. Mil'kov and Yu. N. Tsesel'chuk pointed out the importance of these investigations for agriculture. A resolution recommended that physical geographers participate actively in setting up a system of qualitative land-type inventory.

The conference at L'vov in 1956 set the task of rendering broader geographic service to agriculture. There were papers devoted entirely to this subject. By that time a number of the geographic faculties of the universities and pedagogic institutes, fulfilling the decision of the First Conference, joined in the experimental work on the qualitative evaluation of lands. Interesting examples of this work were exhibited by the geographers of the Moscow, Kiyev, L'vov, and Latvian universities. In a

number of communications there was talk of special expeditions and the elaboration of purposeful methods of qualitative land evaluation and inventory ("Scientific Notes of L'vov University" [*Nauchnyye zapiski L'vovskogo universiteta*], vol. 40).

Considerable space was also devoted to the questions of geographic services to agriculture by the conference held in Tbilisi in 1958. Finally, the Riga conference of 1959 demonstrated that the geographers' work front had broadened extraordinarily with respect to the improvement of agricultural land use. The universities of Odessa, Chernovitsy, Baku, and other cities had joined in this work. Especially detailed and extensive investigations had been undertaken by the geographers of the Baltic republics. The geographers of a number of republics and rayons had changed from expeditions undertaken on their own initiative to planned work in the system of state organs. In some cases they proposed their own methods of cadastral work; in others, they endeavored to improve the state system of land inventory and evaluation. In a special decision by the Ministry of Agriculture of the Ukrainian SSR it was noted that, in those oblasts of the Ukraine where a soil survey had been made by the geographic faculties, enriching it with the methods of integrated physical geography, had proved most successful and high in quality. Highly rated was the work of the Institute of Geography of the Academy of Sciences of the USSR on the integrated natural regionalization of Transbaykalia, aimed at the improvement of land use and the planning of agriculture.

The work on qualitative land evaluation has been mostly fully developed at the geographic faculty of Moscow University. Various working methods were tried out during the expeditions to the Zaraysk rayon of Moscow oblast, the Volga and Akhtuba interfluve, and the regions of virgin land reclamation in Kustanay oblast. These regions differ greatly in their natural conditions.

The Ryazan' expedition of Moscow University has operated since 1954, and has become a genuine laboratory for methods of study and evaluation of agricultural lands. The expedition has compiled a set of maps to a scale of 1:10,000: (1) soil maps, (2) map diagrams of the dates of readiness of fields for cultivation, reflecting the degree of water supply and drainage,. (3) a set of map diagrams reflecting the characteristics of the history of the fields, including the actual alternation of crops and the introduction of fertilizers during a number of years, and (4) crop-yield maps, synthesizing, as it were, the influence of the factors reflected in the first three maps. An analysis has shown that kindred genetic varieties of soils have the same agroproductional value and require the same cultivation at the modern level of agrotechnology. At the same time, differences in the mechanical composition of the soils and soil-forming rocks radically alter their properties and possible types of utilization.

As a result of the investigations, the more than 100 soil varieties distinguished have been united into 29 classes of lands with different agroproductional properties, and a list of crops has been given for each of them in descending order of advisability of cultivation. Basic agrotechnical and agro-reclamational procedures, the composition of crop rotations and their distribution over the area were also recommended.

The expeditions of the universities have also been used as production practice for the students. Hence, they have possessed numerous cadres of relatively well-trained workers and have been able to cover large territories. Thus, the Ryazan' expedition has made a qualitative land evaluation in approximately 100 kolkhozes, located in various rayons of the oblast. It has held a number of explanatory conferences with local specialists in agriculture and land organization.

In 1957, Moscow University transferred its work on qualitative land evaluation to Stanislav oblast. Here, on the slopes of the Carpathians, four altitudinal belts with different soils and types of farms have been clearly distinguished. The old and intensive farm cultivation of the western Ukraine has resulted in a profound reconstruction of the soils. Three separate classifications had therefore to be created: old plowland, meadowlands, and forestlands. The investigations have been carried to the point of practical realization; the expedition workers have drawn up a draft land-organization project for each kolkhoz investigated. The projects have been discussed at meetings of the kolkhozniks and have been co-ordinated with the technical inspectorate. In the last few years, extensive work on qualitative land evaluation, in which geographers have taken an active part, has been undertaken in the Ukraine, Latvia, and Estonia.

The Ukrainian Agricultural Institute has worked out a classification of the soils of the republic, built on principles close to those which were made the basis of the work of the Ryazan' and Stanislav expeditions of Moscow University ("Agroproductional groups of Soils," 1957). The geographic faculties of L'vov, Kiyev, Odessa, and other universities have created working parties which, together with the specialists of allied branches, compile soil and agroproductional maps of kolkhozes to scales from 1:10,000 to 1:50,000 on the basis of this classification.

We cannot, in a brief chapter, even enumerate the extensive scientific-methodological studies relating to the improvement of agricultural land use made by the specialists in the various branches: soil scientists, geobotanists and land organizers. Some of them are carried out in close contact with geographers conducting integrated investigations and are themselves essentially wholly geographic in character, though devoted principally to one or another specialized problem. Thus, the Soil Institute of the Academy of Sciences of the USSR is working out methods of compiling maps which Yu. A. Liverovskiy (1957) called "agrogeographic." Essentially, they are soil maps showing certain elements of the relief and of other objects important for agriculture and provided with a series of special map diagrams.

In the last few years, co-operation has been arranged between geographers and land organizers. The professors and docents of the Moscow Land-Organization Institute are working actively in the Geographic Society. The geographers of the Academy of Sciences and of Moscow University, on their part, participate in the annual All-Union land-organizer conferences.

Finally, the studies of the geographic series on the improvement and use of lands include geobotanical investigations relating to the evaluation of fodder lands and the elaboration of a forest typology.

Work of the geographic sciences in the study of agricultural land use must be done simultaneously in two directions: improvement of the inventory of the existing land use and study of the natural conditions for the purpose of further improvement of this use. The fullest solution of these tasks requires: (1) close contact between geographic investigation and land-organization work, (2) organization of detailed inspections of agricultural lands mainly by specially trained soil-scientist geographers and botanist geographers, (3) proper provision for the storage of the stock of materials relating to land inspections, (4) compilation of generalized medium- and large-scale agricultural maps, and (5) organization of work on the economic rating of lands.

The experience accumulated in the last few years enables one to determine clearly the role and place of geographers in the work of improving land inventory and use. Geographers must participate in all stages of this work, down to the elaboration of standard projects for internal farm land organization. By "geographers" are meant integrated detachments consisting of physical geographers having broad interests, soil scientists, geobotanists, geomorphologists, etc., and economic geographers with an agricultural bent. These detachments should work in participation or be in close contact with land organizers, agronomists, and reclamationists. The basic cadres of the integrated detachments are formed of soil-scientist geographers graduated from the geographic faculties of certain universities.

BASIC LITERATURE

Agroproductional Groups of Soils *(Agroproizvodstvennyye gruppy pochv)*, Khar'kov, 1957.
Voprosy geografii, no. 19. "The Transformation of Nature and the Economy of the USSR," Moscow, 1950.
Voprosy geografii, no. 23. "The Nature of the Steppe and Forest-steppe and its Transformation," Moscow, 1950.
Voprosy geografii, no. 28. "The Tasks of Physical Geography in Connection with the Great Construction Projects of Communism," Moscow, 1952.
Voprosy geografii, no. 43. "Qualitative land inventory and evaluation," Moscow, 1958.
Voprosy geografii, no. 48. "The Conservation of Nature. Biogeography," Moscow, 1960.
Gvozdetskiy, N. A. "The inter-*vuz* [higher educational institution] Conference on Regionalization," *Izv. AN SSSR, seriya geogr.*, 1958, No. 4.
Geograficheskiy sbornik, vol. 2. "Questions of Steppe Forest Cultivation," Leningrad, 1953.
Geograficheskiy sbornik, vol. 5. "Geographic Questions of Forestry," Leningrad, 1955.
Gerasimov, I. P. "The Present State of the Dokuchayev Concept of the Zonality of Soils and L. I. Prasolov's Scientific Ideas about Soil Provinciality and their Significance for the Theory of Natural Regionalization," *Izv. AN SSSR, seriya geogr.*, 1958, No. 4.
Gerasimov, I. P. "The Tasks of Geographic Science in the Study of Agricultural Land Use," *Izv. VGO*, vol. 90, 1958, No. 3.
Gerasimov, I. P., Ivanova, Ye. N., and Nosin, V. A. "The Tasks and Methods of Large-Scale Mapping of Soils in connection with the Inventory and Qualitative Evaluation of the Country's Land Resources," *Pochvovedeniye*, 1954, No. 6.
Land-organization Designing *(Zemlestroitel'noye Proyektirovaniye)*, 3rd ed., Moscow, 1958.

"The Significance of V. V. Dokuchayev's Scientific Ideas for the Combating of Drought and Erosion in the Forest-steppe Regions of the USSR." *(Znacheniye Nauchnykh Idey V. V. Dokuchayeva Dlya Bor'by s Zasukhoy i Eroziyey v Lesostepnykh Rayonakh SSSR)*. Sbornik (Collection of articles), Moscow, 1955.

Izvestiya Vsesoyuznogo geograficheskogo obshchestva, vol. 87, 1955, no. 5 (number devoted to the First Conference on Landscape-Science Questions).

Kozmenko, A. S. Soil Erosion Control *(Bor'ba s Eroziyey Pochv)*, Moscow, 1954.

Kozmenko, A. S. Principles of Anti-erosion Reclamation *(Osnovy Protivoerozionnoy Melioratsii)*, Moscow, 1954.

Liverovskiy, Yu. A. "Detailed Soil Maps and their Significance for Physical Geography," *Izv. AN SSSR, seriya geogr.*, 1957, No. 3.

Malyshkin, M. N. "Soil Investigations in Connection with Land Organization and the Planning of Agriculture in Kolkhozes and Sovkhozes," Sbornik *Pochvennay s"yemka*, Moscow, 1959.

"Materials on the Study of the Processes of Soil Erosion and the Fertility of Eroded Soils," *Tr. Pochv. in-ta im. Dokuchayeva*, vol. 40, Moscow, 1953.

Scientific notes of the L'vov State University named for Iv. Franko *(Nauchnyye zapiski L'vovskogo gosudarstvennogo universiteta im. Iv. Franko)*, vol. 40, *seriya geogr. nauk, geogr. sbornik*, issue 4, L'vov, 1957.

On the Improvement of the Agricultural Use of the Lands of the Non-chernozem Belt of the European Part of the USSR *(Ob Uluchshenii Sel'skokhozyaystvennogo Ispol'zovaniya Zemel' Nechernozemnoy Polosy Yevropeyskoy Chasti SSSR)*, Moscow, 1952.

Soil Mapping *(Pochvennoye Kartirovaniye)*, Sbornik (Collection of articles), Moscow, 1958.

Agricultural Erosion and its Control *(Sel'skokhozyaystvennaya Eroziya i Bor'ba s Ney)*, Sbornik, Moscow, 1956.

Agricultural Erosion and New Methods of Studying It *(Sel'skokhozyaystvennaya Eroziya i Novyye Metody Yeye Izucheniya)*, Sbornik, Moscow, 1958.

Sel'vestrov, S. I. Relief and Farming *(Rel'yef i Zemledeliye)*, Moscow, 1955.

Sobolev, S. S. The Development of Erosion Processes on the Territory of the European Part of the USSR and their Control *(Razvitiye Erozionnykh Protsessov na Territorii Yevropeyskoy Chasti SSSR i Bor'ba s Nimi)*, Moscow-Leningrad, 1948.

Part V

METHODS OF
GEOGRAPHIC RESEARCH

CHAPTER 39

METHODS OF EXPEDITIONS

V. S. Preobrazhenskiy

One and a half to two decades ago, the question was raised, now in one, now in another article, as to whether methods of research by expeditions had not outlived their usefulness. Life has given the lie to these doubts. The number of expeditions is growing from year to year, and their scope is also increasing. The expeditions of our times have gone far beyond the episodic field excursions made by teachers of higher schools during vacations. A considerable part of the present expeditions organized by scientific institutions (the Academy of Sciences of the USSR, the academies of sciences of the union republics, and the universities), by production institutions (the Main Administration of the Northern Sea Route, and others) and by the designing institutions (the Hydro-Project [*Gidroproyekt*]), the (Field-and-Forest Project [*Agrolesoproyekt*] and others) are powerful research collectives which have operated for a number of years and whose budgets often exceed those of the stationary scientific institutions. The circle of sciences which employ expeditionary methods of research is also broadening. These methods are becoming the property, not only of the geologic, geographic, biologic, and historical sciences, but also of a number of technical, physico-mathematical, and chemical disciplines.

The fact is that expeditionary methods have retained their role as one of the most important means of gathering new material for the solution of complex problems by the comparative method tested in science. The expeditions have consolidated their position in the exploration of little-studied regions, and have also received a new impulse toward energetic development in regions already long studied. This has been promoted to a considerable extent by the immense expansion of the investigations reposing on special-purpose large- and medium-scale mapping, which, from the methodological point of view, amounts to the study of the distribution of the phenomenon under investigation on this or that area precisely by expeditionary methods.

Of course, expeditionary methods, in their development, have felt the influence of rapidly developing production, new ideas, and new techniques. Thus, great influence on their development has been exerted by the well-known proposition of dialectic materialism concerning the universal relationship between phenomena in nature and in society. To say nothing of geographers whose studies embrace diverse fields [*geografy-"kompleksniki"*], it is now usually impossible to imagine a natural scientist or economist who would confine his observations to the object of investigation alone and not make a study of the connections between the object and the other components of the geographic environment and the phenomena of social life. This leads to a mutual penetration of the procedures and methods of one set of branches of science into the procedures and methods of other branches, and thus to the enrichment of the arsenal of methodological means of the whole system of geographic sciences.

The broad development of the concept of the universal connection of phenomena with one another has brought about an endeavor on the part of science to make *integrated* [*kompleksnyy*] *research*. The geographic sciences were among the first to take up the organization of complex investigations, promoting, on the one hand, as their main task, the study of natural objects as intricate natural complexes and, on the other hand, creating integrated detachments and expeditions for the study of individual geographic phenomena.

Naturally, the composition of the complex expeditionary subdivisions is highly varied, being determined primarily by the tasks of the expedition. Characteristic of modern integrated expeditions is the participation of specialists having different interests and the organizational participation of many scientific and practical institutions in the work of one expedition. It suffices to name, for example, the Integrated Antarctic Expedition of the Academy of Sciences of the USSR and the series of expeditions of the Council for the Study of the Productive Forces under the Presidium of the Academy of Sciences of the USSR.

The forms and methods of the organization of the investigations are rather varied. Most widespread are the integrated expeditions and integrated detachments. An integrated expedition consists most often of a number of specialized branch detachments. This structure is usually created when it is necessary to co-ordinate the efforts of the workers of different institutions. The efforts of the detachments are united by their common tasks and by the co-ordination of the programs. To reinforce integration, use is often made of common reconnaissance, joint routes, and field encounters at interesting objects. The merits of this method are its high productivity and the possibility it affords of investigating important questions on a more detailed scale. The drawbacks are the comparatively small purposefulness of the work, the often different depth of the investigations despite the seemingly similar scale of the work, and the incomplete coverage of the connections between the components of the geographic environment.

The practice of making up integrated detachments from researchers with different specialties, traveling the same route under unified organizational guidance, is widely followed in expeditions, principally with co-ordination of the activities of the workers of one institution. Its undeniable merit is the union (applying to everything, including organization) of the researchers in the solution of one task. Its main drawback is the low labor productivity, due to the necessity for all to adjust their tempo to the slow-researching specialist and to the lack of thorough study of the most important details.

For some time there has been a rather sharp discussion about the possibility of the expeditionary study of a complex of natural conditions and of natural complexes of different ranks by one person — a geographer "of broad interests" [*shirokiy profil'*]: a "*kompleksnik*." Numerous studies by productional collectives and scientific institutions have now solved this question in the affirmative. Such investigations usually yield good results with respect to the discovery of new connections between the components of nature, are comparatively simple to organize, and insure rapid procurement of homogeneous report material. Their drawbacks are lesser depth of characterization of each of the components. Investigations of this kind have the greatest values as a basis for planning further large-scale research work, and also in all cases where the time factor is uppermost in importance.

A powerful influence on the methods of expeditionary work has also been exercised by the everyday demand for the study of geographic phenomena in their dynamic development. This influence has manifested itself in the endeavor to combine in various ways the methods of expeditionary and stationary research: in the last few years, semistationary posts designed to operate for several years are not infrequently created on expeditions that extend over a number of years. Another form in which this endeavor manifests itself is the combination, characteristic of present expeditionary tactics of route explorations with a comparatively detailed, all-around study of typical sections of terrain — keys, standards, points, profiles, and "stations." This has resulted in the expansion of the field season beyond the warm period of the year and to the organization of special investigations in wintertime. It also has given new impetus to the development of diverse variants of the interrogation method, whereby data gained from many years, and often many centuries, of experience of an army of attentive observers — people who learn the most minute characteristics of local nature in the process of their diversified labor activity — are mobilized for science. The moral and political unity of the multinational Soviet people creates exceptional preconditions for the fruitful application of this method.

The necessity of giving the practical man precise answers, expressed in figures and measurements, and the endeavor to penetrate into the chemical and physical essence of natural phenomena are leading, in all the geographic sciences, to a growing increase in the representation of the characteristics of the objects and processes studied by means of quantitative indices. Hence the intensive growth of measuring work in expeditionary investigations. The larger part of this work still consists of measurements of the dimensions of natural objects and their components. In the last few years, however, there has also been noted an increase in more complex measuring work, connected with the study of the state of an object (its physical properties, chemical composition, physiologic activity, etc.), and of the intensity of a number of natural processes. A part of the simplest measurements have been transferred to an office setting. The growth of the number of samples taken for subsequent laboratory treatment is also closely connected with this tendency.

The successful completion of the work on the large-scale mapping of our country and the wide development of aerial photogrammetry have also exercised a substantial influence on the methods and tactics of expeditionary research. Thus, in view of the comparatively poor cartographic coverage of the territory, in setting up the network of routes great attention used to be paid to ascertaining the outline of natural objects by the method of surveying the boundaries of an object by traveling around its outlines or traversing it repeatedly. Now, aerial-photography materials in many cases offer wide possibilities for reducing the volume of field work on the ascertainment of the boundaries of natural objects. In this connection, somewhat different requirements arise in planning the network of routes: visits to all the typical configurations, which require a lower route density.

In the preparatory period, reliable cartographic materials enable one to make a careful selection and a good study of the routes, mark the locations of the key sections, i.e., essentially to make an office reconnaissance. This is valuable for the further reason that it enables the investigator to "acclimatize himself," as it were, in the natural setting of the region of impending operations.

Modern expeditionary investigation has grown into a rather complex productional process, consisting of comparatively simple, but at the same time very diversified operations. They usually include: the movement and organization of services having to do with the means of transportation and technical equipment; orientation; preparation of the object for study; observation; recording of the observation materials; field office work; organization of the feeding and recreation of the workers; and safety measures. The further development of expeditionary methods requires a clear notion of the nature of the individual operations and their mutual connection. It is necessary to seek ways of reducing the consumption of time in organizational, economic, and technical measures and of improving the research of operations proper.

Each expedition is to a considerable extent a *transportation* operation. The diversity of the territories in which Soviet researchers operate also produces a diversity of the means of locomotion employed. It is difficult to name any kind of transportation that has not been employed by expeditions. In addition to air transport, developed during the last decades (airplanes and helicopters of various types), and traditional as well as new types of water transport (rafts, boats of various design, cutters, steamers, motor and diesel-electric ships, icebreakers, water-jet cutters, hydroplanes and submarines), wide use is also made of various types of surface transport: wheeled (motor cars capable of traveling in different kinds of terrain, and horse-drawn wagons), tracked vehicles (tractors and many designs of cross-country vehicles), vehicles with runners (aero-sleds, sled-tractor trains, dog, reindeer, and horse teams), and pack transport, employed under especially difficult conditions (horse, camel, reindeer, and so forth), as well as horseback riding. Modern means of locomotion have also revolutionized the character of the observations. Thus, the use of airplanes and helicopters has made it possible to see phenomena that have not been observed at all in surface exploration.

The employment of this or that means of locomotion naturally imposes a definite imprint on the tempo of the work, the expeditionary tactics, the methods of recording observations, the possibility of technical outfitting, and the organization of the workers' living conditions. However perfect the modern means of locomotion may be, no expedition can get along without some expenditure of time and effort on overcoming obstacles: water barriers, complex ascents and descents, seasonal lack of roads, hummock ice, shifting sands, etc. Although it is often a transportation task, every participant in an expedition, regardless of his scientific or productional qualifications, must be conversant with the modern methods of rapidly and safely overcoming obstacles. The collective spirit and sense of duty peculiar to Soviet men and women are a trustworthy guarantee of triumph over any obstacle.

Some time is spent on servicing the means of transportation: current and preventive repair, feeding and veterinary care of animals, etc. The solution of these problems is considerably simplified by the system of operation by radial routes, centering on a previously prepared base.

Modern large-scale maps or aerial photographs considerably reduce the expenditure of time on *orientation,* to which much attention was always paid in the old handbooks on field work. To be sure, the use of the new means of locomotion with their high speeds have required increased attention to orientation in movement. The solution of this problem has contributed to the introduction into orientation practice of methods worked out in marine navigation: by course, velocity, and time of movement (or distance traveled).

However carefully the "keys" may have been selected in the office, *reconnaissance* remains an invariable part of field work — the determination of the most typical section for the given locality and the fixing of its outlines in the terrain. After the object of observation has been definitively chosen on the spot, it usually has to be *prepared* for investigation to a greater or lesser extent, like a "laboratory specimen," so to speak. This process, formerly almost entirely inconspicuous among the other kinds of field work, has, in recent decades, become a rather substantial stage of research with respect to the time consumed, owing to the already noted saturation of research with field measurement work and the growth of the volume of samples taken. It includes, for example, such work as the digging of pits, the cleaning of outcrops, drillings, the sawing down of model trees, control mowings, the setting-up of instruments for observation, the instrumental or semi-instrumental marking of profiles, and the large-scale topographic mapping of areas. The care and speed with which the work is performed at this stage depend not so much on the erudition of the researcher, as on his ability to organize the work of the whole detachment. This stage often requires especially concentrated attention to the organization of safe working techniques (in felling timber, digging pits, handling explosives, and so forth).

The preparation of the object for investigation is often closely intertwined with the *taking of specimens.* This operation is rather varied in investigations of different types. But typicality of the specimen, clear recording of its location, and preservation from contamination or destruction during further transportation remain general requirements. Observance of these rules is promoted by the use of standard labels, previously prepared packing (small bags, envelopes, stiff boxes, etc.), new methods of fastening the material (use of glue, plastic film, etc.), and also by the use of more perfect instruments for taking specimens.

The content of the *observations* is set forth in fair detail in numerous and very detailed scientific programs and official instructions. Of course, the clearness and detail of the observations depend above all upon the researcher's training, his powers of observation (which, of course, can be developed), his experience in field work and his inquisitiveness, i.e., his ability to put questions to nature in new ways — over and above the instructions and the program. Very important are questions of the enhancement of objectivity and the comparability of observations. This is insured by relatively unified programs for the collection of material, by the performance of methodical field work by the whole group of participants with the objective of working out uniform evaluations, by the extensive employment of measurements of the objects under study and their component parts, by the collation of the object studied with standard samples (for example, the use of standard color charts in soil and hydrologic investigations), or with tables of the field criteria of the properties of the object, and by taking specimens whose subsequent analysis, clothed in numerical form, makes it possible to judge the degree of objectivity of the field evaluation.

Recording the observations receives great attention in all the instructions. This is entirely justified, since the rule evolved by many generations of researchers that "what has not been written down has not been observed" remains unshakable. The forms of recording observations are very diverse: notes, maps, profiles, sketches, photos, and motion-picture films.

The written records may be discretionary or may be made according to a special program, having most often a tabular or questionnaire form. A multitude of such programs have, for example, been worked out for describing plant groupings, for gathering information by interrogation, for writing economic geographic descriptions ("Handbook of the Traveler and Local-Lore Student" [*Spravochnik Puteshestvennika i krayeveda*], 1949-1950). Here, too, belong the various climatic and hydrologic "journals."

The tabular, questionnaire, and journal forms of recording have a number of advantages: uniformity (which is extremely important if it is intended to subject the materials to a statistical treatment, or if the materials of many investigators have to be compiled), the constant reminder to the investigator of the necessity of paying attention to the information contained in the table or questionnaire. However, a rigid form of recording also has its negative features. Having been worked out before leaving for the field, it cannot anticipate all the characteristics of the phenomenon or object, it dulls the researcher's "keenness of vision," and accustoms him to look at the natural object or phenomenon as the sum of the individual indices. For this reason, the discretionary form of written record retains its significance in any kind of investigation. It is of especially great significance in doing work in which the most important aspect of the investigation is the establishment, not so much of the dimensions and form of a phenomenon as the connections between several phenomena. However, records in a discretionary form should also be subordinated to definite requirements: they should have a clear address (tie-in), and a date, and should make a sharp distinction between what has actually been observed and what is assumed. One distinguishes journals (consisting of a number of blank forms), a notebook — a field diary for immediate recordings — and a diary for evening or field office recordings. Use is sometimes made of "segregated" diaries or journals recording only one kind of natural phenomena or activities of the researcher: a species diary in the case of zoologists, journals for the collection of specimens, photographs, etc. The usual form of keeping a diary for immediate recordings in investigations by geographers of different specialties duplicates, in the main, the type of recordings worked out at one time by the geologists: the recording is done with a pencil on one side of the unfolded notebook; the other side is left for drawings, diagrams, notation of the serial numbers of specimens, the serial numbers and contents of photographs, etc.

A very widespread method of recording field observation material is to enter it on a map or aerial photo. The simplest procedure is to enter the separate notes in words, conventional signs not to scale, or in letter or figure symbols on the face or back of the photo or map. Most often, this method is employed to record some phenomenon supplementing the contents of the map (showing the micro-relief, the vegetation complexes, the seasonal change in the object, its genesis, etc.) as well as to interpret the air-photo outlines. A more meaningful form of recording is by mapping, done on a general topographic map as a base, on contact prints of air photos, on photo diagrams and photo plans, as well as on tracing paper superimposed on them.

Drawings of the forms of relief, cross sections (geologic, soil, stratigraphy of snow layers, etc.), and of profiles have long since been admitted to the arsenal of means of recording observations. However, the introduction into science of the idea of the close connection between the components of the geographic environment has brought about a broad development of the method of composing integrated or landscape profiles, on which the relationships are shown between the geologic structure, the relief forms, the soils, the vegetation, the ground waters, the level of perennial frost, and other components of nature. The character of the profiles varies greatly — they may also be schematic sketches not drawn to scale, or profiles composed on the basis of instrumental leveling, field drillings, etc.

Photography has found wide employment as a means of recording observations. The techniques of ground, air, and underwater photography have now been sufficiently well worked out. Special note must be taken of stereophotogrammetric surveying, which furnishes material for rather varied measuring work. Of great interest are repeated surveys of objects, enabling one to judge the dynamics of the development of a number of phenomena, as well as surveys of one and the same object to different scales. The drawbacks of many photographic surveys are the lack of strict recording of the direction of the photo, the dominance of qualitative scales (people, automobiles, etc.) and the comparatively rare use of good linear scales (rods, rulers), and the predominance of landscape beauty to the detriment of the number and clarity of scientifically significant details.

The motion picture is still being introduced, at a comparatively slow rate, for recording observations. Thus far, the motion picture figures more often as a scenic illustration of narratives about expeditions than as a scientific document.

Field office work is usually comparatively small in volume. One may class as such: the drawing of maps, the construction of graphs and profiles from field materials, the simplest elaboration of climatic indices, the weighing of dried specimens of vegetation, and the examination of specimens and their partial description. In spite of the small volume and, on the whole, rather incidental character of field office work, which is most often performed during enforced interruptions of field investigations (because of bad weather or while awaiting transportation), its value is quite obvious. It permits one to draw the first conclusions, to note what materials are missing for their full confirmation, and to refine the plans for further work.

The high degree of physical and nervous strain characteristic of expeditionary investigations lasting many months demands considerable daily attention to the *organization of rational feeding and recreation of the members of expeditions*. Most of the expedition workers, for dozens of years of their lives, have to spend from three to eight months from year to year, under field conditions. Without going into details, let us note that measures aimed at creating normal conditions for expeditionary living comprise, for example, the establishment of heated camps and bases (building of dwellings and movable houses), the organization of warm meals sufficiently rich in calories and vitamins, the organization of political information and cultural relaxation (radio, newspapers), and the insurance of communication with relatives and close friends.

Expeditions of any degree of complexity have to pay attention to *safety techniques and to medical and sanitary care*. A considerable part of these measures are carried out even before the departure of an expedition. Here belong medical inspection and inoculations; instruction in safety techniques and first aid; equipment with special clothing adapted to the local climatic conditions, with medicines and means of protection against insects (mosquito nets, curtains, chemicals); and with safety devices (equipment for insuring safety on rocks and on stream crossings, rescue equipment for work on water, weapons in regions abounding in wild animals, etc.). The overwhelming part of these measures is carried out for all personnel at government expense.

Of special significance in conducting expeditions is the maintenance of a high level of discipline to insure the observance of the safety rules under all circumstances when under way (for example, prohibition against traveling alone in mountain or tayga regions, and observance of the control dates for the return of field subdivisions to the bases) and when performing various kinds of special work (felling of timber, etc.). Also essential are the organization of radio communication and the assignment of medical personnel to field subdivisions remote from the bases.

We shall not examine the questions of the organization of rescue work. The whole world knows about the exploits of Soviet men and women, who have more than once gone out on missions to rescue not only Soviet participants (for example, the crew of the "Chelyuskin"), but also many foreign expeditions (the Italian expedition on the dirigible "Italia" in the Arctic, the Belgian explorers in the Antarctic, etc.). Many examples may be cited of the heroism of rank-and-file medical workers who have made parachute jumps under difficult conditions in the tayga or beyond the Arctic Circle to rescue a gravely ill explorer or winter camper.

Naturally, for such a complex kind of physical activity as expeditionary work, the specialist must be sufficiently prepared. Soviet higher schools have worked out an orderly program of instruction in field-work methods. In the universities, this program reposes on courses in the techniques of investigation and educational field practice; upon production practice by the students in the duties of junior scientific-technical collaborators or producers of work on production or scientific expeditions. (The duration of such practice in the last two years of instruction is not less than 6 to 7 months.) Certain elements of field-investigation methods, particularly safety and locomotion, are included in the program of special physical training (horseback riding, stream crossings, etc.).

Of considerable aid to the investigator are the various kinds of methodological instructions and handbooks. Such aids have been created for many branches of the geographic sciences (for example, the series "Basic Methodological Instructions for Glaciologic Exploration" [*Osnovnyye metodicheskiye ukazaniya po glyatsiologicheskim issledovaniyam*], 1957, consisting of 15 issues; the "Methods of Geobotanical Field Investigation" [*Metodika polevykh geobotanicheskikh issledovaniy*], 1938). Of great interest has been the two-volume "Handbook of the Traveler and Local-lore Student" [*Spravochnik puteshestvennika i krayeveda*] (1949-1950), which, however, is now rather obsolete. One should note the definite lag in the generalization of the experience gained in conducting scientific and organizational work on the large complex expeditions, and in the creation of methodological instructions concerning integrated exploration.

It cannot be doubted that, in spite of the growth of other methods of geographic research, the scope and volume of expeditionary work will continue to grow. In this connection it is necessary to bring about further improvement in the methods of this research. This process will apparently follow three directions:

1. Improvement of the programs of expeditionary investigation, above all in the direction of deepening and broadening the study of the connection between phenomena; creation of new methodical guides and handbooks; taking into account the experience gained on modern complex expeditions; rapid introduction of the experience of the allied branches of science; organization of field consultations by allied specialists and highly qualified specialists.

2. Technical improvement and introduction of the most progressive means: (a) of locomotion (helicopters and light airplanes, motor vehicles suited for more difficult going, particularly amphibian), light motorized transport and ferrying craft and submarines, (b) the "preparation" of objects and the investigation and taking of specimens; for example, light movable drills, vibrating hole-diggers, and light measuring apparatus, and (c) recording of observation material (motion-picture apparatus, means of recording sounds en route and at given points from different means of locomotion, light self-recording remote-control and automatic instruments and sets of instruments). At the same time, of course, the energetic improvement must continue of the ordinary lightened expeditionary instruments, gear and tools, and the efforts to make them lighter and more economical.

3. Improvement of the organization and tactics of the conduct of expeditionary work: creation of permanent bases, equipped with gear and tools (possible within the framework of the sovnarkhozes [regional national-economy councils] but not within that of the official central agencies, maximum reduction of the organizational-liquidational period, and creation of guides and handbooks on the organizational and economic problems of expeditionary activity.

BASIC LITERATURE

Borzov, A. A., Shchukin, I. S., Tugarinov, D. N., and Zarutskaya, I. P. "Methods of Geographic Descriptions" [Metodika Geograficheskikh Opisaniy], Tr. TsNIIGA i K, no. 26, Moscow, 1938.

Botanicheskiy institut Akademii nauk SSSR. Methods of Geobotanical Field Investigation [Metodika Polevykh Geobotanicheskikh Issledovaniy], 1938.

Kalesnik, S. V. "The Tasks of Geography and Geographic Field Investigation," Uch. zap. LGU, no. 50, seriya geogr. nauk, no. 2, 1940.

Basic Methodological Instructions in Glaciologic Investigation [Osnovnyye Metodicheskiye Ukazaniya po Glyatsiologicheskim Issledovaniyam]. Responsible editor G. A. Avsyuk, issues 1-15, Moscow, 1957.

Rakitnikov, A. N. "On the Methods of Economic Geographic Expeditionary Work," Izv. AN SSSR, seriya geogr., 1954, No. 1, pp. 74-83.

Solntsev, N. A. "Methods and Results of Landscape Field Investigation in the Oka Terrace State Nature Preserve," Vestn. MGU, 1950, No. 2, pp. 155-162.

Handbook of the Traveler and Local-lore Student [Spravochnik Puteshestvennika i Krayeveda]. Under the editorship of S. V. Obruchev. Vols. 1-2, Moscow, 1949-1950.

CHAPTER 40

AERIAL PHOTOGRAPHY AND STEREOPHOTOGRAMMETRY

V. I. Avgevich

Use of the cartographic method is an indispensable condition for the productivity of geographic research. This method furthers the thorough study not only of the static but also of the dynamic elements of the various landscapes of the Soviet Union. It permits one to ascertain and evaluate natural interrelations and laws that were unknown before or had escaped observation. But the effectiveness of the method depends upon its selective capacity. Hence, it is necessary, in research, to use the most perfect special-purpose maps which fully and reliably reflect the quantitative and qualitative characteristics taken into account in studying natural objects and phenomena. The creation of such maps is promoted by photographic measurement. As a result, phototopographic methods have won the recognition of geographers and are being used more widely every year in the objective recording of the aspect and state of the earth's surface.

The possibilities offered by mensurative photography for the quantitative and qualitative evaluation of natural objects, phenomena, and processes to be studied attracted the attention of geographers in the last century, but it was only the ground photogrammetry method. The development of aviation, which began later, caused rapid improvement in the techniques of aerial photographic survey work. The result was that air-photo surveying, far excelling ground phototopographic surveying, began to be energetically introduced into the field of geographic investigation.

The employment of aerial and ground phototopographic surveying in geographic research is now characterized by the considerable variety of the methods and technical means used. Alongside the large number of diverse topical fields of these surveys, one notes a considerable number of new and original methods specially worked out in application to the content and purpose of certain geographic investigations.

The original method of photographic measurement mastered by geographers—ground stereo-photogrammetric surveying—has not lost its significance, but has even undergone further development. In pre-Revolutionary Russia stereophotography was used only episodically in geographic research. Since the Great October Socialist Revolution, on the other hand, phototheodolite surveying, as an efficient method of recording geographic field observations, has been used much more widely and diversely in our country. Intensive use is being made of it in glaciologic investigations, as well as in the study of the properties of polar sea ice. Ground stereophotography is also employed by geomorphologists in studying flash-flood streams, rock falls, and talus (Iveronova, 1942, 1954), landslides (Khrennikov, 1953), and other natural phenomena which are due to relief and its mutual relations with the soils and underlying bedrock (Slastikhin, 1958).

Ground stereophotogrammetry has undergone especially great development in hydrologic and oceanographic research. The employment of phototheodolite surveying in the study of the waves on water surfaces, begun in 1907 by A. N. Krylov, has now been considerably perfected. This has made it possible to discover new possibilities for ground stereophotography (Kudritskiy, 1956) and to use it in the interest of engineering practice (Gorodetskiy, 1953).

Instead of episodic synchronous surveying with individual stereo-pairs by means of the ordinary phototheodolites loaded with photo plates, wide use is now made of continuous photographing with multiload film apparatus. The modern hydrologic phototheodolite models SFA-1, SFA-2 and FP-14-A (Pugin, 1955) permit the automatic stereophotographing of waves in series containing from 5 to 15 stereo-pairs. Their photogrammetric treatment makes it possible, in addition to determining the height,

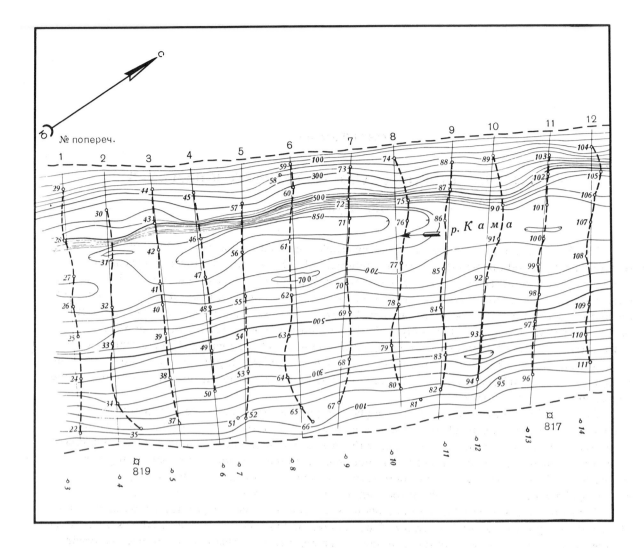

Fig. 24. PART OF THE SURVEYOR'S PLAN OF THE VOTKINSK RESERVOIR ON THE KAMA RIVER (reduced in size). Compiled from echo-sounder mensuration data with photogeodetic tie-in of the tacks with shore-based points. Isobaths given in meters from the working horizon of the water as of 5 October, 1955. Fine straight lines show mensuration ranges; broken lines, the trajectories determined by the photo sightings; numbers of photo sightings are appended.

length, and steepness of the wave, to find its velocity and period, and to study the process of the change in wave form as it approaches the shore.

Ground stereophotography has also begun to be used to determine the velocity of streams and the direction of surface currents, which is of great significance in connection with the designing of big hydrotechnical structures. Since 1938, such investigations have been systematically conducted on rivers of the Soviet Union.

A new variant of ground phototopography is the planned co-ordination of mensuration tacks by means of a system of photogrammetric back sightings. This treatment is due to the wide introduction of the echo-sounder into mensuration practice. Inasmuch as the usual geodetic methods of the planned fitting-together of mensuration tacks have greatly slowed the tempo of mensuration and have not insured a high degree of precision in the co-ordination of the vertical measurements, a method of photogeodetic matching of the echo-sounder mensuration of depths has been evolved (Avgevich, 1951). Use of the echo-sounder permits the measurement of depths to be made really rapidly. Original photo apparatus and new photogrammetric instruments—a precision light panel and a photoprotractor—have been created for this purpose. The method makes it possible to determine automatically, on each mensuration tack, the requisite number of photo-stations. It permits the reproduction, on the planetable, of the course of the measuring vessel (Fig. 24). Owing to the high tempo of field work it is possible to make multiple measurements and obtain comparable plans of the floor relief. The appearance of such plans enables one to study the phenomenon of the transformation of the floor relief under the action of the channel processes, and from this derives the possibility of a fuller knowledge of the channel processes—this least-studied department of the hydrology of the land.

Since 1949, mensuration photography has begun to be used to improve the methods of studying the processes of snow melt (G. R. Rekhtzamer). More recently, in connection with the commencing reclamation of virgin and idle lands, the problem of the detailed and all-around study of the conditions of the formation of runoff has become especially urgent. There has been a need for perfected methods

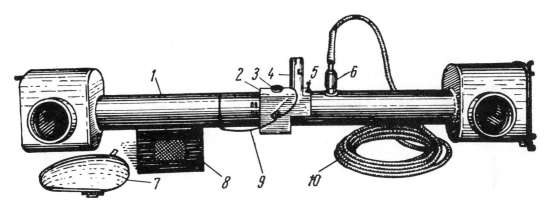

Fig. 25. PHOTOTHEODOLITE SET FOR UNDERWATER STEREOPHOTOGRAMMETRIC SURVEYING

1. Body 2. Sleeve 3. Set screw of inclination sector 4. Supporting fork for setting instrument on rod 5. Base leveling screw 6. Switch of electric cable 7. Cap to first section 8. Adapter case 9. Spring to set base in normal position 10. Electric feed cable

of mapping the snow cover in the various phases of its disappearance. Ground photogrammetry has become the main method of recording the various stages of snow melt on runoff areas.

An original variety of ground stereophotogrammetry is the method of underwater stereo-photography (Loshchilov, 1957), created for the study of the relief of the lower surface of polar sea ice. It permits an objective, quantitative evaluation of its thickness, required for further improvement of the methods of studying the ice regimes of the Arctic seas. The scientific value of the method of underwater stereophotography is not confined to the field of high-latitude oceanographic investigation alone—it will undoubtedly soon be an effective means of study in hydrogeologic or hydrobiologic investigations, as well as in the fields of technology which are connected with the operation of hydro-works, mechanisms and devices operating in the water. From the viewpoint of photogrammetry, this method is interesting because it offers a concrete example of the successful solution of the task of making precise measurements from pictures obtained by photographing through two media. While, in its application to aerophotogrammetry, the solution of the task of two-medium photography was begun abroad, though brought to a conclusion only in the USSR, the problem of its application to underwater stereophoto-grammetry with a horizontal or inclined line of sight was first posed and solved in our country alone. Special apparatus for underwater stereophotogrammetry have already been created (Fig. 25).

Thus, in the USSR, ground photogrammetric surveying is used in geographic investigations on an ever broader list of subjects. Soviet geographic science is making active use of this method, modifying it in application to whatever tasks present themselves.

★ ★ ★

In the integrated process of geographic field and office research, a large role is played by aerial photography. Instantaneously recording the picture of the state of the earth's surface, aerial photography, in addition to high perspicuity and the saturation of the photos with most valuable details, makes it easy to repeat observations many times. The wide range of intervals between surveys guarantees the possibility of any comparison that will assist in ascertaining and studying the elements of the dynamics of the most varied phenomena of nature. Hence, it is now difficult to name any branch of geographic science that does not avail itself of the advantages of aerial photography to one extent or another.

We shall not go into detail here about the techniques of employing aerial photography in general geographic, geomorphologic, zoogeographic, and geobotanical investigations, the groundwork for which was laid by Academician A. Ye. Fersman, a warm advocate of the introduction of aerial photography into the study of the geographic environment. We shall only note that in these investigations aerial photography has long been used very productively in spite of the fact that its employment is still occasional in character.

In a large number of aspects, the leading role in the mastery of the method of aerial photography by geographers has belonged to Soviet scientists. This is true above all of K. A. Salishchev and S. V. Obruchev (1936), who made orographic investigations in the Chukot-Anadyr' district; to B. A. Fedorovich (1948), who was the first to give a filigree analysis of the relief forms of the sands of Middle Asia and to characterize the mutual relations between the vegetation types and the sand relief of the deserts. Innovational also were the works by S. V. Dorofeyev and S. Yu. Freyman (1933), who created aerial photographic methods for the purpose of mapping the lairs of sea animals, for the purpose of taking a census of the droves and working out scientifically based hunting norms.

Comparing our native geographic aerial photo surveys with foreign ones, one has to acknowledge that, on the whole, they have developed parallel, with approximately equal intensity. Let us enumerate a number of examples of the use of aerial photography by Soviet geographers, which can serve to characterize the high level of the requirements for the making of observations of natural phenomena in our country.

The possibility of stereophotographing clouds, first pointed out in 1932 by P. Ret'yen, is already being successfully realized. This kind of surveying makes it possible, by comparing the physical and geometric characteristics of cloudiness of different types, to make a new approach to the study of the laws of transformation of one form of cloudiness into another, which cannot but contribute to the further improvement of the methods of hydrometeorologic forecasting as a whole.

In 1949, the Aero-Methods Laboratory of the Academy of Sciences of the USSR succeeded in sharply broadening the possibility of studying the relief of the sea floor. This was achieved as a result of the properly organized aerial photographing of the Caspian Sea, which proved very efficient in spite of the insufficient transparency of its water. In 1950, V. P. Zenkovich was the first to apply aerial photography to the study of the morphology of sea coasts. Aerial photographs made it possible to elucidate the process of abrasion of coasts of different types, to discover and study new aspects of the process of alluvium accumulation, and to learn the character of the action of sea waves on the floor relief of the coastal strip of the sea.

Since the War, the content of zoogeographic investigations based on the use of aerial methods, including aerial photography, has been considerably enlarged. In the Soviet Union there has been wide development of the application of aerial photography in reconnoitering the locations of shoals of fish, in algological investigations for the purpose of studying the food base, in determining the routes of fish migration, and in obtaining other data necessary for the compilation of fish-hunting charts. Such maps serve as a scientific basis for the organization and planning of the fishing industry. The use of aerial photography for taking a census of the population and geographic distribution of land vertebrates began at the same time. There is still much to be done, however, before aerial photo apparatus becomes an obligatory appurtenance of the zoogeographer. For example, for an objective census of the number of industrial game birds it is necessary, instead of insufficiently perfect panoramic ground photography, to employ aerial stereophotographing of birds previously flushed from their nests. This will help to effect the bird census-taking with the aid of stereomeasuring grid permitting one to observe, within the limits of the stereo-model, a volume-space lattice in the form of the aggregate of cubes of an assigned volume.

The first systematized materials characterizing the methods of mapping soils with the use of aerial photos were published in 1954 (M. S. Simakova). Later, the employment of aerial photography in the study of the geography of soils, based on the wide exploitation of the advantages of photographing on color and spectrozonal aero-film, assumed a systematic character. The methods of soil mapping from aerial-survey materials have already become established.

Fig. 26. FRAGMENT OF A PRINT OF AN AERIAL FILM OF SLIT AXONOMETRIC SURVEY

In geobotanical investigations, the employment of aerial photography began back in 1925, with the study of the country's forest resources. The questions of forest aerophotography have now been worked out very fully and have been successfully systematized, but the process of improving the methods of studying forests with the aid of aerial photography continues to evolve. Axonometric slit aerophotography (Gordeyev, 1954) has been successfully employed in forest assessment. This type of surveying furnishes a photo image (Fig. 26) with like vertical and horizontal scales, and since, in photographing, the projecting rays lie at an angle of 45° to the vertical, it is possible to record the location of the trunks in many-tiered tree stands more fully on the aero-film. This is far from being always achieved in ordinary flat aerial photography.

Axonometric aerophotography does not exhaust the new possibilities discovered in the field of the study of USSR forests. Further improvement of the process of interpreting forest aerial photos, making it possible to establish the boundaries of the lots more accurately in the office and to give a forest-assessment characterization, is due to the introduction of instrumental interpretation.

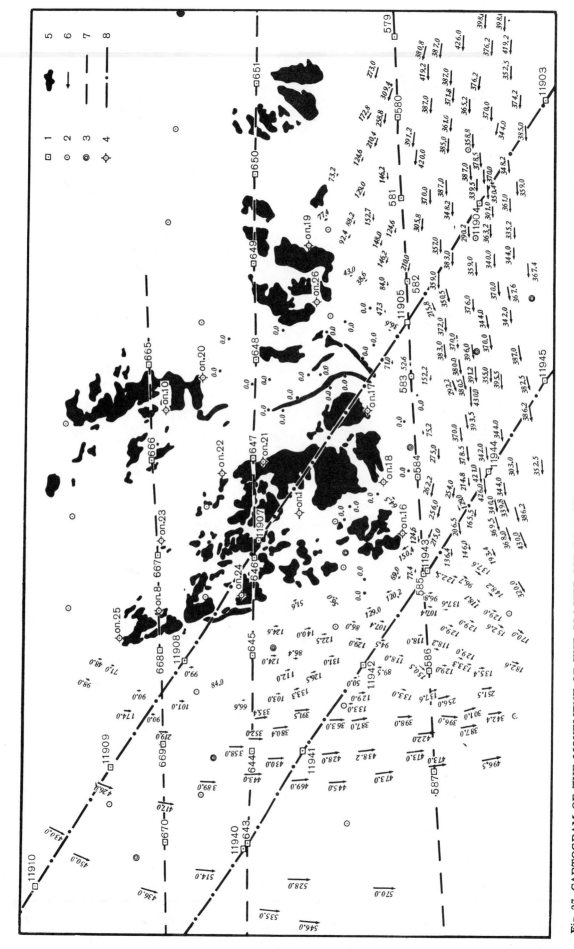

Fig. 27. CARTOGRAM OF THE MOVEMENT OF THE GLACIER ICE OF ANTARCTICA, AS ILLUSTRATED BY THE OBRUCHEV AND SCOTT GLACIERS, according to 1956 and 1957 aerial photographic survey data. (Compiled by V. I. Sil'nitskaya and Yu. I. Fukin.)

1. Numbers and working centers of aerial photos used in compilation of the photogrammetric base. 2. X-points on the aerial photos of the 1956 flight. 3. X-points on the aerial photos of the 1957 flight. 4. Support points on the aerial photos of the 1956-1957 flights. 5. Bedrock exposures. 6. Direction and magnitude of displacement of ice during the interval between aerial photo survey flights. 7. Direction of the aerial photo survey flights (of 1 February 1956). Direction of the aerial photo survey flights.

Fig. 26. FRAGMENT OF A PRINT OF AN AERIAL FILM OF SLIT AXONOMETRIC SURVEY

In geobotanical investigations, the employment of aerial photography began back in 1925, with the study of the country's forest resources. The questions of forest aerophotography have now been worked out very fully and have been successfully systematized, but the process of improving the methods of studying forests with the aid of aerial photography continues to evolve. Axonometric slit aerophotography (Gordeyev, 1954) has been successfully employed in forest assessment. This type of surveying furnishes a photo image (Fig. 26) with like vertical and horizontal scales, and since, in photographing, the projecting rays lie at an angle of 45° to the vertical, it is possible to record the location of the trunks in many-tiered tree stands more fully on the aero-film. This is far from being always achieved in ordinary flat aerial photography.

Axonometric aerophotography does not exhaust the new possibilities discovered in the field of the study of USSR forests. Further improvement of the process of interpreting forest aerial photos, making it possible to establish the boundaries of the lots more accurately in the office and to give a forest-assessment characterization, is due to the introduction of instrumental interpretation.

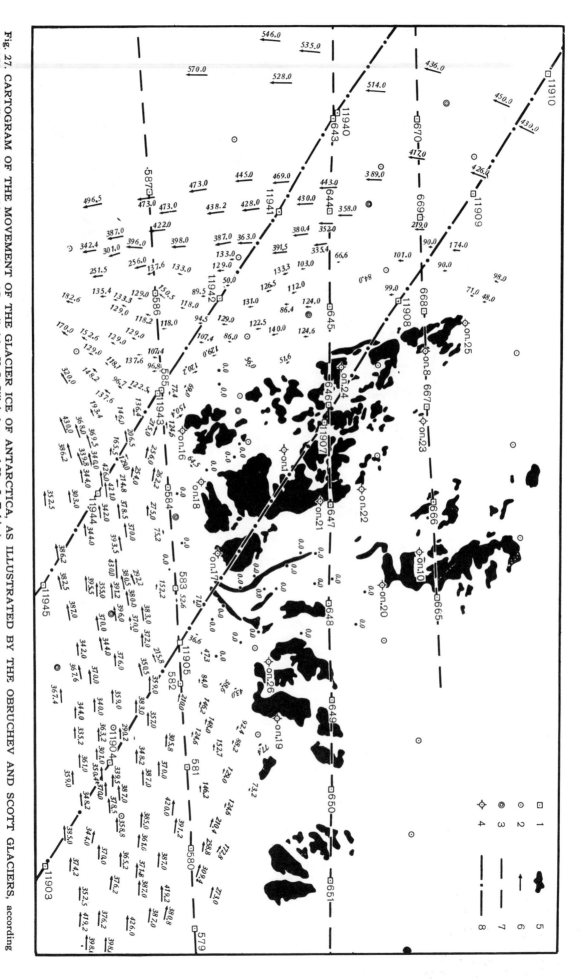

Fig. 27. CARTOGRAM OF THE MOVEMENT OF THE GLACIER ICE OF ANTARCTICA, AS ILLUSTRATED BY THE OBRUCHEV AND SCOTT GLACIERS, according to 1956 and 1957 aerial photographic survey data. (Compiled by V. I. Sil'nitskaya and Yu. I. Fukin.)

1. Numbers and working centers of aerial photos used in compilation of the photogrammetric base. 2. X-points on the aerial photos of the 1956 flight. 3. X-points on the aerial photos of the 1957 flight. 4. Support points on the aerial photos of the 1956-1957 flights. 5. Bedrock exposures. 6. Direction and magnitude of displacement of ice during the interval between aerial photo survey traverses of 24 February, 1956. Direction of the aerial photo survey traverses of 11 March, 1957.

Enhancement of the results of the forest-assessment study of aerial photos is achieved by working up the data obtained by the statistical method. It is precisely in this combination of methods of putting together the initial data and their subsequent elaboration that one must see the basic preconditions for the wide and rapid introduction of mensuration interpretation into other fields of geographic research as well.

In addition to forest aerial photography, there has been a sharp growth in the use of aerial photography in geobotanical research as a whole. Lately, geobotanical investigations have been carried on in an especially broad manner, either in combination with soil investigations (Petrov, 1944), or in searching for an animal-husbandry fodder base, or in combination with the hydrologic study of swamp areas (Galkina, 1958). On the other hand, geobotanical investigations based on air-photo interpretation have also become considerably intensified owing to the exploitation of the mutual relations between the types of vegetation and the lithologic composition of rocks. The use of ecologic data in geologic interpretation has caused the intensive development a new branch of geobotanical research.

The role of aerial photography in geomorphologic research (Rengarten, 1939) is also growing incessantly, with the center of gravity of the use of air-photo materials lying in the field of the interpretation of aerial photographs, without the execution of special surveys.

In recent years there has been a determination of the character of the possible use of aerial photography in glaciologic research, which for a long time has depended exclusively on ground stereophotogrammetric surveying. The first experiment studying the elements of the dynamics of certain glaciers in Antarctica by photogrammetric treatment of aerial photographs has produced methods yielding results which in accuracy, are not inferior to those furnished by the use of ground methods. Soviet methods of using aerial photos in glaciology are adapted above all to the study of glaciers of the sheet type, occupying immense areas. Employing the phototriangulation method for the co-ordinated treatment of air photos of the object under study, taken at considerable time intervals, it provides a system of vectors (Fig. 27) characterizing the direction and magnitude of the linear displacement during the interval between the surveys of a number of points identified on the surface of the glacier. Parallel with the development of methods of treating aerial photographs of glaciers of the sheet type, the Institute of Geography of the Academy of Sciences of the USSR seeks procedures for the photogrammetric treatment of air photos for the purpose of glaciologic cataloguing of high-mountain glaciers of other types.

Lately, owing to the intensive expansion of the sown areas in the arid-climate zone, the need has arisen to investigate the conditions of the occurrence and disappearance of snow over the vast expanses of the virgin lands. Naturally, ground phototheodolite surveying, while suited for observations on runoff areas, no longer proves acceptable in such cases, and aerial photography is called in to help. In 1949, the State Hydrologic Institute proceeded to solve this task and, to begin with, established the fact that the accuracy of the determination of the percentage of a drainage-basin area covered by snow, making allowance for various sources of errors, is of the order of 6 to 7 per cent. In 1954, the work was continued (B. P. Kazantsev) and furnished a basis for working out a more precise method of determining the proportion of snow coverage of a drainage-basin area in various phases of the snow-melt process. This method is based on the use of the photoelectric principle of measurement by aerial photos, the results of which are treated by the statistical method.

The considerable topical diversity of the variants of aerial photography undertaken in the interest of geographers regularly reflects the need for increasing the content of geographic research. This multiformity is especially noticeable in hydrology, in which aerophotogeodetic methods permit the successful solution of a multitude of tasks. Above all, air photos enable one to form a

Fig. 27. CARTOGRAM OF THE MOVEMENT OF THE GLACIER ICE OF ANTARCTICA, AS ILLUSTRATED BY THE OBRUCHEV AND SCOTT GLACIERS, according to 1956 and 1957 aerial photographic survey data. (Compiled by V. I. Sil'nitskaya and Yu. I. Fukin.)

1. Numbers and working centers of aerial photos used in compilation of the photogrammetric base. 2. X-points on the aerial photos of the 1956 flight. 3. X-points on the aerial photos of the 1957 flight. 4. Support points on the aerial photos of the 1956-1957 flights. 5. Bedrock exposures. 6. Direction and magnitude of displacement of ice during the interval between aerial photo survey flights. 7. Direction of the aerial photo survey traverses of 24 February, 1956. 8. Direction of the aerial photo survey traverses of 11 March, 1957.

correct judgment of the elements of geometric order — the configuration of the boundaries of bodies of water and their depths. By interpretation of air photos, combined with their measurements, one discovers the main elements characterizing the channel processes — lateral and depth erosion and evolution of the stream, as expressed in abandoned beds. Aerial photos enable one to provide a geomorphologic characterization of the river valleys and to forecast the direction and rate of development of the channel processes.

Aerial photography insures a quantitative characterization of many hydrologic phenomena and gives definite ideas about the elements of the dynamics of water masses. In this field there are extensive and not fully discovered possibilities which are so obvious that the formerly existing opinion regarding the difficulty of applying aerial photography to hydrometric investigations has proved to be inadequately grounded. Nor has the contention been confirmed that aerial photography is unsuited for judging the physical factors existing in the hydrosphere. From air photos it is possible to interpret with certainty the various forms and conditions of ice with definite and unlike physical properties; the aero-film records the dividing lines between salt and fresh water near river mouths. Finally, winter aerial photography in the regions of geothermal manifestation permits one to ascertain the geographic distribution of hot springs.

Thus, in addition to geometric and mechanical factors, aerial photography enables one to study the factors of a physical order and, in the last analysis, to judge more fully the whole hydrologic regime of the object under study. If we here take into consideration the opinion of Professor G. A. Avsyuk, who thinks that one of the advantages of photogrammetry for the geographer is also the possibility of the photogrammetric, and, on its basis, likewise the physical modeling of the object, this advantage must obviously also be exploited in the interest of hydrology, especially that part of it which is connected with engineering.

Many kinds of geographic work performed on the seas and rivers of the country are regularly based on the use of aerial photographic materials. Here aerial photography facilitates the study of the shore strip of both the sea and the land, and likewise simplifies the technique of substantiating measurements of depths made from launches. Great significance has become attached to the technique of determining depths by the photometric method of interpreting aerial photos (Yantsh, 1958) or by exploiting indirect signs (1958), as well as by the stereophotogrammetric method (Pugin, 1953). In their use of aerial photography for the study of depths, Soviet scientists (Zdanovich and Sharikov, 1954; Potapenko, 1954) have gotten a little ahead of their foreign colleagues. In the Soviet Union there has been a successful solution of the questions of the theory of aerial mensuration photography through two media, and it is here that the necessary precision in the stereophotogrammetric determination of depths from aerial photos was first achieved in practice.

The methods of hydrographic study of river systems (D. M. Kudritskiy, I. V. Popov, Ye. A. Romanova), as well as of lakes and swamp areas (Galkina, 1949-1958), have been greatly systematized through the use of aerophotographic materials.

The phototheodolite surveying of waves is emphatically regional in character. This fact has caused methods to be worked out for applying aerial photography to the study of waves over large expanses of water (Zdanovich and Sharikov, 1954). Unlike the foreign solutions of this question, repeated by the Aero-methods Laboratory of the Academy of Sciences of the USSR, B. V. Dubovskoy and L. I. Perkis in 1955 worked out an original method of the stereophotogrammetric survey of waves from a single airplane. By comparison with the foreign solutions, based on synchronous aerial photographing from two airplanes, the Soviet method is considerably simpler with respect to both technique and organization. With its aid, one can study the character of waves in the open sea and over considerable expanses of water covered by aerial photographing in a short time. Here, regardless of the force of the gale, it is possible to maintain greater uniformity in the elements of external and mutual orientation of the air photos, which substantially facilitates the stereophotogrammetric treatment of the latter.

Of a more utilitarian character is the hydrologic research connected with the designing of irrigation or reclamation systems, as well as of artificial waterways. But in these cases too, the basis is formed by scientific investigations and generalizations permitting one to find important practical conclusions and solutions. Here, aerial photography and photogrammetry also substantially enhance the results of the investigation. This manifests itself especially in the study of reservoirs — both those planned and those already created. In the first case, great efficiency is achieved in the use of aerial photos to mark off the boundaries of the inundation zone and to study the basin of the future reservoir; in the second case, after the reservoirs have been filled, aerial photography in combination with ground observations contributes to the study of the abrasion of the shores and the process of the formation of the natural boundaries of the new body of water. The examples of the three years of investigation on the Tsimlyanskoye More [a part of the Volga-Don Canal system] convinces one that it will soon be possible to create methods of forecasting the magnitude and speed of the reshaping of the shores. This will greatly facilitate the task of planning hydro-construction in cases where one runs up against the prospect of transferring populated points and industrial enterprises from the inundation zone to new sites.

Hydrologic investigations relating to the study of the elements of stream dynamics are of immense aid in planning. The significance and scale of this aid increase sharply in case of the proper application of organized aerial photography. By this method, hydrometric observations can cover a very large stretch of the river under study and one can dispense with insufficiently representative ground methods, the results of which are always local.

The planned aerial photography of river beds enables one, after the photogrammetric or stereophotogrammetric treatment of air photos, to obtain a picture of the location of surface currents and to determine the velocity of the stream in the plane of the water level. Various methods, both of aerial photography proper and of the subsequent processing of the air photos obtained, are being successfully applied for this purpose. B. P. Rodionov has worked out an original method of systems of artificial floats, applicable to the conditions of the ice-free period of observation. Somewhat more recently, G. D. Cheremnykh has applied a new method for the employment of aerial photography in the period of opening and freezing of rivers. This method permits one not only to make hydrometric observations based on the use of natural floats, but also to obtain the data needed for compiling maps of the ice conditions existing in different stages of the opening and freezing of a river. Such maps serve the study of the ice regime of rivers. Their characteristic feature are insets of photo-indicators, i.e., parts of air photos supplementing the characterization of the ice conditions at those spots on the map where conventional symbols are not sufficiently expressive.

Investigation of the precision of the hydrometric characteristics obtained from aerial photographic materials has shown that the velocity of the current is determined with a mean quadratic error amounting to 3-4 per cent of the magnitude of the velocity. Here, unlike the accuracy of the results of ground phototheodolite surveying, the precision achieved is stable both throughout the width of the river, and also throughout the section of river under study.

In complex hydrologic investigations, aerial photography has also gained recognition in the compilation of a water cadaster, where it substantially contributes to the study of the drainage areas, and in estimates of the water balance. This variant of the use of aerial photos is quite natural, since it is known that, in working with air photos in marking watershed lines, there is no need whatsoever for horizontal contours. This fact is especially important in cases where the need arises for determining precisely the boundaries of a basin.

Since the War, still another variety of hydrologic aerial photography has arisen in the Soviet Union, the employment of which has begun considerably later abroad. This is the application of aerial photography to the study of polar sea ice. The oceanographic work connected with the study of sea ice has a history of more than twenty-five years, and has evolved intensively. It is needed to a greater degree than any other branch of hydrology in the objective recording of phenomena observed over the vast expanses of the Arctic seas. This has been the reason for the employment of aerial photography and photogrammetry in ice reconnaissance. As shown by fifteen years of experience, the overwhelming majority of the parameters characterizing sea ice are brought out by aerial photos with a completeness quite unattainable by aero-visual evaluation. The availability of photo representation of the real ice conditions and the special interpretation of ice air photos have made it possible to discover hidden natural mutual connections between the ice and the surrounding medium (Avgevich, 1951-1956).

In the Arctic, traverse ice surveys predominate. Hence, there is a legitimate effort on the part of oceanologists to get the widest survey coverage of the sea surface from each separate traverse. This object is served by the method of combined perspective and planimetric aerial photography. It affords the very detailed data needed not only for the selection of the amount of detail to be put on ice maps, but also for tying each air photo confidently in with the map, without the use of ground control, which is not feasible on drifting ice. The fundamental scheme of the mutual connections between the two kinds of aerial photography and a cyclogram of the method are shown in Figure 28. Let us note that perspective surveying is the main means of covering the surface of the sea with aerial photography, with one series of three air photos embracing a sector with an arc of 184° and a usable depth of 9 kilometers. Planimetric aerial photography is auxiliary in character and insures a trustworthy interpretation of air photos from the line of location of the points of the nadir in the terrain. The geometric relationship between the two types of air photos is shown in Figure 29, page 317.

The regime of duplication of perspective aerial photography by the planimetric type, rigidly maintained by means of special electric control-measurement apparatus, insures the creation of so-called "junction zones" in the middle perspective photos. After passing on to these zones and transferring to them the data to be entered, interpreted in the planimetric air photos, the possibility arises of using these zones as interpreted keys. With their aid it is possible to interpret with assurance

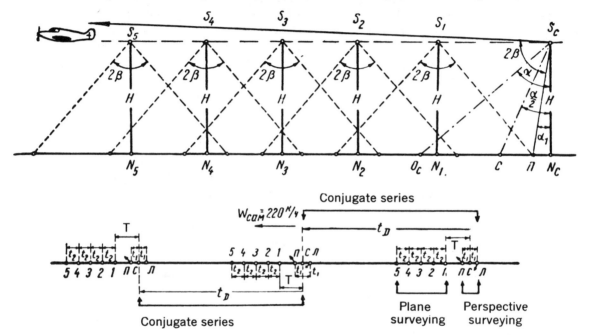

Fig. 28. COMBINED PERSPECTIVE AND PLANE AERIAL SURVEYING

Above: Diagram of interrelationship between pencils of projected rays in combined perspective and plane aerial surveying. *Below:* Cyclogram of combined perspective and plane aerial surveying.

t_1—interval of perspective surveying
t_2—interval of plane surveying

T—interval of conjugation of plane surveying with perspective
t—interval between series of perspective photos

those parts of the perspective photo image which have not been duplicated by the planimetric survey. In this way, it becomes possible to interpret the whole mass of air photos, which is not the case in the "Tri-Metrogon" method. The latter, while efficient enough in interpreting photographs made from great altitudes, is considerably less productive than the Soviet method (Fig. 30, page 318) from an altitude of 400-500 meters, typical of aerial ice reconnaissance.

The principle of stippled planimetric aerial photography used in the combined method is of itself, aside from any connection with perspective photography, also very efficient from the viewpoint of ice-mapping requirements. With a large number of short series of planimetric aerial photos, arranged rather evenly over a considerable expanse of sea, the series assume the functions of photo standards admitting of interpolation. This property of planimetric aerial photography, executed according to the photo-sounding principles, makes it possible, as shown by practice, to obtain new concepts of the processes occurring in ice and of natural interrelations that have not manifested themselves so clearly heretofore.

Let us cite a characteristic example in support of the foregoing. In the course of the 1955 High-Latitude Expedition the Central Polar Basin was covered with a dense network of aerial-

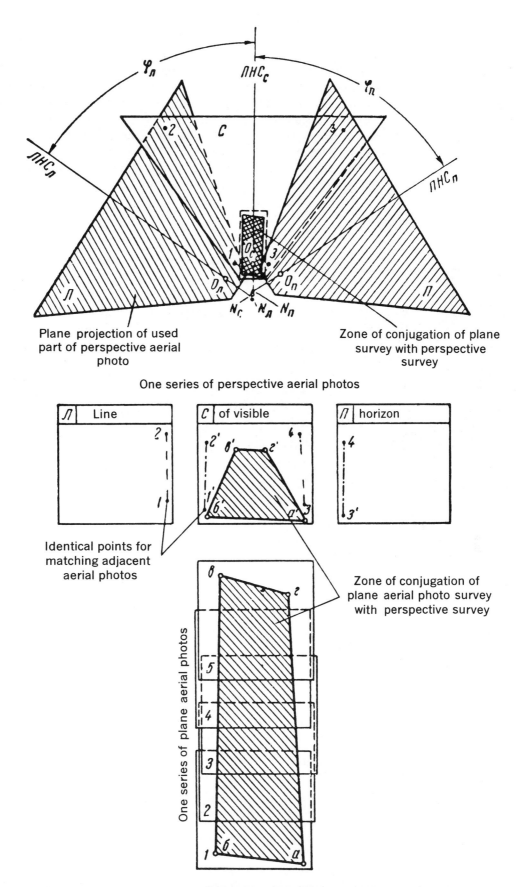

Plane projection of used part of perspective aerial photo

Zone of conjugation of plane survey with perspective survey

One series of perspective aerial photos

Identical points for matching adjacent aerial photos

Zone of conjugation of plane aerial photo survey with perspective survey

One series of plane aerial photos

Fig. 29. GEOMETRIC DIAGRAMS OF THE INTERRELATIONSHIP BETWEEN THE AERIAL PHOTOS OF ONE SERIES OF COMBINED PERSPECTIVE-AND-PLANE AERIAL PHOTO SURVEYING

Above: Conjugate series of plane aerial photos and perspective [= 3-dimensional] photos converted into plane [= 2-dimensional] photos. *Below:* Conjugate series of contact prints.

photography traverses. The total width of the expanses of clear water for each 150 running kilometers of aerial-photography traverse was measured in the Arctic Institute. Isolines were drawn through the points of the total width obtained on the map, producing a pattern similar to the image of the sea-floor relief. Having obtained, *without a unified measurement of the depths*, a picture of the bathymetry of the Central Polar Basin, with the clearly pronounced M. V. Lomonosov Submarine Ridge, it was possible to establish the nature of the relationship of the location of the polar ice to the sea depths (Fig. 31). An analysis of this map, by Ya. Ya. Gakkel', has permitted a precise delineation of the framework for the application of Professor N. N. Zubov's well-known rule concerning the direction of

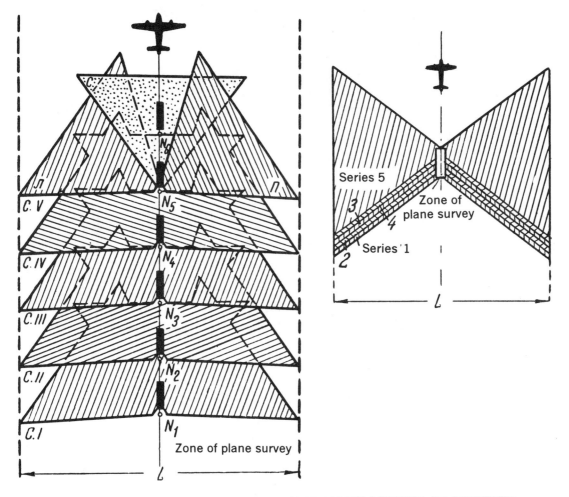

Fig. 30. COMPARISON OF THE PRODUCTIVITY OF THE SOVIET METHOD OF COMBINED PERSPECTIVE-AND-PLANE AERIAL PHOTO SURVEYING WITH THE "TRI-METROGON" METHOD

Left: Diagram of the overlapping of the surface of the sea in surveying by the *Anii* [? sic!] method. Altitude from which taken: 450 meters; dimensions of photo 24 x 24 centimeters; 3 perspective and 5 plane photos in each series; lengthwise overlap of plane aerial survey 60 per cent; of perspective survey, 50 per cent; cross-wise overlap of perspective survey 25 per cent; linear intervals between series of perspective photos 3.8 kilometers; of plane photos 1.9 kilometers; depth covered by survey 7.6 kilometers; width of survey strip 19.5 kilometers; total number of photos per 100 running kilometers of traverse: 174.

Right: Same by the "Tri-Metrogon" method. Altitude from which taken: 450 meters; dimensions of photo 24 x 24 centimeters; 1 plane and 2 perspective photos in each series; lengthwise overlap of plane aerial photo survey 60 per cent; of perspective survey, 95 per cent; (simplified variant, 25 and 92 per cent, respectively); cross-wise overlap within one series of photos: 25 per cent; linear interval between series: 0.28 kilometers (0.53 kilometers); depth covered by survey: 7.6 kilometers; width of survey strip: 15.2 kilometers; total number of photos per 100 running kilometers of traverse: 1,100 (563 in simplified variant).

ice drift. Inasmuch as consideration of the ice drift, which exercises a great direct influence on the ice balance, is of immense significance for the study of the ice regime, Gakkel's conclusions testify that aerial photography is indeed a powerful means of attaining a new level of concepts concerning the processes taking place in the Arctic ice.

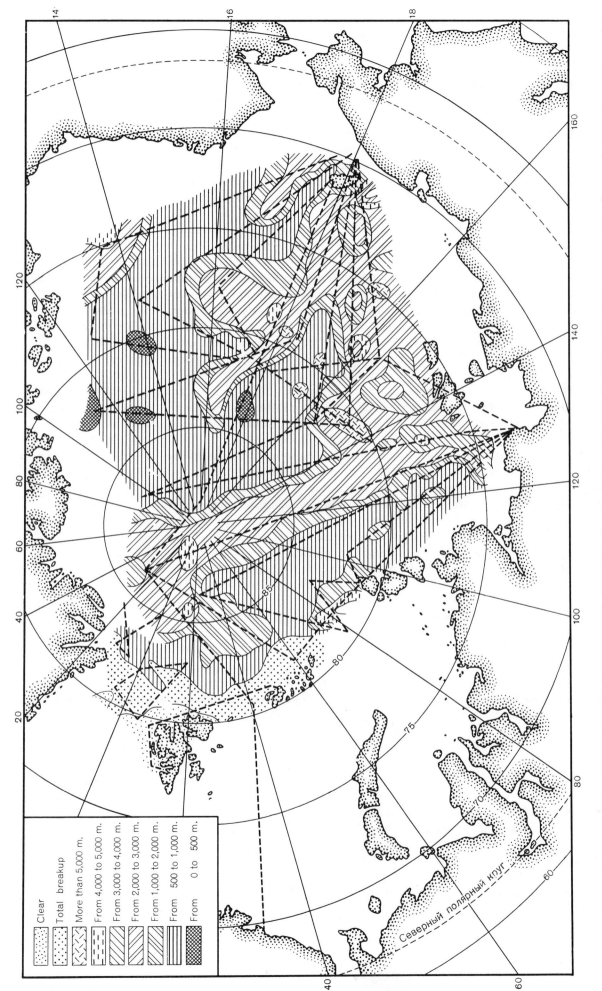

Fig. 31. SYNOPTIC MAP OF THE DISTRIBUTION OF FISSURES, CHANNELS, AND LEADS IN THE ARCTIC OCEAN, April 1955. (Compiled by A. V. Bushuyev from aerial reconnaissance and aerial photographic survey data.)

Clear
Total breakup
More than 5,000 m.
From 4,000 to 5,000 m.
From 3,000 to 4,000 m.
From 2,000 to 3,000 m.
From 1,000 to 2,000 m.
From 500 to 1,000 m.
From 0 to 500 m.

Северный полярный круг

Geographic investigations reposing on the use of air photos may be subdivided into two main groups. The first comprises all the work connected with the study of natural objects in a state of relative rest, or of processes which are evolving extremely slowly. The second group comprises work on the study of the elements of the clearly pronounced dynamics of the geographic environment.

In the first case, geographers may be satisfied by aerial surveys from flights by central government agencies or surveys for a nationwide purpose. Having contact prints and a finished topographic map, geographers merely make a special interpretation of air photos, exploiting their portraying and measuring properties to bring out the detail to be put on special-purpose maps, the basis of which are the topographic maps.

In the second case, aerial surveys admitting of comparison are required. Sometimes this is accomplished by using surveys executed earlier and covering the region under study twice. Much more often, repeated surveys have to be organized, duplicating nationwide or government-agency surveys made earlier. But here one often runs into difficulties, since the possibility of comparison is complicated by the lack of homogeneity in the materials from the two flights and the precision of the photogrammetric treatment is reduced. Specially instituted, at least double surveys, made under unified technical conditions and answering the specific purpose, should be regarded as the best variant of aerial photography for the study of the elements of the dynamics of the geographic environment.

The principle of breaking down the alternatives of geographic aerial photography into two groups is not unshakable. In the last few years, a tendency toward wide use of colored and spectrozonal air photos, the interpretational properties of which are considerably higher, has arisen in work relating to the first group. Such photos are used above all in geobotanical investigations and in the study of soil geography. It is obvious that special flights are needed to obtain colored or spectrozonal air photos, since the former surveys were made only on ordinary aero-film.

Thus, it becomes evident that the subdivision of the geographic alternatives of aerial photography into two groups, according to the character of the materials used and their origin, is becoming a conventional òne under present conditions. In the future, the difference in principle between these groups will be evened out still more. This can be foreseen because, with air photos available, geographers, in creating interpretational keys, are beginning to make more and more frequent use of helicopters. With their aid, in addition to interpreting key air photos on landing, they are able, on flights as well, to make an aero-visual interpretation of the majority of photos, which further enhances the completeness and reliability of the interpretation as a whole. Hence, it must be expected that in the near future a broad need will arise for the organization of summer work, even in geographic investigations which until not so long ago were conducted with the use of air photos studied principally under office conditions, with a limited number of interpretational keys, created through not always easily realizable ground field explorations.

Such a prospect is of great importance, and it is necessary to prepare in various ways for such investigations. Above all, work must be intensified on the creation of new aerial photographic and photogrammetric apparatus. In combination with the available technical means, this will afford opportunities for choosing those instruments which will best contribute to the solution of concrete problems connected with geographic aerial photography and the processing of its results. Simple and portable apparatus is required, suitable for use under expedition conditions and insuring both photogrammetric treatment and work on measurement interpretation.

At the same time, the need remains to seek rational and productive methods of processing air photos without field control of the photos. Great significance must be attached to the use of air photos in the study of the micro-relief in geomorphologic investigations in steppe and desert regions to be drawn into the orbit of socialist farming. In principle, this can be accomplished by means of the photometric method, but serious experimental work in this direction is necessary. The groundwork for this has already been laid.

Inasmuch as the development of instrumental measurement interpretation is of extraordinary importance for geographers, most serious attention must be directed toward the possibilities of the photometric and diffractional methods of analyzing air photos and their use in the process of the geographic study of air photos.

The co-ordinated solution of the questions forming the circle of tasks to be encountered in the further development of the process of applying aerial photography in geographic investigations should substantially broaden the possibilities of using this method in studying the geographic environment, creating a basis for the elaboration and solution of important national-economic problems.

BASIC LITERATURE

Avgevich, V. I. "The Application of Aerial Photography to the Study of the Ice Regime," no. 8, *Izyskaniya Severnogo Porta v Obskoy Gube* (Explorations for a northern port in Ob' Bay), izd-vo Glavsevmorputi, Moscow-Leningrad, 1951; *Trudy Mosk. in-ta inzhenerov geodezii, aerofotos"yemki i kartografii*, no. 11 (1950), 19 (1954), 24, 25 and 26 (1957).

"Airplane Reconnaissance of Fish" *(Aviarazvedka Ryby)*. Sbornik statey (collection of articles), *Tr. Vsesoyuzn. in-ta morskogo rybnogo khozyaystva i okeanografii*, no. XXXVI, 1958.

Avsyuk, G. A. "Concerning the Question of Applying Ground Photogrammetry in Physical Geographic Investigations," *Vestn. Kaz. FAN*, nos. 4-5, 1946.

Belov, S. V. Aerophotography of Forests *(Aerofotos"yemka Lesov)*, izd-vo AN SSSR, Moscow-Leningrad, 1959.

Galkina, Ye. A. "The Use of Aerophotography Materials for the Hydrographic Study of Swamps," *Tr. Gos. gidrolog. in-ta*, no. 13/67, Leningrad, 1949.

"Geobotanical Methods in Geologic Investigations," Sbornik statey, *Tr. Vsesoyuzn. aerogeolog. tresta*, no. 1, Moscow, 1955.

Geodeziya. Reference handbook under the editorship of M. D. Bonch-Bruyevich, vol. VIII, izd. N. K. Zoza, RSFSR, Moscow, 1940.

Gorodetskiy, S. F., and Denisenko, V. D. "An Experiment in the Stereophotogrammetric Surveying of Waves on Port Waters," *Nauchnyye trudy Odesskogo in-ta inzhenerov morskogo flota*, no. 16, 1958, pp. 3-14.

Dorofeyev, S. V., and Freyman, S. Yu. "Aerophotography as a Method of taking a Quantitative Inventory of the Greenland Seal," Sb. *Vozdushnyye puti Severa* (Collection; Air ways of the North), izd. Sov. Aziya, Moscow, 1933.

Dubovskiy, B. V., and Perkis, L. I. "The Aerial Stereophotographing of Waves from One Airplane," *Tr. in-ta Soyuzmorproyekt*, vol. 3, Moscow, 1956.

Zdanovich, V. G., and Sharikov, Yu. D. "Some Tasks of the Study of Sea Waves from Aerial Photographs," *Sbornik statey Laboratorii aerometodov AN SSSR*, Leningrad, 1954.

Ivernova, M. I. "The Movement of Taluses," *Tr. in-ta geogr. AN SSSR*, no. 4, Moscow, 1954.

Kort, V. G. "Concerning the Question of the Study of the Relief of the Bottom from Air Photos," *Zapiski po gidrografii*, no. 1, Leningrad, 1948.

Kudritskiy, D. M., Popov, I. V., and Romanova, Ye. A. Fundamentals of the Hydrographic Interpretation of Air Photos, *(Osnovy gidrograficheskogo deshifrirovaniya aerosnimkov)*, Gidrometeoizdat, Leningrad, 1956.

Loshchilov, V. S. "The Method of Underwater Stereophotography in Oceanographic Investigations," *Problemy Arktiki*, no. 2, 1957.

Materials on the Use of Aerial Methods in Studying the Soils and Vegetation of Northern Kazakhstan *(Materialy po Ispol'zovaniyu Aerometodov pri Izuchenii Pochv i Rastitel'nosti Severnogo Kazakhstana)*, Sbornik statey (Collection of articles) under the editorship of V. P. Miroshnichenko, Izd-vo, AN SSSR, 1957.

Potapenko, B. G. "Stereophotogrammetric Mapping of Underwater Relief," *Tr. Vost.-Sib. fil. AN SSSR*, no. 10, 1959.

Soil Surveying *(Pochvennaya s"yemka)*. Methodical handbook. Izd-vo AN SSSR, Moscow, 1959.

"The Application of Aerial Photography in Hydrologic Investigations" *(Primeneniye Aerofotos"yemki v Gidrologicheskikh Issledovaniyakh)*. Sbornik (Collection) under the editorship of A. P. Yushchenko, Leningrad, 1936.

Pugin, A. A. "Fundamentals of the Stereophotographic Method of Measuring Depths from Air Photos," *Tr. Gos. gidrol. in-ta*, no. 18, Leningrad, 1953.

Pugin, A. A., and Rekhtzamer, G. P. "Investigation of Waves on Seas, Lakes and Reservoirs by the Stereophotogrammetric Method" *(Issledovaniye Volneniya na Moryakh, Ozerakh i Vodokhranilishchakh Metodom Stereofotogrammetricheskoy S"yemki)*, Leningrad, 1955.

Rengarten, P. A. "The Use of Air-photo Materials for Geomorphologic Investigations under various Physico-geographic Conditions," *Izv. VGO*, 1939, No. 6.

Salishchev, K. A., and Obruchev, S. V. The 1932-1933 Summer Expedition *(Letnyaya ekspeditsiya 1932-1933 gg.)*, izd. Arkticheskogo in-ta, Nos. I and II, Leningrad, 1936.

Samoylovich, G. G. The Employment of Aviation and Aerophotography in Forestry *(Primeneniye Aviatsii i Aerofotos"yemki v Lesnom Khozyaystve)*, Moscow-Leningrad, 1953.

Sil'nitskaya, V. I., and Cheremnykh, G. D. "An Experiment in the Photogrammetric Treatment of Air Photos for the Purpose of Determining the Speed of Movement of the Ice in Glaciers," *Izv. AN SSSR, seriya geogr.*, 1959, No. 5.

Slastikhin, V. "Evaluation of Soil Erosion from Photographs," *Zemledeliye i zhivotnovodstvo Moldavii* (Farming and animal husbandry in Moldavia), No. 2, 1958.

Fedorovich, B. A. "The Relief of the Sands of Asia," *Tr. Vtorogo geogr. s"yezda*, vol. II, Leningrad, 1948.

Khrennikov, N. A. "Investigation of Landslide Phenomena on the Basis of Phototheodolite-survey Materials," *Tr. Odesskogo s.-kh. in-ta*, vol. 6, part 1, 1953.

CHAPTER 41

RESEARCH IN PHYSICAL GEOGRAPHY IN FIXED STATIONS

D. L. Armand, S. V. Bass, M. A. Glazovskaya,
M. I. Iveronova, Yu. L. Rauner, L. Ye. Setunskaya, L. N. Sobolev,
D. F. Tumanova, A. N. Formozov, and N. S. Chochia

The old concept of physical geography as a science which studies only the distribution of various natural objects over the earth's surface has played out its role and, at least in the Soviet Union, has long since entered the domain of history. The ascertainment of the distribution of natural objects and complexes cannot be severed from a study of their development in time, or from knowledge of the mechanism of their mutual relations with the surrounding environment. For this reason, the geographic environment or envelope and its changes in time and space have become the object of the study of modern physical geography.

This understanding of the object of physical geography has required the expansion of the arsenal of scientific methods of geographic research. Formerly, geographers drew their material from travels and expeditions, which enabled them to record the state of the territories studied at the moment of the researcher's visit. But this method is not suited for the systematic observation of changes taking place in time. This has given birth to the idea of creating fixed scientific research *stations,* i.e., points at which observations are made continuously the year around concerning natural processes and phenomena occurring on small sections, under conditions as typical as possible of more or less extensive territories.

Observations are made at fixed research stations concerning changes of two orders: (1) seasonal changes recurring annually, although with numerous deviations, and (2) the directions reflecting the secular development of the geographic environment or individual components of it. The stations make it possible to establish the relative significance of the factors determining the course of the development of the landscape or of its components, to ascertain the principal ones among them, and to determine the quantitative indices of the intensity of their manifestation. All these observations require lengthy work by the stations in accordance with a unified program, which is their chief methodological principle.

According to the scope of their topics, the stations may be specialized or complex geographic. Their significance varies for the different geographic scientific disciplines. The geographic disciplines having to do with especially variable components of the environment (for example, climatology, hydrology, and biogeography) are at present entirely unable to develop without stationary observations. The disciplines studying the more stable components of the geographic environment (geology, geomorphology and, in part, soil science) can, in a first approximation, be satisfied with occasional observations and repeated expeditions. However, for them too, the stationary method opens wide prospects for a thorough penetration into the course of natural processes.

Stationary posts have now been evolved in many scientific institutions of the USSR. Depending upon the qualifications of the personnel, they either confine themselves to observations, sending them for treatment to the scientific-research institutions, or they themselves work up the primary data and draw generalized conclusions from them.

Earlier than in any other field, stationary observations were first applied in the investigation of *climate.* Their organization was dictated by the very specificity of the investigation of the object. As is known, climate represents a weather regime viewed in the multi-year cross section, with periodic repetition of the main phenomena and a continuous succession of innumerable variations.

Naturally, in studying the climatic conditions of any region the question of making multi-year observations of atmospheric processes assumes prime importance.

The idea of organizing systematic stationary observations of individual elements of the weather and climate over the whole territory of our country was expressed 150 years ago by the eminent meteorologist V. N. Karazin. In 1810, in a paper read to the Moscow Society of Naturalists, he proposed the creation of a network of stations that would embrace the whole territory of the Russia of that time. This network of permanent observation stations was to operate on a unified system and furnish uniform results which would be worked up by a scientific society specially created for that purpose.

As early as 1849, the year of the creation of the Main Geophysical Observatory, there was operating in Russia a network of about fifty meteorologic stations scattered over the vast territory of the country. By the next year, owing to the rapid development of meteorologic and climatic investigations, techniques for the stationary observation of weather elements were being developed and perfected. At the same time, big observatories were being organized, which became scientific centers performing a wide complex of hydrometeorologic work. As an example, one may name the Irkutsk Observatory, where a great amount of work was done in the study of the hydrometeorologic conditions of the Angara River, climatic descriptions of the regions of eastern Siberia were compiled, and so forth.

In the years of Soviet rule, the number of stations and observatories has increased several times by comparison with the pre-revolutionary period. Of special significance was the creation of a network of actinometric stations making observations of the elements of the radiation balance of the earth's surface and of the atmosphere. There has been an extraordinary expansion of observations of the temperature of the soil and measurement of the snow cover, as well as aerologic observations. Great attention has been paid to the organization of stationary meteorologic work in the sparsely settled and not easily accessible regions, especially in the Arctic. During the periods of the International Polar Year (1932) and the International Geophysical Year (1957-1959), many special meteorologic stations were created to make observations in accordance with an extensive program. In particular, the Institute of Geography of the Academy of Sciences of the USSR, in order to execute the work in accordance with the IGY plan, organized four specialized stations (three in the Arctic regions and one near Moscow) with an extensive complex, not only of standard meteorologic but also of special heat-balance and actinometric observations.

The unified Hydrometeorologic Service of the USSR has succeeded in solving in a very successful manner the problem of the rational distribution of the network of meteorologic stations over the vast territory of the country. This network now represents a scientifically based system in which the territorial position of each station has been so chosen as to be representative of a specific climatic region. At the same time, all the stations are arranged by types which correspond to complexes of observations of greater or lesser intricacy.

The scientific conclusions obtained through many years of operation of the meteorologic stations and observatories embrace the problems of the genesis of climate, synoptics, the relation of weather to solar radiation, to the general circulation of the atmosphere, and to the state of the underlying surface, and so forth.

One of the most important tasks at present facing stationary climatic research is the organization of the observation by networks everywhere of the components of the water-and-heat balance of the earth's surface, the ground layer of the air, and the upper horizons of the soil and subsoil. Here it is necessary to make wide use of the latest achievements of telemetry, which is being applied more and more widely in hydrometeorology. The execution of such a complex of observations under special physical geographic conditions (in mountains, forests, and Arctic regions) has become one of the first-priority tasks of physical geography.

In *hydrology,* as in climatology, all theoretical generalizations can be made only on the basis of a study and analysis of the data on the change in the state of bodies of water and soil moisture, obtained by stationary research methods. Before the October Revolution, the stationary hydrologic network satisfied only the interests of water transportation and, in part, power on the big rivers. They were purely hydrometric observations, which began to be made systematically in Russia in the 1880's.

In the Soviet period, the hydrometric network began to grow rapidly. Simultaneously, the observation program was also expanded. At present, there are more than 5,000 hydrometric stations in the Hydrometeorologic Service system alone. With respect to objects of observation, they are divided into river, lake, glacier, and swamp stations; and with respect to the character of their activity, into observational and operative stations (the latter serve the national economy with current information and compile forecasts of hydrologic phenomena). However, the data of the extensive network situated on the big and medium rivers, furnish only a general, integral characterization of the physical geographic and economic conditions of the formation of the hydrologic regime. They are inadequate to analyze the primary runoff and ascertain the factors of its formation. The concept of the geographic distribution of river runoff obtained on the basis of these data is too general in character.

The fullest study of the water balance and runoff can be organized at special stations—runoff stations. The idea of creating these was advanced by M. A. Velikanov in the 1920's. At present, about forty such stations are operating. The largest among these are the integrated and well equipped Valday and Zelenogorsk (on the Karelian Peninsula) stations of the State Hydrologic Institute.

Usually, the greatest attention is paid to the study of the climatic factors of runoff. However, V. V. Dokuchayev already pointed out that, to discover fully the genesis of runoff, it also is necessary to study the soil and vegetation conditions. Their practical study, which began twenty to thirty years ago, revealed the possibility of determining the relative role of two groups of factors in the formation of runoff. On the one hand were the cyclic fluctuations of the elements of climate that are accidental in character; on the other hand were the changes in the soil and vegetation cover under the influence of human activity, which changes have a systematic direction. Convincing and well-grounded consideration of these factors will be of great significance for the improvement of the practical techniques of hydrologic calculation, which is extremely important for the rational utilization of the water resources in all fields of the national economy. Moreover, such study will make it possible to establish the intra-zonal characteristics of the hydrologic regime which, under the influence of the preference given to the climatic factor, are often wrongly regarded as having a greatly leveling effect.

The study of the runoff is done on three types of objects: (1) runoff areas permitting the measurement of the slope surface runoff, (2) the drainage basins of glens, gulches, etc., in which the soil runoff and, in part, the subsoil runoff is studied together with the slope runoff, and (3) the rivers and their basins. In the latter case, a study is made of the influence of the complex of physical geographic and economic conditions upon the total surface and subsoil runoff. The experimental investigations at the runoff stations include: meteorologic observations, recording of precipitation; snow-measurement surveys; observations characterizing the weather conditions under snow-melt conditions; determination of the hydrophysical properties of the soil, its moisture and frost; recording of the liquid and solid surface runoff; and the regime of the ground waters nearest to the surface. At present, there has not yet been worked out a unified method of operation of the runoff stations studying the objects of the first and second types, which to a certain degree limits the possibility of obtaining generalized conclusions and hampers the further development of the network of these stations. Hydrologists should work out such techniques in the very near future. The runoff should be studied in the initial stage of its development, i.e., on the slopes. The investigation of the runoff should be done on the basis of the water balance, which will permit a more profound analysis of the runoff factors and the processes of its formation. The runoff areas should be similar to one another in the whole complex of physical geographic factors and economic conditions, and differ only in the one factor under study.

At the runoff stations of the USSR, the two main scientific problems at present are: (1) study of the hydrologic efficiency of the agrotechnical, hydroreclamational, and forest-reclamational measures aimed at improving the water regime of the agricultural lands, particularly the study of the methods of water retention on the fields in the zone of unassured moisture, (2) the study of the influence of the same measures on the stream runoff and its regime, for the purpose of refining the methods of calculating hydrotechnical works on rivers in view of the rapid changes in the methods of managing agriculture.

Among the most important subjects of stationary hydrologic observations on rivers is the study of the channel processes, i.e., the interaction between the stream and the bed (the formation of the river's lengthwise and crosswise profile, the shifting of the meanders, the formation of shoals and bars), as well as the search for ways to control these processes.

Geomorphological station observations have the purpose of studying the dynamics of the transformation of the relief under the influence of exogenic processes, primarily the processes of erosion and denudation. The methods of these observations differ for mountain and plains regions. The former are inseparably linked with glaciologic observations; the latter, with hydrologic observations.

Stationary observations in mountains began around the 1920's, and in the 1930's the first permanent stations were organized. In the USSR, the "Apatit" Trust organized in 1936 an avalanche station in the Khibiny on Mount Yukspor; the station now belongs to the Geographic Faculty of Moscow State University. Here observations are made of the snow cover, landslides, avalanches, and the frost and solifluction processes on the slopes.

In 1937, an erosion and flash-flood experimental station was organized in the Chatkal Range for the observation of the formation of flash-flood streams. There are also flash-flood stations in the Caucasus. In 1948, the Institute of Geography of the Academy of Sciences of the USSR created the High-Mountain Tyan'-Shan' Physical Geographic Station in the Terskey-Alatau Range. This station is distinguished by broad coverage of the natural processes chosen as objects of study, and by the integrated character of its investigations. In particular, a study has been made here of a complex of present exogenic geomorphologic processes on the mountain slopes in different altitudinal belts: glacial exaration, formation of moraines, landslides, rock flows, scree, flash floods [*seli*], slope erosion, and river erosion. The ultimate object of these investigations is the determination of the total wear and the ascertainment of the relative magnitude of its individual varieties.

In studying erosional processes on dissected plains and on low elevations, main attention is paid to accelerated erosion due to the economic and especially the agricultural activity of the population. Stationary investigations should occupy an important place in the study of erosion alongside expeditionary investigations, which permit one to cover large territories and provide a comparative evaluation of the intensity and character of the erosional processes in various regions. Only through systematic multi-year observations can the course of harmful erosional processes be traced in detail, their mechanism be ascertained, and methods for suppressing them be worked out.

Stationary investigations of erosional processes in the USSR are conducted according to a broad program. They include: ascertainment of the intensity of the surface and gully erosion (the former, by measuring the erosion from the runoff areas; the latter, by setting up datum marks at the heads of ravines and making repeated surveys); recording the influence on the erosion of forest stands of various composition and design, the different agrotechnical methods of tilling the soil and sowing various agricultural crops; observations of the runoff and intensity of precipitation, the infiltrating properties of soils, and so forth.

Stationary erosion investigations were first initiated in our country after the October Revolution. Support points and scientific-research stations to combat erosion were created in a number of regions of the European part of the USSR. The oldest — the Novosil' zonal agroreclamation station of the All-Union Scientific-Research Institute for Field and Forest Reclamation (in Orel oblast) — was founded in 1923 and was headed for many years by A. S. Kozmenko, a great specialist in erosion questions. Stationary observations of erosion are also conducted at the Kamyshin and Kletskaya support points in Stalingrad oblast, the Desna River station in Chernigov oblast, the Anti-Erosion Station of the Moldavian Soil-Science Institute, and others.

Alongside stationary investigations, great significance in the study of erosion and the elaboration of measures to combat it has been acquired by the key, i.e., semistationary methods of research, intermediate between the stationary and expeditionary methods. As an example of the employment of the key method, one may point out the work done in 1952-1955 by the Erosion Detachment of the Institute of Geography and the Forest Institute of the Academy of Sciences of the USSR. The detachment's investigations were concentrated in the most eroded regions of the Middle Russian Uplands and Volga Heights. The program was based on the complex approach to the study of erosion, which was insured by the participation of specialists in various branches of knowledge. New was the extensive employment of quantitative methods, both in field and in office (cartometric) work.

Mathematical statistical methods were used to work up the series of figures obtained. As a result, the Erosion Detachment has worked out practical recommendations for combating erosion, based on the correct organization of the territory of a kolkhoz.

Stationary methods of the study of erosion are being employed by a number of the scientific-research institutes and institutions. In addition to the institutes already mentioned, a great contribution has been made to this endeavor by the All-Union and Ukrainian Scientific-Research Institutes for Field and Forest Reclamation, the V. V. Dokuchayev Soil Institute of the Academy of Sciences of the USSR, and others. Stationary methods are also employed in studying the movement of sands and of other processes occurring in the desert. Best known in this field is the work of the very old Repetek Sand Station. The practical observations of geomorphologic processes are based on theoretical investigations of the balances of moisture, heat, and solid matter in the lithosphere.

The chief object of stationary *soil* observations is the dynamics of the soil processes, governed by the daily, seasonal, annual, and perennial rhythm of the climate and the biologic processes connected with them. The study of the rhythm of the soil processes is of great theoretical importance for physical geography, since it permits one to discover the closest interrelations between the phenomena occurring in the landscape. Establishment of the characteristics of the dynamics of the soil processes is important for the elaboration of a scientific classification of soils. These observations are of great practical significance because they contribute to a differentiated and rational utilization of the soils and a correct organization of the territory.

One of the earliest stationary methods employed in soil science was the study of the water-and-heat regime of the soils, which was first carried out by G. N. Vysotskiy and A. A. Izmail'skiy. In Soviet times, in connection with the solution of big national-economic tasks in the field of agriculture, reclamation, forest cultivation and hydrotechnical construction, stationary soil investigations have come to be applied in an especially broad manner. At the initiative of Academician V. N. Sukachev, founder of the doctrine of biocoenoses, integrated stationary investigations were commenced in the 1930's in the Central State Forest Nature Preserve and later, in 1947-1948, on the expedition for forest shelter-belt cultivation conducted by the Academy of Sciences of the USSR, in a number of higher educational institutions and institutes of the Hydrometeorologic Service.

There has been considerable development of stationary investigations of the water and salt regime of soils. The elaboration of stationary observation methods has made it possible to change from the study of the regimes of individual phenomena to the study of their entirety, i.e., the soil-forming process as a whole. Examples of such work are the investigations being conducted by the Forest Institute of the Academy of Sciences of the USSR at the Derkul and Telerman stations;* the joint work of the Forest Institute and the Soil Institute of the Academy of Sciences of the USSR at the Dzhanybek, Beloprudskiy, and Arshan'-Zel'men stations; the work of the Soil Institute of the Academy of Sciences of the USSR in the Kursk steppe nature preserve, in the Kamennaya Steppe, in the Stepanovskoye sovkhoz, in the Kolos kolkhoz, and at the Moscow Experimental Swamp Station; the work of the Far Eastern Rice Station, as well as the work at Dzhezkazgan, in the region around Lake Balkhash, conducted by the Academy of Sciences of the Kazakh SSR; in the Tyan'-Shan' by the Kirgiz Academy of Sciences; and at the Vakhsh experimental station in Tadzhikistan.

The high adaptability of the organic world to changes in the geographic environment lends exceptional significance to the stations' observations in the field of *biogeography*. By tracing the reaction of organisms to these changes, as expressed in the deviation of their forms and vital processes from the norm, as well as in the change in the composition of the biocoenoses, the biogeographer can learn many laws governing the development of animals and plants, and also understand the role of the bio-element in the evolution of every natural process.

Physiologic and anatomic investigations and geobotanical experiments may be introduced into the circle of operation of the botanical stations. They may be used to solve vital problems of agriculture and forestry. Before the wide development of stationary botanical work, the range of a species was given a principally historical explanation; as stationary data were accumulated, there appeared the possibility of explaining its boundaries on an ecologo-physiologic basis.

---

*The Derkul station is now under the management of the Ukrainian Scientific-Research Institute of Forestry and Field and Forest Reclamation, and the Telerman station under that of the Forestry Laboratory of the Academy of Sciences of the USSR.

V. V. Dokuchayev pointed out the importance of stationary soil and botanical work in various zones; later, this work was instituted by his pupils, G. I. Tanfil'yev and especially G. N. Vysotskiy, who is responsible for the classic investigations of the environment and behavior of plants in connection with the tasks of steppe forest cultivation in the Ukraine (at Velikiy Anadol). Stationary methods were worked out later by L. G. Ramenskiy; using the Don floodplain (region of Pavlovsk) as an example, he created the method for the geobotanical investigation of floodplains which underlies the study of synecologic series and scales. Later, he laid the groundwork for the stationary study of sandy deserts. V. N. Sukachev organized a number of stationary studies, principally on forests, which laid the groundwork for the elaboration of a forest typology and the study of the biogeocoenosis. Important stationary meadow-science investigations have been conducted by A. P. Shennikov, who has worked out the method of phenologic spectra. The life of steppe coenoses has been studied at stationary points by V. V. Alekhin.

The establishment of stations in mountains presents special geographic interest. Thus, rich material has been furnished by the Pamir High-Mountain Station, situated at an altitude of about 4,000 meters and studying, along with other subjects, the relationship of the anatomy, physiology, and chemistry of plants with the geographic environment, and the influence of the latter on photosynthesis and transpiration. A study of the intensity of the action of plant ferments has also been successfully carried out by the Institute of Geography of the Academy of Sciences of the USSR on the altitudinal profile of the High-Mountain Tyan'-Shan' Physical Geographic Station.

In 1957, a group of institutes of the Academy of Sciences of the USSR began work on a broad front on the study of key sections in a number of successive zones of the regions of new development—in the Far East, Siberia, and Kazakhstan. Here a study is being made of the "biocomplexes" as a whole, i.e., the biologic parts of the biogeocoenoses.

The broadest study being made everywhere at stations is that of the dynamics of the accumulation of organic matter and the vital activity of forest species, and phenologic observations are being conducted here. Also engaged in the latter are the natural preserves, the network of stations of the Hydrometeorologic Service, the *Gossortset'* [network of stations for distribution of improved seed varieties] and the correspondents of the phenological commission of the Geographic Society of the USSR. Large summaries are created on the basis of their data; for example, concerning wheat, forest species, and grapes. Botanico-geographic station work is also conducted by botanical gardens, which observe the behavior of acclimatized plants. Experiments are also being conducted in the transfer of whole phytocoenoses with turf to new conditions. The experience gained from botanico-geographic station work was generalized at a special conference in Leningrad in December, 1951, and at a conference on high-mountain botanical investigations in 1956.

As early as the first half of the past century, some eminent Russian zoologists realized the necessity of making a sufficiently lengthy and systematic collection of zoogeographic materials within a chosen region. Only such observations have made it possible to ascertain which of the present factors account for the presence or absence of this or that species and what their connections are with the physical geographic environment. This contention was most clearly enunciated by the celebrated traveler and biogeographer A. F. Middendorf. His contemporary N. A. Severtsov was the first in our country to attempt to characterize faunas not only from the angle of their species composition, but also according to differences in dates, duration, and intensity of the periodic phenomena of the life of characteristic species (for example, according to the duration of the nesting period, flights, the moulting of ducks; propagation, hibernation of mammals, and so forth). He emphasized the necessity of studying the full annual cycles of the life of animals to understand the close relation existing between the characteristics of a given fauna and the physical geographic surroundings.

The possibility of investigating the annual life cycles for a number of years and of comparing them with the course of the climatic, hydrologic, and biotic conditions is a very important advantage of stationary zoogeographic and ecologic investigations. In the process of multi-year observations the seasonal aspects of the faunas, and their difference in various years and series of years are well brought out. Fluctuations in the numerical strength of the dominant species of animals, including those which are very important from a practical standpoint, result in sharp changes in their distribution with respect to habitat. The presence of few-membered and rare species in a fauna can usually be established only with difficulty by expeditionary investigations, but is necessarily revealed by stationary ones. Finally, with lengthy stationary observations it is easy to establish with great accuracy the perennial fluctuations of the boundaries of distribution of animals and the direction of their changes (broadening or narrowing of the ranges). The successions caused by economic activity, for example, the stages of change and restoration of zoocoenoses on cut-over and reviving sections of forest, as well as the formation of the fauna of a cultivated landscape in regions of new economic development are most accurately and easily traced by stationary investigations.

The appearance of the first special zoogeographic stations in Russia goes back to the end of the last century and the beginning of the present one. Hydrobiology went over to planned ecologic geographic investigations earlier than any other branch. First to be founded were the marine biologic stations: on the Solovestkiye Islands (later transferred to the Kola Gulf) and the Sevastopol' station, then lake stations, and finally river stations (for example, the Volga Biologic Station at Saratov).

A sharp increase in the number of research stations of different types occurred in the period of the first five-year plans: there arose a network of state nature preserves with their bio-stations, stations for the protection of plants from pests, hunter's biologic stations, and the large station network of the anti-epidemic institutions of the Ministry of Health of the USSR, including anti-malarial, anti-plague, and anti-tularemia stations. In the process of the activity and growth of these institutions, original methods of stationary investigation were worked out, instructions were published, and the work was directed toward the standardization of techniques. Such, for example, were the series of instructions on the census of the distribution and numerical strength of infection-carrying rodents, the census of game animals, and many others. Various methods of taking censuses of vertebrates became widely disseminated; the visual method, by trails, on permanent long itineraries, and with the use of traps, as well as the mass marking of animals to study their migrations, etc. Especially valuable results are afforded by the integration of stationary investigations—the joint, co-ordinated work of zoologists, botanists, climatologists, parasitologists, bacteriologists, epidemiologists, etc.

In the last few years zoogeographic works have been published, based on lengthy observations in the Bashkir and Caucasian nature preserves, the investigation of the influence of snow cover on the life and distribution of animals, and many others.

At present, the zoogeographic stations are confronted by the following very important problems: (1) the study of the dynamics of the distribution of animals and the factors influencing them, for the purpose of forecasting and controlling these processes, (2) the detailed study of the permanence and degree of plasticity of the seasonal life phenomena in connection with the course of the processes in the plant world and in non-living nature, (3) the study of the structure and internal relationships in biogeocoenoses, and (4) the ascertainment of the laws governing the spatial distribution of the bio-mass of terrestrial animals in their seasonal and perennial aspects.

A higher form of stationary observations are the integrated *physical geographic* (landscape) observations. They comprise all the above-enumerated specialized observations, but are not simply the sum of them. Integrated observations are not merely concentrated in one place which is representative of this or that zone or type of landscape, but are also conducted according to a unified program compiled in such a manner that the observations of the individual components of the landscape can be easily compared and directed toward the revelation of their interaction and mutual causation.

Integrated stationary investigations are of great practical significance because they permit one to find the levers for controlling the natural processes. They make it possible to give an objective evaluation of man's interference in the life of nature, particularly through reclamation work. Specialized investigations, while determining the direct effect of measures, often disregard their important indirect consequences.

Every natural complex possesses a daily and a seasonal rhythm. This rhythm is a consequence of the fact that the internal landscape relationships differ in various parts of the 24-hour period and in different times of the year. There is a change in the heat and moisture ratio and the aspects of the biocoenoses vary therewith. Thus, the individual natural complexes—facies, tracts, and the larger taxonomic units—differ from one another not only in the character of the combination of the relief, soils, vegetation, and other components, but also in their seasonal rhythm and dynamics. A comparison of the cycles of the seasonal development of the various taxonomic units makes it possible to discover their qualitative characteristics and to define their boundaries more precisely.

In spite of the importance, theoretical and applied, of integrated stationary investigations, they still have not undergone considerable development. At the end of the 1930's and before the beginning of the Great Patriotic War, the first integrated station of the Institute of Geography of the Academy of Sciences of the USSR operated near Moscow (Zelenaya Sloboda). The main subject of its work was the study of the heat and moisture balances and the influence of the other landscape components on them. After the war, the High-Mountain Tyan'-Shan' Physical Geographic Station, mentioned above in connection with geomorphologic, glaciologic, and geobotanic investigations, was founded. Actually, this station's observations have covered a full complex of natural processes, from the weathering of rock to the life of the fauna. The station has now been transferred to the management of the Academy of Sciences of the Kirgiz SSR. The Geographic Faculty of Moscow State University has four stations, which in their program approach an integrated physical geographic station: the Khibiny station, the station near Moscow (Krasnovidovo), and others.

Widely employed in stationary work practice are geophysical, meteorologic, hydrologic, soil, geodetic (including aero- and stereophotogrammetric) and many other observation techniques, interpreted in application to the characteristics of the processes studied, and various special installations are also being built for the direct quantitative recording of their intensity. Passive observation is sometimes combined with active experimentation (releases of water from reservoirs, artificial rain making, acceleration of snow and ice melt, diversified actions upon vegetation, etc.).

As an example of how a complex of physical geographic investigations is instituted, one may point out the operation of a special station organized in the northeastern part of the Karelian Isthmus by the Geographic Faculty of the Leningrad State University. At this station, field stationary landscape observations have been conducted for five years (1954-1958). The program has included microclimatic, phenologic, hydrologic, geologogeomorphologic and soil observations. In wintertime, observations have been made of the snow cover, the ice regime, the microclimate, and the state of hibernating plants. Depending on the objectives and tasks of a local order, other observations have also been included.

The results of the integrated stationary observations, despite their inadequate development, are already rather extensive and cannot be enumerated in a brief article. They are specific for each region, inasmuch as the stations thus far created have been located in very different zones and relief conditions. The results would have been incomparably still more valuable if a network of integrated physical geographic stations, distributed and operating according to a common program and method, had been organized in a planned fashion. The organization of such a network made up initially of five or six zonal stations, as well as the maximum introduction of quantitative, particularly geophysical and geochemical methods, into their mode of operation, is the most urgent first-priority task of the scientific institutions working in the field of integrated physical geography.

BASIC LITERATURE

Abramova, M. M. "The Seasonal Variability of Certain Chemical Properties of the Forest Podzol Soil," *Tr. Pochv. in-ta AN SSSR*, No. 25, 1947.

Aver'yanov, S. F. "On Soviet Hydrologic Science," *Izv. AN SSSR, Seriya geogr.*, 1952, No. 6.

Antipov-Karatayev, I. N. and others. "Investigations into the Influence of Irrigation on the Salt Composition and Physico-chemical Properties of Soils," *Tr. Komissii po irrigatsii*, No. 4, Izd-vo AN SSSR, 1935.

Armand, D. L. "Fundamentals of the Methods of Balances in Physical Geography," *Izv. VGO*, vol. 79, 1947, No. 6.

Afanas'yeva, Ye. A. "Seasonal and Annual Shifts of Carbonates in the Fatty Chernozems of the Streletsskaya Steppe," *Tr. Tsentral'no-Chernozemnogo zapovednika*, No. II, Moscow, 1948.

Bol'shakov, A. F. "The Water Regime of the Soils of Uzbekistan," *Tr. Pochv in-ta im. V. V. Dokuchayeva*, No. 32, 1950.

"The Combating of Soil Erosion through Forest Cultivation," *Tr. in-ta lesa AN SSSR*, vol. XLIV, Moscow, 1959.

Braude, I. D. The Novosil' Field and Forest Reclamation Experiment Station, *(Novosil'skaya Agrolesomeliorativnaya Opytnaya Stantsiya)*, Moscow, 1953.

Vasil'yev, V. S. "The Water Regime of Podzol Soils," *Tr. Pochv. in-ta AN SSR*, No. 32, 1950.

Velikanov, M. A. The Water Balance of the Land *(Vodnyy Balans Sushi)*, Leningrad, 1938.

Velikanov, M. A. The Hydrology of the Land *(Gidrologiya Sushi)*, Leningrad, 1948.

Vysotskiy, G. N. "Biologic, Soil, and Phenologic Observations and Investigations at Veliko-Anadol," *Tr. opytnykh lesnichestv*, St. Petersburg, 1902.

Dokuchayev, V. V. "Our Steppes Before and Now," *Selected Works (Izbr. Soch.)*, vol. 2, Moscow, 1949.

Drozdov, O. A. "Method of Constructing a Network of Meteorologic Stations in a Plains Locality," *Tr. GGO*, No. 12, 1936.

Zonn, S. V. "Materials on the Study of the Water Regime of Chernozem under Forest Stands," *Tr. In-ta lesa AN SSSR*, No. 15, 1954.

Isachenko, A. G. "Tasks and Methods of Landscape Investigation," *Izv. VGO*, vol. 87, 1955, No. 5.

Kachinskiy, N. A. The Freezing, Thawing, and Moisture of the Soil in the Winter Season in the Forest and on Field Plots *(Zamerzaniye, Razmerzaniye i Vlazhnost' Pochvy v Zimniy Sezon v Lesu i na Polevykh Uchastkakh)*, 1927.

Kirikov, S. V. Birds and Mammals under the Conditions of the Landscapes of the Southern Urals *(Ptitsy i Mlekopitayushchiye v Usloviyakh Landshaftov Yuzhnogo Urala)*, Moscow, 1953.

Kovda, V. A. The Origin and Regime of Salinified Soils *(Proiskhozhdeniye i Rezhim Zasolennykh Pochv)*, vol. I, 1946; vol. II, 1947.

Koz'menko, A. S. The Combating of Soil Erosion *(Bor'ba s Eroziyey Pochvy)*, Moscow, 1957.

L'vovich, M. I. "Foreword to the Transactions of the GGI" *(Predisloviye k trudam GGI)*, No. 17, seriya IV, Sverdlovsk-Moscow, 1945.

L'vovich, M. I. "Hydrology in Pre-revolutionary Russia," *Meteorologiya i gidrologiya*, 1948, No. 2.

L'vovich, M. I. "On the Transformation of the Hydrologic Process under the Influence of the Dokuchayev-Kostychev-Vil'yams Complex," *Voprosy geografii*, No. 23, Moscow, 1950.

Materials on the Study of the Processes of Soil Erosion and the Fertility of Eroded Soils, *Tr. Pochv. in-ta im. V. V. Dokuchayeva AN SSSR*, vol. XL, Moscow, 1953; vol. XLVIII, Moscow, 1955.

Nasimovich, A. A. "The Role of the Regime of the Snow Cover in the Life of Ungulates on the Territory of the USSR," *(Rol' Rezhima Snezhnogo Pokrova v Zhizni Kopytnykh Zhivotnykh na Territorii SSSR)*, Izd-vo AN SSSR, Moscow, 1955.

"The Work of the Tyan'-Shan' Physical-Geographic Station," *(Raboty Tyan'shanskoy Fiziko-geografichskoy Stantsii)*, No. 1, 1950; No. 2, 1952; No. 2-a, 1953; No. 3, 1953; No. 4, 1954; No. 5, 1956.

Remezov, N. P., Bykova, L. N., and Smirnova, K. M. "The Biologic Circulation of Nitrogen and Ash Elements in Forest Stands," *Tr. In-ta lesa AN SSSR*, No. 24, 1955.

Rode, A. A. "The Dzhanybek Station, its Tasks and Organization," *"Tr. kompleksnoy nauchnoy ekspeditsii po voprosu polezashchitnogo lesorazvedeniya,"* vol. 2, 1952.

Rubenshteyn, Ye. S. "The Principles of the Distribution of the Climatic Network over the Territory of the USSR, *Voprosy geografii*, Izd-vo AN SSSR, 1956.

Severtsov, N. A. Periodic Phenomena in the Life of Wild Animals, Birds and Reptiles of Voronezh Guberniya *(Periodicheskiye Yavleniya v Zhiniz Zverey, Ptits i Gad Voronezhskoy Gubernii)*, 1855.

Severtsov, N. A. The Vertical and Horizontal Distribution of Turkestan Animals *(Vertikal'noye i Gorizontal-noy Rasprostraneniye Turkestanskikh Zhvotnykh)*, 1873.

Agricultural Erosion and its Control *(Sel'skokhozyaystvennaya Eroziya i Bor'ba s ney)*, Moscow, 1956.

Agricultural Erosion and New Methods of Studying It *(Sel'skokhozyaystvennaya Eroziya i Novyye Metody yeye Izucheniya)*, Moscow, 1958.

Skrynnikova, I. N. "An Experiment in the Study of the Dynamics of the Chemical Composition of the Soil and Subsoil Waters of the Podzol Zone," *Tr. Pochv. in-ta AN SSSR*, vol. 31, 1950.

Smirnova, K. M., and Gronyasheva, B. N. "The Dynamics of the Chemical Properties of the Soil under Green-moss Coniferous Forests," *Pochvovedeniye*, 1955, No. 6.

Tverskoy, P. N. Course in Meterology *(Kurs Meteorologii)*, Gidrometeoizdat, 1954.

Transactions of the Institute of Geography of the Academy of Science of the USSR *(Trudy Instituta geografii AN SSSR)* XLV, XLIX, LVI, LX, LXVII.

Tumanova, D. F. "Concerning the Question of the Role of Phenologic Observations in Intra-landscape Regionalization," *Tr. phenolog. soveshchaniya*, 1957; Gidrometeoizdat, Leningrad, 1959.

Tumanova, D. F., and Chochia, N. S. "Phenologic Observations and Landscape Investigations," *Vestn. LGU*, 1959, No. 18.

Tushinskiy, G. K. Avalanches *(Laviny)*, 1949.

Tushinskiy, G. K., Gus'kov, Ye. F., and Gubareva, V. D. "The Recrystallization of Snow and the Occurrence of Avalanches" *(Perekristallizatsiya Snega i Vozniknoveniye Lavin)*, 1953.

Formozov, A. N. "The Snow Cover in the Life of Mammals and Birds of the USSR," *Materialy k poznaniyu fauny i flory SSSR, izd. Moskovskogo ob-va ispytateley prirody. Novaya seriya. Otd. zoologii*, No. 5 (XX) Moscow, 1946, p. 152.

Chochia, N. S. "Some Questions of the Methods of Stationary Investigations. Talk at the 2nd Landscape Conference," *Nauchn. zap. L'vovsk. gos. un-ta im. Iv. Franko*, vol. 40, No. 4, 1957.

Shavrygin, B. P. "The Salt Regime of the Soils and Soil Cross Sections of the Central Baraba," *Tr. Pochv. in-ta AN SSSR*, 42, 1954.

CHAPTER 42

LABORATORY ANALYSIS AND EXPERIMENT IN THE GEOGRAPHIC SCIENCES

A. A. Velichko, I. P. Gerasimov, N. I. Makkaveyev,
M. I. Neyshtadt, A. I. Perel'man, and N. V. Khmeleva

As is known, laboratory (analytic) and experimental methods have never played as large a role in the development of the geographic sciences as they have played and are playing in the field of physics, chemistry, and biology. It is obvious, however, that such methods have lately been employed on an ever-increasing scale for the solution of the scientific questions of modern geography. This is not due solely to the general progress of laboratory and experimental technology, which makes it possible to study complex natural phenomena and processes with increasingly simple and economical means. The constant expansion of the use of laboratory and experimental methods in geography has been due primarily to the requirements and characteristics of the development of the geographic sciences themselves. These sciences endeavor, with the aid of such methods, to widen more and more the sphere of application of relatively precise procedures for the *quantitative study* of certain geographic phenomena and the ascertainment of the physical, chemical, and biologic essence of the various natural processes.

This need is felt at present in almost all the geographic disciplines, but its keenness and practical satisfaction still differ very greatly in the various disciplines. This depends both upon the specific characteristics of the object of investigation of this or that geographic discipline, lending itself in different degrees to study by laboratory and experimental methods, and upon the level of development attained by the science itself. For these reasons, the methods to be discussed are applied in different degrees in the various geographic disciplines. In some geographic sciences (for example, in soil science and in hydrology), laboratory (analytic) and experimental methods have been employed for a long time and have been rather thoroughly worked out. In others (for example, geomorphology and climatology), the employment of such methods has begun comparatively recently, and here many methodological details still remain to be worked out. For these reasons it is extremely difficult to give a general survey of the question under discussion that would embrace uniformly all its aspects, the accumulated experience, and the contemplated prospects. It is necessary to limit the undertaking substantially and to include in our review only those areas of geographic research and methods of laboratory and experimental work which have by now become more or less established and in which substantial results have been achieved. Moreover, one must obviously give priority in this characterization to the methods employed in the scientific elaboration of the biggest *integrated* scientific geographic problems, the more so because many other laboratory and experimental methods employed for the more special scientific and practical questions treated with the participation of geographers are described in numerous methodological handbooks on the chemical, physical, biologic, and other sciences.

We shall direct our main attention to the following laboratory-experimental methods in the geographic sciences: spore-and-pollen analysis; lithologic (petrographic, mineralogic, granulometric, and other) methods of studying the material composition of surface deposits; geochemical methods; and laboratory experiment.

THE SPORE-AND-POLLEN METHOD*

Very promising among the various laboratory-experimental methods is that of spore-and-pollen analysis, which has already yielded considerable practical results. This method is widely used in investigations by Soviet geographers. It enables one to establish the character of the historical (paleogeographic) development of the natural environment (mainly the landscape zones, vegetation, and climate) by separate stages of the Pleistocene and Holocene. It has been found suitable to use this method for paleogeographic purposes to a certain extent with respect to the Tertiary period as well.

The spore-and-pollen method has made it possible to combine the principles of time and space for paleogeographic purposes. Thanks to this, it has become possible to establish the historical development of certain elements of the natural environment and of the landscape complex over extensive territories. This has required the preliminary treatment of a number of important methodological questions. A study has been made of the spore-and-pollen spectra in the present surface deposits of different landscape-geographic zones and botanico-geographic areas [oblasti] and provinces [provintsii]. Ascertainment has been made of the character (composition) and differences in the pollen spectra of of the tundra, the forest, and the steppe, and the vegetation types transitional between them, and principles have been worked out for discovering the regional types of pollen diagrams reflecting the development of the vegetation of individual sections of the land during a definite interval of time. At the same time, great progress has also been achieved in analysis technique: in the extraction of pollen and spores from various rocks of a mineral character. This has permitted the use of great thicknesses of Quaternary deposits for spore-and-pollen analysis.

The methods of spore-and-pollen analysis itself are generally known. When used in the geographic sciences, it is aimed primarily at the ascertainment of spatial changes, so it is necessary to carry out series of spore and pollen analyses at different points of a territory used for comparison and confrontation of the geographic changes of various character. This does not rule out the value of individual series of spore-and-pollen analyses for the solution of more narrow scientific tasks.

The spore-and-pollen method has also been applied in the geographic sciences to the solution of other questions, such as the interrelationship of forest and tundra and of forest and steppe; the origin of loess; the geographic differences between inter-stage and inter-glacial deposits; the origin of fossil ice and peat mounds; and the character of the pre-glacial vegetation during the glaciations.

The spore-and-pollen method has proved especially productive for the more detailed treatment of many biogeographic problems. For example, the so-called "steppe" problem, i.e., the problem of the mutual relation between forest and steppe, failed for a long time to find a satisfactory, well-grounded solution. On the basis of the data of the spore-and-pollen method, it has been shown that principally steppe-forming phases were observed in the glacial epochs, and forest-forming phases in the inter-glacial epochs. Furthermore, it has been possible to establish the time of formation of steppes on this territory as a special type of vegetation.

The spore-and-pollen method is of especial significance for ascertaining the natural conditions of human life in the various periods of the Pleistocene and Holocene. The spore-and-pollen analyses of specimens taken directly from the cultural layers of the abodes, as well as from the synchronous layers of the deposits of organic or mineral origin, enable one to reconstruct a number of the elements of the geographic environment of that time. The archeologic data are substantially supplemented by the conclusions obtained by this method, which is very important, since man's dependence upon the natural conditions, as is known, increases as one goes farther back into the ages.

There have lately been demonstrated the great possibilities of using the spore-and-pollen method to analyze the bottom deposits of seas and oceans.

LITHOLOGIC METHODS OF STUDYING THE COMPOSITION OF SURFACE DEPOSITS**

No small role in modern geographic research is played by the methods of studying the material composition of surface deposits, i.e., petrographic, mineralogic and granulometric analyses, the study of the textural characteristics of strata, and the extent of rolling undergone by large

---

*Written by M. I. Neyshtadt   **Written by A. A. Velichko

fragments of material and grains of sand. These methods find principal application in two geographic disciplines, paleogeography and geomorphology.

In combination with other methods and sometimes also independently, with the aid of the study of the material composition, it will be possible to solve important paleogeographic questions both of a theoretical and of a practical character (Baturin, 1947).

In Soviet geography, lithologic methods are used to solve a wide range of problems. Let us name the principal ones: the reconstruction of the physical geographic, primarily climatic, conditions of the past; the tectonic regime, age, and type of the relief; the character and velocity of the transporting agent; the history of the hydrographic network; the search for bedrock and alluvial minerals, etc. It is no accident that a proposal has been made to unite this group of methods into a separate branch of geography — so-called "dynamic paleogeography" (Khabarovsk, 1948).

However, conditions for the employment of the individual lithologic methods are not everywhere alike. Thus, in the field of the ancient sheet glaciation the main attention is directed toward the study of boulder material and moraines, their mineralogy, petrography, and degree of working of the large fragmented material. It has long since been shown that, by studying the relationship between the local and the adventitious material in moraines, it is possible to establish the sources of the material and the paths of the movement of the glacial streams. Subsequently, this approach to the study of glacial deposits has been widely employed both in scientific research and in searches for minerals. Thus, for example, S. A. Yakovlev, studying the petrographic composition of boulders, their stratigraphic position, orientation, and the direction of the furrows on their surfaces, has established the fact of the displacement of the center of maximum glaciation of the Russian Plain from Scandinavia to Novaya Zemlya and has reconstructed the direction of movement of the glaciers.

On the other hand, many attempts have been made to use mineralogical analysis and determination of the degree of weathering of boulders to distinguish glacial deposits of different ages. Despite the usually similar mineralogical composition of the different horizons of moraines, they usually differ in every small section as to percentage, above all that of the minerals of the heavy fraction. However, mineralogical analysis has not brought out any general differences between moraines of different ages. The microstructural method of studying moraines also deserves great attention. It will possibly permit a fairly reliable reconstruction of the direction of movement of the glaciers, and also the division of the moraine horizons.

Of a different significance are the lithographic methods of studying the composition of surface deposits in the periglacial regions, the most typical representatives of which are the thick loess deposits. Mineralogical and granulometric analyses are now coming to the fore in the solution of the questions of the origin of loess. A very large amount of analytic material on loess deposits, which have an undoubted stratigraphic position, has been accumulated for many decades in the geographic literature; the material, however, furnishes comparatively little for paleogeographic reconstructions. With the aid of mineralogical analysis, a definite connection is being established between loess rocks and glacial deposits, chiefly from the similarity of the heavy fractions. But the data on the mineralogical composition have not furnished enough material to solve the more general questions of the genesis of loess. The same may be said of the significance of granulometric analysis.

Apparently, micromorphologic analysis is considerably more promising for the study of loess formations, as it helps to bring one closer to a solution of the problem of the genesis of loess and the buried soils lying within it. This method is now beginning to be applied in geographic research. The morphoscopic and morphometric study of the grains of sand found in loess may also furnish additional material for judging the genesis of loess.

In studying periglacial deposits it is of no little importance to ascertain how their physical-mechanical properties vary from top to bottom of a section. This enables one to obtain objective criteria for distinguishing the individual stages of development of the periglacial zone, as well as for comparing the data from different regions. The work being done by the Institute of Geography has shown, in particular, a diminution of porosity toward the horizons of buried soils, and a change in the granulometric composition within the buried soils which is similar to the granulometric variation in the genetic horizons of the present soils of similar type. These data, obtained in the system of other analyses, enable one, when taken altogether, to judge objectively the conditions of formation of the periglacial zone and the stages of its development.

Finally, in studying the periglacial zone, great attention should be paid to a detailed study of the textural characteristics of the deposits. The latest investigations of this sort have shown that the stratification in loess increases in pronouncedness from south to north, in the direction of the boundaries of the last glaciation. On the other hand, it has been possible to trace a gradual diminution of the dimensions of permanently frozen structures (wedges, fissures) in the opposite direction, from north to south.

In the zone of deserts and semideserts, granulometric analysis (the investigation of the character of the rolling of sand grains), as well as mineralogic analysis, have found the most application among the methods under discussion. Employment of these methods in studying the sands of the Karakum and Kyzylkum deserts has helped to ascertain the origins of the sand material composing them.

The most thoroughly lithologic methods of investigating the composition of surface deposits are used in studying the history of the development of the hydrographic network. Sand and pebble alluvial deposits are chiefly studied by these methods. The methods of studying the petrographic composition of pebbles, their rounding, form, and orientation have been discussed in detail by Soviet authors (Rukhin, 1953; Sarkisyan and Klimova, 1955; Rukhina, 1950; Khabakov, 1951; and others). The employment of all these methods furnishes valuable results concerning the history of the development of stream valleys. Here, wider use is made in the USSR of the morphoscopic classification of the pebble form proposed by A. V. Khabakov than of other classifications. Alongside this, morphometric indices (particularly A. Kayye's rolling coefficient) are now also beginning to be used. It is characteristic that the data obtained according to Khabakov's morphoscopic classes of rolling coincide well with the data obtained from Kayye's rolling coefficients.

Of no small significance is the study of the characteristics of sand strata. On the basis of purely granulometric data alone it is possible to undertake the determination of the genesis of sediments and the conditions of their formation. The investigation of stratification and its dip, as worked out by Yu. V. Zhemchuzhnikov (1940) and other authors, enables one to determine not only the genetic type of sediment, but also the dynamics of the environment in which it was formed, as well as the direction of the transfer. The study of the rolling of sand grains is also conducted mainly by morphoscopic methods, as well as by the method of analyzing the velocity of the rolling of grains down a plane having different angles of inclination, which was proposed by I. A. Preobrazhenskiy (1940).

The application of mineralogic, granulometric, and other analyses to alluvial deposits enables one to solve a number of geomorphologic problems. With their aid, Soviet geomorphologists analyzing the history of the hydrographic network have discovered more than one deposit of bedrock or alluvial minerals, including diamonds in the eastern regions of the country. Slime analysis, done directly under field conditions, occupies a special place in these investigations.

Finally, one should mention the study of pebbles and sand in the investigation of the processes of the development of the shores of seas and oceans. The analyses made by V. P. Zenkovich, A. V. Zhivago, and others of the movement of alluvial flow, its composition, size, and places of origin have led to interesting scientific conclusions, and also to valuable practical recommendations in connection with the building of ports and their operation. In this work, wide use is made of methods of coloring the fragmented material, luminophors (phosphors), and tagged atoms.

We have examined only a few aspects of the lithologic methods of studying the composition of surface deposits that are employed by Soviet geographers. This is far from being a full list of the directions in which they are employed, but it does show their importance and their promise for further investigation. At the same time, it is possible to note a certain evolution in the employment of lithologic methods. In geographic research, such analyses as petrographic, mineralogic, and granulometric are primarily used. Then, and sometimes also simultaneously with them, various morphoscopic methods of studying form, rolling of fragments and, of course, texture, have come to be employed. In the last few years, alongside the usual petrographic mineralogic analyses of the data, which are sometimes not enough to solve certain important paleogeographic questions, use is made of micromorphologic methods of studying thin sedimentary rocks. As regards sand and pebble deposits, morphoscopic methods are here usually accompanied by morphometric methods.

GEOCHEMICAL METHODS*

One of the forms of the circulation of matter on the earth is the migration of the chemical elements in the natural landscapes. A chemical element, in the course of its migration, passes from the atmosphere or the rocks into living organisms, from the latter into the water, from the water into the soil, and again into organisms, etc. Hence, by studying the migration of the elements we learn the relations between the individual components of the landscape and the nature of the earth's surface as a single whole, which, as is known, constitutes one of the chief tasks of physical geography.

The necessity of applying methods of geochemistry to the solution of geographic problems has long been understood by the representatives of both sciences. This has been discussed, in particular, by V. I. Vernadskiy and A. Ye. Fersman, who was especially close to geography, as well as by the Soviet geographers L. S. Berg and A. A. Grigor'yev. However, geochemical methods were not widely employed in geography until the works of Academician B. B. Polynov (1877-1952), who elaborated appropriate methods and furnished classic examples of geochemical analysis of certain types of landscape.

Polynov's landscape-geochemical investigations, begun at the end of the 1920's, have gradually led to the development of the geochemical direction in geography, which has received the name of *geochemistry of the landscape*. During the last few years, a considerable amount of work has been done in this field: investigations have been executed into general theoretical problems, the geochemistry of a number of types of natural landscapes has been studied, and generalizing and popular scientific works have been published.

A precondition for the use of geochemical methods in geography has been progress in analytic technique, insuring the possibility of a rapid and precise determination of the majority of chemical elements in rocks, soils, waters, and plants. The modern methods of analysis (spectrographic, radiometric, luminescent, and others) make it possible in a single laboratory to make hundreds and thousands of determinations per day with a 10^{-5} to 10^{-8} per cent sensitivity of determination of the individual elements.

Also of great significance for the introduction of methods of geochemistry into physical geography has been the chemical study of the various components of the natural geographic environment, primarily soil and water. The detailed chemical study of the soils of different regions is traditional for Soviet soil science. The soil-geography investigations made in the USSR during the last few years contain a special wealth of material widely exploited in the geochemistry of natural landscapes. Extensive investigations have also been conducted into the chemical geography of the surface and ground waters.

The geochemistry of natural landscapes, however, is not restricted to the use of the data of the different geographic sciences: it also possesses original methods of its own. It is extremely important, for example, to study the biologic circulation of atoms in the natural landscapes, in the course of which chemical elements are absorbed by organisms (photosynthesis, animal food, mineral food of plants, etc.) and which then abandon the bodies of the organisms as a result of breathing and other processes of metabolism. As a result of the circulation, a living substance rich in free energy is accumulated in the natural landscape. This energy is released while the organisms are still alive, but chiefly after their death. The bearers of this energy are principally the natural waters: they are enriched with the products of disintegration of the organisms, such as CO_2 and the organic acids, which possess high chemical activity. In the course of the biologic circulation of atoms, solar energy, through the mechanism of photosynthesis, is converted into the active energy of the chemical processes occurring in the landscape. Hence, the most important geochemical characteristics of the natural landscape are *determined by the biologic circulation of atoms,* and primarily by the quantity of annually forming living matter, its total mass, and the quantity of disintegrating organic matter. In all these "geochemical indices," the basic types of landscapes differ sharply from one another (Fig. 32). The intensity of the biologic circulation depends largely upon the chemical elements contained in the soils, waters, and atmosphere. The elements whose addition to the landscape from outside intensifies the biologic circulation (there are not enough of them in the landscape for the organisms) are called *deficit* elements, while the elements whose removal heightens biologic productivity are called *excess* elements.

Agrochemists have long since demonstrated the deficiency of nitrogen, phosphorous, and

---

*Written by A. I. Perel'man.

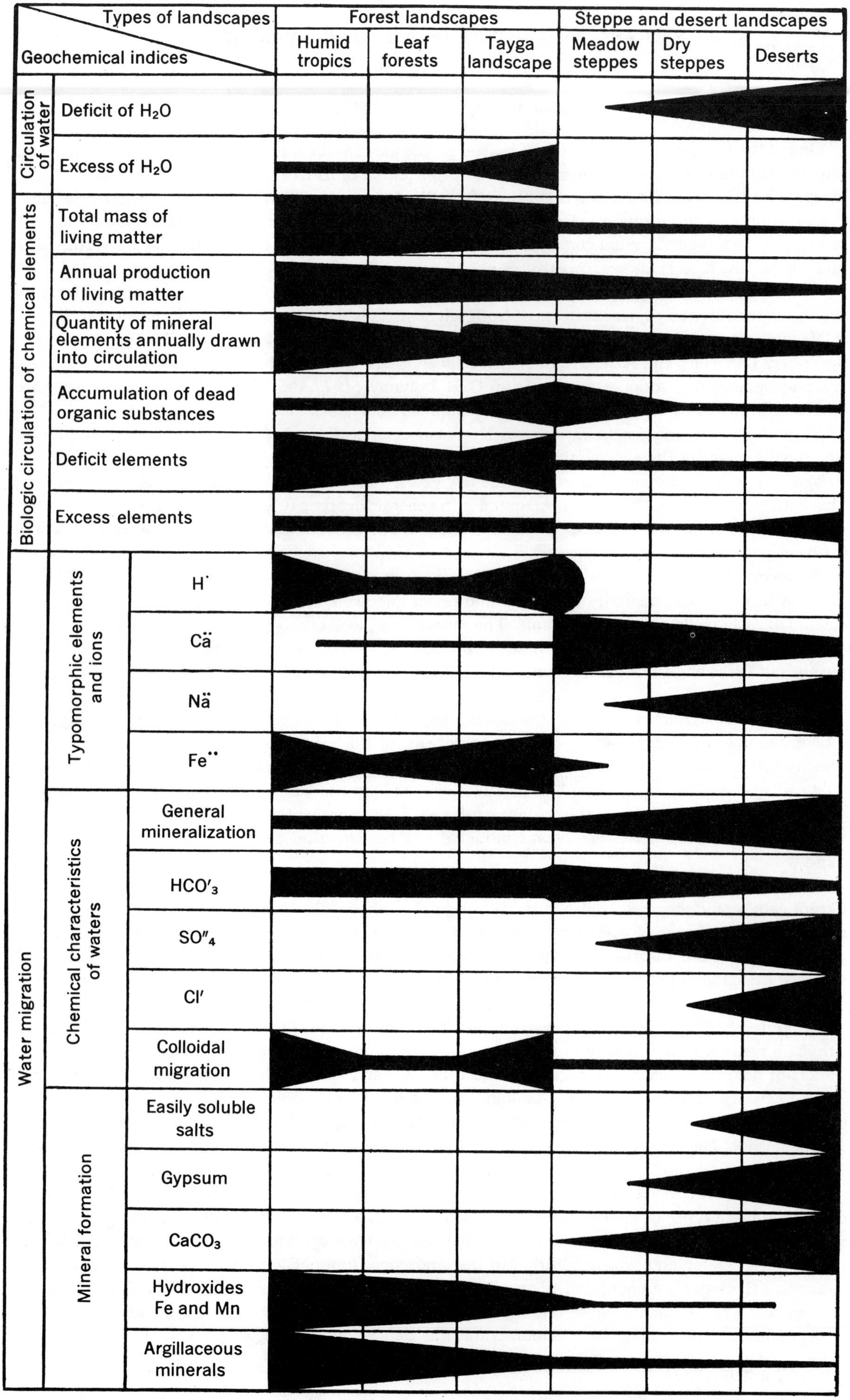

Geochemical indices	Types of landscapes	Forest landscapes			Steppe and desert landscapes		
		Humid tropics	Leaf forests	Tayga landscape	Meadow steppes	Dry steppes	Deserts
Circulation of water	Deficit of H_2O						
	Excess of H_2O						
Biologic circulation of chemical elements	Total mass of living matter						
	Annual production of living matter						
	Quantity of mineral elements annually drawn into circulation						
	Accumulation of dead organic substances						
	Deficit elements						
	Excess elements						
Water migration	**Typomorphic elements and ions**	$H^{\cdot}$					
		$Ca^{\cdot\cdot}$					
		$Na^{\cdot\cdot}$					
		$Fe^{\cdot\cdot}$					
	Chemical characteristics of waters	General mineralization					
		HCO'_3					
		SO''_4					
		Cl'					
		Colloidal migration					
	Mineral formation	Easily soluble salts					
		Gypsum					
		$CaCO_3$					
		Hydroxides Fe and Mn					
		Argillaceous minerals					

Fig. 32. GEOCHEMICAL CHARACTERISTICS OF CERTAIN TYPES OF LANDSCAPES

potassium in the majority of natural regions. These elements are introduced into the soil with fertilizers. Among the other elements deficient in various landscapes one should also list oxygen (for swamp landscapes, and partially for high-mountain landscapes, where the phenomenon of mountain sickness is observed in human beings and domestic animals), calcium (diseases of the skeleton in domestic animals in many landscapes of the tayga zone), sodium and chlorine (requirement of common salt by animals in the same places), iodine (endemic goiter, due to the lack of iodine in human beings and animals in the mountain regions), fluorine (tooth diseases, caries), cobalt (anemia in domestic animals in the tayga landscapes), copper (diseases of cultivated plants on drained swamps), and others. The greatest deficit of elements is characteristic of the upland swamps (nearly all the elements of the periodic system are in short supply), the tundra, the tayga, and the humid tropics. The least deficit of elements is in the forest-steppe and meadow-steppe landscapes.

A very considerable excess of elements is characteristic of salt marshes, where the large quantity of Na, Cl, and S, and at some places also boron and other rare elements, is fatal for plants and animals. Demonstrated in certain landscapes is an excess of iron and hydrogen ions (swamps, tayga, and tundra), of fluorine (tooth diseases in volcanic regions and in regions where phosphorites are developed), copper (anemia in domestic animals in copper-deposit areas), molybdenum (gout in humans), nickel (blindness in domestic animals in areas where nickel ores are developed), etc.

Some tens of years ago, only ten to fifteen of the most widespread elements had been drawn into the orbit of the chemical study of nature, but now a study is being made of the migration of nearly all the chemical elements of the periodic system, including many rare and dispersed ones (iodine, fluorine, boron, molybdenum, uranium, radium, strontium, barium, lithium, etc.). However, not all these elements participate to a like degree in the migration and exercise an influence on the landscape. In this connection, the *principle of mobile components* has been formulated (Perel'man, 1955), according to which the greatest influence on the processes occurring in the landscape is exerted by the energetically migrating elements, which are simultaneously capable of a certain accumulation in a given landscape. Feebly migrating, "inert" elements (for example Ti, Zr, Hf, Ta, Nb, Y, Sc, and others) hardly affect the geochemical characteristics of the landscape, i.e., they do not influence the living organisms, the properties of the water, soil, or atmosphere.

Among the intensively migrating elements may be singled out the "typomorphic elements and ions," whose migration determines the characteristic and essential features of a given landscape. Characteristic of the steppes, for example, are the high calcium content in the soil, the crust of weathering, and the waters (hydrocarbonate-calcium waters); the good supply of this element to the organisms (sturdy skeleton, absence of rickets, etc.); the neutral reaction of the soil; the weak development of colloidal solutions (Ca—a strong coagulator), and so forth. Hence, Ca is a typomorphic element of the steppes. Analogously, H-ion (acid soils and waters, "acid" plants, lack of Ca, etc.) is typomorphic for many tayga landscapes, Na and Cl for deserts, H and Fe for tayga swamps, and so forth. (See Fig. 32.)

Because of all these characteristics, a *joint* analysis of the various elements is necessary in the geochemical study of natural landscapes. For example, in the study of the biologic circulation, one determines the chemical composition of the soils and of the plants growing on them (Polynov, 1956). This enables one to penetrate deeper into the processes occurring in the landscape and to compose so-called *series of biologic absorption*. The study of the composition of surface waters and the rocks drained by them enabled B. B. Polynov to establish series of migrations of the chemical elements in the crust of weathering which are of fundamental significance for the geochemistry of the landscape.

Emphasizing the role of the migration of elements in the formation of landscapes, Polynov introduced the concept of the *geochemical landscape*, i.e., a section of the earth's surface distinguished by definite migration conditions. In each geochemical landscape it is possible to distinguish three basic "elementary landscapes": a kind of "atom of geography," which is autonomous, and two subordinate ones, above and under water (Fig. 33). The autonomous elementary landscape receives chemical elements only from the rocks and the atmosphere, whereas the subordinate ones receive them, in addition, from surface and underground runoff. Inasmuch as the subordinate landscapes receive a part of the substances from the autonomous landscape, their geochemical characteristics are largely determined by the processes occurring in the autonomous landscape. This permits us to state that in each geochemical landscape there exists between the autonomous and the subordinate landscapes a

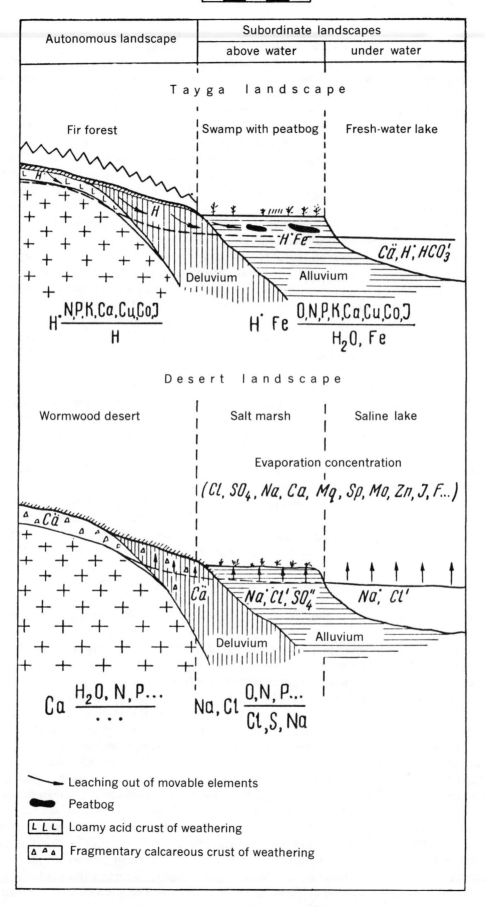

Fig. 33. **GEOCHEMICAL CONJUGATION OF ELEMENTARY LANDSCAPES**

geochemical conjugation whose study forms one of the tasks of landscape geochemistry. Thus, for example, B. B. Polynov has established that, in the humid subtropics of Adzharia, nearly all the mobile elements are energetically carried out of the autonomous landscape with the surface and underground runoff, so that the soil and crust of weathering are united by them. This determines the relatively high SiO_2 content in the waters of the local rivers and brooks and the accumulation of this compound in the bamboos growing in the subordinate landscapes and fed by siliceous waters.

The distribution of geochemical landscapes is portrayed on special maps, compiled to different scales both for general scientific and for practical purposes. Within the outlines corresponding to specific kinds of geochemical landscapes, these maps show the typomorphic elements, as well as other geochemical characteristics.

The study of the migration of the chemical elements thus enables one to give a characterization of the natural landscape as an integral natural formation and introduces new concepts and quantitative indices into geography. The aggregate of all these indices, as applied to a given concrete landscape, is what constitutes its *geochemical characteristics.*

In the last few years, landscape geochemistry has come to be applied in searching for minerals. No less promising is the use of geochemical methods in the solution of questions relating to integrated physical geographic regionalization, agriculture, and medicine.

LABORATORY EXPERIMENTATION*

In geography, as in a number of other systems of sciences, laboratory experimentation is becoming one of the research procedures enjoying full rights. Although the scale of laboratory-experimental work in geography is at present still very modest, a great future awaits it. With its further development, geography must make ever-wider use of such methods as will enable one to penetrate deeply into the mechanism of the natural processes, to find well-grounded solutions for the questions arising in the designing of various measures for the exploitation of natural resources, and to forecast those changes in nature which are caused by man's economic activity.

As is known, in his research work the geographer endeavors to ascertain the leading factors at present determining the development of the geographic landscape. But even if the task of prognostic study is set, it is necessary to ascertain in addition how the introduction of new factors or the alteration of existing ones will influence the character and rate of development of a landscape. In such research, experimental work affords invaluable aid: it permits one to reproduce a process artificially in the laboratory, to establish the significance of each landscape-forming factor and, by applying various combinations of them, to investigate the basic details of the mechanism determining the course of the natural processes.

But, in undertaking the organization of experimental research, one must not overestimate it and, in particular, must not close one's eyes to the fundamental difficulties connected with the problem of the scale of the phenomena and processes, and with the establishment of the conditions of experimentation. Changes in quantity and quality are always closely related to one another. Hence, in scaling space and time we inevitably introduce into the process or phenomenon some new quality which distinguishes to one extent or another the laboratory processes and phenomena from those in nature. Resolution of the resulting conflict is the most important problem in experimental methodology, and is still far from having been achieved even in those branches of it which have had long experience in research connected with the drafting of technical projects and precise forecasts (for example, in hydrotechnology).

The modeling of water flows, for example, has been done since the time of Leonardo da Vinci, and there now exist hundreds of hydraulic, hydrotechnical, and channel laboratories performing a great amount of scientific work connected with the solution of a multitude of practical problems such as hydrotechnical construction, agricultural reclamation, improvement of navigation conditions, water supply, and so forth. Yet the basic principles of modeling flows are still far from resolved. If the calculation of the model is based on the principle of the preservation of the force characteristics of the flow (the same measure, in nature and in the model, of the kinetics of the flow; in other words, the

_____

*Written by N. I. Makkaveyev and N. V. Khmeleva.

preservation of the Froude number), the degree of turbulence of the current is greatly distorted by comparison with nature. But if one preserves in the laboratory "river" the same degree of turbulence as in nature (the same number of Reynolds), the force characteristics are greatly distorted. With a reduction in the scale of the model to preserve the turbulent regime of flow, one has to introduce a distortion into the geometric resemblance of the model, enlarging its vertical scale by comparison with the hoizontal, which inevitably affects the hydraulic structure of the flow, i.e., the character of the currents forming the channel.

The task of modeling is further complicated when the flow in a bed undergoing erosion is investigated. With a reduction in the dimensions of the particles of the ground, there is a change in the nature of the forces offering resistance to the erosion. While the resistance of pebbles, gravel, or sand to erosion is determined mainly by the weight of the individual particles, cohesion between the particles plays the main role in the case of finer mechanical composition. Hence, in order to diminish the resistance of the ground to erosion in conformity with the reduced force of the flow in the model, it is necessary, instead of changing the size of the particles, to change their specific weight. The reduction of the specific weight is accomplished by using coal, bitumen, jet, and other substitutes for natural ground. However, it is practically impossible to impart to the particles of the substitute the same form and the same roughness as the particles of alluvium.

In spite of the absence of a rigorous theory, it has been possible, as a result of many years of research work in the field of modeling water flows, to find a number of procedures which permit one to choose the conditions for the experiments in such a way that their results furnish a sufficiently trustworthy basis for the solution of many practical tasks. The invariable and sole criterion of the evaluation of the accuracy of an experiment is the degree of similarity of the process in the laboratory to the natural processes. Hence, "matches" of the model with nature are made at all stages of the experiment, wherever it is possible.

In introducing the experimental method into the practice of geographic research, one has to overcome considerable difficulties. The multiformity of the factors, differing in their physical nature, which influence the development of the geographic landscape, the small extent of the study of the mechanism of individual processes, the indefiniteness of the quantitative characterization of many phenomena—all this poses problems that thus far cannot yet be solved in a general form, by giving a universal methodology of modeling. Nevertheless, in some fields of geographic research the experimental method is developing rather successfully and is gradually gaining one position after another.

We are unable, within the framework of the present essay, to set forth systematically the experience gained in the application of the experimental method to geographic research. Let us, therefore, dwell solely upon two trends characterizing very different fields of geography, namely (1) the development of fluvial forms of relief, and (2) the development of tectonic structures.

Great interest in fluvial processes has been aroused by those changes in the landscape of stream valleys and watershed expanses which occur as a result of the execution of a broad program of hydroelectric construction and a number of reclamation works. The successful development of experimental research has been aided by the fact that, in the methods of experimentation, it would be possible in many ways to rely on the rich experience gained in hydrotechnical modeling. The experimental research of the last few years has covered the processes of both surface (slope) and linear (channel) erosion.

Surface erosion has also been studied with special care in the Dokuchayev Soil-Science Laboratory of the Academy of Sciences of the USSR. The employment of the microscope, combined with motion picture apparatus, has made it possible to observe directly the character of the phenomena in the area of contact between the water and the ground. The distribution of the velocities and directions of the streams of liquid in the area of the so-called "border layer"—the microscopic thickness of the layer of liquid bordering directly on the surface of the soil—was first recorded. Investigating the erosional work, not only of the water flow, but also of the flows of other liquids, V. B. Gussak (1949) established that the process of soil erosion is very complex from the physical angle. It is determined not only by the mechanical action of the flows, but also depends upon electrical phenomena (resulting from the movement of the liquid), acting upon the character of the surface tension, and upon the dissolving capacity of the liquid. It is characteristic, for example, that two samples of soil having different indices of erosion in water exchanged places with respect to their resistance to erosion, when acted upon by a flow of kerosene.

The influence of rain water falling on slopes has been studied on rain installations in the laboratories of the institutes of Geography and Soil Science of the Academy of Sciences of the USSR. Small sand-covered areas were sprinkled with rain devices permitting changes in the intensity of the precipitation. A. I. Spiridonov's experiments (1951) succeeded in establishing that the upper part of a sandy slope is subject to the greatest erosion under the influence of rain. In D. L. Armand's experiments (1950), attention was directed chiefly to the characteristics of the development of small erosion furrows on the slopes. The character of this development, in general, fitted into the classic scheme of the development of a hydrographic network on a "primary plain." A "struggle" for the territory of the drainage basin was observed between the erosion forms, being effected through the capture of one furrow by another.

More detailed investigations of small erosion forms arising on slopes under the influence of rain have been made in the laboratory of the Institute of Geography of the Academy of Sciences of the USSR by Ye. A. Nefed'yeva and N. V. Khmeleva (1956). They established the influence of the expenditure of water, the inclination of the primary surface, and the size of the sand composing the slope upon the speed and shape of the ruts formed. The dependences obtained present considerable interest. It is characteristic that, unlike large channeled streams, in which the quantity of the solid material carried grows approximately proportionately to the square of the increase in the discharge of water, the discharge of water in flows occurring during rains exerts a much smaller influence on the transportation of alluvium. Thus, a five-fold increase in discharge caused only a two-fold increase in the quantity of material transported. Great influence is exerted on the suspension of alluvium in a downslope flow by the blows of the raindrops, and the greater the thickness of the layer of water, the more reliably is the surface of the ground protected from the dynamic action of the rain. Thanks to this circumstance, the intensity of the erosion on miniature "watersheds" between ruts may be just as intensive as along the thalweg of the ruts. Hence, in some cases, the surface of the slope may remain undissected by large erosional forms even when the erosion is very intensive.

Investigation of the processes of the development of large fluvial forms was begun in 1947 under the direction of M. A. Velikanov (1950) in the laboratory of the Institute of Geography of the Academy of Sciences of the USSR. A study was made of the process of incision by the flow into a sandy bed with different discharges of water and different inclinations of the primary surface. The duration of the individual experiments reached 1,500 hours. Despite the fact that the erosion base level and the amount of water in the flow during the individual experiment were constant, the incision was always accompanied by the formation of several terrace-like ledges on the slopes of the "valley." The formation of the ledges was due to the wandering of the meanders, which developed very rapidly, radically altering the original form of the channel, given to it in the shape of a rectilinear trench. Contrary to the generally accepted notions, the lateral erosion in the initial stages of incision was always more intense than in the subsequent stages.

In 1954-1957, investigations were made by the geomorphological laboratory of the Geographic Faculty of Moscow State University into the processes of the development of the lengthwise profile of a river on a model 60 meters long, the "river" being formed by the confluence of four tributaries. Aerial photography and automatic profilography [profilografirovaniye] were used to record the experiments. Alluvium in the amount required by the conditions of the experiment was constantly fed in at the source of the water system. The flow emptied into a small pond, where its delta could be freely formed. The level of the pond was regulated by a floodgate and the position of the base level of erosion could be changed. Upon increasing the discharge of water downstream (from the sources) and the alluvium fed into the sources in amounts proportional to the water volume, the flow carved out a parabolic lengthwise profile with the inclination diminishing toward the mouth. An investigation was made of the transformation of this lengthwise profile from various causes: changes in the amount of alluvium received, changes in the size of the runoff and the degree of its unevenness, the fluctuations of the base level of erosion, the development of local tectonic movements and other factors.

An increase in the amount of solid material entering the river caused an accumulation in the bed, which was most considerable in the upper part, and a corresponding rise in the mean level of the water. When the supply of alluvium reverted to the former norm, the flow again incised, and on the slopes of

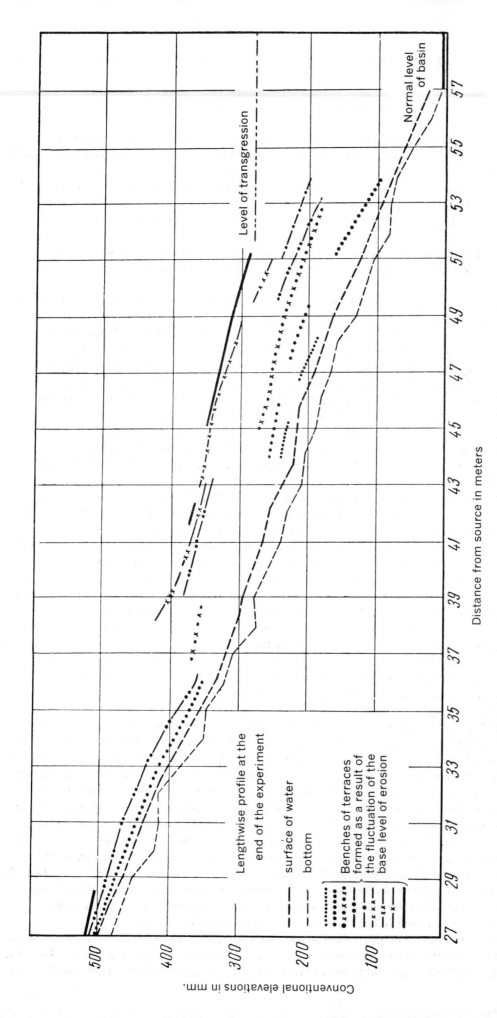

Fig. 34. LEVELS OF THE SURFACES OF TERRACES PRESERVED ON THE VALLEY SIDES AFTER INCISION OF THE CHANNEL CAUSED BY LOWERING THE BASE LEVEL OF EROSION

the "valley" there was formed a series of "terraces," the relative height of which increased gradually upstream, reaching its maximum not far from the main source. Thus, typical "chord" terraces characteristic of a number of rivers of the Russian Plain were obtained.

An increase in the amount of runoff caused incision of the channel with formation of chord terraces, the greatest relative height of which was in the middle course of the river. A similar transformation of the lengthwise profile could be observed when the runoff regime was changed; alternation of an even runoff with an uneven one without any change in its mean magnitude sharply activated the erosion in depth, chiefly in the middle course of the river.

Raising the base level of erosion caused an accumulation at first in the section of the new mouth, which then gradually spread both downstream (owing to the advance of the "marine" edge of the delta) and upstream. The layer of deposits attained its maximum thickness in the area of the marine edge of the delta and gradually diminished upstream. Upon the subsequent lowering of the base level to the old position, the channel cut through the thickness of deposited alluvium, and terraces were formed, the relative height of which increased downstream (Fig. 34).

The lowering of the base level of erosion does not always cause incision of the channel. In one of the experiments, the inclination of the "shelf" in the terminal basin was made ten times smaller than the mean inclination of the river. With such a bottom form, the lowering of the base level caused only a temporary and shallow incision of the channel, localized in the lower part of the old delta. Thereafter there began a rapid accumulation on the gently sloping section of the lengthwise profile, extending upstream, and the incision terrace was totally buried under the layer of alluvium.

It should be noted that in all cases the incision of the channel is accompanied by considerable lateral erosion. On this account, not a single terrace level, but a whole series of them is usually formed, and the individual levels synchronous with respect to time of formation may have a very uneven surface. Lateral erosion is especially considerable in cases where the incision is caused by the lowering of the base level. Relatively weak lateral erosion is observed in the case of incision caused by a reduction in the amount of solid material entering the river.

To study the influence of local tectonic movements, a lifting mechanism was placed on the lengthwise profile under the bed of the river, and with its aid a "mountain ridge" was gradually elevated across the river valley. When the rate of elevation was small (of the order of 1 centimeter per day) no traces of a ledge were discovered on the lengthwise profile, because the flow had time to even out the growing bulge completely. When the rate of elevation was increased 100 times, a through-flowing lake was formed in front of the ridge, while in the antecedent section of the valley a distinct bend was formed in the lengthwise profile, which was then shifted upstream, gradually becoming evened out.

In the field of the modeling of tectonic movements, a great deal of fruitful work has been done in the last few years, permitting the establishment of the basic principles of the approach to this matter. The calculation of models is usually based on the formula of the similarity of plastic deformations:

$\frac{n_1}{n_2} = \frac{P_1}{P_2} \propto t \propto e$ where n_1 and n_2 are the viscosity of the substance in the model and in nature, $P_1 \propto t$ the density of the material employed in the experiments, P_2 the density of the natural rocks, the time scale and $\propto e$ the space scale.

In order to satisfy the conditions of similarity, it is necessary in the experiments to employ viscous semiliquid and liquid substances (oil, petroleum products, etc.). With similar materials, a study was made of the forms of plastic deformation in the local structures of various origin: displacements of blocks having a rigid foundation, intrusions, growth of salt domes, etc.

Attempts are now being made to solve more complex problems—the investigation of the formation of structures under the continuous interaction of endogenic and exogenic processes. Among such attempts is the investigation made in the geomorphological laboratory of Moscow State University into the growth of domelike structures under conditions of delta sediment accumulation. The uplifting of rigid cores of structures was accomplished by hydraulic jacks, which were operated from the shore. The structures were elevated in the river delta simultaneously with its formation. In order to stimulate the regular growth of the delta in height, the base level of erosion was slowly raised. The local characteristics of the accumulation and erosion manifested themselves in the change in thickness of the individual layers in the growing structures (Fig. 35). Alongside this, one common characteristic was

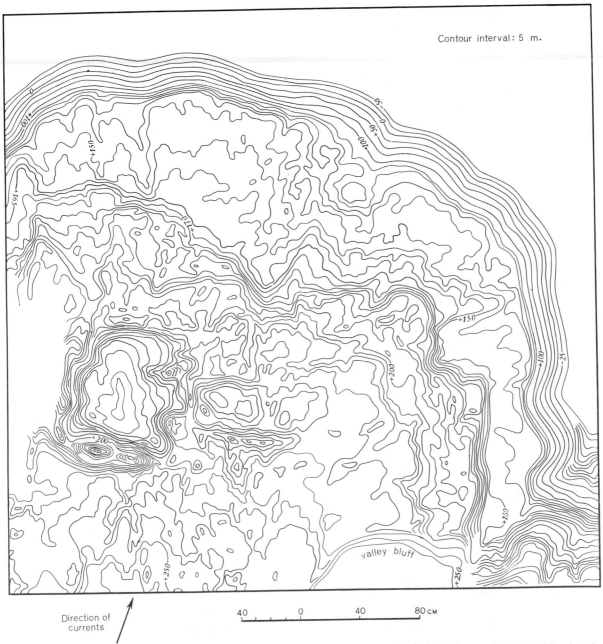

Contour interval: 5 m.

Direction of currents

40   0   40   80 CM

Fig. 35. HYPSOMETRIC MAP OF THE DELTA OF A RIVER, BUILT UP IN THE LABORATORY. The bench on the surface of the delta was caused by the raising of the base level of erosion. The hills correspond to structures that are being intensively uplifted.

discovered in the character of the structures growing under the conditions of delta sediment accumulation. Regardless of the form of the core, the structure received an asymmetric arrangement in the area of the upper layer of alluvium: the axis of folding and the hinges of the flexures (in box folds) were noticeably displaced downstream parallel to their original strike. But in cases where sediment accumulation was absent or was far inferior in intensity to the rate of uplift of the structure, the symmetric form of the latter was preserved throughout the whole thickness of the cross section.

The examples cited above show that experimental research, in spite of its relatively small development, has already made it possible to establish a number of characteristics of the complex natural processes which formerly remained unnoticed or were incorrectly interpreted. For the general success of geographic investigations it is extremely important to employ experimentation in studying, for example, the processes of nivation, solifluction, the erosional and accumulative activity of glaciers, the formation of loess, the development of karst, and so forth, in the mechanism of which there is still much that is unclear and controversial. Instituting these investigations will require a very great deal of preparation both in the field of the theory of modeling and in experimentation techniques, but the fundamental possibility of solving them in the laboratory is quite obvious.

BASIC LITERATURE

Armand, D. L. "The Study of the Geomorphological Processes by the Experimental Method," *Tr. In-ta geogr. AN SSSR,* no. 47, 1950.

Baturin, V. P. Geographic Analysis of the Geologic Past from Terrigenic Components *(Geograficheskiy Analiz Geologicheskogo Proshlogo po Terrigennym Komponentam),* Izd-vo AN SSSR, Moscow, 1947.

Vas'kovskiy, A. P. "The Present Pollen Spectra of the Northern Shore of the Okhotsk Sea and their Application to the Interpretation of the Pollen Analysis of Quaternary Deposits," *Materialy po geologii i poleznym iskopayemym severo-vostochnoy chasti SSSR,* no. 10, 1956.

Veklich, M. F. The Quaternary Deposits of the Right Bank of the Middle Dnepr *(Chetvertinni, Vi Dkladi Pravoberezhzhia Sevedn'ogo Dnipra)* (in Ukrainian), Vid Akademii nauk Ukrain'skoi RSR, Kiyev, 1958.

Velikanov, M. A. "The Modeling of the Channel Process," *Dokl. AN SSSR,* vol. 74, 1950, No. 3.

Glazovskaya, M. A. "Tasks and Methods of the Study of the Geochemistry of Geographic Landscapes," *Vestn. MGU,* 1956, No. 3.

Grichuk, V. P. "An Experiment in the Characterization of the Composition of Pollen in Contemporaneous Deposits of the various Vegetation Zones of the European Part of the USSR," *Probl. fiz. geogr.,* no. 11, 1942.

Gussak, V. B. "An Experiment in the Investigation of the Process of Soil Erosion with Models," sb. *Problemy sovetskogo pochvovedeniya,* No. 15, 1949.

Zhemchuzhnikov, Yu. A. "Oblique Stratification and its Geologic Interpretation," *Tr. VIMS,* no. 163, 1940.

Kovda, V. A. Geochemistry of the Deserts of the USSR *(Geokhimiya pustyn' SSSR),* 1954.

Makkaveyev, N. I., Kapitsa, A. P., and Khmeleva, N. V. "Experimental Investigations of the Processes of the Development of the Lengthwise Profile of a River," *Vestn. MGU,* No. 2, 1955.

Maksimovich, G. A. The Chemical Geography of the Waters of the Land *(Khimicheskaya Geografiya Vod Sushi),* Geografgiz, 1955.

Markov, K. K. and others. "The Interrelations between Forest and Steppe in the Light of History," *Voprosy geografii,* no. 23, 1950

Neyshtadt, M. I. The Spore-and-pollen Method in the USSR *(Sporovo-pyl'tsevoy Metod v SSSR),* 1952.

Nefed'yeva, Ye. A., and Khmeleva, N. V. "The Study of the Erosional Forms of Relief by the Experimental Method," *Tr. In-ta geogr. AN SSSR,* vol. 68, 1956.

Perel'man, A. I. Essays on the Geochemistry of the Landscape *(Ocherki Geokhimii Landshafta),* Geografgiz, 1955.

Perel'man, A. I. "Geochemistry and the Landscape," *Priroda,* 1960, No. 3.

Polynov, B. B. "Geochemical Landscapes," in the book: B. B. Polynov, *Izbr. trudy* (selected works), Izd-vo AN SSSR, 1956.

Polynov, B. B. The Study of Landscapes *(Ucheniye o Landshaftakh),* ibidem.

Polynov, B. B. "Guiding Ideas of the Modern Study of the Formation and Development of Soils." *Ibidem.*

Preobrazhenskiy, I. A. "On the Forms of Grains," *Tr. In-ta geol. nauk AN SSSR,* no. 21, 1940.

Rukhin, L. B. Fundamentals of Lithology *(Osnovy Litologii),* Gostoptekhizdat, 1953.

Rukhina, Ye. V. "The Rounding of Pebbles in the Present Alluvium of the Laba River," *Uch. zap. LGU, seriya geol.,* issue I, No. 102, 1950.

Sarkisyan, S. G., and Klimova, L. T. The Orientation of Pebbles and Methods of Studying Them for Paleogeographic Constructions *(Oriyentirovka Galek i Metody ikh Izucheniya dlya Paleogeograficheskikh Postroyeniy),* Izd-vo AN SSSR, 1955.

Sidorenko, A. V. "An Experiment in the Dissection of the Continental Strata of the Kara-Kums according to the Gravel and Pebble Particles Contained in them," *"Voprosy geologii Azii,"* Izd-vo AN SSSR, Moscow, 1955.

Spiridonov, A. I. "An Experiment in the Study of Water Erosion and Denudation in the Laboratory," *Pochvovedeniye,* 1951, No. 3.

Fedorova, R. V. "The Quantitative Laws of the Distribution of Oak Pollen by the Wind," *Tr. In-ta geogr. AN SSSR,* vol. 46, 1950.

Fersman, A. Ye. Geochemistry *(Geokhimiya),* vols. I-IV, 1932-1939. Handbook for the Traveler and Local-lore Student *(Spravochnik puteshestvennika i krayeveda),* vol. II, Geografgiz, 1950.

Khabakov, A. V. "Dynamic Paleogeography, its Tasks and Possibilities," *Tr. II Vsesoyuzn. geogr. s"yezda,* 1948.

Khabakov, A. V. "Oblique Stratification of Sediments as an Indication of the Conditions of their Formation," *Priroda,* 1951, No. 4.

Yakovlev, S. A. "On the Relationships between the Ice Sheets of the Quaternary Period issuing from the Scandinavian, Novaya Zemlya and Ural Centers of Glaciation," *"Byull. 4 AN SSSR,"* No. 18, 1953.

Grichuk, V. P. L'analyse pollinique en tant que méthode de reconstitution des formations végétales du passé géologique, *Essais de géographie,* Moscou, 1956.

Neyshtadt, M. I. Geschichte der Vegetation der UdSSR im Holozän. Grana pilynologica, 1959, Vol. 2, No. 1, Uppsala.

CHAPTER 43

NATURE PRESERVES [*Zapovedniki*]

S. V. Kirikov

The word *zapovednik* has existed in the Russian language for a long time. In ancient times it was used in various senses, but in those cases in which it was applied to natural lands, it meant "prohibition." In the 17th century, the forests situated on the abatis line and having great importance for defense were called *zapovednyye*. Here is what was said in a ukase sent from Moscow to the governor of Belgorod in 1665: "Firmly enjoin every serviceman and inhabitant in Belgorod under pain of death that they shall not cut down the Belgorod *forest preserve* [*zapovednyy les*] or strip bark from any tree, nor drive through the *forest preserves*, or lay roads or paths, nor keep or till plowlands in the *forest preserves*."*

It is also known that the Polish kings and the Russian tsars (or their closest relatives) had special exclusive hunting reservations (the Belovezhskaya Pushcha, the Kubanskaya "Okhota"), where no hunting could be done without the king's or tsar's permission. In order to preserve favorable conditions for game animals and birds, the cutting of timber, the clearing of trees for plowland or hayfields, etc., were either forbidden or strictly limited.

From these examples it may be seen that the *zapovedaniye* in former times had very limited and narrowly practical purposes and had no connection either with the scientific investigation of nature or with popular tourism. A much deeper meaning is now infused into the word *zapovednik*. Its sense will become clearer if we examine how the idea of national state nature preserves [*zapovedniki*] originated and developed (in other countries they are called people's or national parks). Already in the last century, many prominent individuals understood that the senseless, shortsighted exploitation of the natural wealth, considering only present-day demands, leaves behind it wastelands and swamps in place of the tayga forests; lands turned to desert by trampling cattle and wind-blown sands in place of steppes; a huge network of ravines and erosion of the most fertile layer of soil in the forest-steppe; rivers polluted with sewage, and so forth.

Soon after the crop failure and the succeeding dreadful famine in 1891 seized nearly the whole of the southeast of the European part of our country, prominent scholars headed by V. V. Dokuchayev undertook the study of the question of what the nature of the steppe zone was before its conversion into a zone of dry fields and grazing ranges, and whether man was managing rightly here. Even at that time Dokuchayev declared that, for a correct understanding of the nature of the steppe it was necessary to select and preserve sections of the steppe in perpetuity (Chebotareva, 1949).

Later, at the 12th Congress of Naturalists, which met in Moscow at the end of 1909, Academician I. P. Borodin, one of the first energetic advocates of the conservation of nature in our country, read a paper on the necessity of nature conservation. Borodin considered it necessary to create, under the Russian Geographic Society, a central nature-conservation committee which would be made up both of the scientific institutions and societies (the Academy of Sciences, the St. Petersburg Society of Naturalists, the Free Economic Society, the Forest Society and others) and of the government departments (the Main Administration of Land Organization and Farming, the Forest Department, and others). Another fundamental idea of this paper was that it is necessary to create special nature-preserve sections in our country. By this he meant extensive sections typical of a definite natural area, withdrawn from economic exploitation and preserved in their natural state, not disturbed by human beings, for very long periods of time, "in perpetuity." Borodin's proposal was supported and approved

---

*Documents [*Akty*] collected in the libraries and archives of the Russian Empire by the Archeologic Expedition of the Academy of Sciences, IV, 1836, p. 274. The italics are mine.—S. K.

by G. N. Vysotskiy and many other participants in the congress. The botanical-geographic sub-section of the congress also named the places where it was necessary to create the first of the nature preserves. The majority of them were located in the steppe and forest-steppe zones (Starobel'skiy, Khrenovskiy, Streletskiy, Bessarabskiy, Kodry, Golubaya Balka, and several others), i.e., where nature was being subjected to the greatest change by human beings.

"Steppe questions are our own, purely Russian questions; yet it is precisely the steppe, the virgin steppe, that we are running the risk of losing first of all," wrote I. P. Borodin (1914). Soon thereafter, the idea of the necessity of creating nature preserves was recognized by the then-ruling circles. By this time, the sable hunting industry, which was of great significance in the economy of Siberia and in the life of its peoples, had declined. In order to restore the numerical strength of this valuable species, not only was sable hunting prohibited, but not long before the revolution (in 1916) the Barguzin Sable Nature Preserve—in the modern meaning of the word—was created.

But the idea of nature conservation and the creation of nature preserves was genuinely realized after the October Revolution. In 1919, the Astrakhan' Nature Preserve was founded, and in 1920, the Il'men Nature Preserve. In September, 1921, V. I. Lenin signed the law (decree) "On the preservation of natural monuments, gardens, and seedbeds," which served as a basis for the further development of nature preserves. In connection with the foundation of nature preserves, it was necessary to give them legalized definition, which was done in 1924 by the then-highest legislative institution of our country, the Presidium of the All-Union Central Executive Committee.

The nature preserves were defined as *"sections of land forever subject to complete preservation and withdrawn from any economic utilization whatsoever"* (Shaposhnikov and Borisov, 1958, p. 97). This definition derived from the above-mentioned law "On the preservation of natural monuments, gardens and seedbeds," which speaks of the "inviolability of the natural monuments."

A large number of nature preserves and small preserve sections [*zapovednyye uchastki*] have now been created in our country, and the Soviet Union rightfully regards itself as one of the world centers in this important matter (Fig. 36 and the Table at the end of the chapter). The nature preserves are located in various natural zones and mountain systems. The opinion has been expressed (Lavrenko and others, 1958)—and it is undoubtedly right—that the small preserve sections situated within one mountain system or one natural area should be united into one big nature preserve. In all probability, a number of other big nature preserves will be established in the next few years.

What is the reason that the idea of preserves—of people's (or national) parks—has proved so vital and has won recognition among nearly all peoples? This question is closely connected with others, namely: what are nature preserves and what should they be?

Undoubtedly, one of the foremost and most important tasks of nature preserves is to preserve large typical sections of the natural areas of our country in their natural state for a long time ("in perpetuity"); to preserve them as a national property belonging to the people in order that the generations following us will be able to see feathergrass steppes with all their inhabitants, and ship oak groves and pine forests, and tayga, and mountains. The nature preserves should be bases of popular tourism.

The "Prospective Plan for a Geographic Network of USSR Nature Preserves" (Lavrenko and others, 1958) has pointed out the extraordinary importance of preserving in the nature preserves the largest possible number of species of plants and animals peculiar to this or that type of life environment (forest, steppe, desert, bodies of water, etc.). The practical significance of the immense majority of plants and animals has not been studied. Our generation regrets that our ancestors, like greedy, reckless plunderers, exterminated the sea cow and the aurochs. The generations following us will evaluate our activity still more severely, if no sufficiently extensive sections of the steppes with all the animals and plants characteristic of them are left in our country. After all, among the steppe animals and plants there may prove to be species no less valuable than the sea cow. But their value for us is still unknown, because they have not been studied, or have been studied only very superficially. Only those species whose harmfulness is indisputable may be totally exterminated. All the remaining species must be preserved (in one quantity or another).

In the creation of nature preserves there is still another, no less important object. The nature of the preserves must not only be carefully preserved, but also studied. Many processes and phenomena

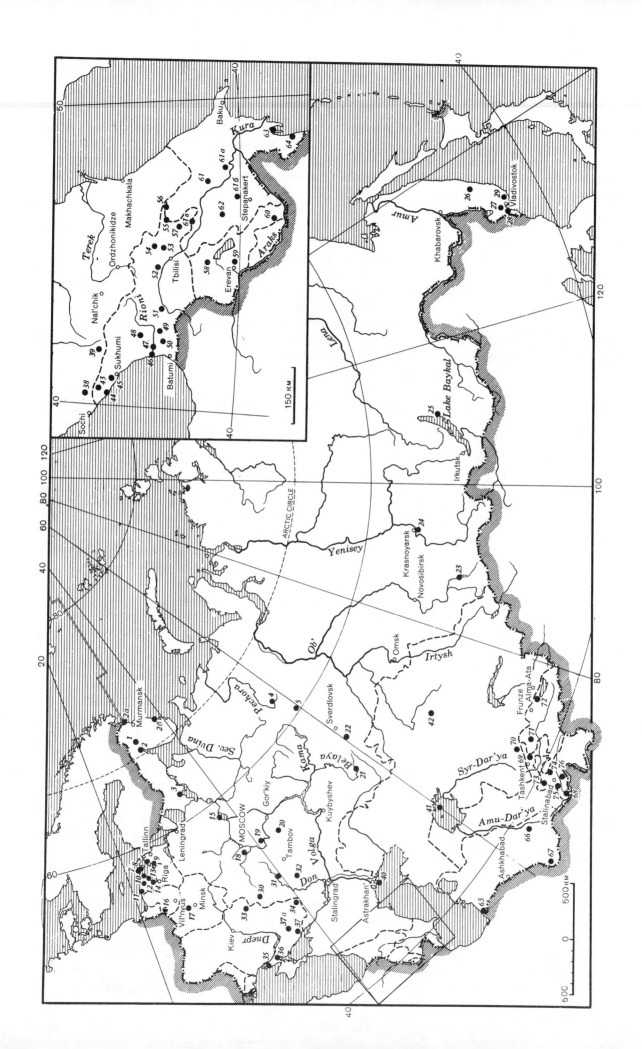

occurring in nature are now taking place under conditions under which human economic activity is making itself felt very strongly. To learn the laws characteristic of such processes and phenomena it is necessary to have control sections, where scientific research can be conducted under natural conditions undisturbed by human beings. Such control sections can only be set aside in nature preserves. Investigations to be based on the comparative method of study under nature-preserve and ordinary conditions will make it possible to foresee what directions the further alterations of nature will follow, and to abandon or change the former directions of human economic activity if it leads to the spoliation or destruction of natural wealth.

Many years of research on permanent sections not subject to man's activity are also needed to learn how and in what directions the continuous change (perennial and secular) in the nature of our steppes, forests, deserts and tundras are proceeding. Investigations of this sort, conducted outside and in disregard of the nature preserves, encounter various difficulties. These difficulties arise because it is often hard to determine what has changed in nature for reasons not connected with human activity and what as a result of it.

In the nature preserves, the continuous changes in nature will stand out most clearly and distinctly. It is quite natural, therefore, that in nature preserves one of the most important scientific investigations is the keeping of a so-called "chronicle of nature." It is kept by scientific workers of different specialties —meteorologists, hydrologists, botanists, zoologists, etc. The immense scientific value of this sort of research will reveal itself, of course, after detailed observations for many years have been accumulated.

The nature preserves, as has been pointed out (Lavrenko and others, 1958), should become the main bases for lengthy stationary study of natural complexes and natural processes. Alongside this, very great attention is paid in the Soviet Union to the investigation of the form of life of the animals and plants under various geographic conditions. Most of the investigations of this sort have concerned chiefly the industrial game mammals and birds (beaver, sable, forest marten, wild hoofed mammals, the grouse family, and aquatic birds, etc.). Scientific research in nature preserves is conducted both by the scientific workers of the preserves themselves and by workers of the academies of sciences, universities, institutes, etc., who visit them.

In most of the union republics there are special administrations which plan and direct the scientific work of the nature preserves. The results of the scientific research are published in the *Trudy* of the nature preserves and, in addition, in the publications of the USSR Academy of Sciences and the union academies, in the *Zapiski* of the universities, and so forth (see the handbook literature on nature preserves).

Fig. 36. SCHEMATIC MAP OF THE DISTRIBUTION OF NATURE PRESERVES [*ZAPOVEDNIKI*] OF THE USSR.

1. Lapland   2. Kandalaksha [Kandalakshskiy] with branches   2a. Aynovy Ostrova [Islands]
2b. Kharlovskiy uchastok [Section]   3. Kivach   4. Pechoro-Ilychskiy   5. Denezhkin Kamen'   6. Matsalu   7. Vayka
8. Viydumee   9. Nibula   10. Slitere   11. Grini   12. Moristsala   13. Greb'i   14. Kemeri   15. Darwin (Darvinskiy)
16. Zhuvintas   17. Berezina   18. Oka River Terrace   19. Oka (River)   20. Mordva   21. Bashkir   22. Il'men'
23. Altay   24. Stolby ["Columns"]   25. Barguzin(skiy)   26. Sikhote-Alin' [Range]   27. Suputinskiy
28. Kedrovaya Pad'   29. Sudzukhinskiy   30. Central Black-Earth (Tsentral'no-Chernozemnyy)   31. Voronezh(skiy)
32. Khopër [River]   33. Mikhaylovskaya Tselina (Virgin Land)   34. Streletskaya Step'   35. Black Sea (Chernomorskiy)
36. Askaniya Nova   37. Khomutovskaya Step' with branch (*filial*)   37a. Kamennyye Mogily ["Stone Graves"]
38. Caucasian   39. Teberda   40. Astrakhan'   41. Barsa-Kel'mes   42. Kurgal'dzhinskiy   43. Ritsa [Lake]   44. Pitsunda
45. Gumista   46. Colchidian (Kolkhidskiy)   47. Pontic Oak (Pontiyskogo Duba)   48. Satapliyskiy
49. Adzhametskiy Les [Forest]   50. Kintrishkiy   51. Borzhomi   52. Saguramskiy   53. Mariamdzhvar   54. Batsar
55. Lagodekhi   56. Zakataly   57. Vashlovan   58. Dilizhan   59. Garni   60. Bartasskiy   61. Turianchay, with branches
61a. Shirvanskiy Uchastok   61b. Fistashkovaya Roshcha [Pistachio Grove] in the Karabakh Steppe
61c. El'darskiy Uchastok   62. Gek-Gel'   63. Kyzyl-Abau   64. Hyrcanian (Girkanskiy)   65. Gasan-Kuli   66. Repetek
67. Badkhyz   68. Tigrovaya Balka ["Tiger Gulch"]   69. Chatkal [Range] (Mountain Forest)   70. Aksu-Dzhebagly
71. Sary-Chilek   72. Keminskiy   73. Iskander-kul' [Lake]   74. Ramit   75. Gazimaylik   76. Childukhtaron (Yakunch)

USSR NATURE PRESERVES (ZAPOVEDNIKI)
(Status as of 1 September, 1959)

NAME OF NATURE PRESERVE (OR SMALL PRESERVE SECTION)	LOCATION		AREA IN HECTARES
	NATURAL ZONE OR MOUNTAIN LAND	UNION REPUBLIC	
Zone of the Deserts			
Astrakhanskiy [Astrakhan]	Seaside-delta preserve, situated in semidesert	RSFSR	75,630
Gasankuliyskiy [Gasan-kuli]	Seaside preserve, located in the zone of the deserts	Turkmenia	69,700
Barsa-Kel'messkiy	Subzone of typical deserts	Kazakhstan	19,800
Badkhyzskiy [Badkhyz]	Subzone of southern deserts	Turkmenia	70,000
Repeteksiy [Repetek]	Subzone of southern sandy deserts	Turkmenia	18,600
Zone of the steppes			
Chernomorskiy [Black Sea]	Seaside preserve, situated in the subzone of dry fescue-and-feathergrass steppes	Ukraine	12,000
(Askaniyskiy preserve section)	Subzone of dry fescue-and-feathergrass steppes	Ukraine	500
(Kamennyye Mogily)	Section of stony steppes	Ukraine	356
(Streletskaya Step')	Subzone of variherbaceous-fescue-feathergrass steppes	Ukraine	525
(Khomutovskaya Step')	Subzone of variherbaceous-fescue-feathergrass steppes	Ukraine	1,024
Kurgal'dzhinskiy	Northern part of the subzone of wormwood-fescue-feathergrass steppes	Kazakhstan	15,000
Forest-Steppe			
(Mikhaylovskaya Tselina) [Virgin Land]	Section of variherbaceous-feathergrass steppes	Ukraine	202
Tsentral'no-chernozemnyy [Central Black Earth]	Small sections of variherbaceous-feathergrass steppes and oak groves	RSFSR	4,200
Voronezhskiy [Voronezh]	Oak groves and pine woods, situated in the southern forest-steppe	RSFSR	30,800
Khoperskiy [Khoper]	Floodplain of the Khoper River with elm-and-oak and black-alder forests	RSFSR	16,000
Mordovskiy	Pine woods and mixed pine-and-broadleaf forests, situated in the northern forest-steppe	RSFSR	30,100
Forest Zone			
Subzone of mixed conifer and broadleaf forests			
Matsalu	Eastern European area of the subzone of mixed coniferous and conifer-broadleaf forests	Estonia	58,800

(Continued on next page)

USSR NATURE PRESERVES (ZAPOVEDNIKI)

(Continued from preceding page) (Status as of 1 September, 1959)

NAME OF NATURE PRESERVE (OR SMALL PRESERVE SECTION)	LOCATION		AREA IN HECTARES
	NATURAL ZONE OR MOUNTAIN LAND	UNION REPUBLIC	
Nigula	Eastern European area of the subzone of mixed coniferous and conifer-broadleaf forests	Estonia	3,000
(Vidumee)	Eastern European area of the subzone of mixed coniferous and conifer-broadleaf forests	Estonia	650
(Vayka)	Eastern European area of the subzone of mixed coniferous and conifer-broadleaf forests	Estonia	35
Kemeri	Eastern European area of the subzone of mixed coniferous and conifer-broadleaf forests	Latvia	46,700
Slitere	Eastern European area of the subzone of mixed conifer-broadleaf forests	Latvia	7,860
(Moristsala)	Eastern European area of the subzone of mixed conifer-broadleaf forests	Latvia	835
(Grini)	Eastern European area of the subzone of mixed conifer-broadleaf forests	Latvia	700
(Greb'i)	Eastern European area of the subzone of mixed conifer-broadleaf forests	Latvia	1,340
Zhuvintas	Eastern European area of the subzone of mixed conifer-broadleaf forests	Lithuania	3,000
Berezinskiy [Berezina]	Eastern European area of the subzone of mixed conifer-broadleaf forests	Belorussia	67,000
Prioksko-Terrasnyy [Oka River Terrace]	Eastern European area of the subzone of mixed conifer-broadleaf forests	RSFSR	4,830
Okskiy [Oka River]	Eastern European area of the subzone of mixed conifer-broadleaf forests	RSFSR	22,000
Kedrovaya Pad'	Far Eastern area of the subzone of conifer-broadleaf forests	RSFSR	15,100
Sudzukhinskiy	Far Eastern area of the subzone of conifer-broadleaf forests	RSFSR	173,000
Suputinskiy	Far Eastern area of the subzone of conifer-broadleaf forests	RSFSR	15,900
Sikhote-Alinskiy [Sikhote-Alin']	Far Eastern area of the subzone of conifer-broadleaf forests	RSFSR	110,590

(Continued on next page)

USSR NATURE PRESERVES (ZAPOVEDNIKI)

(Continued from preceding page)   (Status as of 1 September, 1959)

NAME OF NATURE PRESERVE (OR SMALL PRESERVE SECTION)	LOCATION		AREA IN HECTARES
	NATURAL ZONE OR MOUNTAIN LAND	UNION REPUBLIC	
Subzone of the Tayga			
Laplandskiy [Lapland]	Northern tayga with sections of mountain tundra	RSFSR	158,300
Kandalakshskiy [Kandalaksha]	Seaside preserve, situated in the northern tayga; sections of tundra	RSFSR	20,300
Kivach	Middle tayga	RSFSR	10,315
Pechoro-Ilychskiy	Middle tayga	RSFSR	714,300
Darvinskiy [Darwin]	Southern tayga and shore of the Rybinskoye Reservoir	RSFSR	166,600
Stolby	Middle Siberian pine and pine-and-leaf forests	RSFSR	47,000
Barguzinskiy	Transbaykal mountain-tayga larch and dark-conifer forests	RSFSR	248,180
Urals			
Bashkirskiy [Bashkir]	Mountain pine woods and broadleaf forests	RSFSR	80,100
Il'menskiy mineralogicheskiy [Il'men]	Pine woods and lakes in the eastern foothills of the Urals (at the junction between Middle and Southern Urals)	RSFSR	30,000
Denezhkin Kamen'	Mountain dark-conifer tayga with bald-tops [*gol'tsy*]	RSFSR	36,100
Caucasus			
Dilizhanskiy [Dilizhan]	Northern Slope of the Minor Caucasus with forests of Georgian oak and beech, sparse parkland groves and mountain meadows	Armenia	28,538
Garninskiy [Garni]	The Saraybulak Range and the Khosrov Forest; mountain steppes and scrub growths	Armenia	14,861
Bartasskiy	Transcaucasian broadleaf forests	Armenia	8,178
Lagodekhskiy [Lagodekhi]	Spurs of the southern slope of the Main Caucasian Ridge	Georgia	13,300
Ritsinskiy [Ritsa]	Southern slope of the Main Caucasian Ridge with dark-conifer and broadleaf forests.	Georgia	15,928
Borzhomskiy [Borzhomi]	Mountain oak, beech and dark-conifer forests	Georgia	13,600

(Continued on next page)

USSR NATURE PRESERVES (ZAPOVEDNIKI)

(Continued from preceding page) (Status as of 1 September, 1959)

NAME OF NATURE PRESERVE (OR SMALL PRESERVE SECTION)	LOCATION		AREA IN HECTARES
	NATURAL ZONE OR MOUNTAIN LAND	UNION REPUBLIC	
Adzhametskiy Les	Forest tract of Imeretian oak, dzel'kva [Zelkova carpinifolia, elm fam.] and Hartwiss oak [Quercus hartwissiana]		4,753
Gumistinskiy Les [Gumista]	Forest tract of Caucasian spruce, Oriental fir, chestnut, Georgian oak and Oriental beech	Georgia	2,744
Kintrishskiy	Forest tract of Georgian maple,	Georgia	6,000
Vashlovanskiy	cedar and pomegranate	Georgia	6,600
Saguramskiy	Vegetation of the Colchidian region [Rioni River Lowland]	Georgia	5,000
(Zapovednyy uchastok pontiyskogo duba) [Preserve section of Pontic oak]	Forest of Pontic oak	Georgia	1,400
(Pitsundskaya Roshcha)	Grove [Roshcha] of Pitsunda pine	Georgia	300
(Satapliyskiy zapovednyy uchastok)		Georgia	300
Mariamdzhvarskiy zapovednyy uchastok)		Georgia	1,100
(Kolkhidskiy zapovednyy uchastok)		Georgia	500
Batsarskiy	Yew grove	Georgia	3,052
Zakatal'skiy [Zakataly]	Southern slope of the eastern part of the Main Caucasian Ridge	Azerbaydzhan	25,450
Gekgel'skiy [Gek-Gel']	Northern slope of the Minor Caucasus	Azerbaydzhan	2,500
Turianchayskiy (with the branches [filialy]: Shirvanskiy uchastok The pistachio grove in the Karabakh Steppe El'darskiy uchastok	Sparse pistachio-and-juniper growth on the slopes of the Bozdag Range	Azerbaydzhan	20,000
Lenkoranskiy (Hyrcanian)	Lenkoran' lowland forests	Azerbaydzhan	20,000
Kyzyl-agachskiy	Seaside nature preserve of the S. M. Kirov Gulf	Azerbaydzhan	93,000
Kavkazskiy [Caucasian]	Northern slope of the Major Caucasus; beech and dark-conifer forests; subalpine and alpine meadows	RSFSR	251,780
Teberdinskiy [Teberda]	Northern slope of the Major Caucasus; pine, dark-conifer and beech forests; subalpine and alpine meadows; glaciers	RSFSR	92,580

(Continued on next page)

USSR NATURE PRESERVES (ZAPOVEDNIKI)

(Continued from preceding page) (Status as of 1 September, 1959)

NAME OF NATURE PRESERVE (OR SMALL PRESERVE SECTION)	LOCATION		AREA IN HECTARES
	NATURAL ZONE OR MOUNTAIN LAND	UNION REPUBLIC	
Mountains of Middle Asia			
Chatkal'skiy [Chatkal]	Chatkal'skiy Range; leaf and juniper forests	Uzbekistan	11,000
Aksu-Dzhebaglinskiy	Spurs of the Talas and Ugam Ranges; juniper stands; rocky steppes; high-mountain meadows	Kazakhstan	70,000
Sary-Chilekskiy		Kirgizia	40,000
Keminskiy	Kungey-Alatau; forests of Schrenk fir	Kirgizia	20,000
Tigrovaya Balka [Tiger Gulch]	*Tugai* [floodplain forests] in the valley of the Vakhsh River	Tadzhikistan	41,000
Iskander-kul'	Lake of the same name and the territory to the west of it	Tadzhikistan	30,000
Ramit	Basins of the Sorbo and Sarday-Miyen Rivers (at their confluence)	Tadzhikistan	15,000
Gazimaylik	60 km. to the south of the town of Stalinabad	Tadzhikistan	15,000
Chil'dukhtaron	Basin of the Obi-Surkh and Yakh-su Rivers (40-50 km. to the NNE of the town of Kulyab)	Tadzhikistan	15,000

BASIC LITERATURE

"Documents Collected in the Libraries and Archives of the Russian Empire by the Archeographic Expedition of the Academy of Sciences" *(Akty, Sobrannyye v Bibliotekakh i Arkhivakh Rossiyskoy Imperii Arkheograficheskoy Ekspeditsiyey Akademii Nauk),* vol. IV, St. Petersburg, 1836.

Borodin, I. P. The Preservation of Natural Monuments *(Okhrana Pamyatnikov Prirody),* St. Petersburg, 1914.

Nature Preserves of the USSR *(Zapovedniki SSSR),* vols. I-II, Moscow, 1951 (Description of the major nature preserves. In addition, this publication contains a short list of scientific and popular-scientific literature on nature preserves down to 1951).

Lavrenko, Ye. M., Geptner, V. G., Kirikov, S. V., and Formozov, A. N. "Prospective Plan of a Geographic Network of USSR Nature Preserves. The conservation of Nature and the Nature-preserve Cause in the USSR." *(Okhrana prirody i zapovednoye delo v SSSR),* Bulletin No. 3, 1958.

Makarov, V. N. The Nature Preserves of the USSR *(Zapovedniki SSSR),* Moscow, 1940.

"Scientific-methodical Notes of the Main Administration of Nature Preserves" *Nauchno-metodicheskiye zapiski Glavnogo upravleniya po zapovednikam,* no. X, Moscow, 1948. (This issue contains bibliographic indexes of the published and manuscript studies made in the nature preserves in 1921-1947, and also an index of the literature on nature preserves and the studies executed in them).

Ibid. no. XIII, Moscow, 1949 (Supplement to the bibliographic index of the studies executed in the nature preserves concerning the zoology of vertebrates and parasitology).

"The Sable Hunting Industry on the Northeastern Shore of Lake Baykal," *Materialy Barguzinskoy ekspeditsii G. G. Doppel'maira,* Verkhneudinsk-Leningrad, 1926.

Chebotareva, L. A. "V. V. Dokuchayev. A brief Biographic Sketch" in the book: V. V. Dokuchayev. *Selected Works, (Izbrannyye Trudy)* Moscow, 1949.

Shaposhnikov, L. K., and Borisov, V. A. "The First Measures of the Soviet State for the Conservation of Nature." *Okhrana Prirody i Zapovednoye Delo v SSSR,* Bulletin No. 3, 1958.

CHAPTER 44

METHODS OF RESEARCH IN ECONOMIC GEOGRAPHY

V. V. Poksishevskiy

As has been shown in Chapter 5, on "Economic Geography," the research conducted in the USSR rests upon methodological principles and procedures well tested in practice. Nevertheless, it is far from simple to give in a compact form a general characterization of the modern methods of research in economic geography. This may be explained primarily by the great diversity of the content of the investigations themselves, which, as a rule, have a distinct practical trend toward lending aid in the solution of definite national-economic tasks. These tasks are highly varied, their solution is connected with a very broad range of territorial objects, and the methods employed in the investigations are therefore subjected to considerable individualization in accordance with the dissimilar objectives.

Indeed, economic geographers participate in many kinds of designing and research work, particularly in the location of new industrial construction; in surveying for transportation construction, both of individual lines of trunk-line significance, and for the development of whole networks in the various regions; in work on regional planning; in the solution of questions of the exploitation of territories for agricultural purposes and the correct specialization of agriculture; in forestry surveys, etc. Very characteristic are the investigations conducted in regions of major hydrotechnical construction in connection with the creation of reservoirs. These investigations are connected, on the one hand, with the evaluation of the damage caused by flooding and, on the other hand, with the elaboration of measures to reduce this damage and create a new territorial organization of the economy in the region adjacent to the reservoir (transfer of populated points, reconstruction of the road network, transformation of the agricultural lands and changes in the specialization of agriculture, and so forth).

Alongside such clearly designed investigations and research, which usually have a comparatively narrowly localized territorial object and sometimes also a specialized branch content, economic geographers often participate in broader work intended to furnish an integrated characterization of the productive forces of extensive territories and evaluate the general prospects for their development.

In these cases, special economic geographic expeditions are most often organized, being made up of detachments or groups studying either certain parts of the territory or certain aspects and branches of the economy, or both (local-branch problems). Finally, economic geographers often make investigations (of a semiexpeditionary character) for the purpose of preparing a scientific characterization of this or that region or area, to be used later by the planning and economic organs and reflected in a monograph.

This list of the different kinds of economic geographic investigations alone shows that their methods are inevitably very diverse. Perhaps this is the reason why comparatively few works establishing the general methodological principles of research in economic geography have been published in the USSR. Predominant among them are methodological instructions confined to economic geographic investigations of an educational character, executed in the geographic faculties by way of field exercises. Such investigations naturally cannot be particularly narrowly specialized, since they must provide the students with a whole set of skills. Considerably more works have been published which reveal these principles as applied to individual concrete directions and forms of work. The list of basic literature given at the end of this chapter reflects above all precisely such concrete directions. We have considered it appropriate to indicate only a very few works of a general character.

In this chapter we shall attempt to note some chief general features of the methods employed in economic geographic research, illustrating the discussion with particular instances relating to the various kinds of work.

355

The first basic principle is the purposefulness of investigations in economic geography, which most often are directed toward concrete assistance in the planned development of the economy. Even if the work is conducted, at first sight, for purely research and knowledge purposes (for example, in the line of treatment of questions relating to detailed economic geographic regionalization, the ascertainment of types of populated points, etc.), its list of subjects is such that the results are valuable for the planning organs and can be utilized by them at any moment.

The second general principle is the broad integration [*kompleksirovaniye*] of investigations in economic geography with ones in physical geography, as well as co-operation, in the course of the work, between the geographers and the representatives of many other specialties—geologists, agronomists, engineers, economists having different specialties, town builders, land organizers, and others. Such co-operation makes research in economic geography considerably more concrete and enhances its practical value. This co-ordination presupposes that the economic geographers, especially if the work being done by them is of a field character (see below), have themselves come pretty close to mastering the skills of the respective allied specialties; for example, those of technical economic calculation, the agro-economic evaluation of agricultural lands, etc.

As regards creative co-operation with physical geographers, the organization and methods of research in economic geography illustrate beautifully the interrelationships between economic and physical geography which prevail in the Soviet Union. In each sphere of research, its own specific methodology is applied, inasmuch as the processes and phenomena of a socio-productional character are studied in the first case and the natural ones in the second. The laws studied are accordingly also different. At the same time, however, there is absolute need of interpenetration between both spheres of research: a wide use of the conclusions of physical geographers by economic geographers (and vice versa), and the co-ordination of these conclusions with the general complex.

This co-ordination is based on the nearly-always-existing community between the territorial frameworks of research themselves, i.e., the spatial community of its object (though different aspects of of this object are studied); the close connections and inter-influences between economic and natural phenomena, which exist objectively (a fact which should also be reflected in the sphere of research); and the practical national-economic purposefulness of the final conclusions of the whole circle of investigations.

Characteristic of most of the economic geography investigations conducted in the USSR is the broad combination of "office" methods, connected with the use and working-up of statistical materials, report data, and written sources, with field methods, which have undergone development in the USSR. Economic geographers, in doing thorough regional research, do not work solely on "alien" and ready-made material (report data, official materials, etc.), but also conduct their own field observations and gather primary material.

Many landmarks of primary economic geography field investigation have already been noted; for example, investigations of kolkhoz lands, rural settlements, towns, micro-regions, etc. Experience has been accumulated to show how the collection of ready-made materials and one's own field observations must be combined in the course of investigation.

It should be borne in mind that the State character of economic geography investigations (like any other scientific research in the USSR) provides the investigator with all the materials available in the the local central institutions, departments, and enterprises. Likewise, in organizing field investigations it is always possible to rely on the all-around support of the local organs—down to such primary administrative organs as the rural soviets—and of such centers of economic administration as the directing boards of the kolkhozes, the management of the individual industrial enterprises, sovkhozes, etc. The research programs and tasks themselves are set up in agreement both with the central organs (up to the Gosplan [State Planning Commission] of the USSR) and with the interested local institutions. As a result of the close contacts with the latter, the plan is often enriched by many additional particular questions and aspects already in the course of the investigation.

Information gained from interviews holds a sort of intermediate position between one's own field observations and the various statistical and report data essential for research purposes, obtained from "centralized sources." Such information, when correctly recorded and capable of being co-ordinated clearly enough with a definite territory, subject to indirect verification by data obtained from official materials or through one's own observations, may be of great help in supplementing with the necessary information the characterization of the region given by the generalized data. The ability to obtain and evaluate correctly the information gained from interviews is a very important skill for economic geographers working on regional subjects.

The combination of the use of "centralized" information, of data obtained on the spot, both "officially" and by means of interviews and, finally, of the results of one's own field observations, is the most valuable among the methodological procedures of modern Soviet work in economic geography. This combination may be well illustrated, for example, by the numerous studies in economic geography made in the USSR for the purpose of providing a basis for the reconstruction and development of the motor highway network. To establish the freight traffic density on the individual roads, the investigator may, on the one hand, use the statistical reports obtained from the respective organs and, on the other hand, make a direct count of the motor vehicles passing over the sections of road that especially interest him. Obviously, for all the value of the final conclusions drawn from comprehensive statistical data, direct observations will permit him to ascertain additional important features of a road's work regime (the characteristics of the use of the road by hours of the day and night, in dependence upon the weather, etc.).

Very important from the viewpoint of method is the scale of economic geographic investigation, i.e., the degree of geographic detail. Externally, it is best expressed by the scale of the maps used by the investigator as working material, or the special-purpose maps compiled by himself and reflecting the results of his work.

Economic geography investigations to which 1:1,000,000 or smaller scale maps correspond may be conducted mainly without direct field work, merely on the basis of materials obtained from centralized sources in the various oblast, kray, and republic institutions, on the basis of literature and report data. To be sure, here too traverses through typical localities and visits to individual economic centers are very desirable. They train the economic geographer and help to extract from these data that which would escape his attention without his personal impressions. Also very fruitful is the direct intercourse with the local leading party and soviet workers and various specialists: the agronomists, the managers of the industrial enterprises and transportation organizations, forest organizers, etc.

Work corresponding to 1:100,000 (or larger) scale maps, on the contrary, is connected with field investigations. This work (unless it is a matter of a comparatively compact economic rayon, oblast, or republic) usually pertains only to individual sections of a territory that are important for some reason or other. These scales enable one to a considerable degree to cover the locality to be investigated with working traverses and also to "look" at it visually all over or nearly all over in one degree or another. The official economic data that can be obtained from centralized sources is too schematic for such work: the center of gravity of the work lies in the independent co-ordination of individual economic data with this or that section of the locality. For example, the geographer may establish the confinement of certain crops to valley terraces or watershed plots, determine precisely the topography of distribution of industrial enterprises in a town or city, the location of logging camps with relation to possible road routes, the characteristics of the planning of populated points, and so forth. Such detailed work enables one to discover and analyze directly on the spot and reflect on special-purpose large-scale maps a large number of primary spatial connections both between the individual elements of the economy and between these elements and the geographic environment. An important precondition for this analysis, already made in the course of the field observation of the locality, is the direct surveyability of its constituent elements, resulting precisely from the large scale of the investigation itself. Here the geographer is confronted with sections of terrain capable of being thoroughly examined, traversed by working micro-itineraries, inspected as to all the main types of land, etc.

In the case of intermediate scales, as well as of combined investigations (as is often the case) aimed at treating individual territories in relative detail against the background of the general characterization of an extensive territory, the so-called "method of keys" has undergone broad development in the last few years, having been employed with special success by the economic geographers of Moscow University. With this method, the collection and elaboration of comprehensive materials relating to the whole territory are combined with a detailed study of small, but sufficiently typical sections (individual kolkhozes, groups of mines, etc.). The number of "keys" should be adequate, and all types of economic utilization of the territory should be represented among them. Only then is it possible, with their aid, to establish with great certainty the regular combinations of individual economic phenomena in the locality, as well as their confinement to this or that element of the geographic environment.

Even on the basis of very generalized data averaged for the whole territory and obtained through official channels, the "keys" will make it possible to represent very concretely the distribution of the economic elements and to evaluate the economic processes throughout the territory. When setting the tasks for a medium-scale (and sometimes also a small-scale) investigation, it is important to make a large-scale study of the "keys" as well. The "key method," created by economic geographers after the analogy of the procedure, employed in landscape science, of combining a detailed study of the individual small natural tracts with broad zonal generalizations, is exceptionally effective.

Economic geographers also make wide use of the more general procedure of the selective study of individual objects (the most important, on the one hand, and the most typical, on the other) in combination with the collection of material on the whole territory under study. The objects of selective study may be towns and other populated points, industrial enterprises, kolkhozes and sovkhozes, logging tracts, fisheries, etc. The concrete choice of such objects is determined by the topics of the investigation.

Such methods derive from the methodologic principle of Soviet geography—the discovery of general laws relating to considerable territories through particular (local) manifestations of them and, vice versa, the explanation of the local and particular phenomena by the general tendencies of development. At the same time, Soviet methods of research in economic geography range from direct field observations to the office treatment of comprehensive data obtained from official sources. Inasmuch as both kinds of work are usually done by one and the same collective research team, intermittently with respect to time, wide use is also made, in the course of office work, of all the field materials gathered during expeditions, which greatly expands the possibilities of ascertaining the scientific laws. Let us characterize briefly some methodological procedures of field and office work performed in the course of economic geographic investigations.

Field work includes both economic geography observations during the trip itself and the short stops (or those not caused by the specially set task of studying some point) and work performed at previously designated stations at points requiring a lengthier sojourn. With correct organization of the expedition, travel over an itinerary not only insures the movement of the investigator for work from one place to another, but should itself become a part of his research work, permitting him to make and record observations throughout the itinerary.

It is obvious that at each station there is a possibility of making a considerably more detailed study than during travel, of the complex of natural-geographic conditions and ways of exploiting the natural resources, of interpreting the characteristics of the existing economy, of noting its typical features, etc. Here, the economic geographer is able to penetrate into the essence of each phenomenon and determine the whole multiform of relations between them. But observations at stations always embrace only very small territories, while observations during travel, necessarily much more cursory, have the advantage of covering a considerable area and of permitting one to observe how the phenomena investigated in more detail at the stations are distributed over the territory under study. Hence, observations at stations and in the course of travel should supplement one another mutually. Essentially, this is the application of the principle of "keys" in field work itself. The less inhabited and less economically saturated is the territory under investigation, the greater the significance of such an organization of field work for the integrated economic geographic study of that territory. This procedure is especially important where the economic points, to which stationary observations will most often be confined, are separated from one another by great distances.

While at the stopping points on the itinerary the economic geographer already knows the main questions to be clarified and the process of their clarification is here to a certain degree suggested by the objects of observation and by the relations between the phenomena which are essential for the analysis of those objects, the situation is a different one during the travel sections of the journey. Here, active observation becomes the main method of learning about the territory under study. The circle of phenomena appearing in the field of vision is very great and diversified. Of course, this whole circle must be the object of observation, but in it one has to select the principal things to which attention must be directed. This selection often has to be made on the way and as a result of observations that must not be converted into passive registration of everything that strikes the eye: they must be purposeful observations which repose on an analytic clarification of the mutual relations, and upon the identification of the leading links in these relations. It is for this reason that such observations may be defined as active.

One of the most effective procedures in field work is the compilation of profiles along the itineraries. In their entirety, these profiles covering the territory under study (in accordance with the network of itineraries) permit one to give a sufficiently substantial economic geographic characterization of the whole territory under study, together with detailed descriptions associated with individual populated points and economic units, as well as with the statistical economic materials collected from centralized sources. The pivotal point in this characterization should be occupied by those problems which are topically leading from the viewpoint of the special tasks of the investigation.

Economic geography profiles are usually of two types: one type extends along a strip that is in general fairly uniform with respect to nature and economy (for example, along a river valley); the other type cuts across a territory with sharply differing natural and economic conditions (for example, watershed areas from river to river, considerable elevations of relief, etc.). In the first type, the description along the itinerary loses its profile character to a certain degree and becomes a characterization illustrated by a number of homogeneous and only linearly localized examples. In the second type, the profile method can receive its most vivid expression. The itinerary itself may have, for example, the objective of tracing the change in the features of the economy and population distribution as one moves away from a big city or river, according to a change in the landscape with altitude, and so forth.

Not infrequently, economic geographers are engaged for expeditionary work in sparsely settled or uninhabited regions: for example, in hydro-reclamational surveys and surveys for new railroads. Two questions naturally arise: What should be the field work methods of the economic geographer where there is for the time being still almost no economy? What and how can the economic geographer study here? The tasks facing him may be highly varied, but the central question is that of determining the conditions and prospects for economic exploitation. In so doing, the economic evaluation of those natural resources (for example, mineral wealth) the presence of which makes it advisable to draw the respective territory into economic activity, requires serious specialized explorations. It remains the task of the economic geographer to elucidate the general geographic setting for the settlement, "habitability," and exploitation of the territory containing the resources investigated and evaluated by other specialists. This task is a very important one. After all, even with a preliminary national-economic evaluation of proposals for the exploitation of this or that newly discovered resource, it is essential to have a clear notion of the local conditions which will be encountered in the course of designing and building, and then operation. An integrated economic geographic evaluation of the respective territory with all its auxiliary resources from the angle of the possibilities of locating future settlements, the conditions for road building, the preconditions for the creation of a local agricultural base near the future new construction, the water supply, the availability of building lumber and firewood, the local building materials, etc., is something that only the economic geographer can handle. Such an evaluation can often considerably facilitate the judgment of the real conditions for the utilization of the resources most prominent in the development of this territory.

The situation is a similar one when economic geographers participate in railroad surveys. The justification of a new railroad line is, of course, most often determined by transit considerations lying far beyond the limited territory that can be dealt with in the field work of the economic geographer. Both the course of the line and the whole complex of technical questions connected with the construction conditions, which must always be solved by the designers of railroads, will be determined by means of specialized explorations. But the elucidation of the potential economics of a region to be traversed by a new line requires an integrated economic geographic study of the region, and the treatment of the whole economic geographic setting for the impending settlement of population and for rendering the territory "inhabitable."

In the final analysis, economic geographic field work in sparsely inhabited localities must insure the possibility of a detailed regionalization of the territory under study according to the features of the conditions and methods of exploitation, i.e., for agricultural purposes, according to the circumstances with regard to settlement, road building, and water supply, according to the availability of local building materials, according to the conditions of colonization and inhabitation of the future settlement. Such a regionalization renders much more objective and complete the evaluation and results of specialized explorations. The local resources established by the latter will rest on a definite network of zones and microregions identified by economic geographers, with definite types and conditions of exploitability. Particular questions which can be solved here and which will also be a premise for this unique kind of regionalization will be, for example, the establishment of the general altitudinal-zonal characteristics of the economic activity (which is essential for mountain regions), the ascertainment of the seasonal regime of the economic circumstances in localities of different types, and so forth.

Office work, especially in its concluding stages, must accumulate and generalize all the results of the expeditionary field work and the materials obtained from centralized sources.

Although Soviet economic geographers possess the inestimable advantage that all the data available in the state institutions are accessible to them, it has to be taken into account that these data must be subjected to special treatment (sometimes very considerable) according to the purposes of the investigation. The fact is that the data are usually received in the form of nationwide government statistics and reports, which cannot anticipate the special tasks set in various investigations. One has to make independent groupings, derive relative indices, establish correlative series, etc.

In itself, this treatment represents nothing original; the methods are generally known. The essential thing is that its program is established in accordance with the concrete purpose of a given economic geographic investigation. Thus, if it is aimed at a detailed industrial-economic regionalization, a system of indices is chosen which will give an idea of the decline in "industrial potential" as one moves away from the core of industrial nodes toward their periphery (for example, the per capita volume of industrial production, etc.), and the indices of specialization of industrial production (the proportion of branches with relation to the number of workers, the total production, etc.). To supplement the comprehensive statistical data, information gathered on the spot (including the enterprises) concerning the productional relations and the transportation gravitation of the individual enterprises should be utilized. This makes it possible to refine the outlines of those industrial areas which could be obtained on the basis of the comprehensive statistics alone.

Here the principle of combining the use of centralized materials and those gathered on the spot again comes to the fore. The comprehensive statistics themselves are further subjected to an analysis on the basis of the investigator's personal knowledge of the territory. For example, the statistics often tell the volume of any production as a whole for an administrative rayon, but the investigator knows (from other data or from personal observations) that this production is actually concentrated in one point alone. This gives grounds for not including the whole rayon in the area, but only that part of it in which the production is actually localized, and so forth.

Combination of the analysis of comprehensive statistical materials on agriculture with the data obtained from the study of individual "keys" often enables one to establish a number of agro-economic laws in the course of office work, to note the zones of agricultural specialization, and to justify practical recommendations.

Of especial importance is the mapping of the data obtained. Comparison of specially compiled maps, subsequent analysis of them and the drawing of outlines according to this or that feature on the system of areas (which requires also the working out of legends responding to the tasks of the investigation and the character of the data entered on the maps) are a vital stage of office research work. Soviet economic geographers rightly regard mapping, not as a method of creating illustrations, which may not have to be there, but as a methodical stage of research necessary in almost every study. N. N. Baranskiy, the outstanding Soviet master of methods of economic geographic investigation, writes: "Every geographic investigation proceeds from a map and comes back to the map; it begins with a map and ends with a map.... The map contributes in a high degree to the ascertainment of geographic laws. The larger the scale of the map, the more geographic correlations it allows to be noted on it.... The map is not only an entirely necessary tool of geographic research, but also an indispensable and irreplaceable element of geographic exposition."*

Both for mapping and for the analysis itself of the phenomena studied, it is very essential that the territorial units on which there is information should be as small as possible. As a rule, unless it is a matter of establishing the most general laws, the economic geographer concerned with agricultural

---

*N. N. Baranskiy, "Sketches on the School Methods of Economic Geography" [Ocherki po shkol'noy metodike ekonomicheskoy geografii], 1954, pp. 180-181.

problems is not satisfied with data grouped, for instance, by administrative rayons. He needs statistics by kolkhozes and, in large-scale research, also by individual plots of land of a kolkhoz differing with respect to nature and economy. To obtain such data (at least selectively, in individual "keys"), field work is usually necessary. To a certain extent, field observations can be replaced by analysis of aerial photographs (but with retention of a part of the "keys" investigated in ordinary "ground" work as well). Analysis of air photos is being introduced more and more widely in the USSR into both physical geographic and economic geographic practice. It has also proved very efficient in the analysis of forms of population distribution and in practical work on the problems of regional planning. For these purposes, aerial photographs had been widely used even before the War. Likewise in the solution of problems of the remodeling of the economy in the zones of inundation around the big hydro-stations under construction, office work on the basis of "general" statistics very quickly runs up against the fact that the information on the productional reserves of land in the regions of possible inundation, drawn from the "general" statistics, has no differentiation by altitude, so that office work must invariably be combined with field study on the spot.

The general tendency of the development of the methods of economic geographic research is in the direction of ever-greater intensification of the role of field work. This is also determined by the growing demands upon the scientific level of the work (conclusions based on roughly averaged data are already ceasing to satisfy Soviet economic geographers), and by the increased purposefulness in investigations, which are most often directed at territorially concrete objects. But the growing significance of the investigator's own primary materials "created" directly in the field (instead of ready-made information gathered from official sources) also makes demands upon the office work of economic geographers for further development of its methods, and causes them to strive for more and more refined techniques. Herein lie the moving forces of the improvement of the methods of Soviet economic geographic work in the present stage.

BASIC LITERATURE

Baranskiy, N. N. Economic geography. Economic cartography (*Ekonomicheskaya Geografiya. Ekonomicheskaya Kartografiya*), Moscow, 1956.

Vol'f, M. B., and Klupt, V. S. Inundation in Major Hydro-construction (*Zatopleniye pri Krupnom Gidrostroitel'stve*), Moscow, 1934.

"Town and Rayon as Objects of Geographic Study" (Gorod i Rayon, kak Ob"yekty Geograficheskogo Izucheniya), *Uch. zap. MGPI im. Lenina*, vol. 54, issue I, Moscow, 1947.

Zardalishvili, G. I. Some Questions of Economic Geographic Field Research (*Nekotoryye Voprosy Polevykh Ekonomiko-geograficheskikh Issledovaniy*), Tbilisi, 1953 (in Georgian).

Kovalev, S. A. "An Experiment in the Systematization of Materials for the Characterization of Rural Population Distribution in the Chernozem Center," *Voprosy geografii*, no. 14, Moscow, 1949.

Krylov, N. V. "Methods of Expeditionary Work on the Study of a Territory from the Viewpoint of working out Problems of Agricultural Production," *Materialy k II s"yezdu Geograficheskogo obshchestva SSSR*, Moscow, 1954.

Lavrov, V. I., and Pokshishevskiy, V. V. "Some Methodological Questions of the Conduct of Economic Geographic Field Work and the Compilation of Detailed Regional Characterizations," *Izv..VGO*, 1947, No. 3.

Pokshishevskiy, V. V. "On the Problem of Scales in Economic Geographic Field Work," *Izv. VGO*, 1953, No. 4.

Pokshishevskiy, V. V. "Some Questions of the Content and Methods of Economic Geographic Field Work in Sparsely Inhabited Regions," *Izv. VGO*, 1955, No. 6.

Pomus, M. I. "An Experiment in the Economico Geographic Study of Towns of the USSR," *Izv. AN SSSR, seriya geogr.*, 1958, No. 1.

Rakitnikov, A. N. "On the Methods of Expeditionary Economic Geographic Work," *Izv. AN SSɔR, seriya geogr.*, 1954, No. 1.

Saushkin, Yu. G. "Geographic Study of the Rural Populated Points of the Soviet Union," *Voprosy geografii*, no. 5, Moscow, 1947.

"Handbook of the Traveler and Local-lore Student" (*Spravochnik Puteshestvennika i Krayeveda*), vols. I-II, Moscow, 1949-1950.

Stepanov, P. N. "Methods of Studying an Industrial Enterprise and an Industrial Region," in the book: Stepanov, P. N. Geography of the Industry of the USSR (*Geografiya Promyshlennosti SSSR*), Moscow, 1955.

Khersonskiy, S. A. "Cartographic Work in the Evaluation of Lands," *Voprosy geografii*, no. 43, Moscow, 1958.

Part VI

GEOGRAPHIC EDUCATION AND POPULARIZATION OF SCIENTIFIC GEOGRAPHIC KNOWLEDGE

CHAPTER 45

GEOGRAPHIC EDUCATION IN SECONDARY SCHOOLS

A. I. Solov'yev

Progressive figures in Russian science and culture have always attached great significance to geography as a subject of instruction in the common school. Widely known, for example, are the views concerning the educational significance of geography held by the eminent Russian pedagogue of the 19th century, K. D. Ushinskiy, the great Russian democrats V. G. Belinskiy, N. G. Chernyshevskiy, the writers N. V. Gogol' and L. N. Tolstoy, the renowned surgeon N. I. Pirogov, the well-known geographer D. N. Anuchin, and by many others. All of them saw in primary and secondary geographic education not only an arming of the pupils with knowledge, but also an active means of shaping the realistic world outlook of youth and broadening their horizon, a means of nurturing better qualities in man.

However, the best wishes and endeavors of the progressive figures were slow in penetrating into the pre-revolutionary school, because of the reactionary policy of the Tsarist government. For a long time, geography was taught only in the younger classes of the common school. But even after it had received a considerable place with respect to the total number of hours in the curriculums of the non-classical schools and the boys' classical high schools, it remained primarily a subject of "names." Including primary instruction, geography received 444 hours in the non-classical schools, and 572 hours in the boys' classical schools according to the 1914 curriculum. In the textbooks of Kuznetsov, Lebedev, Smirnov, and Belokha, each class was required to learn ("commit to memory") hundreds of geographic names, which obscured in the minds of the pupils the grains of explanation of geographic phenomena contained in the textbooks.

A certain degree of departure from "name" geography was noted only at the beginning of the 20th century in the textbooks of Lesgaft and Barkov, Grigor'yev, Kruber, and Chefranov, in the 1914 curriculums, and in the resolutions of the first congress of geography teachers (1915). The resolutions, however, were not realized until the October Revolution, and the contemplated tendencies toward improvement of geography teaching were not implemented.

The Communist Party expressed its attitude toward the pre-revolutionary school in the words of V. I. Lenin at the 3rd All-Russian Congress of the Communist Youth League. "In these schools," said Lenin, "the young generation of workers and peasants were not so much educated as trained in the interest of the same bourgeoisie. They were educated in such a way as to create for it suitable servants who would be capable of bringing it profit and at the same time would not disturb its peace and idleness ... The old school was a school of rote, it made the children assimilate a mass of useless, superfluous, dead knowledge that cluttered up their heads and converted the young generation into functionaries all reduced to a common denominator."*

In comparison with the pre-revolutionary school, the new post-revolutionary social conditions of Soviet Russia have cardinally changed the aims, system, and content of general education. By a decree of the Council of People's Commissars dated 13 January, 1918, the church was separated from the state and the school from the church.

The first years of Soviet rule were filled with a search for a more rational system, content, and methodology of teaching in the common school, which became a truly mass school, with free instruction. By the end of the 1920's, the system of common education had been generally defined, but the school still had a number of substantial defects.

In the early 1930's, the Communist Party and Soviet Government undertook further measures for

---

*V. I. Lenin, *Works*, vol. 31, pp. 260-261.

the improvement of popular education. Analyzing the experience in the operation of the schools during the preceding years, the Central Committee of the Communist Party, in a decree of 5 September, 1931, noted that instruction in the schools still "does not provide a sufficient volume of general knowledge and does not solve satisfactorily the task of training for the technical schools [*tekhnikumy*] and for the higher schools fully literate persons who have a good grasp of the fundamentals of the sciences." Among the other educational disciplines, mention was also made here of geography, which was confronted with new tasks. The decree required a clearly defined range of knowledge in the curriculums, the systematic study of it, the liquidation of "fancy methodological planning," etc.

The basic requirements for geography as a subject of instruction were defined in a decree of the Central Committee of the All-Union Communist Party dated 25 August, 1932, "On the Curricula and Routine in the Primary and Secondary Schools." The geography program, it was pointed out therein, "should provide a knowledge of maps, particularly those of the USSR, basic concepts of physical geography, basic elements of the physical, natural, and economic geography of the USSR both as a whole and each of the republics, krays, and oblasts separately; the geography curriculums should also include knowledge of the geography of the capitalist countries in appropriate volume." The execution of these tasks required an intensification of geographic education, expansion of the geography course to include the older classes of the secondary school, elaboration of a clear system of knowledge by classes, a careful selection of the teaching material as fundamentals of science, a deepening of the pupil's knowledge in the field of the geography of the USSR and foreign countries, a clearer subdivision of the teaching material on physical and economic geography (the former was oriented mainly toward the younger, the latter toward the older classes), the simplification of knowledge about maps, the ability to read and understand them, and making the educational material on countries and regions deeper and more concrete. These tendencies were reflcted in the newly established geography programs (1933).

On 16 May, 1934, the Government of the USSR and the Central Committee of the Party adopted a special resolution "On the Teaching of Geography in the Primary and Secondary Schools of the USSR," which noted the most important defects then existing in the teaching of geography in the schools: the abstractness and dryness of the presentation of the subject in the textbooks and in the classroom, the insufficiency of physical geographic material, the poor orientation of the pupils concerning maps, and the overloading of geography teaching and textbooks with economic-statistical material and general diagrams.

To eliminate these shortcomings, the decree provided for the following system of geography teaching: in the primary school (3rd and 4th classes), the imparting of solid knowledge about geographic maps within the limits set by the program, with an intelligible, popular, and entertaining presentation of the educational material and greater use than theretofore of visual aids in teaching; in the 5th class of the secondary school, the teaching of the basic concepts of physical geography at a level accessible for the pupils of that class with respect to their age characteristics; in the 6th class, the teaching of the physical geography of the continents with the addition of basic information about the most important states (political system, national economy); in the 7th class, a general physical geographic survey of the USSR and a survey by republics, krays, and oblasts, with a decisive simplification of the programs and their relief from economic and statistical details; in the 8th class, the economic geography of the USSR with a general survey of the distribution of the productive forces of the USSR, the state of the national economy, and a detailed economic geographic characterization of the country's economic regions; in the 9th class, the economic geography of foreign countries.

To insure the success of the new system of geographic education in the secondary schools, stable textbooks were introduced in 1935, and in the following years readers, methodological aids, bibliographic indexes, and a series of books for home reading by pupils were published to aid the teachers. Numerous school maps, pictures, tables, and later also new school atlases corresponding to the programs and textbooks were issued. The methodologic journal "Geography in the School" [*Geografiya v shkole*] began to be published. The necessary conditions were thus created for setting before teachers and their pupils, and for realizing, the task of "knowing geography very well." The significance of geography as a subject for school instruction which arms the pupil with concrete knowledge, orients him in the geographic laws of nature and the social phenomena, and nurtures a genuinely materialistic world outlook and a feeling of Soviet patriotism and internationalism has been notably enhanced.

The new system of instruction reflected the best experience in geography teaching that had by that time been gained in the mass school, and the necessary conditions for the full realization of progressive tendencies had been assured.

For twenty years, Soviet schools worked with stable geography textbooks: that of N. Ye. Vitkovich for the 4th class, of A. S. Barkov and A. A. Polovinkin for the 5th, of G. I. Ivanov for the 6th, and of S. V. Chefranov for the 7th class. Their basic content and trend was physical geographic. In the 8th class, the textbook on the economic geography of the USSR by N. N. Baranskiy was used; in the 9th, the textbook on the economic geography of foreign countries by I. A. Vitver. The last two books have been awarded Stalin Prizes for their high quality.

But life moves ahead at a strenuous pace and makes ever-new demands upon the instruction and rearing of Soviet youth. The tempestuous development of the national economy of the USSR in the postwar years, the further uplifting of culture, the unparalleled achievement in science, technology, and art, and the nationwide drive toward the construction of communism have predetermined the possibility, and insured the conditions, for such an organization and arrangement of popular education that all young citizens of the USSR without exception may get an education at the level of the eight-year common school and, in the very near future, also a complete secondary education. This poses the task, which is a complex one so far as its realization is concerned, of insuring, in the process of instruction, the possibility of an all-around intellectual and physical development of the pupils without lowering the attained level of general secondary education; of bringing the school still closer to life; of developing and nurturing more and more a love of work in the pupils and inculcating work skills in them; and of providing them with a broad polytechnical horizon which will help to lead them to an intelligent choice of calling in accord with their interests, inclinations, and abilities. In the light of these tasks, especial significance attaches to the combination of instruction with socially useful productive labor.

The urgent need of transforming the schools and altering their course was subjected to nationwide discussion, and in 1958 the Supreme Soviet of the USSR adopted the law "On the Strengthening of the Ties of the School with Life and on the Further Development of the System of Popular Education in the USSR." In accordance with this law, there will exist in the country an eleven-year secondary general education labor polytechnical school with production instruction. The eight-year school, affording pupils solid foundations of common educational and polytechnical knowledge, will be a compulsory labor polytechnical school, giving free instruction to all children. It will instill in the children a love of work and a readiness for socially useful activity and give them a moral, physical, and esthetic training, and will likewise prepare them to continue their secondary education, both general polytechnical and vocational (in the vocational-technical schools, technical high schools [tekhnikumy], etc.).

A system of evening (shift, seasonal, extension) common-education schools is being created for pupils going into production after eight years of schooling, so that they may continue their education. Thus, all young citizens of the USSR are offered the full opportunity of a complete secondary eleven-year education.

A conspicuous place is assigned to geography as a subject of instruction both in the incomplete secondary (eight-year) school and in the eleven-year school, as heretofore. In the draft curriculum of the incomplete secondary (eight-year) school, the introductory (primary) elements of geography are provided in the 4th class according to the program for the natural-science course. A systematic course in geography is given in the 5th to 8th classes to the extent of 286 teaching hours.

Unlike the hitherto effective curriculum, the curricular material on geography is distributed somewhat differently by classes, namely: 5th class and first half of the 6th class, general geography; second half of the 6th and all of the 7th class, geography of the continents; 8th class, geography of the USSR.

A certain lengthening (by a semester) of the general geography course formerly studied in the 5th class has been caused by instructional requirements—to give the best-grasped and most solid possible grounding in general geography, on the basis of which it will be possible to reveal the geographic features and characteristics of the continents as a whole and of individual countries. Fundamentally, the course of the 5th to 8th classes is physical geographic, but contains certain information about population geography and about economic and political geography. In studying this course, the principle of co-ordinating the phenomena studied with the reality surrounding the pupils is strictly observed. The formation of general concepts is built on the foundation of concrete phenomena known to the pupils from everyday observation. By virtue of this principle, acquaintance with "one's own district" is acquiring ever greater significance in teaching practice. The principle of local studies, expanded from class to class—from one's own school and its surroundings to the rayon, the oblast, and the republic—is recognized by teachers as the most reliable support in the formation of general concepts and clear notions. In addition to the visual aids and devices for class work which have been created in the last few decades, the use of a specially equipped outdoor "geographic field station" next to the school also helps a good deal in the development of skills for local studies, and is now being introduced more and more into teaching practice. Obligatory elements provided in this station are a meteorologic station for systematic weather observations by the pupils, elementary devices for observing the movements of the sun, the position of the North Star in the celestial sphere, solar time, a series of measuring devices (meter, etc.), as well as three-dimensional models, for example of a hill, even a high hill, where it is possible to show the vertical belting of the vegetation, a mountain glacier, a river valley with its basic geologic geomorphologic elements, etc. In a word, in the practice of school geography work, the endeavor is felt more and more, in the study of physical geographic phenomena, to start from what is observed in nature, to proceed from "verbal" instruction to live observation and to make wider use of "nature's own laboratory" in the natural setting. This same purpose is served by the subjects of "Our own District" and "Our own Oblast," which have long since been introduced into the program; by the time provided for excursions into nature and to local places of production; by the work with pupils in the summer pioneer camps; by tourism, widely developed in the USSR; and by short- and long-distance hikes for educational purposes.

Of course, the principle of local studies can be carried out more easily while taking the course in general geography (5th-6th classes) and in the geography of the USSR (8th class). As regards the course in the geography of the continents (6th-7th classes), the use of it is extremely limited and is possible only upon acquaintance with new concepts of a general geographic character, inevitably "sprinkled" in the program of the course on the continents.

One of the substantial defects of the previous programs of the seven-year school has been the inadequate attention paid in the course in the geography of the continents to population geography, the elements of ethnology and ethnography, the characteristics of the culture of the various peoples of the globe. In the drafts of the new programs, this defect has been eliminated insofar as the teaching time permits.

The program for the 8th class course—geography of the USSR—, in addition to the study of nature, the processes occurring in it, the inexhaustible natural resources, and the diversity of the country's landscapes from the icy expanses of the Arctic to the subtropics, includes the acquaintance of the pupils, to the extent of their capacity, with the physical geographic conditions of the individual major natural areas of the USSR and an evaluation of their favorable and unfavorable qualities for the economic conquest of the territory. Here, special attention is paid to the expanses of virgin lands now being newly won and to the regions to be won in the near future.

The curricula of the schools of the union republics of the USSR provide for a considerable share of teaching time for the study of nature, population, the main features of the economy of the given republic and the national [= ethnic] characteristics of the culture of its population.

Thus, substantial changes are now being introduced into the teaching of geography in the compulsory incomplete secondary school on the basis of work experience. They reinforce the significance of this educational subject by bringing the school closer to life and strengthening its ties with practice; by nurturing in the pupils a love of work and the understanding of the demands of life, love and respect for the laboring man, a materialistic view of the natural phenomena surrounding them, a striving for the beautiful in nature, in the way of living and culture of men and women, and high personal moral qualities.

There was a certain "concentricity" in the hitherto-existing system of geography instruction. For many youths and girls, education was concluded in the compulsory eight-year school. The curricula of this concentration contained a considerable proportion of economic geographic material difficult for the pupils. Now that the possibility is offered to all to get a full secondary education in this or that type of school (evening, shift, seasonal, without separation from productive work, etc.), the formerly inevitable "concentricity" can be abated to a considerable degree. The more fundamental study of physical geography in the eight-year school makes it possible to lay less stress on the attention of the pupils in the older classes to general geographic concepts and accordingly to strengthen the economic geographic training. In appraising their practical experience, very many teachers express themselves in favor of having the 10th and 11th classes take the economic geography course henceforth in the eleven-year secondary school. The raising of the age level of the pupils will undoubtedly make it possible to make this course more thorough than formerly in the 8th and 9th classes. The new programs now worked out provide for a more fundamental study of the economic geography of foreign countries in the 10th class and the economic geography of the USSR in the 11th class.

It will now be possible, in a definite system, to give the pupils basic economic and, in part, political economic concepts, the principal indices of the economic phenomena and their nature; to reveal more thoroughly the socioeconomic processes manifesting themselves in the system of capitalism and socialism; and to show more clearly the advantages of the socialist system and, in the course in the economic geography of the USSR, to study more fully the structure of the economy of the country as a whole and of its economic regions.

The course in the economic geography of the USSR is of special significance in the system of school geography. It not only gives the pupils concrete knowledge for the understanding of reality, but also prepares them for practical activity. It is, furthermore, a discipline of the polytechnical cycle, revealing the basic technological processes of the principal types of production, and the productional and economic relations between the branches of production and the economic regions.

In order that the pupils may acquire practical skills in the use of economic data, the program of this course includes (a) practical exercises closely connected with the geographic map, (b) economic reference books and other material, both that of significance for local studies and that on a broader plane, (c) excursions to places of production, museums, exhibits of the economic achievements of their own district, rayon, oblast, and republic. In addition, a certain amount of time is assigned in the programs to the subjects of "Our own District," "Our own Oblast," and "Our own Republic." In the schools of the union republics, as has been pointed out, teaching time is furthermore provided for the study of population, economy, and culture of the pupils' own republic. In the 10th class course—the economic geography of foreign countries—attention to the main international events is considerably intensified.

During all the classroom exercises in geography and, to some extent, in the home assignments, the teacher's work is, of course, constantly supported by the geographic map and its study as the most important means of developing "geographic thinking."

From the first to the last year of geography instruction, the Soviet teacher strives to nurture in the pupils proletarian internationalism, respect for people of all races and nationalities, and a profound urge to fight for peace throughout the world.

For the successful teaching of geography and the fulfillment of its educational and training tasks, the school must be assured a supply of qualified teachers. In the USSR, special concern has always been and is now being displayed about this. In the 1930's, there were founded in our country about 70 pedagogic institutes comprising geographic and natural-geographic faculties. (For more details see the following chapter on "Geographic Education in Institutions of Higher Learning.") Nor has the task of training teachers been taken away from the geographic faculties of the universities. In addition to the special chairs of physical and economic geography, chairs of geography-teaching methods have been created in a number of pedagogic institutes. Since 1945, there has existed a laboratory of geography methodology for scientific-research work in the field of methodology in the Institute of Teaching Methods of the Academy of Pedagogic Sciences of the RSFSR. Systematic work is being done by the institutes for the improvement of teachers, assisting pedagogues to master the latest achievements of science and augment their methodological skill. The growth of the scientific qualifications of teachers is also promoted by their identification with the departments of school geography of the Geographic Society of the USSR, by participation in the congresses of this society, in scientific conferences and geographic congresses of the USSR, as well as by participation in teachers' meetings, held regularly twice a year (in January and August) on the spot, by regions or by clusters of several neighboring schools.

The Soviet common school is fully supplied with teachers of geography who possess special scientific and methodological training. This army of teachers is ready to apply all its forces to the very important cause of the remodeling of the secondary school and to the effort to bring it still closer to life and to the demands of the construction of communism in the USSR.

BASIC LITERATURE

Ganelin, Sh. I. "Essays on the History of the Secondary School in Russia" *(Ocherki po Istorii Sredney Shkoly v Rossii)*, Moscow, Uchpedgiz, 1954.

"Law concerning the strengthening of the ties of the school with life and concerning the further development of the system of popular education in the USSR." In the book "Laws of the USSR and decrees of the Supreme Soviet of the USSR" *("Zakony SSSR i Postanovleniya Verkhovnogo Soveta SSSR"). Adopted at the second session of the Supreme Soviet of the USSR, fifth convocation (22-25 December, 1958),* izd-vo "Izvestiya Sovetov deputatov trudyashchikhsya SSSR," Moscow, 1959, pp. 8-28.

Konstantinov, N. A. Essays on the History of the Secondary School *(Ocherki po Istorii Sredney Shkoly)*, Moscow, Uchpedgiz, 1957.

Medynskiy, Ye. N. "Popular Education in the USSR," *(Narodnoye Obrazovaniye v SSSR),* Moscow, izd-vo APN RSFSR, 1952.

Medynskiy, Ye. N. Education in the USSR *(Prosveshcheniye v SSSR),* Moscow, Uchpedgiz, 1955.

Popular Education in the USSR *(Narodnoye Obrazovaniye v SSSR).* Under the ed. of I. A. Kairov, N. K. Goncharov, N. A. Konstantinov, F. F. Korolev, M. P. Malyshev and V. Z. Smirnov, Moscow, izd-vo APN RSFSR, 1957.

"Statute concerning the eight-year school of the RSFSR. Concerning the common labor polytechnical school with productional instruction. Concerning the evening (shift) secondary common school" (Polozheniye o vos'miletney shkole RSFSR. O sredney obshcheobrazovatel'noy trudovoy politekhnicheskoy shkole s proizvodstvennym obucheniyem. O vecherney (smennoy) sredney obshcheobrazovatel'noy shkole,) *Uchitel'skaya gazeta,* August, 1959.

"Curriculums of the eight-year and secondary school of the RSFSR" (Uchebnyye plany vos'miletney i sredney shkoly RSFRS), *Uchitel'skaya gazeta,* No. 103, dated 29 August, 1959.

School Affairs *(Shkolovedeniye).* Under ed. of A. N. Volkovskiy and M. P. Malyshev, Moscow, izd-vo APN RSFSR, 1952.

CHAPTER 46

GEOGRAPHIC EDUCATION IN INSTITUTIONS OF
HIGHER LEARNING

O. A. Konstantinov, V. L. Kotel'nikov, and A. M. Ryabchikov

Special higher training of geographers in the USSR for scientific-productional and pedagogic activity is given, according to data as of 1 January, 1959, in 30 universities (of which five train geographers in day, evening, and extension departments, 18 in day and extension departments, six only in a day department and one only in an extension department), in 62 pedagogic institutes (of which two train geography and biology teachers for the secondary schools in day, evening, and extension departments, 37 in day and extension departments, 15 only in a day department, and eight only in an extension department) and in five engineering institutes. Among the latter are two institutes for engineers in geodesy, aerial photography, and cartography (in Moscow and Novosibirsk), two hydrometeorologic institutes (in Leningrad and Odessa) and the Leningrad higher marine engineering school named for Admiral S. O. Makarov, where hydrology specialists are also trained along with other specialties. In addition, a number of indispensable geographic disciplines are taught in economic, agricultural, forestry, and certain other institutes and faculties.

UNIVERSITIES*

The development of higher geographic education in our country is closely connected with the very large and very old Moscow and Leningrad universities and goes back to the time of the fruitful activity of the great M. V. Lomonosov, founder of Moscow University.

In spite of the fact that Russian science has given birth to eminent geographers, university geography developed feebly in the 19th century. Down to 1884, geography as a general educational discipline was taught in only a few of our universities, principally by professors of physics, history, or law, or by sub-librarians. In 1884, a chair of geography was created in Moscow University, and later in Leningrad, Odessa, and Kazan' universities. In 1912, D. N. Anuchin succeeded in having the specialty of geography instituted at Moscow University.

Although university geography in our country has already passed the two-century mark, its vigorous development is chiefly connected with the last four decades, i.e., with the period of the establishment and development of the Soviet Socialist State. In 1918, the first geographic educational institute in the USSR was founded in Leningrad, being to a certain extent a model for the geographic faculties and departments that followed it in the various universities and pedagogic institutes. The Geographic Institute subsequently became a part of the Leningrad University as a full-fledged faculty.

Of great significance for the development of geography in the institutions of higher learning was the decree of the Central Committee of the Communist Party and Soviet Government dated 16 May, 1934, "On the Teaching of Geography in the Primary and Secondary Schools" (see Chapter 45), after which the bulk of the now-existing geographic faculties and departments were created in the universities and pedagogic institutes. During the whole pre-revolutionary period, Moscow University trained a little more than 100 geography specialists, while during the 40 years of Soviet rule 2,400 persons have received higher geographic education at Moscow University.

In 1958, there were 160 doctors and 1,440 candidates [graduates of a 3-year postgraduate course] of the geographic sciences in the USSR, the larger part of whom (54 per cent) were working in higher educational institutions. Altogether, there were 3,799 scientific workers having geographic qualifications in the USSR, according to data as of 1 October, 1958.

*Written by A. M. Ryabchikov.

The system and organization of higher geographic education in the USSR, the structure of the geographic faculties (staffs of the chairs and laboratories), the list of specialties and specializations, and the makeup of the curricula and programs reflect, in the main, the theoretic concepts of the scientific essence of geography and its place in the economics, science, and culture of the country. However, in some cases the real structure of geographic education differs from the theoretic one. Firstly, the list of geographic specialties and chairs does not exhibit equal completeness in the various universities; secondly, geographic sciences such as soil science and permafrost science and the training of personnel in these specialties are handled almost entirely in the biology-and-soil and geologic faculties alone, not in the geographic faculties.

Of the 39 universities in the USSR, 18 have geographic faculties, five have geologic-geographic faculties and six have natural-science and biologic-geographic faculties, in which geographers are trained in the following specialties: geography (in 24 universities), physical geography (in four universities), economic geography (in four universities), geomorphology (in three universities), cartography (in two universities), hydrology of the land, meteorology, and climatology (in six universities) and oceanology (in two universities). In addition to these specialties, the geographic faculty of Moscow University offers specialized training for paleogeographers, glaciologists, soil-science geographers, biogeographers, and geochemist geographers, and there are also certain regional specializations: the physical geography of the USSR, the economic geography of the USSR, the geography of the polar lands, the physical geography of foreign countries, the economic geography of the countries of the people's democracy, and the economic geography of capitalist and dependent countries (Fig. 37).

The geographic faculty of Leningrad University has almost the same list of specialties, with the exception of soil geography and regional specializations.

The annual admission of geography students to the higher educational institutions is determined by the country's requirements for the respective specialists and, for a given geographic faculty, it also depends upon the existence of this or that chair and the availability of laboratories and qualified teachers.

The training of young geography specialists has until recently lasted five years, and training in the extension and evening departments, six years.

In connection with the law, adopted at the beginning of 1959 by the Supreme Soviet of the USSR, "On the Strengthening of the Ties of the School with Life and the Further Development of the Popular-education System in the USSR," the higher educational institutions are now renovating their curricula with the object of bringing the training of specialists closer to the requirements of economics, science, and culture. In particular, it is proposed to introduce into the curricula protracted work by students in production, for the training of geography specialists in the advanced courses.

In enrolling students in the last few years, preference has been given to those among the winners of passing grades in the competitive entrance examinations who have a labor record of not less than two years in production since graduating from secondary school. Eighty per cent of the places of the acceptance contingent are assigned to persons of this category.

Also contemplated is differentiated training of geographers in universities for subsequent work, principally in the secondary schools, on the one hand, and in scientific-productional organizations, on the other. For this purpose, the new curricula provide for a broader set of geographic specialties and specializations. They will be distinguished by special disciplines in the advanced courses and by the character of the probationary work (schools or scientific-productional organizations). Furthermore, inasmuch as the school year begins on the first of September, geography teachers will have to study five years and finish university on the first of July (vacation in July and August), while geographers specializing in scientific-productional work will have to go through a longer period of practical work and write a diploma thesis based on the primary materials gathered during the probationary work period and then worked up by them personally. The duration of the term of instruction of the second group of geography specialists is to be 5½ years. Graduates will finish the university on the first of January.

Although, as has been noted, the list of geographic specialties and specializations is not the same in the different universities, the system of geographer training, the makeup of the curricula and the programs are in general unified. As an example, let us examine the process of training geographers at

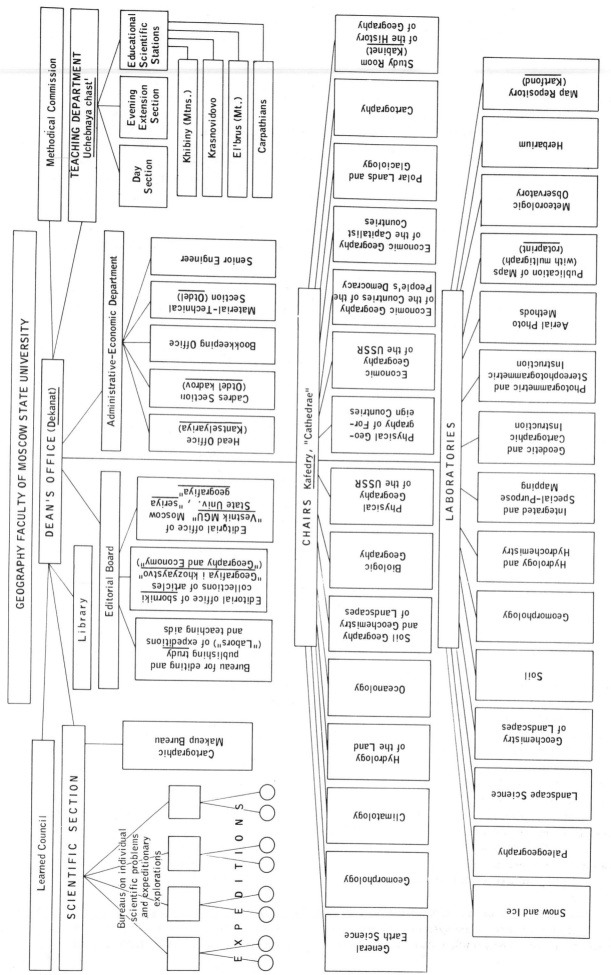

Fig. 37. ORGANIZATION OF THE GEOGRAPHY FACULTY OF MOSCOW STATE UNIVERSITY NAMED FOR M. V. LOMONOSOV

Moscow University, where geography is more broadly represented than in any other higher educational institution of the country.

The *first-year students,* regardless of their specialty, are engaged in one single flow of instruction. In the lessons, seminars, and laboratory work they study general educational and broad geographic disciplines (political economy, introduction to physical and economic geography, fundamentals of biogeography, the history of geographical discoveries and explorations, geodesy, general geology, a foreign language, higher mathematics, physics, and chemistry), which create the necessary foundation for special training. Moreover, much attention is paid to the physical training of the students.

In the *second course,* alongside the general educational and broad geographic disciplines (a foreign language, general geomorphology, meteorology and climatology, general hydrology, the fundamentals of soil science, cartography, the political economy of socialism, the fundamentals of industrial and agricultural production), the students take special geographic courses, supplemented by seminars, which determine their specialization.

In the *third course,* there is a further division of the students by specialties. The number of hours offered for the study of the general educational and integrated geographic disciplines (a foreign language, dialectical and historical materialism, paleogeography, the physical geography of the continents and oceans, and the economic geography of foreign countries) corresponds approximately to the time assigned to special courses and seminars. To supplement the lectures, topical seminars having the object of stimulating the students' activity in independent work are also introduced in addition to the laboratory exercises. In those disciplines which are provided with good textbooks, the lecturer usually does not read all the material in accordance with the program, but only deals with the main problems, sets forth the scientific-methodological principles of study, supplements the textbook with new information, and gives advice on the organization of the student's independent work with the textbooks and supplementary scientific literature. Of course, in the tests and examinations demands are made upon the student's knowledge to the full extent of the program.

In the *fourth course,* only the physical and economic geography of the USSR are retained from among the integrated geographic disciplines taken by students of all specialties, and only the history of the Communist Party of the Soviet Union from among the general educational disciplines. The rest of the time is devoted to a study of the special geographic disciplines. Integrated courses of lectures on the physical and economic geography of the USSR and foreign countries are taken by the students after they have heard a whole series of so-called "underlying" courses: on geology, geomorphology, climatology, hydrology, soil science, biogeography; and, for economic geography, on political economy and the geography of the branches of the national economy. Thus, the special geographic disciplines which form the area of concentration of the future geography specialist are stratified on a solid foundation of general education and broad geographic disciplines.

The *fifth course* is devoted to the study of special disciplines and the writing of the diploma thesis.

Lack of space prevents us from giving a full list of the special subjects in all the specialties. We shall therefore confine ourselves to a few examples.

On the physical geography of the USSR: the geology and tectonics of the USSR; hydrology; geomorphology; the climates, hydrography, soils, and vegetation of the USSR; Quaternary geology and lithology of unconsolidated deposits; the study of landscapes and the geochemistry of landscapes; the interpretation of aerial photographs; reclamation; engineering geographic investigations; methods of physical geographic field research.

On the economic geography of the USSR: economic statistics with the fundamentals of demography; the economic geography of the branches of the national economy; population geography; economic cartography; the fundamentals of economic research and project designing; planning of the national economy; economic regionalization; geography of the world economy; geology of the USSR and minerals. In addition, the students participate in seminars on specific problems (by choice); the geography of agriculture; the geography of industry and construction; transportation geography; population geography; the geography of the structure of an economic region. Let us note that in the case of economic geographers the physical-mathematical disciplines in the earlier courses are studied according to a special program: the fundamentals of mathematical statistics and the physical-chemical fundamentals of modern production.

On cartography: map science; drawing and makeup of maps; compilation and editing of integrated and special-purpose maps; mathematical cartography; photogrammetry; interpretation of aerial photographs; integrated and special mapping under field conditions; publication of maps; ecomonic cartography and economic mapping.

On geomorphology: historical geology; geotectonics and geology of the USSR; the study of facies; Quaternary geology and historical earth science; mineralogy and petrography; glaciology and permafrost science; geomorphology of the USSR; applied geomorphology; geomorphology of the shores and bottom of the sea; runoff and channel processes; geomorphology of foreign countries; methods of geomorphological field exploration and geomorphological mapping; fundamentals of lithology; fundamentals of prospecting for minerals; fundamentals of geologic surveying and the organization of geologic prospecting; engineering geology and hydrogeology; fundamentals of the mechanics of the ground and soil erosion.

On climatology and meteorology: general, dynamic and synoptic meteorology; agrometeorology; aerologic methods of investigating the free atmosphere; general climatology; microclimatology; the climates of the USSR and foreign countries; synoptic, meteorologic, and climatologic practical exercises.

On the hydrology of the land: hydrometry; hydrology of river mouths; limnology; swamp science; hydromechanics and hydraulics; water research; hydrography of the USSR; the study of runoff; hydrogeology; fundamentals of hydrotechnology; hydrologic forecasting; water-economy estimates; hydrochemistry; biohydrology and general oceanology.

Of very great significance in the training of geography specialists is the summer educational and productional practice by the pupils. It serves as a logical continuation and completion of the lectures heard in the auditoriums. The use of "summer semesters" after the first and second years of instruction is one of the most important features of the organiaztion of higher geographic education in the USSR. The students' summer academic practice is conducted under the direction of the teachers at permanent teaching stations (Moscow University, Leningrad University, and others) or at leased bases and on excursions. During this practice, which continues for three months after the first and second courses, the students occupy themselvse with geodesy, geology, geomorphology, hydrology, climatology, botanical geography, zoogeography, as well as with practice in their chosen specialty.

The summer productional practice is done on expeditions or in scientific-productional institutions of the respective qualification range after the 3rd and 4th courses, occupying altogether not less than half a year.

The student's total schooling time, according to the curriculum for the training of geography specialists and not counting independent work, is distributed approximately in the following manner: 20 per cent is assigned to the study of general educational disciplines, 20 per cent to the broad geographic disciplines, 22 per cent to the special geographic disciplines, 32 per cent to educational and productional practice, and 6 per cent to diploma work.

Great significance is attached to the students' independent work with scientific materials. For this purpose, the chairs give the students assignments and subjects for the composition of reports and course studies, and for the preparation of papers to be read in seminars or in the student scientific circle. The students of the advanced courses are assigned a special day in the schedule for independent work, when they are freed from classroom exercises.

In order to stimulate independent work with scientific materials by students, to instill interest and cultivate their inclination to scientific work, the activity of the scientific student societies and circles associated with the different chairs is encouraged in every possible way, and scientific student conferences are held annually. The best scientific studies by students are published.

Thus, the system of geographic education in the geographic faculties of the universities is based on a combination of broad geographic training with specialized training, which makes it possible to satisfy the demands of the national economy and to make a successful contribution to the development of geographic science. Students who have displayed a capacity for scientific work are offered positions in scientific-research institutions. In addition, the learned councils of the faculties recommend students capable of scientific work for retention in postgraduate work with the faculty chairs or in one of the scientific-research institutes, with the object of preparing a dissertation for the acquisition of the degree of candidate of geographic sciences.

As is known, requirements for candidate dissertations in the Soviet Union are about the same as for dissertations for the degree of doctor of philosophy in a number of Western European countries.

Published in full or in part, they are publicly defended at a session of the Learned Council, concerning which due announcement is made in the local newspapers, and not less than 150 copies of the theses (reports) developed in the dissertation are distributed to interested institutions and persons. In addition to two official opponents, anyone present may engage in the debate. Upon termination of the debate, a secret vote is taken by the members of the Larned Council, and if a majority of them evaluate the dissertation affirmatively, the dissertator is awarded the degree of candidate of sciences. In the USSR there also exists the degree of doctor of sciences, which is awarded in an analogous manner to a mature researcher, a candidate of sciences who has a number of published works to his credit, for a published monograph making a great contribution to scientific theory, or for the investigation of an important scientific-productional problem. In addition to the learned degrees, the Learned Councils in the higher educational institutions confer, by secret ballot, the learned title of docent upon experienced candidates of sciences having published scientific works to their credit, and that of professor upon doctors of sciences.

With the object of stimulating scientific growth and attracting talented scholars from elsewhere, particularly from the scientific-production organizations, into scientific institutions and higher educational institutions, contests are announced periodically (every five years) to fill new positions and vacancies. The election following the contest is also done by secret vote of the members of the Learned Councils of the faculties and institutes.

In addition to exercises with the students, the professors, docents, scientific research associates, and assistants of the higher school do a considerable amount of research and scientific-methodological work. In particular, they have written a number of textbooks and teaching aids. The scientific results are published in the non-periodic "Transactions" or in "Learned Notes" of the universities. Moscow and Leningrad universities also publish periodic journals: "Journal [*Vestnik*] of Leningrad University" and "Journal [*Vestnik*] of Moscow University." Along with articles by well-known professors, the most deserving studies by students are also printed in these publications. In addition, the publishing houses of the universities, that of "Soviet Science" [*Sovetskaya Nauka*], the Publishing House of Geographic Literature, the Educational-Pedagogic Publishing House, and the Hydrometeorologic Publishing House issue a considerable number of textbooks and teaching aids.

The list of all the textbooks and teaching aids on the geographic sciences published during the last two decades numbers many dozens of titles, the more so because many universities print a number of teaching aids in small editions, primarily for their own students. For example, the geographic faculty of Moscow University multigraphs annually as many as 200 folio sheets (20 to 30 titles) of teaching aids and scientific works on the main problems of geography.

Although Soviet geography students are adequately supplied with textbooks and teaching aids, a gap is nevertheless felt in the educational literature on the economic geography of the USSR and especially on that of foreign countries. Thus far, our students do not have textbooks on the geomorphology and soils of foreign countries. There is no summary textbook on the physical geography of the continents. In the next few years, it is intended to eliminate this gap. The Leningrad economic geographers have prepared a textbook on the economic geography of foreign countries, and the economic geographers of Moscow University are completing a textbook on the economic geography of the USSR. At the same time, two textbooks are being prepared on the physical geography of the continents: one for the pedagogic institutes, the other for the universities. A textbook is also being written on the soils of foreign countries.

PEDAGOGIC INSTITUTES*

In pre-revolutionary Russia, no geography teachers at all were trained for the secondary school. Not until shortly before the First World War were teachers' institutes and higher women's courses for teacher training opened in some guberniya towns. By 1917 there were 14 such educational institutions for all of Russia. The specialty of "geography" was missing in them. In the classical high schools and elementary schools [*gimnazii* and *progimnazii*] geography was taught either by persons without proper training or by university graduates who know the fundamentals of the science but had not been methodically trained.

The development of school geography was greatly promoted by the better (for that time)

*Written by V. L. Kotel'nikov.

geography textbooks compiled by the teachers of the St. Petersburg *Gimnaziya G. I. Ivanov*. These textbooks, first published in 1902, went through more than 20 editions—a fact which had no precedents in pre-revolutionary Russia. The textbooks by S. Mech, composed in the style of readers also played a positive role, chiefly through development of the method of enlivening the teaching of geography.

Much credit for the popularization of new ideas in geography and in the methods of teaching it belongs to the pupils of D. N. Anuchin (the so-called school of Moscow geographers): A. A. Kruber, A. A. Borzov, S. G. Grigor'yev, A. S. Barkov, and S. V. Chefranov.

In the first decade of Soviet rule, searches were made for new organizational forms of teacher training. But neither were geography teachers trained during this time, because geography was removed as a school subject and dissolved among other subjects. By the end of the 1920's it had become evident that the training of teachers for the secondary schools did not answer the country's requirements either qualitatively or quantitatively. The year 1930 was a turning point in the development of pedagogic education in the USSR. On the basis of the pedagogic faculties at the universities, more than ten specialized pedagogic institutes were created. This was the beginning of a period of vigorous growth of pedagogic personnel for the secondary schools. But even during this time geography still failed to undergo any development owing to the continued undervaluation of this subject.

A decisive role in the development of the Soviet school, including geography as a school subject, was played by the decrees of the Central Committee of the All-Union Communist Party and the Council of People's Commissars of the USSR, dated 5 September, 1931, "On the Primary and Secondary Schools" and that of 25 August, 1932, "On the Educational Programs and Regime in the Primary and Secondary Schools." Geography was restored as an independent subject and occupied its place among the other disciplines. However, the undervaluation of geography was not fully overcome until the decree of the Central Committee of the All-Union Communist Party and the Council of People's Commissars of the USSR, dated 16 May, 1934, "On the Teaching of Geography in the Primary and Secondary Schools." This decree played an exceptional role in the development, not only of geography in school, but also in higher educational institutions and also of scientific-research geography. In all the republics of the Soviet Union, specialized geographic faculties began to be created at the pedagogic institutes in the oblast centers and major cities. The demand for qualified groups of teachers was so great that so-called teacher institutes with a two-year term of instruction were created en masse alongside the pedagogic institutes with a four-year term. Persons graduating from the teacher institutes were permitted to teach in the younger classes of the secondary schools or in the incomplete secondary school. Out of concern for the enhancement of the qualifications of teachers who were already working but did not have sufficient education, evening and extension departments were organized in accordance with a decision of the Soviet Government for various specialties at the pedagogic institutes.

An idea of the rate of training of geography teachers in the USSR is given by the table compiled from archive materials of the Ministry of Education of the RSFSR and the Ministry of Higher Education of the USSR (Table 1).

Table 1. Number of Departments of Geography in Pedagogical Institutes in the USSR, 1932-1950

	1932	1933	1934	1935	1936	1937	1938	1939	1940	1950
Separate geography faculties	2	7	14	24	32	37	40	48	50	61
Combined naturalist-geography departments	—	6	13	20	28	31	36	45	59	149

The number of specialists graduated by the institutes has also grown accordingly. The first graduates of the 1933/34 school year numbered only a few tens of teachers. But already in 1937, 1,306 persons completed the course of instruction in the geography faculties. In addition, 31 naturalist-geography departments, teaching 2,660 students, were functioning in the teachers' institutes. Three years later, at the beginning of the Great Patriotic War, there were 50 geography faculties in the pedagogic institutes, with 4,950 students in them, of whom 1,517 graduated. About 5,000 persons were being taught in the 59 naturalist-geography departments in the teachers' institutes. Furthermore, extension instruction was being widely practiced.

The chief methodological problem of those times was the improvement of the system of geographic education in the pedagogic institutes. There was no experience. For a long time, the curricula of the geographic faculties of the universities were copied in spite of the differences in the type of the specialists to be trained. The chief trouble with the curricula was their great number of subjects, in which the specialized courses "drowned." The most important aspect of the teacher's training—the methodology of geography instruction—penetrated slowly and only with great difficulty into the geographic faculties.

Through the efforts of outstanding pedagogues and geographers, organizers and old heads of the chairs of the geographic faculty of the Moscow State Pedagogic Institute named for V. I. Lenin— N. N. Baranskiy and A. S. Barkov—and of one of the heads of the geographic faculty of Moscow City Pedagogic Institute named for V. P. Potemkin—A. A. Borzov—, the specialization of students of the geographic faculties in the pedagogic institutes was defined with sufficient clarity after repeated changes in the curriculum. Later, the curricula were merely refined, and improvements were made in the arrangement of this or that course and in the whole pedagogic process.

The prewar period was marked by important achievements in the training of highly qualified geography teachers: production practice was instituted directly in the schools, methods were worked out for summer field practice by geography students, good textbooks and teaching aids were created on a number of school disciplines. Among the textbooks, those by Academician L. S. Berg, *Natural Regions of the USSR [Priroda SSSR]* and "Geographic Zones of the Soviet Union" [*Geograficheskiye Zony Sovetskogo Soyuza*] have occupied a prominent place.

Durting the Great Patriotic War, teacher training was greatly curtailed because many institutes in the theater of military action and in the regions temporarily occupied by the enemy did not operate. On the other hand, in the eastern regions of the country, new pedagogic institutes were opened even in the war years, and in them were five geographic faculties and 16 geography-science departments in the teachers' institutes. In that same difficult period, the Government in 1943 permitted the organization of special chairs of methodology of geography teaching at the major geographic faculties of the pedagogic institutes of Moscow, Leningrad, and other cities.

The postwar period has been characterized by the broad development of teachers' institutes. Thus, from 1944 to 1950, six new geographic faculties were opened with a four-year term of instruction, and four naturalist-geographic departments with a two-year term. The country required that the war-disturbed balance between the demand for teachers and the possibility of satisfying that demand be restored in the shortest possible time. It was for this reason that both evening and extension instruction assumed hitherto unknown proportions.

In the 1955/56 school year a new stage began in the system of training geography teachers. By this time the secondary schools throughout the country had in the main been fully provided with geography instructors. The incomplete secondary schools, located principally in small populated points (in villages, sovkhozes, and other settlements), continued to experience a lack of teachers with higher education. But these schools, owing to the small number of pupils, could not provide full-time jobs for teachers of certain subjects, including geography. At the initiative of the geographic faculty of Moscow Pedagogic Institute named for V. I. Lenin, a way out of this situation was found. It was proposed that the whole system of higher pedagogic education be altered in the direction of training teachers in accordance with a so-called broad profile. The teachers' institutes with a two-year term of instruction were found to be unnecessary under the established conditions and were either converted en masse into pedagogic institutes or were closed. By the beginning of the 1958/59 school year, there remained only two of them in the whole Soviet Union: in Vil'nyus (Lithuanian SSR) and in Krasnoyarsk (RSFSR).

What constitutes a "broad profile"? It means training the teacher not in one specialty, as was the case heretofore, but in two (in certain cases even three). At present there are 208 pedagogic institutes in the USSR, including one evening institute, four extension institutes, and two teachers' institutes. Only three geography faculties of the former type (with the narrow specialization of geography) have remained. Fifty-eight of the former geography faculties have been converted into geography-biology faculties. At 43 of them, geography and biology teachers are trained; at 15, teachers of geography, biology, and the fundamentals of agriculture. In addition, the students at four geographic faculties have a supplementary specialization in history. The large network of geographic extension faculties continues to exist.

In the next few years, the number of geography faculties is to be reduced by four units: 60 of them will remain, with an annual acceptance of 4,000 persons. In addition, 31 geography faculties giving extension instruction will function with an annual admission of 17,000.

Curricula of a new type, differing greatly from those of former years, have been worked out for training broad-profile specialists. From now on, there will be five years of instruction in the pedagogic institutes instead of the former four-year term. Thirty-six subjects are included in the compulsory minimum of disciplines studied, being distributed by groups as shown in the following Table 2:

Names of groups of disciplines	Number of subjects	Number of hours		
		Lectures	Practical exercises	Production practice
General historical	3	280	230	——
General educational	3	——	328	——
Pedagogic (including methodology)	8	286	282	1,050
Biologic	11	736	722	704
Geographic	11	953	545	640
Total	36	2,255	2,107	2,394

The principal achievement of the new system of training is undoubtedly the inclusion in geographic education of a large group of disciplines of the biologic cycle, which will certainly have a positive effect on the quality of geography teacher training. Another important achievement of the new curriculum is the large proportion of production practice, occupying 35.4 per cent of the whole instruction time. The significance of production practice is also increased by the fact that the geography and biology teacher is charged with promoting the polytechnical education of the rising generation, a task of exceptional importance and responsibility.

The newly created geography-biology faculties are now confronted by two very important tasks. The first is the compilation of textbooks, teaching aids, practical exercises in laboratory work, seminar and practical exercises in application to broad-profile instructions. The second task is the working out of methods of geography and biology teaching in the secondary schools of the new type, based on the polytechnical system of instruction. Work on these tasks has already been commenced

Now, in the period of the evolved construction of communism in our country, life has confronted the school in general and school geography in particular with truly grandiose tasks. The corps of instructors in the pedagogic higher educational institutions understand these tasks and are adopting all measures to execute them successfully.

ECONOMIC AND OTHER HIGHER EDUCATIONAL INSTITUTIONS*

Economic geography is the most widespread geographic discipline in the higher educational institutions of the Soviet Union. It is taught in the geographic (geology-geography, naturalist-geography, etc.) faculties of the universities and pedagogic institutes, and at all the economic and engineering-economic institutes, in all the economic and engineering-economic faculties and in many special higher educational institutions (party, transportation, etc.). Outside the system of higher geographic education, economic geography is studied in more than a hundred higher educational institutions, so that the total number of higher educational institutions of the Soviet Union whose curricula include economic geography amounts to more than two hundred.

In the geographic faculties, economic geography, as a rule one of the specialized sciences, is usually divided into a number of subjects. Thus, the geography of industry, agriculture, and transportation, population geography, and special courses in individual regions are often detached from the economic geography of the USSR. The economic geography of foreign countries is divided into the ecoonmic geography of the countries of the people's democracy and the countries of capitalism, etc. These economic geographic disciplines are studied principally in the advanced

*Written by O. A. Konstantinov.

courses and, consequently, are preceded by a number of physical geographic and humanistic disciplines. In the other higher educational institutions, economic geography figures as a general scientific discipline (like the history of the national economy, the general theory of statistics, etc.). Hence, it is taught in the first or in the first and second years. The larger part of the time assigned by the curriculum to economic geography is naturally devoted to a study of the Soviet Union. In some cases, the economic geography of foreign countries, because of the strain on the curriculum, is not studied at all or is optional. In courses in the economic geography of the USSR, the main attention (usually up to 70 per cent of the time) is devoted to the economic regions and republics. In specialized higher educational institutions, it is sometimes advisable to reduce the regional section somewhat and to enlarge the topical section at its expense. Some specialized higher educational institutions, in addition to the economic geography of the USSR as a general scientific discipline, include in the curriculum supplementary study of the geography of the given topic (for example, the geography of water transportation, etc.). Such disciplines are already of a special character and are studied in one of the advanced courses.

There are not a few special characteristics in the teaching of economic geography as a general scientific discipline. The study of political economy, the history of the national economy, and certain other economic disciplines do not precede economic geography, but run parallel with it. Hence, in giving instruction in economic geography, only partial use can be made of the knowledge gained on these subjects. At the same time, economic geography must prepare the student to take a number of special subjects to be studied later, such as specialized economics, national-economic planning, economic statistics, etc. Economic geography should afford an understanding of such economic phenomena and processes as the geographic division of labor, economic regionalization, territorial-productional complexes, etc. Students undertake the study of economic geography with the knowledge of physical geography that they received in the secondary school some years before; usually, this knowledge has already been forgotten to some extent. Economic geography is confronted with the task of restoring this knowledge and reinforcing it in some part and, above all, of teaching the students to give an economic evaluation to physical geographic conditions. An understanding of the laws of the distribution of production under socialism and under capitalism and of the manifestations of those laws in the individual countries and regions is acquired on the basis of a study of a large amount of factual material.

Economic geography is of great significance for the political education of the student. It teaches the distribution of production in the USSR and other countries from Marxist-Leninist standpoints. In the course in the economic geography of the USSR, it is very important to show how the economic policy of the Communist Party and Soviet Government, single for the whole country, has been and is being conducted in the individual regions and republics, with consideration for local conditions. V. I. Lenin repeatedly warned against the stereotype, against the mechanical transfer of the experience of the central regions to the margins, against the ignoring of local characteristics. It is necessary for students to understand well and feel deeply this Lenin principle of taking into account the diversity of conditions in the various regions of the USSR, so that, in their further work, they may be able, in application to the local (natural, historical, ethnical, etc.) characteristics, to carry out correctly and flexibly a single economic policy for the whole country.

Of great significance in the course in USSR economic geography is the study of the national-economic plans (especially their territorial cross section), and of the decisions of the higher governmental and party organs on questions of the distribution of production in the USSR. As noted in Chapter 5, the large amount of work in the field of economic geography accomplished by the numerous groups of scientists and practical workers receives its generalization in these decisions. These documents contain not only the latest report and prospective data, but also important economic geographic ideas in which the future economists and other specialists must be trained. The use of these documents is necessary for the further reason that the textbooks, statistical handbooks, and other educational aids are to some degree lagging behind life even at the moment they come off the press, in view of the rapid rate of development of our national economy.

The study of the economic geography of foreign countries brings out the radical differences in the laws of the distribution of production under capitalism and under socialism and the characteristics of the manifestation of these laws according to the concrete conditions of this or that country.

Just as in scientific work, generalization is of exceptional importance in teaching economic geography. In order to avoid being captivated by mere facts or, on the contrary, by general considerations not reposing on precise data, it is necessary (on the basis of a profound scientific study) to generalize the factual material and to deduce the most typical features of a given country, region, or city.

The sources for the study of economic geography are the works of the classicists of Marxism-Leninism, national-economic plans, governmental and party documents, textbooks, monographs on countries and regions, separate articles, statistical collections, as well as various maps and atlases. Many higher educational institutions publish (in multigraphed, offset, or duly printed form) separate lectures, parts of courses, methodological guides, and other teaching aids which are especially important for extension students. Great attention is paid to the use of maps and atlases. Systematic work with maps and a good knowledge of them are indispensable conditions for the successful mastery of economic geography as, indeed, they are for any other geographic discipline.

BASIC TEXTBOOKS AND TEACHING AIDS ON GEOGRAPHIC DISCIPLINES

Alekhin, V. V., Kudryashv, L. V., and Govorukhin, V. S. The Geography of Plants with Fundamentals of Botany (*Geografiya Rasteniy s Osnovami Botaniki*), Moscow, Uchpedgiz, 1957.

Alekhin, V. V. The Vegetation of the USSR in the Main Zones (*Rastitel'nost' SSSR v Osnovnykh Zonakh*), 11th ed., Moscow, "Sovetskaya nauka," 1951.

Alisov, B. P. Climatic Areas of Foreign Countries" (*Klimaticheskiye Oblasti Zarubezhnykh Stran*), Moscow, Geografgiz, 1950.

Alisov, B. P. The Climate of the USSR (*Klimat SSSR*), Moscow, izd-vo MGO, 1956.

Alisov, B. P., Drozdov, O. A., and Rubinshteyn, Ye. S. Course in Climatology (*Kurs Klimatologii*), parts I and II, Gidrometeoizdat, 1952.

Alisov, B. P., Berlin, I. A., and Mikhel', V. M. Course in Climatology, part III. Climates of the globe by countries (*Klimaty Zemnogo Shara po Stranam*) Leningrad, Gidrometeoizdat, 1954.

Apollov, B. A. The Study of Rivers" (*Ucheniye o Rekakh*), izd-vo MGU, 1952.

Armand, D. L., Dobrynin, B. F., Yefremov, G. K., Ziman, L. Ya., Murzayev, E. M., and Sprygina, L. I. Foreign Asia (*Zarubezhnaya Aziya*), Uchpedgiz, 1956.

Barkov, A. S. *Afrika*. Uchpedgiz, 1953.

Berg, L. S. Fundamentals of Climatology (*Osnovy Klimatologii*), 2nd ed., Leningrad, Uchpedgiz, 1938.

Berg, L. S. The Geographic Zones of the Soviet Union (*Geograficheskiye Zony Sovetskogo Soyuza*), Moscow, Geografgiz, vols. I and II, 1952.

Berg, L. S. Nature in the USSR (*Priroda SSSR*), 3rd ed., Moscow, Geografgiz, 1955. [Also published in English as *Natural Regions of the USSR*. Translated by Olga Adler Titelbaum. Edited by John A. Morrison and C. C. Nikiforoff. New York, Macmillan, 1950.]

Bliznyak, Ye. V. Water Investigations (*Vodnyye Issledovaniya*), 5th ed., revised and enlarged, Moscow, Rechizdat, 1952.

Bobrinskiy, N. A. The Geography of Animals (*Geografiya Zhivotnykh*), Moscow, Uchpedgiz, 1951.

Breyterman, A. D. Economic Geography of the USSR (*Ekonomicheskaya Geografiya SSSR*), part I, Geography of Heavy Industry (*Geografiya Tyazheloy Promyshlennosti*) Leningr. inzh.-ekonom. in-t, izd. LGU, 1958.

Bykov, V. D. Hydrometry (*Gidrometriya*), Leningrad, Gidrometeoizdat, 1949.

Vilenski, D. G. Soil Science (*Pochvovedeniye*), 3rd ed., Moscow, Uchpedgiz, 1957. (English translation: D. G. Vilenskii. *Soil Science*, third enlarged edition, published for the National Science Foundation, Washington, D. C. and the U. S. Department of Agriculture, by the Israel Program for Scientific Translations, 1960. Available from the Office of Technical Services, U. S. Department of Commerce, Washington 25, D. C.).

Vol'pe, V. M., and Klupt, V. S. Lectures on the Economic Geography of the USSR (*Lektsii po Ekonomicheskoy Geografii SSSR*), part I, Leningr. fin.-ekonom. in-t, izd. LGU, 1957.

Gvozdetskiy, N. A. Karst. Questions of General and Regional Karst Science (*Karst. Voprosy Obshchego i Regional'nogo Karstovedeniya*), 2nd ed., revised and enlarged, Moscow, Geografgiz, 1954.

Gvozdetskiy, N. A. Physical Geography of the Caucasus (*Fizicheskaya Geografiya Kavkaza*), a course of lectures, issues 1-2, Moscow, izd-vo MGU, 1954-1958.

Gerasimov, I. P., and Markov, K. K. Quaternary Geology (Paleogeography of the Quaternary Period) (*Chetvertichnaya Geologiya Paleogeografiya CHetvertichnogo Perioda*), Uchpedgiz, 1939.

Glazovskaya, M. A. A Soil-geography Sketch of Australia (*Pochvenno-geograficheskiy ocherk Avstralii*), Moscow, Geografgiz, 1952.

Davydov, L. K. Hydrography of the USSR (*Gidrografiya SSSR*), part I, 1953, part II, 1955, Leningrad, Gidrometeoizdat.

Davydov, L. K., and Konkina, N. G. General Hydrology (*Obshchaya Gidrologiya*), Leningrad, Gidrometeoizdat, 1958.

Dobrynin, B. F. Physical Geography of Western Europe (*Fizicheskaya Geografiya Zapadnoy Yevropy*). Teaching aid for the geography faculties of state universities and pedagogical institutes, Moscow, Uchpedgiz, 1948.

Dobrynin, B. F. Physical geography of the USSR. European part and the Caucasus (*Fizicheskaya Geografiya SSSR. Yevropeyskaya Chast' i Kavkaz*). Textbook, 2nd ed., Moscow, Uchpedgiz, 1948.

Zubov, N. N. Sea Water and Ice (*Morskiye Vody i L'dy*). Teaching aid for the hydrometeorologic *vuzy*, Moscow, Gidrometeoizdat, 1938.

Zubov, N. N. Dynamic Oceanology (*Dinamicheskaya Okeanologiya*), Leningrad, Gidrometeoizdat, 1947.

Il'inskiy, A. P. The Vegetation of the Globe (*Rastitel'nost' Zemnogo Shara*), Moscow-Leningrad, 1937.

Kalesnik, S. V. General Glaciology (*Obshchaya Glyatsiologiya*). Teaching aid for universities and pedagogical institutes, Leningrad, Uchpedgiz, Leningr. otd., 1939.

Kalesnik, S. V. Fundamentals of General Geography *(Osnovy Obshchego Zemlevedeniya)*, 2nd ed., Uchpedgiz, 1955.

Kalesnik, S. V. Short Course in General Geography *(Kratkiy Kurs Obshchego Zemlevedeniya)*, Geografgiz, 1957.

Karandeyeva, M. V. Geomorphology of the European part of the USSR *(Geomorfologiya Yevropeyskoy Chasti SSSR)*, Moscow, izd-vo MGU, 1958.

Lavrenko, Ye. M. The Plant Cover of the USSR *(Rastitel'nyy Pokrov SSSR)*. Explanatory text to the 1:4,000,000 geobotanical map of the USSR, Moscow-Leningrad, izd-vo AN SSSR, 1956.

Leont'yev, O. K. The Geomorphology of the Sea Shores and Bottom *(Geomorfologiya Morskikh Beregov i Dna)*, Moscow, izd-vo MGU, 1955.

Lukashova, Ye. N. South America *(Yuzhnaya Amerika)*, Moscow, Uchpedgiz, 1958.

L'vovich, M. I. The Elements of the Water Regime of the Rivers of the Globe *(Elementy Vodnogo Rezhima Rek Zemnogo Shara)*, Sverdlovsk-Moscow, Gidrometeoizdat, 1945.

Markov, K. K. The Basic Problems of Geomorphology *(Osnovnyye Problemy Geomorfologii)*, Moscow, Geografgiz, 1948.

Makkaveyev, N. I. The Channel of a River and the Erosion in its Bed *(Ruslo Reki i Eroziya v yeye Basseyne)*, izd-vo AN SSSR, 1955.

Magidovich, I. P. Essays on the History of Geographic Discoveries *(Ocherki po Istorii Geograficheskikh Otkrytiy)*, 2nd ed., Uchpedgiz, Moscow, 1957.

Perel'man, A. I. Essays on the Geochemistry of Landscapes *(Ocherki Geokhimii Landshaftov)*, Moscow, Geografgiz, 1955.

Ramenskiy, L. G. Introduction to the Integrated Soil-geobotanical Investigation of Lands *(Vvedeniye v Kompleksnoye Pochvenno-geobotanicheskoys Issledovaniye Zemel')*, Moscow, Sel'khozgiz, 1938.

Rode, A. A. Soil Science *(Pochvovedeniye)*, Moscow-Leningrad, Goslesbumizdat, 1955.

Salishchev, K. A., and Gedymin, A. V. Cartography *(Kartografiya)*, Geografgiz, 1955.

Saushkin, Yu. G. Introduction to Economic Geography *(Vvedeniye v Ekonomicheskuyu Geografiyu)*, Moscow, izd-vo MGU, 1958.

Spiridonov, A. I. Geomorphological Mapping *(Geomorfologicheskoye Kartografirovaniye)*, Moscow, Geografgiz, 1952.

Stepanov, P. N. Geography of the Industry of the USSR *(Geografiya Promyshlennosti SSSR)*, 2nd ed., Moscow, Uchpedgiz, 1955.

Sumgin, M. I., and others. "General Permafrost Science" *(Obshcheye Merzlotovedeniye)*, Moscow-Leningrad, 1940.

Suslov, S. P. Physical Geography of the USSR. Asiatic Part. *(Fizicheskaya Geografiya SSR. Aziatskaya Chast')*, Moscow, Uchpedgiz, 1954. (English translation: S. P. Suslov: *Physical Geography of Asiatic Russia*. Translated by Noah D. Gershevsky and edited by Joseph E. Williams. San Francisco: W. H. Freeman and Co., 1961).

Khromov, S. P. Fundamentals of Synoptic Meteorology *(Osnovy Sinopticheskoy Meteorologii)*, Leningrad, Gidrometeoizdat, 1948.

Cherdantsev, G. N., and others. Economic Geography of the USSR *(Ekonomicheskaya Geografiya SSSR)*, 3 volumes, Moscow, Uchpedgiz, 1956, 1957, 1958.

Shokal'skiy, Yu. M. Oceanography *(Okeanografiya)*, 2nd ed., Leningrad, Gidrometeoizdat, 1959.

Shchukin, I. S. General Morphology of the Land *(Obshchaya Morfologiya Sushi)*, vols. 1-2, Moscow, Gornefteizdat, 1933, 1938.

Edel'shteyn, Ya. S. Fundamentals of geomorphology. Short course *(Osnovy Geomorfologii. Kratkiy Kurs)*, 2nd ed., 1947.

CHAPTER 47

LOCAL STUDIES AND GEOGRAPHY

Yu. K. Yefremov

The term *krayevedeniye* [local studies, home-district lore, "Heimatkunde," or literally, "Landeskunde"] has several meanings. Some geographers understand by it the large-scale geography of small areas and contrast it to *stranovedeniye* [regional geography or "Länderkunde"] as the knowledge of extensive territories on a smaller scale and to *zemlevedeniye* [general geography or "Erdkunde"] as the knowledge of the earth as a whole. More widespread is the understanding of *krayevedeniye* as the all-around study of a limited territory by independently acting local forces. Finally, in the broadest sense of the word, *krayevedeniye* is a whole social movement, uniting any forces (local inhabitants and newcomers, specialists and dilettantes, children and adults) in the study of a given district [*kray*]. In this case, usually no rigid boundaries are drawn to fix the size of the territory subject to study: the object of *krayevedeniye* may be either a separate populated point with its surroundings, or any administrative unit (rayon, okrug, or oblast), or even a whole republic, though usually not a large one in area. In the latter case, the boundary between *krayevedeniye* and *stranovedeniye* becomes effaced.

Krayevedeniye studies the nature, economy, and population of specific territories. But the interests of the *krayevedy* [home-lore students] reach in a number of directions beyond the direct interests of the geographer; for example, into culture, history, and archeology, into the study of folklore, etc. It is no accident, therefore, that, alongside integrated geographic local studies, one also speaks of historical, archeologic, ethnographic and other kinds of local studies.

In Soviet local studies, several basic organizational forms have become established. One of them is the association of home-lore students and voluntary societies, circles, and sections: the so-called social home-lore study. The second form is local studies practiced by children and youth, usually united under the name of school home-lore study, although extracurricular forms of work are also widely employed in it. The third form is local studies which are connected with the activity of the state home-lore museums, that is, museum local studies. Actually, this is the most widespread form of a broader state home-lore study, which, in addition to museums, is represented by special home-lore institutes, libraries, and local scientific-research institutions. State home-lore study is also carried on by the employees of many local official agencies—by economists, statisticians, land organizers, agronomists and reclamationists, foresters, meteorologists, hydrologists, geologists, and by many others.

The tasks of the Soviet home-lore students were formulated about thirty years ago in a special governmental act, as follows:

"The study of the productive forces and natural wealth of the country, the search for additional local resources capable of being exploited in the interest of socialist construction and the acceleration of the cultural growth of the country."[*]

Indeed, home-lore study, in addition to its great educational significance, exercises a positive influence on the development of the economy and stimulates the activity of the broad popular masses, mobilizing their attention to the expansion of our knowledge of the natural resources and to the search for rational ways of exploiting, conserving, and enriching them. Many thousands of the mineral deposits now under exploitation were discovered by home-lore students or with their co-operation. Hundreds of useful plants are known whose curative or industrially important properties were discovered by home-lore students.

The work of Soviet home-lore students proceeds in close co-ordination with the general tasks

---

[*]Decree of the Council of People's Commissars of the RSFSR dated 30 March, 1931. *Sobraniye uzakoneniy i rasporyazheniy Raboche-Krest'yanst'yanskogo Pravitel'stva RSFSR,* 1931, No. 16, p. 185.

confronting the planning, economic, cultural-enlightenment, educational, and scientific institutions. The home-lore students are worthy participants in the fulfillment of the seven-year plan for the development of the USSR national economy, actively collaborating in the construction of a communist society.

Before the Great October Socialist Revolution, social home-lore study was represented in Russia by only 160 amateur societies, totaling about 15,000 members. After 1917, the vigorous growth of home-lore organizations began, and by 1930 their number had already surpassed 2,000. A special form of home-lore study were mass hikes for the study of the country's natural wealth under the first five-year plans (1928-1941). Similar hikes on a mass scale are now organized in Siberia. Many thousands of persons take part in such walking tours, and their activity has resulted in obtaining information about new mineral deposits, the habitats of useful plants, etc. During the Great Patriotic War (1941-1945), home-lore students substantially aided in finding additional medicinal plant resources for public health needs.

Since the War, the tasks of social home-lore study have grown especially in connection with remodeling the administration of industry and construction effected in the USSR, with the movement of economic management nearer to the localities concerned, and with the enhancement of the role of prospective planning on the spot. The regional national-economy councils [sovnarkhozy] as well as the republic, kray, and oblast planning organizations, are beginning to see in home-lore students their closest advisers and helpers, and with their co-operation are becoming more fully acquainted with the history of the economy of the region, with the integrated geographic characteristics of the natural conditions, with ways of exploiting the resources, with the natural and cultural-historical objects to be conserved, with the methods of insuring an expanded reproduction of the replenishable natural wealth, etc.

Home-lore students can be used not only as consultants, but also as social inspectors who exercise supervision over the natural appearance of the territory as a whole, over the observance of the norms of economic exploitation of the resources, and over the progress of preserving the monuments of nature, culture, and antiquity.

The cultural-enlightenment role of home-lore societies is very great. Lectures and excursions, articles in the press and publication of books and guides, radio and television broadcasts on home-lore subjects enlarge the geographic horizon of the people, acquaint the inhabitants with the history and wealth of their native district, teach them methods of conservation and rational exploitation and contribute to the nurturing of local patriotism as an integral part of socialist patriotism—love for the native land as a whole.

Considerable aid in organizing and strengthening the home-lore movement is given by the Geographic Society of the USSR and its numerous branches, departments, and cells in the various cities of the USSR.

School home-lore study is destined to contribute to the study of their native district by children and youth, above all in the course of their instruction in geography and history, as well as in natural science and a number of disciplines connected with the study of local lines of production (physics, chemistry). School excursions, the gathering of scientific collections, drawing and photographing—all help to enliven instruction and implant knowledge firmly in the pupils' minds. Home-lore study is the school's big window on life, one of the excellent forms of acquainting students with the demands of practical life, and an important means of polytechnicizing school instruction.

Like social home-lore study, school home-lore study is of great significance for upbringing. "The nurturing of patriotism begins with a thorough knowledge of one's homeland," said M. I. Kalinin.

No less important are the forms of extracurricular home-lore work with children and youths—home-lore circles, hikes, and excursions. Their staffs are organized not only in the schools, but also in the homes of pioneers and in the youth sections of the various clubs and palaces of culture.

An especially wide range of extracurricular home-lore study has been attained in the course of the activity of the All-Union Expedition of Pioneers and School Children, which has now operated for several years and counts tens of thousands of detachments; it unites about 10 million young home-lore students. The methodical guidance of this expedition is accomplished by a system of children's excursion and tourism stations with its central staff in Moscow. Using the vacation periods for their tours, young home-lore students travel on foot or on skis, ride bicycles or travel in boats for hundreds of kilometers and not only acquire the skills of outdoor life, of making collections and field observations but also carry out independent investigations. Not infrequently, these investigations terminate in practically valuable finds and discoveries; the youthful home-lore students enrich the museums and study rooms with their collections, organize exhibitions, and write interesting reports on what they have seen. From these young boys and girls often develop natural-science specialists enamored of their subject—geographers, geologists, botanists, zoologists, as well as historians, and collectors of folklore.

No small role, both as to upbringing and with respect to the economy, is played by the socially useful work performed incidentally by the youthful home-lore students. For example, they gather the seeds of wild plants, care for forest stands, and participate in the supervision of nature conservation. The youthful home-lore students also act as a cultural force and as propagandists of the ideas of nature conservation, as the preservers of traditions and the cultural and historical heritage of their district.

Still more fruitful is the activity of adult home-lore tourists. From among the tourists who have fallen in love with, and who have systematically visited some region are formed *krayevedy* who sometimes are not inferior to the local inhabitants, and occasionally even surpass them in the fullness and depth of their knowledge of the geography of a district. Also important here are the direct contributions by tourists to science and economy (finds, discoveries), and the role of tourists as propagandists of the ideas of conserving and enriching nature, and of respect for the monuments of culture and antiquity.

Home-lore museums, in the aggregate, form a whole network of special state institutions which in many cases have become the centers of attraction for all home-lore work in a given city, rayon, oblast, or kray. In the museums is concentrated and generalized the scientific-methodical work on the local studies of the respective territories, and around the museums is grouped the active force of students of the area.

Along with their scientific-methodological and organizational work, the museums collect, preserve, and exhibit the local materials, which usually embrace both the nature and the population, economy, culture, way of living, and history of the region.

The characterization of territories is based on the landscape-geographic principle, the endeavor to reflect the relations between phenomena and to create in the visitor impressions of the integral appearance of a territory.

A large place in such museums is occupied by a display of collections (geologic-mineralogic, soil, botanical, and zoologic), as well as scientific graphic representation (maps, diagrams, cross sections), portraits of explorers of the given district, prominent persons connected with the district, chronicles of noteworthy historical events, landscape dioramas, models of biocoenoses, and many other things.

The home-lore or local-study museums systematically put on exhibitions devoted to the achievements of economy and culture, and to noteworthy dates in the life of the city or district. In the historical sections of the museums, special displays show the course of the revolutions of 1905 and 1917 in the given city (oblast or district), its role in the Great Patriotic War, its tasks in the seven-year plan and in the prospective development of the national economy. Many local museums also carry on scientific-research work including subjects relating to the physical geographic and economic geographic study of the locality.

At the beginning of 1960, the local-study museums in the USSR numbered more than 500 (in 1922 there were 285). Museums have been founded in all the capitals of the union and autonomous republics, in all the kray and oblast centers, and in most of the historically important cities and populated points (for example, Suzdal' and Pereyaslavl').

Growth of the network of local-study museums is especially contemplated in the union republics, where before the October Revolution there were either none at all or only a few isolated ones. Now there are local-study museums even in a number of rayon centers. Many local-study museums of the western republics and oblasts of the USSR were destroyed and plundered during the Fascist occupation, were robbed of very valuable collections, and in a number of cases are being restored from the ground up.

Deserving of mention among the richest local-study museums of the country, with a widely evolved display of geographic materials, are the museums of Vladivostok, Gor'kiy, Ivanovo, Irkutsk, Kazan', Krasnodar, Krasnoyarsk, Kyakhta, L'vov, Minusinsk, Novgorod, Noril'sk, Riga, Saratov, Sverdlovsk, Tbilisi Uzhgorod, Khabarovsk, Yakutsk, and Yaroslavl'. The number of visitors to a good oblast local-study museum usually amounts to 100,000 persons a year.

The work of the whole network of local-study museums is directed by the committees on the affairs of cultural-enlightenment institutions and by the ministries of culture of the union republics.

Lately there has appeared a tendency to unite the forces of social and state local studies, and proposals are being discussed for the creation of a special state geographic or local-study service in the form of scientific local-study bureaus, inspectorates, or boards for the stock-taking, rational exploitation, preservation and enrichment of the natural resources under the oblast (kray or republic) organizations.

In the larger cities, particularly in the capitals of the union republics, the role of such centers of state local study is performed by the local (republic) academies of sciences or by the branches of the Academy of Sciences of the USSR, as well as by various special institutes (geographic, agricultural, forestry), and, in part, by the geographic, geologic, biology-and-soil, and historical faculties of the universities and pedagogic institutes. There is to be an especial growth in the role of the local local-study libraries and repositories, where the acquisitions resulting from the exploration of the given territory are to be concentrated.

An important task of Soviet local study in the coming years is the further strengthening of the mass character of this movement, while raising the scientific level of investigation, and the still greater concentration of the attention of local students on the most burning practical questions of both economic and cultural life. Those who are interested in local areas can assist the appropriate official agencies to perform the immense job, wholly geographic in nature, of taking an inventory of the natural resources—making a qualitative evaluation of the lands and compiling a land cadaster, as well as conserving the soils and combating soil erosion, and conserving the waters and forests, pasturelands, and valuable animals.

The fulfillment of such work can be promoted by strengthening the local-study specialization of the graduates of the geographic faculties of the universities and pedagogic institutes. N. N. Baranskiy proposes that a "geographic division of labor" be made between the country's universities so that they may insure the training of local-study groups for the respective regions. For this purpose, it is necessary to provide, in the programs of the geographic faculties, for special courses in the geography, history, and ethnography of a concrete region and to organize, in the process of instruction, one or two local-study exercises by students in local museums, at tourist bases, or on excursions.

Soviet local study students are helpers of the party, Soviet, and economic organizations, fosterers of patriotic love for one's land, chroniclers of their own district, its guardians, zealous managers, and judicious transformers.

CHAPTER 48

DEVELOPMENT OF TOURISM AND ALPINISM

Yu. K. Yefremov

Tourism is one of the best forms of active recreation, combining cultural learning, esthetic, sport-and-health, and moral-educational aspects. The active kinds of touristic travels help to develop endurance, resourcefulness, familiarity with outdoor life, and readiness to overcome unforeseen difficulties. Physical exertion and the wholesome effect of fresh air exercise a healthful influence on the tourist.

These properties of tourism alone enable one to regard it as an especially valuable means of training and forming future natural scientists-geographers, geologists, and other specialists in expeditionary professions. Tourism is the first school of geographers.

However, the role of tourism as a means of propagating geographic knowledge is still more important. It facilitates international contacts, and contributes to a knowledge of other countries and peoples. Furthermore, the widening of one's general horizon, the acquisition of geographic, historical, ethnographic, and many other kinds of knowledge, is afforded by tourism during recreation; this knowledge is retained better in the memory than that obtained from any book or film on geography.

The vastness of the territory of the Soviet Union, the grandeur and diversity of its nature, the abundance and beauty of the monuments of past and present culture, the might of the socialist economy, the achievements of science and technology — all create remarkable opportunities for the development of tourism in the USSR.

The alpine peaks of the Pamirs and Tyan'-Shan' surpass the highest points of many mountain systems of the world. The mountains of the Caucasus and of the Altay exceed the Alps in height, without in any way yielding to them in picturesqueness. The Crimea and the Ukrainian Carpathians, the Khibiny and the Urals, the Maritime Region and Sakhalin are full of the charm of medium-high mountain landscapes.

Every one of the great rivers of Eurasia—the Lena and the Amur, the Ob' and the Yenisey, the Volga and the Dnepr, or any one of a hundred smaller rivers—is a tourist itinerary. Some tourists are lured by the sea shores—the Black Sea, the White Sea, the Baltic—; others by lakes—Lake Baykal, Issyk-Kul', Sevan, Seliger, and others.

The country's water arteries have been transformed during the years of Soviet rule. The Volga, already converted into a stairway of placid reservoirs, drives the turbines of the biggest hydroelectric stations. On the Angara and the Yenisey are being built the largest hydro-power stations in the world. The tourist's interest is also attracted by the new man-made fresh-water "seas," and by the new waterways such as the Moscow Canal (Volga-Moskva), by the Stalin White Sea - Baltic Canal, and the Lenin Volga-Don Canal.

The lovers of untouched nature push into remote parts of the country, into the heart of the mountains, into the nature preserves. But no less interest is offered by the observation of already-transformed nature, such as the parks in the environs of Leningrad, the orchards and vineyards of the Ukraine and Moldavia, the lovingly tilled fields of the Baltic lands, or the cotton plantations in Middle Asia.

Centers of attraction to great masses of tourists are the major governmental, cultural, and industrial centers of the country, above all Moscow, Leningrad, Kiyev, Riga, Tbilisi, Yerevan, Tallin, Sverdlovsk, and many others.

The tourist is captivated by the present flowering of culture, science, and technology, observed in the course of any journey through the Soviet land. A visit to the modern industrial enterprises, ports, electric stations, sovkhozes and kolkhozes acquaints him with the diversity of the Soviet economy, with its technical equipment, with the labor achievements of the foremost collectives, and with the new features of the culture and way of living of Soviet men and women.

A number of cities attract the tourist not only by their present cultural and economic significance, but also by monuments of the past. Millions of visitors crowd into the Moscow Kremlin, seeing in it both an incarnation of the grandeur of the age-long history of Russia and one of the bulwarks of the socialist revolution, the place where V. I. Lenin worked, and the headquarters of the construction of socialism and communism in the Soviet Union. The heroic cities of Stalingrad, Sevastopol', Odessa and, of course, Leningrad are visited by masses of both Soviet and foreign tourists who pay tribute to the exploits of the Soviet people in the Great Patriotic War. The memorable sites of the Civil War, the 1812 battlefield of Borodino, Sevastopol' as the arsenal of the heroic defense of 1855 are also objects of constant attention from tourists. The places associated with the life and activity of V. I. Lenin (Ul'yanovsk, Razliv, Gorki, Shushenskoye, etc.), the Pushkin sites (Mikhaylovskoye and others), Lev Tolstoy's Yasnaya Polyana, the house of P. I. Tchaikovsky in Klin and a multitude of other memorial museums, manorhouses, and monuments are all objects of mass tourism. Immense in number are the historical, archeologic, and artistic treasures attracting tourists in their journeyings over the USSR.

For the Soviet people, tourism, by acquainting them with the grandeur and richness of the nature and culture of the Fatherland, serves as one of the powerful means of fostering the socialist patriotism and the geographic culture of the nation. For foreign guests in our country, tourism is a means of learning the truth about the Soviet Union and of convincing themselves personally of the achievements of Soviet government, economy, and culture.

Well-known are the direct contributions of tourists to the country's science, culture, and economy —finds of new mineral deposits and valuable plants, the delivery of collections to museums and schools, composition of guides, essays, photo albums, and motion picture films on the regions visited. Thus, for example, it was tourists who discovered the industrial value of the wild rubber-bearing plant kok-sagyz in the mountains of Middle Asia. Tens of thousands of persons are now participating in mass exploration campaigns in Eastern Siberia, co-operating in the search and prospecting for valuable ores. Tourists were the first to "untangle" the orographic patterns of many not easily accessible mountain nodes, to reconnoiter the approaches to passes and glaciers and to make glaciologic observations.

Tourists not infrequently exercise an effective social supervision over the conservation of nature and cultural monuments. It was the action of tourists that helped to prevent the reduction of the area of the Caucasian Nature Preserve contemplated in 1956 and that later contributed even to the enlargement of the protected territory.

The forms of the tourist movement in the USSR are very varied. Widespread is *excursion tourism*, the touring of noteworthy cities and regions by the use of the common means of transportation: trains, automobiles, steamers, and airplanes.

Another mass form of tourism is that of so-called *active travels*, connected with an expenditure of physical energy by the tourists themselves and hence also embodying the elements of sport. Such are journeys on foot (including mountain and alpinist trips), by boat, bicycle, skis, and other forms of tourism.

Independent travels are usually made by small groups over itineraries chosen by them, including such as are not provided with tourist bases, and often pass through remote and sparsely inhabited places and rely largely on self-service.

A distinctive feature of Soviet tourism is its genuinely mass character. As many as three million persons a year participate in hikes, rallies, campings, and similar touristic enterprises.

An important form of tourism in the USSR is the children's mass tourist movement, under the guidance of the children's excursionist-and-tourist stations. The Pioneer Section of the All-Union Lenin Communist Youth League guides the tourist work in the pioneer detachments, and in the Pioneer Homes and Palaces. Under the Ministry of Education of the RSFSR there operates the Central Children's Tourist-and-Excursionist Station, which generalizes the achievements in the methods of tourist work with children. A noteworthy form of children's tourism is the participation of children in the excursions of the All-Union Home-Lore Expedition of Pioneers and School Children, numbering tens of thousands of detachments. For more details, see Chapter 47.

The "Intourist" Stock Company, which has existed since 1929, serves foreign tourists in the Soviet Union.

A number of publishing houses put out guides for tourists. The Main Administration of Geodesy and Cartography, as well as the Geografgiz, have undertaken the publication of specialized tourist maps of individual regions of our country and of foreign countries.

One of the most complex forms of tourism is *alpinism,* the opportunities for which are truly unlimited in the USSR. The six- and seven-thousand meter summits of the Pamir-Alay and the Central Tyan'-Shan', the five-thousand meter summits of the Caucasus, the very high snow-capped volcanoes of Kamchatka, the multitude of summits of alpinistic class exceeding 4,000 meters in the mountains of the Altay, the Northern and Western Tyan'-Shan'—such is the field of activity for summit-climbing alpinists. But the lesser-altitude objects of alpinistic sport also enjoy deserved renown: the fantastically shaped precipices of the Krasnoyarskiye Stolby, excellent for rock-climber training (it was here that the famous Russian alpinist brothers Ye. and V. Abalakov acquired their skill), the impassable Bzyb Canyon in the Western Caucasus, and a number of not easily accessible caves.

The requirement of alpinistic skills was first felt in Russia by the explorers of nature: Parrot, a professor of Tartu University, on his ascent of Mt. Ararat in 1829, the celebrated traveler Przheval'skiy and his fellow-adventurers in the study of all Central Asia, the topographers and geodesists Khodz'ko, Pastukhov, and others in their survey work in the Caucasus, the geologists Abikh and Mushketov and the geographer Radde on their numerous ascents in the Caucasus and in Middle Asia. At the end of the 19th century, mountain clubs and societies began their activity (the Tiflis, Crimean, later the Crimean-Caucasian, and others). Down to 1917, however, alpinism was confined to a few individual enthusiasts, among whom the remarkable revolutionary and statesman S. M. Kirov deserves special mention for his achievements in conquering Mt. Kazbek 50 years ago (1910) and El'brus in 1912.

The first woman alpinist in Russia, M. P. Preobrazhenskaya, made ten ascents of the summit of Mt. Kazbek. In doing so, she conducted scientific-research work in meteorology and glaciology.

The year 1923 is reckoned as the date of birth of Soviet alpinism, when two ascents of Mt. Kazbek were completed at once under the guidance of Professor Nikoladze and Didebulidze. Twenty-eight persons were on the summit of this mountain in five days, whereas only 46 persons had reached it during the preceding 55 years.

The organization of specialized alpinist camps began in 1929, and they now number 20, and in certain seasons there have been as many as 36. In 1933, the first mountain ski schools were founded and mass ascents of summits—so-called "alpiniads"—were held. These forms have since insured the remarkable mass character of alpinistic sport in the USSR. During 90 years before the Revolution only 59 ascents of El'brus had been made (47 of them by foreigners), but in 1935 alone there were more than 2,000 Soviet alpinists on El'brus. It is important to stress that representatives of the local mountain peoples participated widely in these "alpiniads." Great progress in the development of alpinism has been achieved in a number of the union republics, especially in Georgia, Kazakhstan, and Kirgizia.

A most important feature of alpinism is its ties with life and the satisfaction of vital practical demands. Alpinists helped the Soviet armed forces to repulse the onslaught of the Fascist armies in the passes over the Main Caucasian Ridge in the hard days of 1942.

Alpinists are faithful helpers of the scientist exploring the high mountains and in many cases are themselves keen and self-sacrificing explorers. Meteorologists have wintered on El'brus (*Priyut Devyati*) ["Shelter of the Nine"], 4,250 meters and on the Fedchenko Glacier. Alpinists have participated in explorations in accordance with the programs of the Second International Polar Year (1932-1933), the International Geophysical Year (1957-1958) and the continuing International Geophysical Collaboration (including participation in the exploration of Antarctica). They have given aid to topographers in making phototheodolite surveys, have broadly co-operated with geologists in surveying, search, and prospecting work, and even aided in the organization of the exploitation of the mineral wealth of the high mountains; for example, the Olovyannaya Stena ("Tin Wall") in the Turkestan Range at an altitude of over 4,000 meters. Such are the manifold forms of service rendered by alpinists to scientific and practical needs. The experience gained by alpinists in exploratory work is studied by commissions on high-mountain explorations under the Geographic Society of the USSR in Leningrad and in its Moscow branch.

Among the greatest exploration and sport achievements of Soviet alpinists, the following deserve special mention:

1928: The entire Fedchenko Glacier was traversed under the guidance of O. Yu. Shmidt.

1929: The so-called Garmo Knot was "untied" under the leadership of N. V. Krylenko, N. P. Gorbunov, and geodesist I. G. Dorofeyev. The true position of Garmo Peak was established and Stalin Peak [*Pik Stalina*] was identified.

1931: The ascent of Khan-Tengri (6,995 meters) by the Ukrainian expedition of M. T. Pogrebetskiy.

1932-1933: Study of the glaciers of the Central Tyan'-Shan' (Inyl'chek and others) by the Ukrainian expedition of M. T. Pogrebetskiy.

1932-1938: Explorations by the expeditions of the Moscow House of Scientists (*Dom uchenykh*) under the guidance of A. A. Letavet in the Kokshaal-Tau Range and in other regions of the Central Tyan'-Shan', leading to the discovery of a summit "not inferior in altitude to the Khan-Tengri."

1933: The Tadzhik-Pamir Expedition. Ascent of the highest summit in the USSR—Pik Stalina (7,495 meters)—by Ye. M. Abalakov.

1934: Ascent of the Pik Lenina (7,127 meters) by V. M. Abalakov's group (3 persons). Establishment of automatic radio stations on a number of Pamir peaks.

1936: The ascent of Khan-Tengri by alpinists of Kazakhstan and V. and Ye. Abalakov's groups.

1937: Repeated ascents of the Pik Stalina and the Pik Lenin,a conquest of the Pik Yevgenii Korzhenevskoy.

1940: Organization of a high-altitude physiologic laboratory on the Muzkol Ridge of the Pamirs (6,200 meters) by Odessa alpinists.

1943: Topographic survey of the Central Tyan'-Shan' under the direction of P. N. Rapasov and measurement of the summit, discovered by Professor A. A. Letavet, which proved to be the highest in the Tyan'-Shan' (7,439 meters) and second in elevation in the USSR. At the very climax of the Great Patriotic War this summit was given the name of Pik Pobedy [Victory Peak].

1946: Ascent of Pik Patkhor (6,052 meters) in the Southwestern Pamirs by Ye. A. Beletskiy's group.

1956: The conquest of Pik Pobedy by a group of Moscow and Kakakh alpinists under the leadership of V. M. Abalakov (11 persons).

1956: The Soviet-Chinese ascent of Pik Mustag-Ata (7,546 meters) in the Range in Sinkiang (China). Thirty-one persons reached the summit, including 12 alpinists from China.

1956: A group under the leadership of K. K. Kuz'min ascended Mt. Kongur-Tyube (7,595 meters) in the same Kashgar Range.

1957: K. K. Kuz'min's group penetrated in the Pamir Firn Plateau, first noted in 1934 by geologist A. V. Moskvin and shown in 1954 on the map by geographer-alpinist Ye. V. Timashev (1909-1951).

1957: K. K. Kuzmin's group (10 persons) repeated the ascent of Pik Stalina.

1958: Soviet-Chinese ascent of Pik Lenina (38 persons, of whom 17 were Chinese alpinists).

1959: New ascents of Pik Stalina by the groups of K. K. Kuz'min (5 persons) and Ye. Ivanov (14 persons).

Alpinism, like other forms of tourism, is a valuable means of molding a man or women and a powerful aid in the exploration of the nature of high-mountain regions.

BASIC LITERATURE

Al'pinizm. Under the editorship of I. A. Cherepov, Moscow-Leningrad, 1940.

Abalakov, V. M. Fundamentals of Alpinism (*Osnovy Al'pinizma*), Moscow, 1941.

Zatulovskiy, D. M. On the Glaciers and Summits of Middle Asia (*Na Lednikakh i Vershinakh Sredney Azii*), Moscow, 1948.

Kirov, S. M. The Ascent of Mt. Kazbek (*Voskhozdeniye na Kazbek*), Terek, 1910, no. 3815.

Pobezhdennyye Vershiny (Conquered Summits), Annual of Soviet Alpinism, 1949, 1959.

Simonov, Ye. D. "Main Stages in the Development of High-mountain Sport in the USSR," *Teoriya i praktika fizicheskoy kul'tury,* 1946, vol. 9, no. 8-9.

Tourist Travels in the USSR (*Turistskiye Puteshestviya po SSSR*), Moscow, 1958.

Tourist Trails (*Turistskiye Tropy*). Al'manakh, book I, Moscow, 1958; book 2, Moscow, 1959.

CHAPTER 49

PUBLICATION OF GEOGRAPHIC LITERATURE*†

V. V. Pokshishevskiy

As shown in most of the chapters in this book, the development of geography is regarded in the USSR as an important state task, inseparable from the practical requirements of the knowledge and the planned exploitation of the natural wealth and other economic resources of the country. Hence, the publication of scientific literature, necessary for the growth of geography, is also done in the USSR directly by state scientific institutions or with the organizational and material support of those institutions. Likewise, the state organizes the publication of popular geographic literature, which plays above all an important cultural-enlightenment role.

The forms of publishing activity are very diversified. Let us name the principal ones:

1. *Publication by the scientific institutions of the results of the investigations made by them.* This relates primarily to the Academy of Sciences of the USSR and to the academies of sciences of the union republics, and also to the local sections and branches of the Academy of Sciences of the USSR. The largest main academic geographic institution in our country is the Institute of Geography of the Academy of Sciences of the USSR; many republic academies and peripheral sections and branches also have similar institutes or sectors of geography. All these institutions carry on a great deal of expeditionary work and make office or theoretical investigations. The major integrated expeditionary work with the participation of specialists in diverse fields is organized by the Council on the Study of Productive Forces *(SOPS)* under the Presidium of the Academy of Sciences of the USSR. The distribution of productive forces is studied by the Institute of Economics of the Academy of Sciences of the USSR, as well as by specialized academic institutions such as the Forest Institute, the Institute of Integrated Transportation Problems, the Institute of Oriental Studies, etc. The results of all such work are usually published by the Publishing House [*Izdatel'stvo*] of the Academy of Sciences of the USSR, or in the local academy publications. Thus, many studies on geography have been published by the Eastern Siberian branch of the Academy of Sciences of the USSR or by special scientific publishing houses such as the special Publishing House of Oriental Literature under the Institute of Oriental Studies of the Academy of Sciences of the USSR.

The forms of publication themselves are very diversified: in some cases they are individual fundamental monographs such as the *Subarktika* [Subarctic] by Academician A. A. Grigor'yev, and a number of books on the natural-historical regionalization of the USSR prepared by the *SOPS;* in other cases, they are serial publications of the *trudy* of the expeditions, e.g., *Trudy* of the Aral-Caspian Expedition of the Academy of Sciences of the USSR; in still other cases, they are continuing non-periodic publications [*Problemy fizicheskoy geografii*], published by the Institute of Geography of the Academy of Sciences of the USSR. In addition, separate articles on leading geographic problems or the results of particular investigations are published in the geographic journals issued by these same institutions (for example, six issues of the journal *Izvestiya Akademii Nauk SSSR, seriya geograficheskaya* come out each year). The academy journals and serial publications of the Institute of Geography of the Academy of Sciences of the USSR [*AN SSSR*] have also reflected all the most important discussions on the theoretical questions of geography that have taken

---

*This chapter does not touch upon the publication, in the USSR, of atlases, maps, and other cartographic productions, nor on the publication of scientific literature on cartography by specialized publishing houses, and journals. Concerning this, see Chapter 7, on "Cartography." The scientific literature on cartography is considered only insofar as it appears in general geographic publications.

†[See the Appendix for a list of the serial publications referred to in this book — Ed.]

place in the USSR (on the problem of moisture circulation, on monoglacialism and polyglacialism, on the object of economic geography. Here, too, are usually published, above all, the important results of the expeditionary work of Soviet geographers, e.g., in the Arctic and Antarctic. The journal *Izvestiya AN SSSR, seriya geograficheskaya*, devotes great attention to the elucidation of the state of geography abroad and to international geographic relations. Much geographic material is also published in the popular academic natural-history journal "Nature" [*Priroda*] designed for wide circles of scientific workers and the intelligentsia.

2. *Publications by scientific societies with the co-operation of the state* (often also through the Publishing House of the Academy of Sciences of the USSR). The respective publications reflect the research done by the members or scientific correspondents of these societies, the most important of which is the Geographic Society of the USSR [*Geograficheskoye obshchestvo Soyuza SSR*]. In addition to the publications of its central organization,* located in Leningrad, there is considerable publishing activity on the part of its local branches [*filialy*] and sections [*otdely*], which total about one hundred.** The largest branch, that of Moscow, has since 1946 regularly issued topical scientific collections entitled "Questions of Geography" [*Voprosy geografii*]. Altogether, fifty such collections have appeared.*** Not infrequent are cases of co-operation in the preparation of publications between local branches of the Geographic Society and the academic institutions, and the issuance of joint collections and monographs. Such co-operation is facilitated by the fact that, as a rule, the scholars working in the field of geography in the academic institutions are also active members of the Geographic Society of the USSR. Besides the Geographic Society, studies on geography (along with other fields of knowledge) are also published by certain other scientific societies such as the Moscow Society of Investigators of Nature [*Moskovskoye obshchestvo ispytateley prirody*], the republic societies for the conservation of nature, and others.

3. *Scientific publications of the higher educational institution, reflecting the investigations made by the chairs of the geographic faculties or those of kindred specialties.* The network of geographic faculties in the universities of the USSR, and of geographic or biologic-geographic faculties in the pedagogic institutes, is very great. (For more details, see Chapter 46, "Geographic Education in Institutions of Higher Learning.") Numerous specialized geographic chairs or individual geographic chairs operate in these faculties. Geography courses are also given in certain other higher educational institutions (agricultural, economic, forestry, etc.) Scientific-research subjects are also included in the work plan of the chairs of the higher educational institutions of the USSR, which unite the considerable forces of the professor and teaching staff; hence, the scientific production of the workers of the higher educational institutions is very great in the aggregate. In the geographic faculties, it is very often connected with expeditionary work or field practice conducted with the students. Such, for example, were the Caspian, Eastern Siberian, and Pamir expeditions, conducted by the geography faculty of Moscow State University. Most of the higher educational institutions publish their own *Uchenyye zapiski* or *Trudy*, in the makeup of which works on geography occupy a prominent place. Some faculties such as those of Leningrad, Voronezh, and Odessa State universities, the V. I. Lenin Moscow State Pedagogic Institute, the A. I. Hertsen State Pedagogic Institute in Leningrad, and the pedagogic institutes in Vologda, Chelyabinsk and elsewhere have become great centers of scientific geographic thought, putting out very valuable publications. Thus, the geography faculty of Moscow State University has issued during the last few years such monographs as "Geography of Soils" [*Geografiya pochv*] by I. P. Gerasimov, "Physical Geography of the Caucasus" [*Fizicheskaya geografiya Kavkaza*] by N. A. Gvozdetskiy, "Introduction to Economic Geography" [*Vvedeniye v ekonomicheskuyu geografiyu*] by Yu. G. Saushkin, and "Economic Geography of Hungary" [*Ekonomicheskaya geografiya Vengrii*] by I. M. Mayergoyz. Since 1958, this faculty has also issued periodic collections of articles entitled "Geography and

---

*The non-periodic "Notes" [*Zapiski*] and "Geographic Collections" [*Geograficheskiye sborniki*] as well as the journal *Izvestiya Vsesoyuznogo geograficheskogo obshchestva*, which appears periodically at the rate of six numbers a year; every six numbers (per year) form a volume, Volume 91 being issued in 1959.

**These are listed in Chauncy D. Harris and Jerome D. Fellmann, *International List of Geographical Serials* (University of Chicago, Department of Geography, Research Paper No. 63, Chicago, 1960) as items 1252-1336 — Ed.

*** Among the non-periodic continuing publications put out by the peripheral branches one may name the "Questions of the Geography of Siberia" [*Voprosy geografii Sibiri*], "Questions of the Geography of the Far East" [*Voprosy geografii Dal'nego Vostoka*], and others. For more details, see Chapter 50, "The Geographic Society of the USSR."

Economy" [*Geografiya i khozyaystvo*], which deal with many questions of applied geography. Khar'kov University published in 1958 a survey book on "Economic Geography of the European Countries of the People's Democracy" [*Ekonomicheskaya geografiya yevropeyshikh stran narodnoy demokratii*]. In addition to the *Uchenyye zapiski* and *Trudy* some faculties and chairs also issue teaching aids on geography or textbooks for their students.

4. *Publications of the State Publishing House of Geographic Literature* [*Geografgiz*]. This specialized publishing house (so far as we know, it is the only one of its kind in the world) was founded in 1946. It publishes geographic books of various character, from serious scientific monographs to travel sketches and popular brochures. At one time, republication of the geography classics, especially the works of Russian travelers, occupied a prominent place in its activity. During its existence, Geografgiz has published such fundamental works as "The Geographic Zones of the Soviet Union" [*Geograficheskiye zony Sovetskogo Soyuza*] by L. S. Berg, the three-volume edition of selected works on the geography of Asia by V. A. Obruchev, the "Essays on Geomorphology" [*Ocherki po geomorfologii*] and *Paleogeografiya* by K. K. Markov, the two-volume edition of the selected works of N. N. Baranskiy, etc. Lately, Geografgiz has put out a good many detailed regional economic-geographic monographs on individual republics and regions of the USSR, a number of books on foreign countries (for example, "France" by I. A. Vitver and A. Ye. Sluka, and "Great Britain" by A. S. Dobrov), on the Polar regions (on the Soviet sector of the Arctic and on the Antarctic), and others.

5. *School literature on geography* (textbooks for schools and higher educational institutions, as well as a considerable number of books to aid geography teachers) *is published by the State School Pedagogic Publishing House* [*Uchebno-pedagogicheskoye izdatel'stvo*] *of the Ministry of Education of the RSFSR.* The significance of its activity is defined, not so much by the number of publications put out as by the huge number of copies made at one printing, which insures the spread of geographic culture "in breadth" throughout the USSR. For example, the first edition of N. I. Lyalikov's textbook, "Economic Geography of the USSR" [*Ekonomicheskaya geografiya SSSR*] intended for the ninth year of instruction, came out in 1957 in more than two million copies. Some textbooks put out for the secondary school have been republished abroad, where they are used to teach the geography of the USSR in the higher educational institutions, e.g., "Economic Geography of the USSR" by N. N. Baranskiy, and "Economic Geography of Foreign Countries," by I. A. Vitver. In addition to school literature proper, this publishing house prints much methodological literature on geography, as well as a special scientific-methodological journal "Geography in the School" [*Geografiya v shkole*]. In the union republics, school and methodological literature on geography (chiefly in the native language) is published by similar local publishing houses (for example, in the Ukrainian SSR by the publishing house *Radyan'ska shkola* ["Soviet School"].

6. A considerable amount of geographic material (both reference and scientific) is contained in the *publications of the "Sovetskaya Entsiklopediya" Publishing House.* In addition to the encyclopedias themselves, this house has put out many geographic reference books on individual countries, and in 1959 undertook the publication of a special "Short Geographic Encyclopedia" [*Kratkaya geograficheskaya entsiklopediya*] in four volumes. Many geographic materials published by the "Great Soviet Encyclopedia" Publishing House have been translated and published abroad (in Germany, China, etc.).

7. The wide interest of Soviet men and women in geography is also reflected in the makeup of the published output of many other houses which gladly publish geographic books. Among the central publishing houses, one may list here, in particular: (a) the Publishing House of Foreign Literature, which publishes translations [in Russian] of books issued abroad which are of most interest to the Soviet reader. It has, for example, translated and published, the "Essays on Geomorphology" by Baulig, monographs by Baker, James, George, Gourou, Stamp and Beaver, Trewartha, Ch'u Shao-t'ang, and many other well-known foreign scholars. A translation of the symposium "American Geography: Inventory and Prospect" has also been published; (b) the Publishing House "Young Guard" [*Izdatel'stvo "Molodaya Gvardiya"*]; (c) the State Publishing House of Children's Literature [*Gosudarstvennoye izdatel'stvo detskoy literatury*]. These publishing houses put out chiefly popular-scientific and scientific-artistic books on geography, thereby fulfilling the important social task of widely propagating geographic knowledge; (d) the

Izdatel'stvo "Znaniye" ["Knowledge"] prints large editions of many brochures on geography prepared by the Society for the Dissemination of Political and Scientific Knowledge; (e) a number of other central publishing houses (for example, *Sovetskaya Rossiya,* which deals broadly with geographic objects of the RSFSR). Designed for wide circles of readers, especially for youth, is the popular geographic journal ("Around the World") [*Vokrug Sveta*], published by the *Molodaya Gvardiya.*

Individual books on geographic topics are put out by the publishing houses of the agricultural, economic, transportation, and other branches of industry. The specialized publishing house "Hydrometeorological Publishing House" [*Gidrometeoizdat*] produces a considerable amount of scientific material on geography: monographs, agroclimatic reference books, water cadaster, the *trudy* of the scientific-research institutions of the Hydrometeorologic Service of the USSR, the journal "Meteorology and Hydrology", and much more.

Besides the central publishing houses, local publishing houses also print many geographic and home-district books, mainly on the geography of their own republics, krays, oblasts, and cities (the geography literature on the Ukrainian SSR and Siberia is especially rich). All this adds up to a rather impressive number of publications, which not infrequently have practical significance. Local and republic popular-scientific journals are also issued, for example "Nature in Estonia" and "Urals Pathfinder."

8. Finally, one should mention the considerable work done in the publication of references to geographic literature and on the bibliography of geographic literature. Soviet geographers have at their disposal the fundamental monthly Reference Journal: "Geography," which now deals each year with as many as 30,000 publications on geography published in all countries of the world. Together with the indexes (by author, subject, etc.) published by this journal, this is the fullest bibliographic reference periodical in the world. For example, its fullness by comparison with the American "Current Geographical Publications" or with the French "Bibliographie géographique internationale" is defined, in particular, by the fact that the Institute of Scientific Information of the Academy of Sciences of the USSR which publishes this journal, possesses not only all the most important foreign special geographic periodic and continuing publications, but also those on allied fields of knowledge. These enable the journal to include geographic topics from non-geographic journals, from various collections of articles, *Trudy,* etc. In addition to the systematic publication of references and geographic bibliography, done from month to month by the Reference Journal, other similar publications are printed in the USSR. For example, the bibliographic handbooks prepared by the Institute of Geography of the Academy of Sciences of the USSR, bibliographies on individual problems or individual regions, the recommendatory bibliographic indexes published by the V. I. Lenin State Library, and so forth. The Institute of Scientific Information of the Academy of Sciences of the USSR in 1957-1958 issued "Indexes of New Literature on Nature, Resources, and the Economy" by economic administrative regions of the USSR (14 issues in all).

Our enumeration of the channels through which geographic literature is released in the USSR is evidence of the fact that Soviet geographers possess manifold and flexible opportunities for effecting a broad exchange of their theoretical achievements, for promoting by their publications the solution of the practical tasks of socialist construction, for insuring the training of new personnel in the higher educational institutions, and for satisfying the demands of the secondary school, as well as the broad circles of Soviet men and women, for geographic knowledge.

While the publications of the Academy and of the higher educational institutions and "fat" geographic journals (as well as certain books issued by the Geografgiz and, in part, by other special publishing houses) primarily serve qualified geography specialists, other forms of publication are addressed to the wider type of reader, satisfying his interest in his country, and in nature and the economy of its regions, as well as his interest in all the countries of the world. Publications of the regional type, for the mere reason that a more mass type of reader is interested in them in the USSR, are often given a somewhat "easier" character. In the main, even such publications are written by geographers, are based on their own research, and thus are not reduced to the status of a mere compilation. More special questions, without the analysis of which it would be difficult to perform the whole work, are usually presented by the authors in simultaneously published separate items not printed in any collection or journal. This explains why the names of the same geographer-scholars are found on both the title pages of specialized studies and of books designed for the propagation of geographic knowledge and for the use of students, practical workers in the provinces and, in general, for wide circles of readers. This diversity in the system of publications reflects the general trend of Soviet science, which sets itself the task of serving the people and their practical needs and is alien to professional exclusiveness.

With respect to topics, the original geographic publications in the USSR, regardless of their form as articles, books, etc., may be broken down for the last few years approximately as follows [Table I]. The estimate was made on the basis of the 1955-1958 publications of the Geografgiz, the three leading geographic journals, the collections "Voprosy geografii," and the publications of Moscow State University. Altogether, about 2,500 publications entered into the estimate. The percentages given are typical of all Soviet geographic literature of the years named. Inclusion in them of the peripheral publications might somewhat increase the proportion of economic geographic, particularly regional literature.

TABLE I

GEOGRAPHIC PUBLICATIONS IN THE SOVIET UNION, 1955-1958, BY TYPE

1. General theoretical questions of geography	2.9%	⎫
2. Questions of geographic education in the higher and secondary schools (including methodology and textbooks, except those of the higher educational institutions which represent monographs or special aids)*	14.6%	37.9%
3. History of geography, re-publications of classics, notes of travelers, etc.	7.0%	
4. Contributions on questions of the organization of geography, personalia, and other general questions	13.4%	⎭
5. Physical geography as a whole	25.3%	25.3%
5a. Theoretical and topical questions 10.5%		
5b. Regional questions 14.8%		
6. Economic geography (except population geography)	14.6%	⎫
6a. Theoretical and topical questions 2.9%		16.3%
6b. Regional questions** 11.7%		
7. Population geography	1.7%	⎭
8. Cartography	2.9%	2.9%
9. Criticism and bibliography (surveys, critical articles, and major reviews of fundamental significance)	17.6%	17.6%

*Such school aids for the higher educational institutions are included in Nos. 1, 3, 5 and 6, respectively.

**The concept of a "single, unified geography" has not gained ground in the USSR. Hence, reigonal studies can, by an overwhelming majority, be subdivided into physical geographic and economic geographic. A comparatively small number of integrated regional studies are distributed among these headings in the estimate according to which aspect—the physical geographic or the economic geographic—predominates in them or reflects the author's own research to a greater extent. Of course, this involves a certain amount of unavoidable conventionalism, but it concerns only a relatively small number of studies. A different method of estimation—distinction of a separate heading for integrated regional-geography [stranovedcheskiy] studies— would create a false idea of the existence of a "single, unified geography" in the USSR.

If one singles out from among the publications included in Table I those whose object is territorially concrete (whether the topic be some branch of geography or an integrated regional one), the proportion of studies relating to the territory of the USSR will be about 60 per cent and that relating to foreign countries 40 per cent.

The percentages in Table I give some idea of the thematic structure of the geographic publications in the USSR, but not of their total volume, which, of course, is considerably higher than the printed output of the limited circle of publications used for the estimate. The total number of Soviet geographic publications can only be fixed with a great deal of approximation. The Reference Journal "Geography" reflected, in its 1956-1958 issues, 21,500 Soviet geographic publications (or those on subjects akin to geography), i.e., approximately 7,000 titles a year. The "Indexes of New Literature on Nature, Resources and the Economy" of the economic administrative regions of the USSR, which are published by the Institute of Scientific Information and have covered the

TABLE II

QUANTITATIVE INDICES OF THE PUBLICATION OF GEOGRAPHIC LITERATURE

Data on the volume of publishing activity with respect to geographic works along the line of some of the channels named above are given in the following Table II:

Publishing house, series, or journal	Period	Unit of Measurement	Index	Remarks
1. Geografgiz	1946-1958	Number of titles	858	From 1955 to 1958:
		Total in author's pages	11,305	
		Total in millions of printed pages	353	409 titles, totaling 4,380 author's pages
2. Publishing House of Foreign Literature (geographic books only)	1947-1958	Number of titles	98	From 1955 to 1958:
		Total in author's pages	2,300	45 titles, totaling about 1,000 author's pages
3. Publishing House "Bol'shaya Sovetskaya Entsiklopediya"	1949-1957	Number of "geographic words" in 2nd ed. of "Great Soviet Encyclopedia"	17,000	In addition to book production (handbook of geographic books on individual countries, etc.).
		Total in author's pages	130	
4. Publications of the Institute of Geography of the Academy of Sciences of the USSR (apart from No. 7)	1951-1958	Number of serially issued *trudy* and topical collections of articles	53	From 1955 to 1958 the Institute published a total of 79 books, totaling 1,571 author's pages
		Total in author's pages	973	
		Number of monographs (those published through Geografgiz are counted under No. 1)	29	
		Total in author's pages	610	
		Number of other books	10	
		Total in author's pages	202	
		Number of other books	92	
		Total in author's pages	1,785	

(Continued on next page)

(Continued from preceding page)

Publishing house, series, or journal	Period	Unit of Measurement	Index	Remarks
5. Collections of articles in *Voprosy geografii*, published by Moscow Branch of the Geographic Society of the USSR	1946-1958	Number of issues Number of contributions in them	44 819	From 1955 to 1958: 8 numbers containing 165 contributions
6. Journal: All-Union Geographic Society, *Izvestiya*	1955-1958	Number of issues Number of contributions in them	24 477	Oldest geographic journal in the USSR (published continuously since 1865)
7. Journal: Academy of Sciences, *Izvestiya, seriya geograficheskaya*	1955-1958	Number of issues Number of contributions in them	24 550	Down to 1950, a geographic and a geophysical series were combined
8. Journal: "Geography in the School"	1955-1958	Number of issues Number of contributions in them	24 550	
9. Reference journal: "Geography"	1956-1958	Number of issues Number of references (*referaty*) there, in thousands	35 84.6	In 1954-1955, a combined reference journal: "Geography and Geology" was published

literature for 1953-1957 (and only in individual cases from 1950 on), total about 18,000 titles of regional literature on the USSR. To be sure, the topics of this literature touch on some allied questions and are not solely geography.

Concurrent with the above quantitative indices relating to geographic contributions proper, geographic topics are usually widely represented at various congresses and conferences dealing with the problems of augmenting the productive forces—both in the regional and in the topical aspects. As an example, one may mention the Irkutsk Conference of 1958 on the development of the productive forces of Eastern Siberia, which was preceded by regional conferences in the oblasts and republics. The *trudy* of such conferences reflect the participation of geographers in them. The significance of such contacts between geographers and the representatives of the other scientific specialties is great, because here geography is really placed at the service of the national economy. In just the same manner, the abundance of contributions on geographic topics published by the specialized publishing houses (technical, agricultural, economic), as well as by the various journals and local publishing houses which are sometimes on the whole very far removed from geography in their field, testifies to the close ties between Soviet geography and the practice of socialist construction.

Part VII

THE GEOGRAPHIC SOCIETY
OF THE USSR

CHAPTER 50

REVIEW OF ACTIVITY

S. V. Kalesnik

The Geographic Society of the USSR [*Geograficheskoye obshchestvo SSSR*] is among the oldest in the world: it was founded on 6 August, 1845, in St. Petersburg. Among its founders were the great scholars K. I. Arsen'yev, K. M. Ber, F. P. Vrangel' [Wrangel], and F. P. Litke. Since the very first years of its existence, the Geographic Society has carried on an extensive expeditionary, publishing, and educational activity.

Before 1845, geographic exploration and work in Russia had been engaged in principally by the Academy of Sciences, which achieved admirable progress in this line of endeavor. The famous Kamchatkan expeditions, which studied the northern coasts of Siberia and Kamchatka and discovered the Kuril and Aleutian islands as well as northwestern North America, rank with the most noteworthy expeditions of the epoch of great discoveries.

The Geographic Society, although it originated as a voluntary social and scientific organization, never lost touch with the Academy. From the moment of its foundation down to the October Revolution, it was a kind of successor to the Academy of Sciences in the field of the further development of geographic exploration. The first president of the Society and one of its founders, the well-known Polar explorer and around-the-world traveler F. P. Litke, was also president of the Academy of Sciences. Among the outstanding figures of the Geographic Society were many academicians and corresponding members of the Academy, and in 1938 the Society officially became a part of the Academy of Sciences of the Soviet Union.

The All-Union Geographic Society has played an enormous role in the scientific and cultural progress of our country. Its leaders and most active members have been and are now scholars whose names occupy a prominent place in science. Among them are the first Russian circumnavigator of the globe, I. F. Kruzenshtern; the well-known author of the "Explanatory Dictionary of the Living Great-Russian Language" [*Tolkovyy slovar' zhivogo velikorusskago yazyka*], V. I. Dal'; the first explorer of the Tyan'-Shan', P. P. Semenov-Tyan-Shanskiy; the India traveler I. P. Minayev; the noteworthy ethnographer and humanist N. N. Miklukho-Maklay; the great explorers of middle and central Asia, N. M. Przheval'skiy, the brothers M. Ye. and G. Ye. Grumm-Grzhimaylo, G. N. Potanin, M. V. Pevtsov, P. K. Kozlov, N. A. Severtsov, A. P. Fedchenko, I. V. Mushketov, and V. A. Obruchev; one of the founders of the science of climate, A. I. Voyeykov; the outstanding explorers of Siberia and eastern Asia, P. A. Kropotkin, I. D. Cherskiy, A. L. Chekanovskiy, and V. L. Komarov; the well-known oceanographer, cartographer, and geographer, Yu. M. Shokal'skiy; the eminent geographer and naturalist L. S. Berg; and many others.

The expeditions of the Geographic Society and its local sections have won the Society world renown. Their participants were the first to make known to the world the natural characteristics of a number of extensive territories in the Urals, the Altay, and the Tyan'-Shan', the Turukhan District, the Lake Baykal region, the Ussuri District (Ussuriyskiy kray), Sakhalin Island, Kamchatka, and the Chukot Peninsula, in eastern China and on the Tibetan Plateau, in Mongolia, Iran, New Guinea, etc.

The Geographic Society, which has always paid great attention to the problems of the Arctic, was a pioneer in the stationary study of the northern Polar lands. It was also the first to organize special explorations on the territory of our country: geologic and oceanographic explorations, the study of glaciers, earthquakes, investigation of the weather, climate, and relief, geodetic and cartographic work, etc.

The Geographic Society has also invariably been one of the centers of foremost social thought. According to the testimony of an archive document of 1852 — a denunciation to the Tsarist government — admission to the Geographic Society was so broad that "persons saturated with the utopian ideas of Proudhon, Louis Blanc, Mazzini, Garibaldi and other dreamers could easily invade it...and spread their ideas of communism, socialism, democracy, and atheism, so destructive for the welfare of kingdoms and the happiness of mankind." Chekanovskiy, Cherskiy, Dybovskiy, and Godlevskiy, banished to Siberia, enjoyed the unceasing support of the Geographic Society and, with its cooperation, carried out noteworthy explorations in the region of Lake Baykal. Many members of the Society were involved in the Petrashevtsy affairs.

The presidents of the Society before the Revolution were: F. P. Litke (1845-1850); M. N. Murav'yev (1850-1857); F. P. Litke again (1857-1873); and P. P. Semenov-Tyan-Shanskiy (1873-1914).

During the Soviet years, the Geographic Society has grown greatly in size and strength. After the October Revolution it was converted into a genuinely mass social-scientific association, embracing scientific workers, teachers, and practical men in the field of geographic sciences.

The highest organ of the Geographic Society of the USSR is the Congress, convoked every five years. Between congresses, the Society is directed by the Learned Council (elected by the Congress) and by its Presidium headed by the President. The presidents of the Society in Soviet times have been: Yu. M. Shokal'skiy (1914-1931), N. I. Vavilov (1931-1940), L. S. Berg (1940-1950); this post is now occupied by Ye. N. Pavlovskiy (since 1952).

Before the October Revolution, the Society had 11 sections [otdely] and a thousand members; by 1959, the number of active members had reached 10,000. The Society now consists of a Central Organization (in Leningrad), 24 branches [filialy], and 84 sections in the various cities of the USSR. The branches, i.e., the largest subdivisions of the Society, are located in Armenia, Azerbaydzhan, Bashkiria, Belorussia, Buryatia, Georgia, Dagestan, Kazakhstan, Karelia, Kirgizia, Komi ASSR, Latvia, Lithuania, Moscow, the Amur region (Priamur'ye), the Maritime region (Primor'ye), Tadzhikistan, Tataria, Turkmenia, Uzbekistan, the Ukraine, the Urals, Estonia, and Yakutia. The branches of the Geographic Society in the union republics are at the same time republic geographic societies (the Geography Society of the Georgian SSR, the Geographic Society of the Estonian SSR, and so forth).

Among the main tasks of the Society are:

1. All possible co-operation in the development of research and exploration and of geographic science in general, and in the application of the results attained by geography to the requirements of the national economy.

2. Organization of broad aid to the members of the Society and improvement of their scientific qualifications.

3. Participation in measures for the promotion of cultural ties with the peoples of other countries, in the struggle for peace against the instigators of aggressive wars.

4. Investigation and popularization of the history of our native geography.

5. Co-operation in the correct arrangement and development of instruction in the geographic sciences in the secondary and higher schools.

6. Popularization and propagation of geographic knowledge among the broad masses of the population.

7. Posing and elaboration of scientific-technical, methodological, and organizational questions.

8. Co-operation in the development of local studies, mass tourism, excursions, and alpinism.

9. Co-operation in the conservation of nature, co-ordination of geographic research and exploration, as well as regulation and unification of geographic terminology and geographic names.

The Geographic Society of the USSR fulfills the functions of social initiative, control, and co-ordination in the field of the geographic sciences, and in a number of cases, acts also as an actual executer of scientific work. In its work, the Society employs the following forms of activity:

1. Discussion of scientific papers at meetings of departments and commissions. In the central organization of the Society there are the following departments: physical geography, biogeography, economic geography, history of geographic knowledge, mathematical geography and cartography, school geography, and ethnography. In the branches and sections, depending upon the

characteristics of their work and staff of specialists, the structure may be different; the number of departments and their names are determined by the branches and sections themselves. The same is to be said of the commissions [*komissii*] which are formed within the departments (or independently of the departments) to discuss papers on the various branches or major problems of geographic science.

2. Organization and holding of broad scientific conferences. Examples of such conferences are the all-union conferences on landscape-science questions (in Leningrad in 1955, in L'vov in 1956, in Tbilisi in 1958, in Riga in 1959); the phenologic conference (1957); the conference on the transcription of geographic names (1955); on the physical geographic regionalization of the Urals (1954); on the natural-historical regionalization of the Ukraine (Kiyev, 1958); on the application of aerial methods in landscape research (1959). Participating in conferences of this sort are representatives of the numerous interested institutions from the various cities of the USSR.

3. Convocation of all-union geographic congresses to review the progress of the geographic sciences during a specific period, as well as to discuss the tasks, ways and prospects of the development of geography in connection with the demands of the national economy and culture. The First All-Union Geographic Congress was held on 11-18 April 1933, the Second on 25-31 January, 1947 (both in Leningrad).

4. Rendition of expert opinion and advice on all geographic questions.

5. Organization of expeditions and scientific trips. It should be noted that before the October Revolution the outfitting of expeditions to study the Fatherland or foreign countries had become a sort of monopoly of the Geographic Society, while after the Revolution this form of Society activity was given less weight, because hundreds of new scientific-research institutes and institutions having a geographic or naturalist interest, and annually outfitting hundreds of expeditions, parties, and detachments to go to various regions of the Soviet Union, had been created in the Soviet state, which was striving to place the natural productive forces at the service of the people. Still, the Society continues even under the new conditions to outfit large expeditions. One may note the Mongolian-Tibetan Expedition of P. K. Kozlov (1923-1926), the Western Siberian Expedition of B. N. Gorodkov (1923), the Kol's Expedition to the Taz River (1926-1927), and the Ladoga Expedition of P. F. Domrachev (1940). After the Second World War, the Society's expeditionary activity was concentrated in its branches and sections, which annually organize 20 to 30 large or small expeditions, depending upon the assignment and the means of the local scientific and economic institutions. Thus, in 1958 the Buryat branch made biogeographic investigations on the Vitim Plateau; the Novosibirsk section organized an integrated expedition to study the region of the Ob' reservoir; the L'vov section is conducting broad-scale soil-geographic surveys in the kolkhozes of the western oblasts of the Ukraine, and so forth.

6. A great amount of work is being done by the Geographic Society in the propagation and popularization of geographic knowledge. For this purpose, special free geographic lectures have been instituted in the central organization of the Society and in many of its branches and sections. The Society's members also go out to give lectures in factories, plants, schools, Houses of Culture, etc. In the Society's lecture rooms, 2,500-5,000 popular-scientific lectures are given annually.

7. The Society has created in the USSR a voluntary phenologic network, which in 1959 numbered 400 points. The correspondents of this network—home-district students, teachers, agronomists, workers of the meteorologic stations, scientific workers, etc.—systematically send in their observations of the seasonal natural phenomena to the Phenologic Sector of the Society, where the observations are subjected to preliminary treatment. To strengthen its ties with these correspondents, the Phenologic Sector publishes an *Informatsionnyy byulleten'*.

8. The Society encourages the authors of the best scientific works on geography by awarding them gold medals and prizes. The Grand Gold Medal of the Society (together with the accompanying prize of 25,000 rubles) and the Semen Dezhnev Prize, amounting to 15,000 rubles, are awarded once every three years by the Learned Council of the Society. The Litke, Przheval'skiy, and Semenov Gold Medals (each accompanied by a prize of 10,000 rubles) are awarded once every two years.

9. During its existence the Geographic Society and its branches and sections have produced more than 1,500 volumes of various publications containing an extraordinary wealth and variety of material on the geography of our state and neighboring countries. At present, in addition to separate monographs, bulletins and brochures, the Society publishes the oldest Russian scientific

geographic journal, "Bulletin of the All-Union Geographic Society" [*Izvestiya Vsesoyuznogo geograficheskogo obshchestva*], issued continuously since 1848 under changing titles, and also systematically issues the "Notes of the All-Union Geographic Society" [*Zapiski Vsesoyuznogo geograficheskogo obshchestva*] (new series since 1948; down to 1959, 18 volumes have appeared), and the "Geographic Collection" [*Geograficheskiy sbornik*] (since 1952; down to 1959, 13 volumes have appeared). Besides the central organization of the Society, 30 branches and sections of the Society have (in 1959) their own publications, under the titles: "Scientific Notes," "Yearbook," "Questions of Geography," "Transactions," etc., which appear with varying degrees of regularity. These branches and sections are: Amur, Bashkir, Belorussian, Buryatian, Vologda, Voronezh, Eastern Siberian, Georgian, Western Kazakhstan, Kazakh, Komi, Crimean, Kirgiz, Kyakhta, Lithuanian, Moscow, Novozybkov, Novosibirsk, Omsk, Perm', Amur (Priamurskiy), Tadzhik, Tomsk, Turkmen, Uzbek, Ukrainian, Urals, Chernovitsy, Chelyabinsk, and Estonian. Especially widely known is the "Questions of Geography" published by the Moscow branch of the Geographic Society. Fifty collections of articles have appeared since 1946.

The Geographic Society of the USSR has its own building in Leningrad, constructed in 1908 and specially equipped for scientific meetings and the scientific work of its members. Here there is a library numbering over 326,000 volumes, a map collection, and a Scientific Archive.

Since 1956, the Society has belonged to the International Geographical Union (through the National Committee of Soviet Geographers).

APPENDIX

SOVIET SERIALS CITED IN THIS BOOK

(An appendix prepared by Chauncy D. Harris)

This appendix consists of: (1) enumeration of the serials most frequently cited, (2) a listing in the form typically used by American and British libraries, and (3) an index of the abbreviated forms cited in this book.

SOVIET SERIALS MOST FREQUENTLY CITED

Since *Soviet Geography, Accomplishments and Tasks* is a general survey of the progress and programs of the broad field of Soviet geography, the references at the end of each chapter provide a highly selected list of articles and books considered to be of especial significance in Soviet geographical research. An analysis of the frequency of citations to various periodicals or nonperiodical serials may provide some clue to the serials which should be ordered by libraries and regularly consulted by scholars interested in following further developments in Soviet geography and related disciplines. I mention the most cited serials with the names of the issuing institutions translated into English. Libraries list these serials, of course, under Russian titles as given in the following section of this appendix. Numbers following each title refer to the location in that list.

Three Soviet geographical serials are clearly of key importance in terms of frequency of references:

Academy of Sciences of the USSR, *Izvestiia*. Geographical Series (8). This is edited in the Institute of Geography of the Academy of Sciences, the greatest concentration of research geographers in the country.

The *Izvestiia* of the Geographic Society of the USSR (49), the oldest of the continuously published geographical periodicals in the Soviet Union.

Voprosy Geografii (Questions of Geography) (140) published by the Moscow Branch of the Geographic Society of the USSR.

All three of these geographical serials include a table of contents in English as well as in Russian. Selected articles from them are translated into English and published in *Soviet Geography: Review & Translation* issued ten times a year by the American Geographical Society.

Other serials often cited include some primarily geographic, some in closely related disciplines, and some of a general nature but frequently containing articles of geographic significance:

Trudy formerly issued by the Institute of Geography of the Academy of Sciences but recently closed (14).

Problemy Fizicheskoi Geografii (Problems of Physical Geography), formerly issued by the same institute (114).

Geograficheskii Sbornik (Geographical Collection) published irregularly by the Geographic Society (48).

Zapiski of the Geographic Society (50).

Trudy of the Central Scientific-Research Institute of Geodesy, Photogrammetry, and Cartography in Leningrad (70).

Pochvovedenie (Soil Science) issued by the Academy of Sciences (111).

Trudy of the Soil Institute of the Academy of Sciences (32).

Trudy of the Main Geophysical Observatory in Leningrad (63).

Trudy of the State Hydrological Institute in Leningrad (65).

Meteorologiia i Gidrologiia (Meteorology and Hydrology) issued by the Main Administration of the Hydrometeorological Service (83).

Zoologicheskii Zhurnal (Zoological Journal) published by the Academy of Sciences (150).

Doklady (Reports) of the Academy of Sciences (12), with scholarly articles of broad interest.

Priroda (Nature), a popular journal of the Academy of Sciences (112).

Vestnik of Moscow State University, first as a general series (93), later with a series for biology, soils, geology, and geography (94), but since 1960 with a separate series for geography.

SERIALS CITED IN THIS BOOK

A listing in the form typically used by American and British libraries

Individuals wishing to consult books listed in the bibliographies usually will have no difficulty in locating such works, if they are in the libraries, since the name of the author is usually a clear and sufficient guide. In the case of serials, however, some difficulties may be experienced. In order to aid the reader, serials referred to in this book are listed below in alphabetical order in the form typically used by American and British libraries. The entries provide the minimum essential bibliographical data.

In order to facilitate use of these serials, data are provided in parentheses on (a) the location in various union lists of data on identity of American and Canadian libraries having holdings of the serial in question, and (b) the Library of Congress call number.

The following union lists are referred to:

(1) S. *Serial Publications of the Soviet Union, 1939-1957: a Bibliographic Checklist.* (Washington, D. C.: Library of Congress, 1958.) For example, the notation (S-4819) under *Voprosy geografii* signifies that under entry 4819 in this union list data are provided on the 13 American libraries which have holdings of this serial. This invaluable union list is the most complete and up-to-date American listing of recent Soviet serials.

(2) U. *Union List of Serials in the Libraries of the United States and Canada,* 2nd edition. (New York: H. W. Wilson, 1943.) Numbers refer to pages and letters to columns. This is the basic union list for serials published up to 1940.

(3) UG. *List of Serial Publications of Foreign Governments.* (New York: H. W. Wilson, 1932.) Occasionally useful for older government serials.

(4) N. *New Serial Titles, Second Series: 1959 Cumulation.* (Washington: Government Printing Office, 1960.) The basic source of data on new serials launched after 1957.

(5) *British Union Catalogue of Periodicals: A Record of the Periodicals of the World, from the Seventeenth Century to the Present Day, in British Libraries* (London: Butterworths Scientific Publications, 4 vols. 1955-1958), and *Catalogue Collectif des Périodiques conservé dans les Bibliothèques de Paris et dans les Bibliothèques Universitaires de France. Périodiques Slaves en Caractères Cyrilliques. Etat des Collections en 1950.* (Paris: Bibliothèque Nationale, 1956.) Both of these were consulted in confirming titles or other bibliographic data. They provide data on library holdings in Britain and France.

The Library of Congress call number, if known to me, has been listed in parentheses. Since the Library of Congress has the most complete holdings in the United States of Soviet serials and since its classification system is followed by many other libraries, such information may speed the finding and use of Soviet serials. The word "monograph" indicates that the Library of Congress classifies each number of a given serial separately according to the subjects of each number. "Unclassified" indicates that, at the date of the publication consulted, the Library of Congress had not yet classified its holdings of the serial.

The number in parentheses at the end of each entry records the number of times articles in this serial have been cited in the bibliographies in this book.

1. Akademiia nauk Gruzinskoi SSR, Tiflis. *Soobshcheniia.* Tbilisi. 1- (1940-). (S-86) (AS262.A5893) (1)
2. Akademiia nauk Kazakhskoi SSR, Alma-Ata. *Izvestiia. Seriia geograficheskaia.* Alma-Ata. 1- (1948-). (S-128) (QE1.A24952) (1)
3. ————. *Vestnik.* Alma-Ata. 1944-. (1944-1948 as Akademiia nauk SSSR. Kazakhskii filial). (S-140) (AS262.A5913) (4)
4. ————. Institut ekonomiki. *Trudy.* Alma-Ata. 1957-. (S-141b) (1)
5. Akademiia nauk SSSR. *Doklady. Novaia seriia.* Moscow. 1- (1933-). (S-153) (AS262.S3663) (12)
6. ————. *Izvestiia. Otdelenie literatury i iazyka.* Moscow. 1- (1940-). (S-156) (AS262.A6243) (1)
7. ————. ————. *Seriia geofizicheskaia.* Moscow. Mr 1951-. (Continues in part *Seriia geograficheskaia i geofizicheskaia.*) (S-160) (QC801.A35) (1)
8. ————. ————. *Seriia geograficheskaia.* Moscow. Mr 1951-. (Continues in part *Seriia geograficheskaia i geofizicheskaia.*) (S-161) (G23.A35) (56)

9. ————. ————. *Seriia geograficheskaia i geofizicheskaia. Moscow.* 1-15 (1937-F 1951). Closed. (In 1951 split into two separate series: *geograficheskaia* and *geofizicheskaia*.) (S-162) (AS262.A6246) (5)

10. ————. ————. *Seriia geologicheskaia.* Moscow. 1936-. (S-163) (AS262.A62465) (1)

11. ————. *Vestnik.* Moscow. 1- (1931-). (S-172) (AS262.A627) (1)

12. ————. Azerbaidzhanskii filial, Baku. Botanicheskii institut. *Trudy.* 1- (1936-). (U-64b) (1)

13. ————. Geologicheskii institut. *Trudy.* Moscow. 1-9 (1931-1939). ns 1- (1956-). (S-226) (QE1.A335) (1)

14. ————. Institut geografii. *Trudy.* Moscow. 1-80 (1931-1960). Closed. (S-243) (GB236.A4) (17)

15. ————. Institut geologicheskikh nauk. *Trudy.* Moscow. 1-165 (1938-1956). (S-245) (QE1.A34) (3)

16. ————. Institut iazykoznaniia. *Doklady i soobshcheniia.* Moscow. 1- (1952-). (S-253) (P25.A452) (1)

17. ————. ————. *Trudy.* Moscow. 1952-. (S-254) (P381.R8A7) (1)

18. ————. Institut lesa. *Nauchnye voprosy polezashchitnogo lesorazvedeniia.* Moscow. 1- (1951-). (S-269) (SB437.A5) (1)

19. ————. ————. *Trudy.* Moscow. 1- (1947-). (S-271) (SD1.A335) (3)

20. ————. Institut merzlotovedeniia imeni V. A. Obrucheva. *Trudy.* Moscow. 1- (1944-). (S-280) (TA713.A4) (1)

21. ————. Institut okeanologii. *Trudy.* Moscow. 1- (1946-). (S-291) (GC1.A4) (1)

22. ————. Kol'skaia baza. *Trudy.* Moscow. 1-5 (1935-1940). (S-340) (Q60.A635) (1)

23. ————. Komissiia po estestvenno-istoricheskomu raionirovaniiu SSSR. *Trudy.* Moscow. 1-2 (1947-1948). (S-345) (GB236.A42) (4)

24. ————. Komissiia po irrigatsii. *Trudy.* Leningrad. 1-7 (1933-1937). (U-66c) (1)

25. ————. Komissiia po izucheniiu chetvertichnogo perioda. *Biulleten'.* Moscow. 1- (1929-). (S-348) (QE696.A35) (1)

26. ————. ————. *Trudy.* Moscow. 1- (1932-). (S-350) (QE696.A34) (3)

27. ————. Komitet po vechnoi merzlote. *Trudy.* Moscow. 1-10 (1932-1940). (1-5, 1932-1937, by Akademiia nauk SSSR. Komissiia po izucheniiu vechnoi merzloty.) (S-354) (S599.R9A7) (1)

28. ————. Laboratoriia ozerovedeniia. *Trudy.* Moscow. 1- (1950-). (S-365) (GB1603.A45) (1)

29. ————. Mongol'skaia komissiia. *Trudy.* Moscow. 1- (1932-). (S-374) (DS793.M7A423) (2)

30. ————. Morskoi gidrofizicheskii institut. *Trudy.* Moscow. 1- (1948-). (S-375) (GC1.A45) (1)

31. ————. Pochvennyi institut imeni V. V. Dokuchaeva. *Problemy sovetskogo pochvovedeniia.* Moscow. 1- (1936-). (S-395) (S590.A65) (1)

32. ————. ————. *Trudy.* Moscow. 1- (1926-). (S-397) (QE1.A35) (8)

33. ————. Vostochno-Sibirskii filial, Irkutsk. *Trudy.* Moscow. 1- (1954-). (S-425) (Q60.A646) (1)

34. ————. Zapadno-Sibirskii filial, Novosibirsk. Transportno-energeticheskii institut. *Trudy.* Novosibirsk. 1- (1951-). (S-430) (TJ4.A656) (1)

35. ————. Zoologicheskii muzei. *Ezhegodnik.* Leningrad 1-32 (1896-1931). (U-68c) (1)

36. ————. Zoologicheskii institut. *Trudy.* Moscow. 1- (1932-). (S-432) (QL1.A4253) (2)

37. Akademiia nauk Tadzhikskoi SSR, Stalinabad. *Trudy.* Stalinabad. 1- (1956-). (S-434a) (DK921.A45), (1)

38. ————. Otdelenie obshchestvennykh nauk. *Izvestiia.* Stalinabad. 1- (1952-). (S-438a) (DK921.A462) (1)

39. Ashkhabad. Turkmenskii sel'skokhoziaistvennyi institut. *Trudy.* Ashkhabad. 1- (1935-). (S-594) (Yudin S13.T7) (1)

40. *Biulleteni pochvoveda.* Moscow. (Biuro upolnomochennykh pochvovedov SSSR). 1926-1930? (U-475b) (1)

41. *Botanicheskii zhurnal.* Moscow. (Vsesoiuznoe botanicheskoe obshchestvo). 1- (1916-). (S-788) (QK1.V713) (3)

42. Erivan. Universitet. *Nauchnye trudy.* Erevan. 1- (1925-). (S-922) (AS262.E77) (1)

43. *Fauna S.S.S.R. Novaia seriia.* Moscow. (Akademiia nauk SSSR. Zoologicheskii institut). 1- (1935-). (S-938) QL281.F3) (1)

44. *Geodeziia i kartografiia.* Moscow. (Glavnoe upravlenie geodezii i kartografii SSSR). 1956-. (Succeeds *Geodezist,* 1925-1940, and Russia (1923- U.S.S.R.) Glavnoe upravlenie geodezii i kartografii. *Sbornik nauchno-tekhnicheskikh i proizvodstvennykh statei po geodezii, kartografii, topografii, aeros"ëmki i gravimetrii,* 1940-1955.) (S-979a) (QB275.G45) (3)

45. *Geodezist.* Moscow. (Glavnoe upravlenie geodezii i kartografii SSSR). 1925-1940. (See no. 44 above). (S-981) (QB296.R813) (1)

46. *Geofizika.* Moscow. 1932-. (U-1098b) (2)

47. *Geograficheskii vestnik.* Leningrad. (Leningrad. Geograficheskii institut). 1-4 (1922-1925). (U-1098c) (Slavic Division) (1)

48. Geograficheskoe obshchestvo SSSR. *Geograficheskii sbornik.* Leningrad. 1- (1952-). (S-983) (GB58.G34) (7)

49. ————. *Izvestiia.* Leningrad. 1- (1865-). (S-984) (G23.G16) (35)

50. ————. *Zapiski. Novaia seriia.* Leningrad. 1- (1948-). (S-985) (monographs) (6)

51. ————. *Zapiski . . . po obshchei geografii.* Leningrad. 1-51 (1867-1916). (Imperatorskoe Russkoe geograficheskoe obshchestvo). (U-1139c) (G23.R67) (1)

52. ————. Statisticheskii otdel. *Zapiski.* Leningrad. 1-14 (1866-1915). (U-1140b) (G23.R65) (1)

53. *Geografiia i khoziaistvo.* Moscow. (Moscow. Gosudarstvennyi universitet. Geograficheskii fakul'tet). 1- (1958-). (N-529b) (1)

54. *Geografiia v shkole.* Moscow. (Ministerstvo prosveshcheniia RSFSR). 1934-. (S-993) (G1.G313) (4)

55. *Gidrologicheskii vestnik.* Leningrad. 1-3 (1915-1917) (U-1121b) (1)

56. *Gidrotekhnicheskii sbornik.* Moscow. (Moscow. Vysshee tekhnicheskoe uchilishche). 1-2 (1927-1929). (U-1121b) (1)

57. Irkutsk. Universitet. *Trudy.* Moscow. 1- (1932-). (S-1087) (Q60.I7) (1)

58. *Istoricheskie zapiski.* Moscow. (Akademiia nauk SSSR. Institut istorii). 1- (1937-). (S-1099) (DK1.I8) (1)

59. *Istoriia S.S.S.R.* Moscow. (Akademiia nauk SSSR. Institut istorii). 1957-. (S-1100b) (DK40.I895) (1)

60. Kazan. Universitet. *Uchenye zapiski.* Kazan. 1- (1834-). (S-1192) (AS262.K2) (1)

61. Leningrad. Arkticheskii i Antarkticheskii nauchno-issledovatel'skii institut. *Trudy.* Leningrad. 1- (1932-). (S-1547) (G600.I4) (3)

62. ————. Geograficheskii institut. *Izvestiia.* Leningrad. 1-6 (1919-1926). (U-1565a) (G23.I4) (2)

63. ————. Glavnaia geofizicheskaia observatoriia. *Trudy.* Leningrad. 1- (1934-). (S-1568) (QC801.I46) (8)

64. ————. Gosudarstennyi gidrologicheskii institut. *Izvestiia*. Leningrad. 1- (1921-). (U-1565b) (1)

65. ————. ————. *Trudy*. Leningrad. 1- (1936-). (S-1574) (GB651.L38) (6)

66. ————. ————. *Zapiski*. Leningrad. 1- (1926-). (U-1565b) (1)

67. ————. Gosudarstvennyi pedagogicheskii institut imeni A. I. Gertsena. *Uchenye zapiski*. Leningrad. 1- (1935-). (S-1581) (AS262.L4143) (4)

68. ————. Inzhenerno-stroitel'nyi institut. *Nauchnye trudy*. Leningrad. 1- (1934-). (1-7, 1934-1940 as: Leningrad. Leningradskii institut inzhenerov kommunal'nogo stroitel'stva. *Trudy*). (S-1603) (TA4.I43) (1)

69. ————. Sanitarno-gigienicheskii meditsinskii institut. *Trudy*. Leningrad. 1949-. (S-1651) (R95.L443) (1)

70. ————. Tsentral'nyi nauchno-issledovatel'skii institut geodezii, aeros"ëmki, i kartografii. *Trudy*. Moscow. 1- (1931-). (S-1672) (QB280.L42) (14)

71. ————. Universitet. *Uchenye zapiski*. Leningrad. 1- (1935-). (S-1690) (AS262.L422) *Seriia geograficheskikh nauk*. 1- (1939-). (1)

72. ————. ————. ————. *Seriia geologii*. 1- (1950-). (1)

73. ————. ————. ————. *Seriia vostokovedcheskikh nauk*. 1- (1949-). (2)

74. ————. ————. *Vestnik*. Leningrad. 1946-. (S-1691) (AS262.L463) (2)

75. ————. Vsesoiuznyi geologicheskii institut. *Trudy*. Moscow. 1- (1950-). (S-1721) (QE1.L438) (1)

76. Lietuvos TSR Mokslu akademija, Vilna. Geologijos ir geografijos institutas. *Moksliniai pranesimai*. Vilna. 1- (1955-). (Akademiia nauk Litovskoi SSR, Vilna. Institut geologii i geografii. *Nauchnye soobshcheniia*.) (S-1828b) (QE1.L448) (1)

77. Lvov. Universytet. *Naukovi zapysky*. *Nauchnye zapiski*. Lvov. 1- (1946-). (S-1891) (QE1.L96) (4)

78. *Materialy i issledovaniia po arkheologii S.S.S.R.* Moscow. (Akademiia nauk SSSR. Institut istorii material'noi kul'tury). 1- (1940-). (S-1926) (DK30.M3) (1)

79. *Materialy k poznaniiu fauny i flory S.S.S.R. Novaia seriia. Otdel zoologicheskii*. Moscow. (Moskovskoe obshchestvo ispytatelei prirody). 1- (1940-). (S-1960) (QL1.M35) (2)

80. *Materialy po chetvertichnomu periodu SSSR*. Moscow. (Akademiia nauk SSSR. Komissiia po izucheniiu chetvertichnogo perioda). 1- (1936-). (S-1962) (QE696.M45) (2)

81. *Materialy po issledovaniiu reki Volkhova i ego basseina*. Leningrad. (Vysshii sovet narodnogo khoziaistva). 1-24 (1924-1929). (U-1679a) (1)

82. *Meditsinskaia parazitologiia i parazitarnye bolezni*. Moscow. (Ministerstvo zdravookhraneniia SSSR). 1- (1932-). (S-1981) (RC960.M4) (2)

83. *Meteorologiia i gidrologiia*. Leningrad. (Glavnoe upravlenie gidrometeorologicheskoi sluzhby SSSR). 1935-. (S-2001) (QC851.M27) (6)

84. Mezhdunarodnyi geofizicheskii god (International geophysical year). *Informatsionnyi biulleten'*. Moscow. (Akademiia nauk SSSR. Prezidium. Mezhduvedomstvennyi komitet po provedeniiu Mezhdunarodnogo geofizicheskogo goda.) 1958-. (N-853c) (1)

85. Moscow. Gosudarstvennyi institut po proektirovaniiu morskikh portov i sudoremontnykh predpriiatii. *Trudy*. Moscow. 1- (1956-). (S-2129a) (1)

86. ————. Gosudarstvennyi okeanograficheskii institut. *Trudy*. Leningrad. 1- (1931-). (S-2153b) (GC1.M58) (1)

87. ————. Institut istorii, filosofii i literatury im. N. G. Chernyshevskogo. *Trudy*. Moscow. (S-2162) (monographs) (1)

88. ————. Moskovskii gosudarstvennyi pedagogicheskii institut imeni V. I. Lenina. *Uchebnye zapiski*. Moscow. 1- (1934-). (S-2217) (AS262.M6) (3)

89. ————. Moskovskii institut inzhenerov geodezii, aerofotos"ëmki i kartografii. *Trudy*. Moscow. 1- (1940-). (S-2218) (unclassified) (1)

90. ————. Nauchno-issledovatel'skii institut geologii Arktiki. *Trudy*. Moscow. (S-2239a) (unclassified) (2)

91. ————. Tsentral'nyi institut prognozov. *Trudy*. Moscow. 1- (1947-). (S-2350) (QC851.M64) (1)

92. ————. Universitet. *Uchenye zapiski*. Moscow. 1- (1933-). (S-2395) (Q60.M868) (3)

93. ————. ————. *Vestnik*. Moscow. 1946-1955. (In 1956 divided into subseries, one of which was: *Seriia biologii, pochvovedeniia, geologii, geografii*, no. 94, below). (S-2396) (Q60.M86812) (5)

94. ————. ————. ————. *Seriia biologii, pochvovedeniia, geologii, geografii*. Moscow. 1956-1959. (In 1960 a separate geography series was formed, *Seriia 5. Geografiia*.) (S-2396b) (QH301.M566) (4)

95. ————. Vsesoiuznyi nauchno-issledovatel'skii institut mineral'nogo syr'ia. *Trudy*. Moscow. 1- (1923-). (S-2485) (TN4.M65) (1)

96. ————. Vsesoiuznyi nauchno-issledovatel'skii institut morskogo rybnogo khoziaistva i okeanografii. *Trudy*. Moscow. 1- (1935-). (S-2487) (SH1.M65) (1)

97. Moskovskoe obshchestvo ispytatelei prirody. *Biulleten'*. Moscow. 1- (1829-). (S-2569) (Q60.M8) (4)

98. ————. ————. *Otdel biologicheskii*. 1- (1917-). (S-2570) (Q60.M8) (2)

99. ————. ————. *Otdel geologicheskii*. 1- (1922-). (S-2571) (Q60.M8) (1)

100. *Movoznavstvo; naukovi zapysky* (in Ukrainian). Kiev. (Akademiia nauk URSR. Instytut movoznavstva). 1- (1941-). (S-2577) (PG3801.A415) (2)

101. *Na planovom fronte*. Moscow. 1929-1931. (U-1849b) (1)

102. *Nauchnye doklady vysshei shkoly: geologo-geograficheskie nauki*. Moscow. (Ministerstvo vysshego obrazovaniia SSSR). 1958-1959 no. 2. Closed. (N-927c) (3)

103. *Nevropatologiia i psikhiatriia*. Moscow. (Ministerstvo zdravookhraneniia SSSR). 1937-1951. (S-5283) (RC321.Z47) (1)

104. *Ocherki po istorii geologicheskikh znanii*. Moscow. (Akademiia nauk SSSR. Institut geologicheskikh nauk). 1- (1953-). (S-2730) (QE13.R9A562) (1)

105. Odessa. Institut inzhenerov morskogo flota. *Nauchnye trudy*. Moscow. 1- (1935-). (S-2740) (1)

106. ————. Sil's'ko-hospodars'kyi instytut (Sel'skokhoziaistvennyi institut). *Pratsi. (Trudy)*. Odessa. 1- (1939-). (S-2748) (1)

107. *Okhrana prirody i zapovednoe delo v S.S.S.R.; biulleten'*. Moscow. (Akademiia nauk SSSR. Komissiia po okhrane prirody). 1- (1956-). (S-2773) (unclassified) (2)

108. *Onomastica*. Wroclaw, Poland. 1- (1955-). (N-1000b) (1)

109. *Parazitologicheskii sbornik.* Moscow. (Akademiia nauk SSSR. Zoologicheskii institut. Otdel parazitologii). 1-
    (1930-). (S-2843) (QL757.A32) (1)
110. *Planovoe khoziaistvo.* Moscow. (Gosudarstvennaia planovaia komissiia SSSR). 1923-. (S-2896) (HC331.P52) (1)
111. *Pochvovedenie.* Moscow. (Akademiia nauk SSSR). 1- (1899-) (S-2901) (S590.P6) (11)
112. *Priroda.* Leningrad. (Akademiia nauk SSSR). 1912-. (S-2952) (Q4.P8) (10)
113. *Problemy Arktiki.* Leningrad. (Glavsevmorput'. Arkticheskii nauchno-issledovatel'skii institut). 1937-1946.
    (S-2959) (G600.P7) (3)
114. *Problemy fizicheskoi geografii.* Moscow. (Akademiia nauk SSSR. Institut geografii). 1-17 (1934-1951). (S-2964)
    (G1.P67) (14)
115. *Problemy severa.* Moscow. (Akademiia nauk SSSR. Sovet po izucheniiu proizvoditel'nykh sil. Komissiia po
    problemam severa). 1- (1958-). (N-1093b) (GB395.P7) (3)
116. *Raboty Tian'shanskoi fiziko-geograficheskoi stantsii.* Moscow. 1-6 (1950-1959). A subseries of Akademiia nauk
    SSSR. Institut geografii. *Trudy.* q.v.
117. *Referativnyi zhurnal: geografiia.* Moscow. (Akademiia nauk SSSR. Institut nauchnoi informatsii). 1954-.
    (1954-1955 as combined series: *geologiia i geografiia*). (S-3105; N-1128a) (G1.R35) (1)
118. Russia (1923- U.S.S.R.). Gidrograficheskoe upravlenie. *Zapiski po gidrografii.* Leningrad. 1887-1949. (S-3292)
    (VK4.R87) (2)
119. ————. Glavnoe upravlenie geodezii i kartografii. *Sbornik nauchno-tekhnicheskikh statei po geodezii, kartografii,
    topografii, aeros"ëmki i gravimetrii.* Moscow. 1-31 (1940-1955). (Succeeds *Geodezist;* succeeded by *Geodeziia
    i kartografiia.*) (S-3310) (QB301.R8) (3)
120. ————. Glavnoe upravlenie gidrometeorologicheskoi sluzhby. *Trudy nauchno-issledovatel'skikh uchrezhdenii. Seriia
    4: Gidrologiia sushi.* Moscow. 1-40 (1941-1947). (S-3319) (GB653.R82) (2)
121. ————. Glavnoe upravlenie po zapovednikam i okhotnich'emu khoziaistvu. *Trudy tsentral'no-chernozemnogo
    gosudarstvennogo zapovednika.* Moscow. 1- (1940-). (S-3375) (unclassified) (1)
122. ————. Glavnoe upravlenie Severnogo morskogo puti. Gorno-geologicheskoe upravlenie. *Trudy.* Moscow. 1-37
    (1937-1947). (S-3394) (monographs) (1)
123. Saransk. Mordovskii nauchno-issledovatel'skii institut iazyka, literatury, istorii i ekonomiki. *Zapiski.* Saransk. 1-
    (1940-). (S-3759) (unclassified) (1)
124. Smolenskoe obshchestvo estestvoispytatelei i vrachei pri Smolenskom gosudarstvennom universitete. *Trudy.*
    Smolensk. 1-4 (1926-1930). (U-2556b) (1)
125. Sovetskaia antarkticheskaia ekspeditsiia, 1955-1958. *Informatsionnyi biulleten'.* Leningrad. 1- (1959-). (Arkticheskii
    i antarkticheskii nauchno-issledovatel'skii institut). (N-1243a) (4)
126. *Sovetskaia botanika.* Moscow. 1-15 (1933-1947). (S-3939) (QK1.S85) (1)
127. *Sovetskaia etnografiia.* Moscow. (Akademiia nauk SSSR). 1931-. (S-3941) (GN1.S65) (1)
128. *Sovetskaia geologiia: sbornik statei.* Moscow. (Ministerstvo geologii i okhrainy nedr SSSR). 1- (1944-). (S-3942)
    (QE1.S952) (1)
129. *Sovetskaia meditsina.* Moscow. (Ministerstvo zdravookhraneniia SSSR i RSFSR). 1- (1937). (S-3950) (R91.S68)
    (1)
130. *Sovetskoe zdravookhranenie.* Moscow. 1- (1942-). (S-4023) (RA727.S6) (1)
131. Tashkend. Universitet. *Trudy. s.12a. Geografiia.* Tashkend. 1- (1928-). (U-2737b; S-4285 main series) (DS1.T3) (1)
132. *Teoriia i praktika fizicheskoi kul'tury.* Moscow. (Vsesoiuznyi komitet po fizicheskoi kul'ture i sportu). 1- (1937-).
    (S-4346) (GV201.T4) (1)
133. Tomsk. Gosudarstvennyi pedagogicheskii institut. *Uchenye zapiski.* Tomsk. 1- (1939-). (S-4418) (AS262.T48A15)
    (1)
134. ————. Universitet. *Trudy.* Tomsk. 1- (1889). *Seriia geograficheskaia.* (S-4428) (AS262.T5) (1)
135. *Trudy po sel'skokhoziaistvennoi meteorologii.* Leningrad. (Vsesoiuznyi institut rastenievodstva). 1-26 (1901-1948),
    (S-4464) (QC989.R49T7) (1)
136. Ulan-Ude. Buriat-Mongol'skii gosudarstvennyi nauchno-issledovatel'skii institut kul'tury. *Zapiski.* Ulan-Ude. 1-
    (1936-). (S-4580) (DK771.B8U45) (1)
137. *Vokrug sveta.* Moscow. (Vsesoiuznyi Leninskii kommunisticheskii soiuz molodëzhi. Tsentral'nyi komitet). 1861-
    (S-4789) (G1.V6) (1)
138. *Voprosy ekonomiki.* Moscow. (Akademiia nauk SSSR. Institut ekonomiki). 1948-. (S-4807) (HC10.V67) (1)
139. *Voprosy filosofii.* Moscow. (Akademiia nauk SSSR. Institut filosofii). 1947-. (S-4814) (B8.R9V6) (2)
140. *Voprosy geografii.* Moscow. (Geograficheskoe obshchestvo SSSR. Moskovskii filial). 1- (1946-). (S-4819)
    (G23.V6) (37)
141. *Voprosy geografii Dal'nego Vostoka.* Khabarovsk. (Geograficheskoe obshchestvo SSSR. Priamurskii filial).
    1- (1957-). (S-4820) (Unclassified) (1)
142. *Voprosy geografii Sibiri.* Tomsk. (Geograficheskoe obshchestvo SSSR. Tomskii otdel). 1- (1949-). (S-4822) (1)
143. *Voprosy iazykoznaniia.* Moscow. (Akademiia nauk SSSR. Institut iazykoznaniia). 1- (1952-). (S-4830) (P9.V6) (1)
144. Vsesoiuznoe geologo-razvedochnoe upravlenie. *Trudy.* 1- (1930-). (1930-1931 as Glavnoe geologo-razvedochnoe
    upravlenie. *Trudy.*) (UG-670c) (1)
145. Vsesoiuznyi aerogeologicheskii trest. *Trudy.* Moscow. 1- (1955-). (S-5101) (QE1.V84) (1)
146. *Zashchita rastenii.* Leningrad. (Vsesoiuznyi institut zashchitu rastenii). 1-19 (1935-1939). (S-5233) (SB599.Z3)
    (1)
147. *Zemledelie i zhivotnovodstvo Moldavii.* Kishinev. (Ministerstvo sel'skogo khoziaistva Moldavskoi SSR). 1956-.
    (S-5251) (1)
148. *Zemlevedenie.* (Moscow. (Moskovskoe obshchestvo ispytatelei prirody). 1-40 (1892-1938); ns. 1-4 (1940-1957).
    (S-5252) (G1.Z7) (1)
149. *Zhurnal mikrobiologii, epidemiologii i immunobiologii.* Moscow. (Ministerstvo zdravookhraneniia SSSR). 1924-.
    (S5278) (QR1.Z5) (1)
150. *Zoologicheskii zhurnal.* Moscow. (Akademiia nauk SSSR). 1- (1916-). (1-10, 1916-1930, as *Russkii zoologicheskii
    zhurnal*). (S-5297) (QL1.Z747) (5)

INDEX TO SERIALS CITED IN THIS BOOK

(In the form cited)

The following list, arranged in alphabetical order, records the forms (mostly abbreviated) used in references to serials in the original of this book and preserved in the translation. The numbers refer to the preceding list of full titles in the forms typically used in American and British libraries. Of the 158 different serials cited, 150 have been so identified. The notation "not identified" indicates that the serial in question was not confirmed as being listed by an American, British, or French library or union list; there are 8 such serials, each cited but once in the book.

It has not been thought necessary to list the intermediate steps in the transformation of the abbreviated form of titles to the full transliterated library form, but the following five examples will illustrate the process and problems:

(1) The most frequently cited periodical in the bibliographies is cited as *Izv. AN SSSR, seriya geogr.* Removing the abbreviations, this becomes *Izvestiya Akademii nauk SSSR, seriya geograficheskaya.* Listing under the issuing agency, changing slightly the transliteration scheme to follow the Library of Congress system (rather than that of the Board on Geographic Names used in the text of this book), and making the appropriate changes in cases (Russian is a declined language), this entry becomes: *Akademiia nauk SSSR. Izvestiia. Seriia geograficheskaia. (8).*

(2) There are frequent citations to *Izv. RGO* and *Izv. VGO.* These refer to the same periodical issued by the Geographic Society of the USSR, which in its long history has undergone several name changes. The periodical is typically listed in Russian as *Izvestiya Vsesoyuznogo Geograficheskogo Obshchestva* and in American libraries as *Geograficheskoe obshchestvo SSSR, Izvestiia (49),* with the notation that the name of the society was earlier *Russkoe geograficheskoe obshchestvo.*

(3) *Tr. TsNIIGAiK.* Here there are two problems: first, determining what institute is represented by this barrage of initials, and second, ascertaining how the institute is listed by the library. The initials stand for *Tsentral'nyi Nauchno-Issledovatel'skii Institut Geodezii, Aeros"ëmki i Kartografii* but a search of library catalogues may not turn up any such agency in its alphabetical order. Libraries often list such institutions under the name of the city in which located and it is thus necessary to know that this institution is in Leningrad. *(70).* Similarly with *Tr. GGO* and *Tr. GGI* one looks under Leningrad for the *Glavnaia geofizicheskaia observatoriia. Trudy (63),* and *Gosudarstvennyi gidrologicheskii institut. Trudy (65).*

(4) One citation reads *Tr. NIU.* This turns out to be considered a part of a government department and therefore is listed by libraries under the heading: *Russia (1923 — USSR). Glavnoe upravlenie gidrometeorologicheskoi sluzhby. Trudy nauchno-issledovatel'skikh uchrezhdenii. Seriia 4: Gidrologiia sushi. (120).* Similarly with *Sb. GUGK* for *Glavnoe upravlenie geodezii i kartografii. Sbornik... (119).*

(5) Many institutes are part of the Academy of Sciences of the USSR and therefore listed under the Academy. Thus *Tr. Pochv. in-ta im. Dokuchayeva* is listed under *Akademiia nauk SSSR. Pochvennyi institut imeni V. V. Dokuchaeva. Trudy. (32).*

Istoriya SSSR. 59
Izv. AN Kaz. SSR. Seriya geogr. 2
Izv. AN SSSR, Otd. literatury i yazyka. 6
Izv. AN SSSR, seriya geof. 7
Izv. AN SSSR, seriya geogr. 8
Izv. AN SSSR, seriya geogr. i geof. 9
Izv. AN SSSR, seriya geol. 10
Izv. GGI. 64
Izv. In-ta geogr. 62
Izv. otd. obshch. nauk AN Tadzh. SSR. 38
Izv. RGO. 49
Izv. VGO. 49
Izvestiya Akademii nauk SSSR. Seriya
    geograficheskaya. 8
Izvestiya VGO. 49
Izvestiya Vsesoiuznogo geograficheskogo obshchestvo. 49
Latvijas PSR vietvardi I, no. 1, Riga, 1956.
    Not identified.
Leningr. gos. ped. in-t im. A. I. Gertsena, Uchen. zap. 67
Materialy i issled. po arkheol. SSSR. 78
Materialy k poznaniyu fauny i flory SSSR, Novaya
    seriya. Otd. zoologii. 79
Materialy po chetvertichnomu periodu SSSR. 80
Materialy po geologii i poleznym iskopayemym
    severo-vostochnoy chasti SSSR, vyp. 10, 1956.
    Not identified.
Materialy po issledovaniyu R. Volkhova i yego
    basseya. 81
Medits. parazitologiya i parazitarnyye bolezni. 82
Meteorol. i gidrol. 83
Mosk. gos. in-t istorii, filosofii i literatury. 87
Na planovom fronte. 101
Nauchn. tr. Yerevansk. un-ta. 42
Nauchn. zap. L'vovsk. gos. un-ta im. Iv. Franko. 77
Nauchn. zap. L'vovsk. un-ta. 77
Nauchnyye doklady vysshey shkoly, geol.-geogr.
    nauki. 102
Nauchnyye trudy Odesskogo in-ta inzhenerov morskogo
    flota. 105
Nevropat. i psikhiatr. 103
Ocherki po istorii geologicheskikh znanii. 104
Ocherki po zemlevedeniyu i ekonomike Vostochnoy
    Sibiri, vyp. 11, Irkutsk, 1926. Not identified.
Okhrana prirody i zapovednoye delo v SSSR,
    Byulleten'. 107
Onomastica. 108
Parazitol. sbornik AN SSSR. 109
Planovoye khozyaystvo. 110
Pochvovedeniye. 111
Priroda. 112
Probl. severa. 115
Problemy Arktiki. 113
Problemy fiz. geog. 114
Problemy sovetskogo pochvovedeniya. 31
Raboty Tyan'shanskoy fiziko-geograficheskoy
    stantsii. 116
Referativnyy zhurnal: geografiya. 117
Russk. zool. zhurn. 150
Sb. GUGK. 119
Soobshch. AN Gruz. SSR. 1
Sov. botanika. 126
Sov. meditsina. 129
Sovetskaya etnografiya. 127
Sovetskaya geologiya. 128
Sovetskoye ugrovedeniye, vyp. 5, Petrozavodsk, 1948.
    Not identified.
Sovetskoye zdravookhraneniye. 130
Teoriya i praktika fizicheskoy kul'tury. 132
Tr. AN Tadzh. SSR. 37
Tr. Arktich. n.-i. in-ta. 61
Tr. Bot. in-ta. 12
Tr. GGI. 65

Tr. GGO. 63
Tr. GGRU. 144
Tr. GOIN. 86
Tr. Geol. in-ta AN SSSR. 13
Tr. Glav. geof. observ. 63
Tr. Glav. geof. observ. im. A. I. Voyeykova. 63
Tr. gornogeol. upr. 122
Tr. Gos. gidr. in-ta. 65
Tr. Gos. gidrolog. in-ta. 65
Tr. in-ta geogr. AN SSSR. 14
Tr. in-ta geol. nauk SSSR. 15
Tr. in-ta lesa AN SSSR. 19
Tr. in-ta merzlotovedeniya im. V. A. Obrucheva. 20
Tr. in-ta okeanol. 21
Tr. in-ta Soyuzmorproyekt. 85
Tr. in-ta yazykozn. AN SSSR. 17
Tr. Irkutsk. gos. un-ta im. A. A. Zhdanova. 57
Tr. Kol'sk. bazy AN SSSR. 22
Tr. Komissii po irrigatsii. 24
Tr. Komissii po izuch. chetvert. perioda. 26
Tr. Komissii po izucheniyu vechnoy merzloty
    AN SSSR. 27
Tr. Komissii po yestestv. geog. rayonirovaniyu
    SOPS AN SSSR. 23
Tr. Kompleksnoy nauchnoy ekspeditsii po voprosu
    polezashchitnogo lesorazvedeniya. 18
Tr. Labor. ozerovedeniya AN SSSR. 28
Tr. Leningr. in-ta inzh. kommun. stroit. 68
Tr. Leningr. san.-gigienich. med. in-ta. 69
Tr. Mongol'skoy komissii AN SSSR. 29
Tr. Morskogo gidrofiz. in-ta AN SSSR. 30
Tr. n.-i. in-ta geologii Arktiki. 90
Tr. NIU, 120
Tr. NIU GUMMS SSSR, seriya IV. 120
Tr. Odesskogo s.-kh. in-ta. 106
Tr. po s.-kh. meteorol. 135
Tr. Pochv. in-ta AN SSSR. 32
Tr. Pochv. in-ta im. Dokuchayeva. 32
Tr. Smolensk. obshch. yestestvoisp. i vrachey. 124
Tr. Sr.-Az. gos. un-ta. 131
Tr. TsIP. 91
Tr. TsNIIGAiK. 70
Tr. Tomsk. gos. un-ta, seriya geogr. 134
Tr. Transp.-energ. in-ta Zap.-Sib. fil. AN SSSR. 34
Tr. Tsentral'no-chernozemnogo zapovednika. 121
Tr. Turkmen. s-kh. in-ta. 39
Tr. VIMS. 95
Tr. VSEGEI. 75
Tr. Vost.-Sib. fil. AN SSSR. 33
Tr. Vsesoyuzn. aerogeolog. tresta. 145
Tr. Vsesoyuzn. in-ta morskogo rybnogo khozyaystva i
    okeanografii. 96
Tr. Zool. in-ta AN SSSR. 36
Trudy Instituta ekonomiki AN Kaz. SSR. 4
Trudy Mosk. in-ta inzhenerov geodezii, aerofotos"yemki
    i kartografii. 89
Uch. zap. in-ta yazykoved. AN USSR, "Movoznavstvo."
    100
Uch. zap. LGU, seriya geogr. nauk. 71
Uch. zap. LGU, seriya geol. 72
Uch. zap. Leningr. gos. un-ta, seriya vostokovedch.
    nauk. 73
Uch. zap. Tomskogo ped. in-ta. 133
Uch. zap. MGU. 92
Uchen. zap. Kaz. gos. un-ta. 60
Uchen. zap. Leningr. ped. in-ta. 67
Uchen. zap. MGPI. 88
Uchen. zap. MGPI im. Lenina. 88
Uchenyye zapiski MGU. 92
Vestn. AN Kaz. SSSR. 3
Vestn. AN SSSR. 11
Vestn. Kaz. FAN. 3